Oxford Cambridge and RSA Examinations

RECOGNISING ACHIEVEMENT

GCSE Mathematics

HIGHER COURSE

GW00570155

SERIES EDITOR BRIAN SEAGER

HOWARD BAXTER, MIKE HANDBURY, JOHN JESKINS, JEAN MATTHEWS, MARK PATMORE

Hodder & Stoughton

A MEMBER OF THE HODDER HEADLINE GROUP

Acknowledgements

The Publishers would like to thank the following individuals and companies for permission to reproduce photographs in this book:

Bubbles Photo Library: Frans Rombout page 248.
Paul Hart: page 220 (top).
Life File Photo Library: Mike Evans page 305, Ron Gregory page 220 (bottom), David Kampfner page 249 (bottom) and Lionel Moss page 247 (bottom).
Robert Harding Picture Library: pages 136, 151, 219, and Phil Robinson page 34.
The Photographers Library: pages 5, 27, 134, 140, 141, 144, 224 (both), 243, 247 (top), 249 (top) and 319.

Every effort has been made to trace ownership of copyright. The Publishers would be happy to make arrangements with any copyright holder whom it has not been possible to trace.

Orders: please contact Bookpoint Ltd, 130 Milton Park, Abingdon, Oxon OX14 4SB. Telephone: (44) 01235 827720, Fax: (44) 01235 400454. Lines are open from 9.00 - 6.00, Monday to Saturday, with a 24 hour message answering service. Email address: orders@bookpoint.co.uk

British Library Cataloguing in Publication Data
A catalogue record for this title is available from The British Library

ISBN 0 340 758708

First published 2001
Impression number   10 9 8 7 6 5 4 3
Year   2005 2004

Copyright © 2001 by Howard Baxter, Mike Handbury, John Jeskins, Jean Matthews, Mark Patmore and Brian Seager.

Designed and typeset by Cambridge Publishing Management.

Printed in Italy for Hodder & Stoughton Educational, a division of Hodder Headline Plc, 338 Euston Road, London NW1 3BH by Canale & C.

Contents

Contents

Contents

Introduction

About this book

This book covers the complete specification for the Higher Tier of GCSE Mathematics. It is particularly aimed at OCR Specification A but is also a suitable preparation for all Higher Tier GCSE Mathematics examinations.

The book aims to make the best of your performance in the examinations:

- Each chapter is presented in a style intended to help you understand the mathematics, with straightforward explanations and worked examples.
- At the start of each chapter is a list of what you need to know before you begin.
- There are plenty of exercises for you to work through and practise the skills.
- At the end of each chapter there is a list of key points and a revision exercise.
- Some exercises are designed to be done without a calculator so that you can practise for the non-calculator paper.
- Some of the answers are given at the end of the book to help you check your progress.
- Some chapters are designed to help you develop the necessary skills to undertake coursework.
- At frequent intervals throughout the book there are Examiner's tips, where the experienced examiners who have written this book offer advice and tips to improve your examination performance.
- Revision tests are provided in the Teacher's Book, after each term's work.

Part of the examination is now a calculator-free zone. You will have to do the first of the papers without a calculator and the questions are designed appropriately.

The marks on the two papers (out of 200) for the Assessment Objectives are:

25 marks	AO1	Using and Applying Mathematics
100 marks	AO2	Number and Algebra
50 marks	AO3	Shape, Space and Measures
25 marks	AO4	Handling Data

The remaining marks to balance AO1 and AO4 are awarded on the internal assessment (coursework).

Other changes are not so obvious from a study of the specification. Most of the marks given for Algebra are for 'manipulative' algebra. This includes simplifying algebraic expressions, factorising, solving equations and changing formulae. Some questions are also being set which offer you little help to get started. These are called 'unstructured' or 'multi-step' questions. Instead of the question having several parts, each of which leads to the next, you have to work out the necessary steps to find the answer. There will be examples of this kind of question in the end-of-term tests and past examination papers.

Top ten tips

Here are some general tips from the examiners to help you do well in your examinations.

Practise:

1. all aspects of **manipulative algebra** in the specification
2. answering questions **without** a calculator
3. answering questions which require **explanations**
4. answering **unstructured** questions
5. **accurate** drawing and construction
6. answering questions which **need a calculator**, trying to use it efficiently
7. **checking answers**, especially for reasonable size and degree of accuracy
8. making your work **concise** and well laid out
9. using the **formula sheet** before the examination
10. **rounding** numbers, but only at the appropriate stage.

Coursework

The GCSE Mathematics examinations will assess your ability to use your mathematics on longer problems than those normally found on timed written examination papers. Assessment of this type of work will account for 20% of your final mark. It will involve two 3-hour tasks taken during your final year. One task will be an investigation, the other a statistics task.

Each type of task has its own mark scheme in which marks are awarded in three categories or 'strands'. The titles of these strands give you clues about the important aspects of this work.

For the investigation tasks the strands are:

- Making and monitoring decisions – what you are going to do and how you will do it
- Communicating mathematically – explaining and showing exactly what you have done
- Developing the skills of mathematical reasoning – using mathematics to analyse and prove your results.

The table below gives some idea of what you will have to do and show. Look at this table whenever you are doing some extended work and try to include what it suggests you do.

Mark	Making and monitoring decisions	Communicating mathematically	Developing the skills of mathematical reasoning
1	organising work, producing information and checking results	discussing work using symbols and diagrams	finding examples that match a general statement
2	beginning to plan work, choosing your methods	giving reasons for choice of presentation of results and information	searching for a pattern using at least three results
3	finding out necessary information and checking it	showing understanding of the task by using words, symbols, diagrams	explaining reasoning and making a statement about the results found
4	simplifying the task by breaking it down into smaller stages	explaining what the words, symbols and diagrams show	testing generalisations by checking further cases
5	introducing new questions leading to a fuller solution	justifying the means of presentation	justifying solutions explaining why the results occur
6	using a range of techniques and reflecting on lines of enquiry and methods used	using symbolisation consistently	explaining generalisations and making further progress with the task
7	analysing lines of approach and giving detailed reasons for choices	using symbols and language to produce a convincing and reasoned argument	report includes mathematical justifications and explanations of the solutions to the problem
8	exploring extensively an unfamiliar context or area of mathematics and applying a range of appropriate mathematical techniques to solve a complex task	using mathematical language and symbols efficiently in presenting a concise reasoned argument	providing a mathematically rigorous justification or proof of the solution considering the conditions under which it remains valid

For the statistics tasks the strands are:

- Specify the problem and plan – choosing or defining a problem and outlining the approach to be followed
- Collect, process and represent data – explaining and showing what you have done
- Interpret and discuss results – use mathematical and statistical knowledge and techniques to analyse, evaluate and interpret your results and findings.

The table below gives some idea of what you will have to do and show. Look at this table whenever you are doing some extended work and try to include what it suggests you do.

The marks obtained from each task are added together to give a total out of 48.

Mark	Specify the problem and plan	Collect, process and represent data	Interpret and discuss results
1–2	choosing a simple problem and outlining a plan	collecting some data; presenting information, calculations and results	making comments on the data and results
3–4	choosing a problem which allows you to use simple statistics and plan the collection of data	collecting data and then processing it using appropriate calculations involving appropriate techniques; explaining what the words, symbols and diagrams show	explaining and interpreting the graphs and calculations and any patterns in the data
5–6	considering a more complex problem and using a range of techniques and reflecting on the method used	collecting data in a form that ensures they can be used; explaining statistical meaning through the consistent use of accurate statistics and giving a reason for the choice of presentation, explaining features selected	commenting on, justifying and explaining results and calculations; commenting on the methods used
7–8	analysing the approach and giving reasons for the methods used; using a range of appropriate statistical techniques to solve the problem	using language and statistical concepts effectively in presenting a convincing reasoned argument; using an appropriate range of diagrams to summarise the data and show how variables are related	correctly summarising and interpreting graphs and calculations and making correct and detailed inferences from the data; appreciating the significance of results obtained and, where relevant, allowing for the nature and size of the sample and any possible bias; evaluating the effectiveness of the overall strategy and recognising limitations of the work done, making suggestions for improvement

Advice

Starting a task

Ask yourself:

- what does the task tell me?
- what does it ask me?
- what can I do to get started?
- what equipment and materials do I need?

Working on the task

- Make sure you explain your method and present your results as clearly as possible.
- Break the task down into stages. For example in 'How many squares on a chessboard', begin by looking at 1×1 squares then 2×2 squares, then 3×3 squares. In a task asking for the design of a container, start with cuboids then nets, surface area, prisms … or in statistics you might want to start with a pilot survey or questionnaire.
- Write down questions that occur to you, for example, *what happens if you change the size of a rectangle systematically*? They may help you find out more about the work. In a statistical task you might wish to include different age groups or widen the type of data …
- Explore as many aspects of the task as possible.
- Develop the task into new situations and explore these thoroughly.
  - What connections are possible?
  - Is there a result to help me?
  - Is there a pattern?
  - Can the problem be changed? If so, how?

Explain your work

- Use appropriate words and suitable tables, diagrams, graphs, calculations …
- Link as much of your work together as possible, explaining, for example, why you chose the tables and charts you used and rejected others, or why the median is more appropriate than the mean in a particular statistical analysis, or why a pie chart is not appropriate. Don't just include diagrams to show identical information in different ways.
- Use algebra or symbols to give clear and efficient explanations; in investigations, you must use algebra to progress beyond about 4 marks. You will get more credit for writing $T = 5N + 1$ than for writing 'the total is five times the pattern number, plus one'.
- Don't waffle or use irrelevant mathematics; present results and conclusions clearly.

State your findings

- Show how patterns have been used and test conclusions.
- State general results in words and explain what they mean.
- Write formulae and explain how they have been found from the situations explored.
- Prove the results using efficient mathematical methods.
- Develop new results from previous work and use clear reasoning to prove conclusions.
- Make sure your reasoning is accurate and draws upon the evidence you've presented.
- Show findings in clear, relevant diagrams.
- Check you've answered the question or hypothesis.

Review/conclusion/extension

- Is the solution acceptable?
- Can the task be extended?
- What can be learned from it?

Example task

On the next page there is a short investigative task for you to try, in both 'structured' and 'unstructured' form. The structured form shows the style of a question that might appear on a timed written paper. The unstructured form represents the usual style of a coursework task. The structured form leads you to an algebraic conclusion. Notice the appearance of algebra from question 4 onwards, through a series of structured questions. These mirror the sort of questions you would be expected to think of (and answer) if you were trying it as coursework.

Comments about the questions, linking the two forms of presentation, are also shown.

Although the task in both forms directs you to investigate trapezium numbers, you would be expected to extend the investigation into considering other forms of number, such as pentagon numbers, to achieve the higher marks.

Other tasks

In chapters 9, 13, 18 and 20, the text has been written using a 'task' approach. More practice for coursework can be obtained by using some or all of these chapters in this way.

There are two options for this part of the assessment. In one, your work is sent to an examiner and in the other your teacher marks it. In each case, the approach to the work is the same.

structured form

Trapezium numbers

These diagrams represent the first three trapezium numbers.

Each diagram always starts with two dots in the top row.

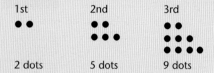

1st	2nd	3rd
2 dots	5 dots	9 dots

So the third trapezium number is 9 because 9 dots can be arranged as a trapezium. There are two dots in the top row, three dots in the next row and four dots in the bottom row.

1. Write down the next two trapezium numbers.

2. (a) Draw a table, graph or a chart of all the trapezium numbers, from the first to the tenth.
   (b) Work out the 11th trapezium number.

3. The 19th trapezium number is 209. Explain how you could work out the 20th trapezium number without drawing any diagrams.

4. Find an expression for the number of dots in the bottom row of the nth trapezium number. Test your expression for a suitable value of n.

5. Find, giving an explanation, an expression for the number of dots in the bottom row of the diagram for the $(n + 1)$th trapezium number.

6. The nth trapezium number is x. Write down an expression in terms of n and x for the $(n + 1)$th trapezium number. Test your expression for a suitable value of n.

unstructured form

Trapezium numbers

These diagrams represent the first three trapezium numbers.

Each diagram starts with two dots in the top row.

1st	2nd	3rd
2 dots	5 dots	9 dots

So the third trapezium number is 9 because nine dots can be arranged as a trapezium.

Investigate trapezium numbers

NB Although the task in this form directs you to investigate trapezium numbers, you have the freedom to – and are expected to – extend the investigation to consider other forms of number such as pentagon numbers.

Commentary

This question allows you to show understanding of the task, systematically obtaining information which **could** enable you to find an expression for trapezium numbers.

This question provides a structure, using symbols, words and diagrams, from which you should be able to derive an expression from either a table or a graph. Part (b) could be done as a 'predict and test'.

In the unstructured form you would not normally answer a question like this.

From here you are **directed** in the structured task, and **expected** in the unstructured task, to use algebra, testing the expression – the **generalisation**.

In the unstructured form this would represent the sort of 'new' question you might ask, to lead to a further solution and to demonstrate symbolic presentation and the ability to relate the work to the physical structure, rather than doing all the analysis from a table of values.

1   Numbers

You will need to know:

- about place value, for example 378.46 is 3 hundreds, 7 tens, 8 units, 4 tenths and 6 hundredths
- how to change fractions and percentages into decimals
- how to compare fractions
- about equivalent ratios, working with ratios and sharing in a given ratio
- how to add and subtract negative numbers.

Approximating numbers

There are two ways of approximating numbers, or rounding, when an exact answer or number is not required. Both are described below.

Method 1: rounding to the nearest whole number or to a given number of decimal places

Think of a number line.

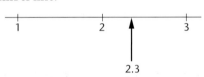

2.3 to the nearest whole number is 2.

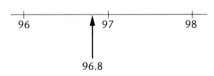

96.8 to the nearest whole number is 97.

Examiner's tip

Remember the rule that if the value of the first digit being ignored is 5 or more then round up.
Examples:
3.75 is 3.8 to 1 d.p.
0.0136 is 0.014 to 2 d.p.

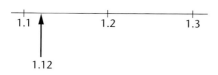

1.12 to the nearest tenth or one decimal place is 1.1.

Examiner's tip

When rounding to a number of decimal places, count the digits after the decimal point.

Example ① Write the following numbers correct to two decimal places (2 d.p.).

(a) 9.368   (b) 0.0438   (c) 84.655

(a) 9.368

> The first two decimal figures are 3 6, the third figure, the 8, is more than 5 so round up.

= 9.37 (to 2 d.p.)

(b) 0.0438

> The first two decimal figures are 0 4, the third figure is 3, which is less than 5, so round down.

= 0.04 (to 2 d.p.)

(c) 84.655

> The third decimal figure is 5 so the convention is to round up.

= 84.66 (to 2 d.p.)

Exercise 1.1a

1. Write these numbers first correct to two decimal places, then correct to one decimal place.
   (a) 5.481   (d) 0.5666   (g) 7.0064
   (b) 12.0782 (e) 9.017   (h) 0.0734
   (c) 0.214   (f) 78.044

2. Use your calculator to find the square root of 55. Write this value correct to:
   (a) one decimal place   (b) two decimal places.

3. Use your calculator to work out the value of $\sqrt{5^2 + 8^2}$.

Write your answer correct to two decimal places.

4. Write these fractions as decimals correct to three decimal places.
   (a) $\frac{1}{3}$ (b) $\frac{2}{7}$ (c) $\frac{3}{11}$ (d) $\frac{4}{13}$

5. Work out the mean of the following numbers. Give your answer correct to one decimal place.
   4, 6, 8, 9, 11, 3, 2, 15

6. Calculate 13.8% of 67.7, giving your answer correct to two decimal places.

Exercise 1.1b

1. Write these numbers first correct to two decimal places, then correct to one decimal place.
   (a) 9.424   (d) 0.85   (g) 7.1111
   (b) 0.8413   (e) 7.093   (h) 8.081
   (c) 0.283   (f) 18.63

2. Use your calculator to find the square root of 75. Write this value correct to:
   (a) two decimal places   (b) one decimal place.

3. Use your calculator to work out the value of $\sqrt{4^2 + 5^2}$.
   Write your answer correct to two decimal places.

4. Write these fractions as decimals correct to three decimal places.
   (a) $\frac{1}{8}$ (b) $\frac{3}{7}$ (c) $\frac{4}{11}$ (d) $\frac{5}{13}$

5. Work out the mean of the following numbers. Give your answer correct to one decimal place.
   3.51, 5.21, 7.91, 8.31, 9.41, 11.71, 13.51

6. Calculate 14.2% of 93.4, giving your answer correct to two decimal places.

Rounding to the nearest 10, 100, …

A number line may also help in rounding numbers to the nearest 10, 100 and so on.

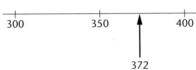

372 to the nearest 100 is 400.

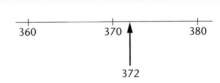

372 to the nearest 10 is 370.

Exercise 1.2a

1. Write these numbers correct to the nearest 10.
   (a) 456   (b) 254   (c) 123   (d) 998
   Write these numbers correct to the nearest 100.
   (e) 5678   (f) 9870   (g) 8801   (h) 151

   As with decimals the convention with a number in which the last digit is 5 is to round up so that, to the nearest 10, 35 would be 40 and 655 would be 660, and to the nearest 100, 550 would be 600 and 1350 would be 1400.

2. Round these numbers to the nearest 10 and then to the nearest 100.
   (a) 125   (b) 450   (c) 545   (d) 4555   (e) 1405

Exercise 1.2b

1. Round these numbers to the nearest 10.

    (a) 97   (b) 111   (c) 374   (d) 444

    Round these numbers to the nearest 1000.

    (e) 1234 (f) 8724 (g) 6789   (h) 9988

2. Round these numbers to the nearest 10 and then to the nearest 100.

    (a) 135   (b) 955   (c) 645   (d) 7555   (e) 1005

Method 2: rounding to a given number of significant figures

Sometimes you may be asked to give an answer to a given number of significant figures. Significant figures are counted from left to right, for example:

5 000 000 has one significant figure (1 s.f.). This is the 5.

5 300 000 has two significant figures (2 s.f.). These are the 5 and 3.

5 340 000 has three significant figures (3 s.f.). These are the 5, 3 and 4.

Rounding 5 340 000:

to one significant figure	
(rounding to the nearest million)	gives 5 000 000
to two significant figures	gives 5 300 000
to three significant figures	gives 5 340 000

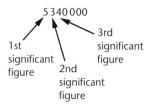

Note that zeros are kept to show the size of the number.

For a number less than 1, for example rounding 0.005 341 23:

to one significant figure	gives 0.005
to two significant figures	gives 0.0053
to three significant figures	gives 0.005 34

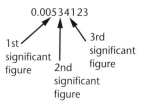

Note that zeros are kept to show the size of the number.

Figures are often rounded to one or more significant figures in newspapers:
- '30 000 see Derby win' when the actual attendance could have been 29 877
- 'Cambridge man wins £3 million' when the actual figure could have been £3 132 677.

Exercise 1.3a

1. Write each of these to the number of significant figures (s.f.) shown.
   - (a) 67 890 (to 3 s.f.)
   - (b) 54.123 (to 3 s.f.)
   - (c) 1789 (to 2 s.f.)
   - (d) 1 564 389 (to 5 s.f.)
   - (e) 0.006 78 (to 2 s.f.)
   - (f) 1.456 (to 2 s.f.)
   - (g) 0.0894 (to 1 s.f.)
   - (h) 45.278 (to 3 s.f.)

2. Work these out.
   - (a) 25% of 16 844 (to 2 s.f.)
   - (b) 80% of 888 (to 3 s.f.)

3. A room is 3.65 m long, 2.44 m wide and 2.2 m high. Calculate the total wall area, correct to two significant figures.

4. The amounts of money taken in a charity shop, over a six-day period, are listed here.
   £245.77, £452.88, £189.52, £212.79, £181.83, £233.56
   - (a) Calculate the average daily takings, correct to three significant figures.

   The shop is open for 51 weeks in the year.
   - (b) Use your answer to part (a) to estimate the yearly takings. Give this answer correct to two significant figures.

5. Round each of these numbers to two significant figures.
   - (a) 76 560
   - (b) 681
   - (c) 0.8099
   - (d) 3.086
   - (e) 0.707

6. Work these out on your calculator. Round your answers to two decimal places.
   - (a) $19 \div 16$
   - (b) $\sqrt{30}$
   - (c) 1.59^2
   - (d) 1.3^3
   - (e) 0.35×1.35

7. Estimate the answers to these calculations by rounding the numbers to one significant figure. Compare your estimates with the calculations worked out on a calculator and with the answers rounded to two significant figures.
   - (a) $5.89 \times 0.186\,75$
   - (b) $19.258 \div 3.889$
   - (c) 36.87×15.87
   - (d) $9.7687 \div 0.0512$
   - (e) $2.14 \times 5.8754 \times 0.9876$

Exercise 1.3b

1. Write each of these to the number of significant figures (s.f.) shown.
   - (a) 12 340 (to 3 s.f.)
   - (b) 76.456 (to 3 s.f.)
   - (c) 1654 (to 2 s.f.)
   - (d) 1 456 789 (to 5 s.f.)
   - (e) 0.007 98 (to 2 s.f.)
   - (f) 1567 (to 2 s.f.)
   - (g) 0.0923 (to 1 s.f.)
   - (h) 54.827 (to 3 s.f.)

2. Work these out.
   - (a) 30% of 17 824 (to 2 s.f.)
   - (b) 70% of 999 (to 3 s.f.)

3. A water tank is 4.45 m long, 3.24 m wide and 1.4 m high. Calculate the volume correct to two significant figures.

4. Find the average of these numbers.
   134.64, 157.92, 194.33, 254.45, 188.88
   Give this answer correct to two significant figures.

5. Work these out on your calculator. Round your answers to two decimal places.
   - (a) $24 \div 17$
   - (b) $\sqrt{40}$
   - (c) 1.78^2
   - (d) 1.5^3
   - (e) 0.42×1.42

6. Estimate the answers to these calculations by rounding the numbers to one significant figure. Compare your estimates with the calculations worked out on a calculator, and with the answers rounded to two significant figures.
   - (a) $4.89 \times 0.196\,54$
   - (b) $24.342 \div 4.874$
   - (c) 34.62×16.34
   - (d) $7.9685 \div 0.0432$
   - (e) $8.16 \times 5.974 \times 0.9325$

Ordering numbers

Ordering numbers means arranging them in size order. It is essential to work with numbers that are all of the same type, for example to compare fractions and decimals, change the fractions into decimals, using a calculator if necessary.

Put these numbers in size order, smallest first.

$\frac{3}{5}$, 0.55, 0.7

$\frac{3}{5} = 0.6$ so the order is 0.55, 0.6, 0.7

To compare fractions with different denominators, either change them into decimals (the simplest approach), or change them into equivalent fractions.

Write these fractions in size order, smallest first.

$\frac{2}{5}, \frac{3}{7}, \frac{4}{9}$

$\frac{2}{5} = 0.4$ $\qquad \frac{3}{7} = 0.428\ 57$ $\qquad \frac{4}{9} = 0.444\ 44$

or $\frac{2}{5} = \frac{126}{315}$ $\qquad \frac{3}{7} = \frac{135}{315}$ $\qquad \frac{4}{9} = \frac{140}{315}$

> Make sure you understand why 315 is in the denominator of each fraction.

They were given in size order.

Exercise 1.4a

1. Make as many fractions as you can, choosing pairs of numbers from those listed.
   3   4   5   6
   Put your fractions in order, smallest first.
2. Write these decimals in order, starting with the smallest.
   0.000 280, 0.0098, 0.0126, 0.0042, 0.5, 0.0014
3. Write these numbers in order, largest first.
   15 065, 15 605, 156 005, 1 560 005, 15 565
4. Write these numbers in size order, from largest to smallest.
   0.6, 0.006 004, 0.0624, 0.62

Exercise 1.4b

1. Make as many fractions as you can, choosing pairs of numbers from those listed.
   6   7   8   9
   Put your fractions in order, smallest first.
2. Write these decimals in order, starting with the smallest.
   0.000 342, 0.0064, 0.0136, 0.004 14, 0.6, 0.0015
3. Write these numbers in order, largest first.
   14 104, 14 140, 141 401, 1 410 401
4. Write these numbers in order, from largest to smallest.
   0.4, 0.424, 0.042 424, 0.442, 0.0044

Ratio

When comparing ratios make sure the units are the same.

Ratios can be used to compare quantities.

The ratio of noughts to crosses in this box is 3 to 1 which can be written as 3 : 1,

| 0 0 0 X |

but the ratio of crosses to noughts is 1 : 3.

The order in which a ratio is given is important.

If a ratio is written as $n : 1$ it means that the first quantity is n times the second quantity, so if a colour is made by mixing yellow and red paint in the ratio 5 : 1, there is five times as much yellow paint as red paint.

Maps often have their scale expressed in the form 1 : n, for example 1 : 50 000 means that 1 cm on the map represents 50 000 cm on the ground.

Exercise 1.5a

1. Copy these statements and complete them.
   (a) 1 : 4 is equivalent to 6 : □
   (b) 2 : 5 is equivalent to 12 : □
   (c) 4 : 5 is equivalent to □ : 40
   (d) 4 : 5 : 6 is equivalent to □ : 15 : □
2. Write these ratios in their simplest form.
   (a) 40p to £4   (b) 100 kg to 25 kg
   (c) 2 to 2.5   (d) 0.5 to 9
3. Write these ratios in the form 1 : n.
   (a) 4 : 20 (b) 9 : 27 (c) 3.5 : 14 (d) 0.1 : 30
4. A map is drawn with a scale of 1 : 30 000.
   Two towns are 7.6 cm apart on the map. How far apart are they on the ground?
5. The scale of a map is 1 : 100 000.
   The length of a road is 2.8 km. How long will the road be on the map?
6. The teacher−student ratio in a school is given as 1 : n.

   (a) If the ratio for a school is 1 : 17.6 about how many staff would you expect in a school with 700 students?
   (b) A school has 84 staff. About how many students would you expect the school to have?
7. Write the following ratios in the form 1 : n.
   (a) 2 cm to 1 m   (b) 1 litre to 5000 ml
   (c) 4 minutes to 4 hours
8. A prize is divided so that one person gets three times as much as the other.
   (a) Write this as a ratio.
   (b) If the prize money were £480 how much should each person get?
9. The Fibonacci series is 1 1 2 3 5 8 ...
   (a) Continue the series for another five terms.
   (b) Use your calculator to investigate the ratio of each term to the previous one. What do you notice?

1. Copy these statements and complete them.
   (a) 1 : 5 is equivalent to 5 : □
   (b) 3 : 4 is equivalent to 12 : □
   (c) 3 : 5 is equivalent to □ : 80
   (d) 5 : 6 : 7 is equivalent to □ : 18: □

2. Write these ratios in their simplest form.
   (a) 30p to £3   (b) 100 g to 10 kg   (c) 3 to 3.6   (d) 0.5 to 5

3. Write these ratios in the form 1 : n.
   (a) 5 : 35   (b) 16 : 48   (c) 5.2 : 26   (d) 0.2 : 30

4. A map is drawn with a scale of 1 : 250 000.
   Two towns are 8.5 cm apart on the map. How far apart are they on the ground?

5. The scale of a map is 1 : 100 000.
   The length of a road is 3.2 km. How long will the road be on the map?

6. On a map, the distance between two towns is 12 cm. How far apart are they on the ground if the scale is 1 : 300 000?

7. Write the following ratios in the form 1 : □.
   (a) 20 g to 5 kg   (b) 1 m to 15 000 cm   (c) 7 days to 4 weeks

8. A prize is divided so that one person gets five times as much as the other.
   (a) Write this as a ratio.
   (b) If the prize money were £480 how much should each person get?

Negative numbers

Multiplying and dividing

When multiplying and dividing the following rules apply.

$(+) \times (+) = (+)$ $(+) \div (+) = (+)$
$(-) \times (-) = (+)$ $(-) \div (-) = (+)$
$(-) \times (+) = (-)$ $(-) \div (+) = (-)$
$(+) \times (-) = (-)$ $(+) \div (-) = (-)$

Examiner's tip

Use the change of sign button, (+/−) on your calculator to give negative numbers.

Example 4

$-3 \times -4 = +12$

$-7 \times +9 = -63$

$-24 \div -6 = 4$

1. (a) $-9 \times -6 =$ (b) $+12 \times -6 =$ (c) $-3 \times +14 =$
   (d) $-8 \times -50 =$ (e) $-7 \times -60 =$ (f) $+12 \times +9 =$
   (g) $+45 \div -15 =$ (h) $-88 \div +4 =$ (i) $+144 \div -9 =$

2. Copy this number square and complete it.

$\times$			4	
10	80	-60		-30
-7		42		21
	24	-18		-9
	-40	30	-20	15

3. Replace the □ with the numbers -6, -3 and 2 to make these statements true.
   (a) $\square \div \square \times \square = 1$ (b) $(\square \div \square) - \square = 0$
   (c) $(\square - \square) \times \square = -30$

4. If $x = -3$ find the value of:
   (a) $3x$ (b) $4 \div x$ (c) $x \div 4$ (d) $3x^2$
   (e) x^3 (f) $4x + 3$ (g) $5x^2 - 6$ (h) $(-4x)^2$

1. (a) $-5 \times -7 =$ (b) $+5 \times -6 =$ (c) $-6 \times +7 =$
   (d) $-9 \times -3 =$ (e) $-6 \times -8 =$ (f) $+8 \times +9 =$
   (g) $+16 \div -4 =$ (h) $-24 \div +3 =$ (i) $+56 \div -8 =$

2. Copy this number square and complete it.

$\times$		-7		
	-9	21		-15
6	18		-54	30
8		-56		40
-9	-27		81	

3. Replace the □ with the numbers -8, -4 and -2 to make these statements true.
   (a) $\square \div \square \times \square = -1$ (b) $(\square \div \square) + \square = 0$
   (c) $(\square - \square) \times \square = 16$

4. If $x = -4$ find the value of:
   (a) $5x$ (b) $8 \div x$ (c) $x \div -2$ (d) $2x^2$ (e) x^3 (f) $4x + 4$
   (g) $3x^2 - 8$ (h) $(-3x)^2$

Indices

Indices (or powers) are a form of mathematical shorthand:

$3 \times 3 \times 3 \times 3$ is written as 3^4 and
$2 \times 2 \times 2 \times 2 \times 2 \times 2 \times 2 \times 2$ is written as 2^8.

Multiplying numbers in index form

$$3^4 \times 3^8 = (3 \times 3 \times 3 \times 3) \times (3 \times 3 \times 3 \times 3 \times 3 \times 3 \times 3 \times 3)$$
$$= 3 \times 3 \times 3 \times 3 \times 3 \times 3 \times 3 \times 3 \times 3 \times 3 \times 3 \times 3$$
$$= 3^{12}$$

The indices or powers are added i.e. $3^4 \times 3^8 = 3^{4+8} = 3^{12}$

The rule is $n^a \times n^b = n^{a+b}$

Powers of numbers can also be raised to powers.

If the numbers are in brackets then powers are multiplied.

Example 5
$$(3^4)^2 = (3^4) \times (3^4) = 3^8$$
$$\text{and } 3^{4 \times 2} = 3^8$$

The rule is $(n^a)^b = n^{a \times b}$

Dividing numbers in index form

$$2^6 \div 2^4 = (2 \times 2 \times 2 \times 2 \times 2 \times 2) \div (2 \times 2 \times 2 \times 2)$$
$$= 2 \times 2$$
$$= 2^2$$

so $2^6 \div 2^4 = 2^{(6-4)}$
$$= 2^2$$

The rule is $n^a \div n^b = n^{a-b}$

If the subtraction gives a negative answer, for example $2^4 \div 2^6$
then the rule gives the result 2^{-2}.

$$\text{But } 2^4 \div 2^6 = \frac{2 \times 2 \times 2 \times 2}{2 \times 2 \times 2 \times 2 \times 2 \times 2}$$
$$= \frac{1}{2^2}$$

so $2^{-2} = \frac{1}{2^2}$

The rule is $n^{-a} = \frac{1}{n^a}$

One important fact can be shown from the following example.

> **Example 6** Work out $4^3 \div 4^3$.
>
> Using the rule established above:
>
> $4^3 \div 4^3 = 4^{3-3} = 4^0$
>
> but $4^3 \div 4^3 = (4 \times 4 \times 4) \div (4 \times 4 \times 4) = 1$
>
> therefore $4^0 = 1$

The rule is $n^0 = 1$

Finally look at the following example.

> **Example 7** Write these in index form.
>
> (a) $5 \times 5 \times 6 \times 6 \times 6 \times 6$
>
> (b) $3x^3 \times 4x^5$
>
> (c) $25x^4 \div 5x^2$
>
> (d) $4^3 \div 4^6$
>
> (a) $5 \times 5 \times 6 \times 6 \times 6 \times 6 = 5^2 \times 6^4$
>
> (b) $3x^3 \times 4x^5 = 12x^8$
>
> (c) $25x^4 \div 5x^2 = 5x^2$
>
> (d) $4^3 \div 4^6 = 4^{3-6} = 4^{-3}$

Exercise 1.7a

1. Write these in a simpler form, using indices.
   (a) $3 \times 3 \times 3 \times 3 \times 3$
   (b) $7 \times 7 \times 7$
   (c) $8 \times 8 \times 8 \times 8 \times 8$
   (d) $3 \times 3 \times 5 \times 5 \times 5$
   (e) $2 \times 2 \times 2 \times 3 \times 3 \times 4 \times 4 \times 4 \times 4 \times 4$

2. Write these in a simpler form, using indices.
   (a) $5^2 \times 5^3$ (b) $6^2 \times 6^7$ (c) $10^3 \times 10^4$
   (d) $3^6 \times 3^5$ (e) $8^3 \times 8^2$ (f) $5^{-2} \times 5^{-4}$

3. Work these out, giving your answers in index form.
   (a) $\dfrac{3^4}{3^5 \times 3^2}$ (b) $\dfrac{(2^3)^4}{2^5}$ (c) $\dfrac{5^2 \times 5^3}{5^4 \times 5^5}$

Exercise 1.7b

1. Write these in a simpler form, using indices.
   (a) $4 \times 4 \times 4 \times 4 \times 4$
   (b) $8 \times 8 \times 8$
   (c) $2 \times 2 \times 2 \times 2 \times 2$
   (d) $5 \times 4 \times 4 \times 4 \times 5$
   (e) $7 \times 7 \times 7 \times 8 \times 8 \times 9 \times 9 \times 9$

2. Write these in a simpler form, using indices.
   (a) $4^2 \times 4^3$ (b) $9^2 \times 9^7$ (c) $10^5 \times 10^2$
   (d) $3^5 \times 3^2$ (e) $8^4 \times 8^2$ (f) $6^2 \times 6^6$
   (g) $7^5 \div 7^3$ (h) $9^7 \div 9^9$ (i) $6^3 \div 6^2$
   (j) $3^6 \div 3^3$ (k) $4^4 \div 4^4$

3. Work these out, giving your answers in index form.
   (a) $\dfrac{4^6}{4^5 \times 4^4}$ (b) $\dfrac{(2^4)^2}{2^4}$ (c) $\dfrac{6^2 \times 6}{6^5 \times 6^4}$

Standard form

Standard form is a very important use of powers and indices. It is a way of writing numbers as a number from 1 to 10 multiplied by a power of 10.

 Example 8

$4\,000\,000 = 4 \times 10^6$

$0.03 = 3 \times 10^{-2}$

Examiner's tip

Standard form is useful for expressing very large or very small numbers.

 Example 9

The speed of light is $300\,000\,000$ m/s

$= 3 \times 100\,000\,000$ ← This line can be omitted.

$= 3 \times 10^8$ m/s

A virus is $0.000\,000\,000\,56$ cm in diameter

$= \dfrac{5.6}{10\,000\,000\,000}$ ← This line can be omitted.

$= 5.6 \times 10^{-10}$ cm

Examiner's tip

In standard form, a number is written as a number from 1 to 10 multiplied by a power of 10.

Exercise 1.8a

1. Write these numbers in standard form.
   (a) 5000 (b) 50 (c) 70 000
   (d) 46 (e) 0.02 (f) 546 000
   (g) 0.000 45 (h) 16 million

2. These numbers are in standard form. Write them out in full.
   (a) 5×10^2 (b) 4×10^5 (c) 6×10^{-3}
   (d) 4.5×10^3 (e) 8.4×10^{-3} (f) 2.87×10^{-5}
   (g) 9.7×10^3 (h) 5.55×10^{-5}

Exercise 1.8b

1. Write these numbers in standard form.
   (a) 6000 (b) 80 (c) 30 000
   (d) 67 (e) 0.08 (f) 897 000
   (g) 0.000 54 (h) 18 million

2. These numbers are in standard form. Write them out in full.
   (a) 7×10^2 (b) 8×10^5 (c) 3×10^{-3}
   (d) 2.5×10^3 (e) 6.7×10^{-3} (f) 3.82×10^{-5}
   (g) 5.7×10^3 (h) 4.65×10^{-5}

Working with numbers in standard form

Always take care when working with numbers written in standard form. With multiplication and division you can deal with the numbers in the normal way.

 Example 10

Work out $(3 \times 10^2) \times (4 \times 10^3)$.

$(3 \times 10^2) \times (4 \times 10^3) = 3 \times 4 \times 10^2 \times 10^3$
$= 12 \times 10^{2+3}$
$= 12 \times 10^5$
$= 1.2 \times 10^6$

Examiner's tip

Find out how your calculator deals with standard form. Most do not require '×10' but have an (EXP) key. On these, to enter 4×10^3 press (4) (EXP) (3).

Addition and subtraction are not so straightforward.

> **Example** Work out $(3 \times 10^2) + (4 \times 10^3)$.
>
> It is safer to write out the numbers in the brackets first, add then change the answer back into standard form.
>
> $(3 \times 10^2) + (4 \times 10^3) = 300 + 4000$
> $= 4300 = 4.3 \times 10^3$

Exercise 1.9a

Work out these calculations. Give your answers in standard form.

(a) $(5 \times 10^3) + (7 \times 10^4)$
(b) $(7 \times 10^6) - (3 \times 10^3)$
(c) $(3 \times 10^3) + (3 \times 10^2)$
(d) $(6 \times 10^3) - (5 \times 10^2)$

Exercise 1.9b

Work out these calculations. Give your answers in standard form.

(a) $(4 \times 10^3) + (5 \times 10^4)$
(b) $(8 \times 10^6) - (4 \times 10^3)$
(c) $(2 \times 10^3) + (4 \times 10^2)$
(d) $(4 \times 10^3) - (3 \times 10^2)$

Powers and roots

The set of whole numbers 1, 4, 9, 16, 25, 36, ... are **squares** of the counting numbers, for example:

$1 = 1^2, 4 = 2^2, 9 = 3^2$

Because $16 = 4^2$ the **square root** of 16 is 4, written as $\sqrt{16} = 4$. Similarly $\sqrt{36} = 6$ and $\sqrt{81} = 9$.

The numbers 1, 8, 27, 64, ... are **cube** numbers because each of them can be written as the cube of a whole number, for example:

$8 = 2^3, 27 = 3^3$

Because $27 = 3^3$ the cube root of 27 is 3, written as $\sqrt[3]{27} = 3$.

Exercise 1.10a

1. Write down the square of each number.
   (a) 7   (b) 12   (c) 25   (d) 40   (e) $(6^2 - 5^2)$
2. Write down the square root of each number.
   (a) 49   (b) 121   (c) 169   (d) 289   (e) $(3^2 + 4^2)$
3. Write down the cube of each number.
   (a) 4   (b) 5   (c) 6   (d) 10   (e) 2^3
4. Write down the cube root of each number.
   (a) 343   (b) 729   (c) 1331   (d) 1 000 000
5. Work these out, giving your answers correct to two decimal places.
   (a) $\sqrt{56}$ (b) $\sqrt{27}$ (c) $\sqrt{60}$ (d) $\sqrt{280}$ (e) $\sqrt{678}$

Exercise I.IOb

1. Write down the square of each number.
   (a) 8 (b) 11 (c) 35 (d) 50 (e) $(7^2 - 5^2)$
2. Write down the square root of each number.
   (a) 81 (b) 144 (c) 196 (d) 361 (e) $(2^2 + 6^2)$
3. Write down the cube of each number.
   (a) 2 (b) 3 (c) 1.5 (d) 7 (e) 2^2
4. Write down the cube root of each number.
   (a) 216 (b) 512 (c) 1728 (d) 1000
5. Work these out, giving your answers correct to two decimal places.
   (a) $\sqrt{70}$ (b) $\sqrt{39}$ (c) $\sqrt{90}$ (d) $\sqrt{380}$ (e) $\sqrt{456}$

Reciprocal

Earlier in this chapter you saw this rule:

$$n^{-a} = \frac{1}{n^a}$$

When the power (the value of a) is 1, the rule becomes

$$n^{-1} = \frac{1}{n}$$

and $\frac{1}{n}$ is called the **reciprocal** of n.

Similarly, n is the reciprocal of $\frac{1}{n}$.

> **Examiner's tip**
>
> If you find the reciprocal of, or divide by, a very small number, the result is very large. (Try $1 \div 0.000\,000\,01$ on your calculator.) If you divide by 0 you will not get a number, but your calculator will probably show E for error. Mathematicians call the result of dividing by zero **infinity**.

> **Example**
>
> Write down the reciprocal of (a) 4 (b) 25.
>
> (a) The reciprocal of 4 is $\frac{1}{4}$.
>
> (b) The reciprocal of 25 $= \frac{1}{25}$.

Exercise I.IIa

1. Write down the reciprocal of each of these numbers.
   (a) 3 (b) 6 (c) 49 (d) 100 (e) 640
2. Write down the numbers of which these are the reciprocals.
   (a) $\frac{1}{16}$ (b) $\frac{1}{9}$ (c) $\frac{1}{52}$ (d) $\frac{1}{67}$ (e) $\frac{1}{1000}$

Exercise I.IIb

1. Write down the reciprocal of each of these numbers.
   (a) 4 (b) 9 (c) 65 (d) 10 (e) 4.5
2. Write down the numbers of which these are the reciprocals.
   (a) $\frac{1}{3}$ (b) $\frac{1}{10}$ (c) $\frac{1}{25}$ (d) $\frac{1}{71}$ (e) $\frac{1}{100}$

Key points

- 23 to the nearest 10 is 20.
- 379 to the nearest 100 is 400.
- 4.569, correct to two decimal places, is 4.57.
- 343, correct to two significant figures, is 340.
- 4 : 16 is the same ratio as 1 : 4.

- Multiplying or dividing a negative number by a negative number gives a positive answer.
- In standard form, $432 = 4.32 \times 10^2$.
- $2^3 = 8$ and $\sqrt[3]{8} = 2$.
- Reciprocals are written as, for example, the reciprocal of $9 = \frac{1}{9}$.

Revision exercise 1a

1. Write the following numbers correct to two decimal places.
   (a) 7.897   (b) 13.1234   (c) 0.243
   (d) 0.6772

2. Work out the value of $\sqrt{6^2 + 5^3}$.
   Write your answer correct to two decimal places.

3. Write these fractions as decimals correct to three decimal places.
   (a) $\frac{3}{7}$ (b) $\frac{2}{11}$ (c) $\frac{2}{13}$ (d) $\frac{7}{13}$

4. Calculate 17.5% of £167.75, giving your answer correct to two decimal places.

5. Write these numbers to the nearest 10.
   (a) 127   (b) 543   (c) 995   (d) 1239
   Write these numbers to the nearest 100.
   (e) 7898   (f) 9820   (g) 8850   (h) 51

6. Write each of these correct to the stated number of significant figures (s.f.).
   (a) 6789 (to 3 s.f.)   (b) 57.123 (to 3 s.f.)
   (c) 1897 (to 2 s.f.)   (d) 1 576 398 (to 5 s.f.)
   (e) 0.005 88 (to 2 s.f.)   (f) 1.756 (to 2 s.f.)
   (g) 0.0812 (to 1 s.f.)   (h) 40.278 (to 3 s.f.)

7. Write these decimals in order, starting with the smallest.
   0.000 980, 0.0098, 0.0926, 0.9042, 0.9, 0.914

8. Write these ratios in the form $1 : n$.
   (a) 6 : 24   (b) 36 : 72   (c) 2.5 : 7.5
   (d) 0.1 : 3

9. A map is drawn with a scale of 1 : 25 000. Two towns are 8.6 cm apart on the map. How far apart are they on the ground?

10. Write the following ratios in the form $1 : n$.
    (a) 10 m to 2 km   (b) 10 g to 5000 kg
    (c) 40p to £4

11. Without using a calculator, work these out.
    (a) $-8 \times -9 =$ (b) $+25 \times -6 =$
    (c) $-6 \times +3 =$ (d) $-12 \times -3 =$
    (e) $-6 \times -5 =$ (f) $+8 \times +12 =$
    (g) $+36 \div -4 =$ (h) $-24 \div +8 =$
    (i) $+56 \div -7 =$

12. If $x = -5$ find the value of each of these expressions.
    (a) $4x$ (b) $10 \div x$ (c) $x \div 2$ (d) $3x^2$
    (e) x^3 (f) $4x + 3$ (g) $5x^2 - 6$ (h) $(-4x)^2$

13. Write these numbers in a simpler form.
    (a) $7^2 \times 7^3$ (b) $6^3 \times 6^6$ (c) $10^9 \times 10^3$
    (d) $3^4 \times 3^8$ (e) $8^9 \div 8^3$ (f) $6^7 \div 6^9$
    (g) $4^2 \div 4^3$ (h) $9^6 \div 9^2$

14. Write these numbers in standard form.
    (a) 7600   (b) 89.9   (c) 60 000
    (d) 466   (e) 0.056   (f) 564 600
    (g) 0.0055   (h) 24 million

15. These numbers are in standard form. Write them out in full.
    (a) 6×10^3 (b) 5×10^2
    (c) 7×10^{-3} (d) 4.5×10^2
    (e) 8.4×10^{-2} (f) 2.87×10^{-3}
    (g) 4.7×10^3 (h) 5.55×10^{-2}

16. Work out these calculations. Give your answers in standard form.
    (a) $(6 \times 10^3) + (8 \times 10^3)$
    (b) $(7 \times 10^4) - (2 \times 10^3)$

You will need to know:

- that the sum of the angles of a triangle is 180°
- in an isosceles triangle the angles opposite the equal sides are themselves equal
- the properties of alternate and corresponding angles.

Exterior angle of a triangle

If one of the sides of a triangle is extended, to form an angle outside the triangle, this angle is called the exterior angle.

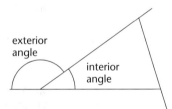

exterior angle

interior angle

Draw a large triangle with sides 10 cm, 12 cm and 14 cm. Extend the length of the base.

Cut off two of the corners, as shown by the shaded angles.

Try to fit them together, next to the remaining angle at the base.

What do you notice?

They should fit over the exterior angle.

exterior angle

Repeat for a different sized triangle with a different exterior angle.

Does the same thing happen?

You have demonstrated that:

The exterior angle of a triangle is equal to the sum of the interior opposite angles.

Activity 2

Try to write a proof of the result you have just found, using some or all of the statements given below. Give reasons if you can.

Note that there is more than one proof.

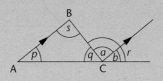

$a + b = r$	because angles on a straight line add up to 180°
$p = b$	because they are alternate angles
$p + s = r$	because they are vertically opposite angles
$s = a$	because they are corresponding angles
$p + s = a + b$	because angles in a triangle add up to 180°

Exercise 2.1a

1. Calculate the sizes of all the angles marked with letters.

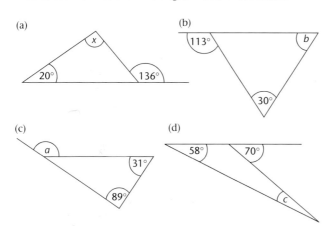

(a)

(b)

(c)

(d)

2. Write down as many different ways as you can to find the value of *e* once you have found the value of *d*.

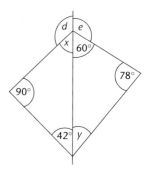

3. Calculate the sizes of all the angles marked with letters.

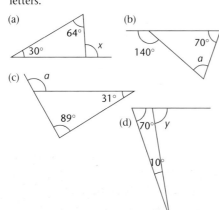

(a)

(b)

(c)

(d)

4. Calculate the sizes of all the angles marked with letters.

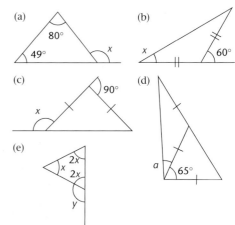

(a)

(b)

(c)

(d)

(e)

1. Calculate the sizes of all the angles marked with letters.

(a)

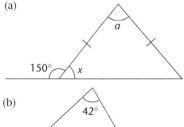

(b)

(c)

2. Calculate the sizes of all the angles marked with letters.

(a)

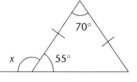

(b)

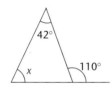

(c)

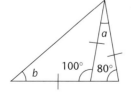

3. Calculate the sizes of all the angles marked with letters.

(a)

(b)

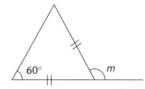

4. Calculate the sizes of all the angles marked with letters.

(a)

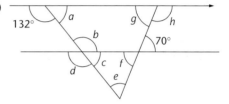

(b)

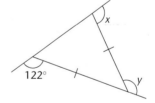

(c)

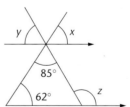

Examiner's tip

Remember all the angle properties you have met. There are several ways of calculating some of these angles.

Chapter 2   Exterior angle of a triangle

23

Angle in a semicircle

- Draw a circle of radius 6 cm.
  On the circumference, mark three points that can be joined up to form a right-angled triangle. Repeat for circles with different radii.
  What do you notice? Write down your idea.
- Now test your idea by drawing a right-angled triangle with sides 6 cm, 8 cm and 10 cm.
  Use a protractor or angle measurer to draw the angles as accurately as you can.
  Draw a circle that passes through the three vertices of the triangle.
  Was your idea correct?
  Check by drawing a different right-angled triangle and then drawing a circle round it.
- An alternative approach is to use a set-square or a piece of card with a right-angled corner, and two nails.
  You could use two points marked on the paper if you prefer to.
  Place the set-square between the two nails so that the edges of the set-square which form the right angle touch the nails.

- Mark a point to represent the position of the tip of the right angle, when the edges of the set-square are firmly against the nails.
  Repeat for different positions of the set-square.
  (a) What shape are the marks forming?
  (b) What can you say about the line joining the two nails (or points)?

(c) What would happen if the angle at the corner were acute?
(d) What would happen if the angle at the corner were obtuse?
(e) In each case, state what shape would be formed.

Now you can prove it. Study the diagram, then work through the statements given below.

Copy statements 1–4 and complete them, filling in the reasons.

1. The lines OA, OP and OB are equal because …
2. The angles marked a are equal to each other because …
3. The angles marked b are equal to each other because …
4. In triangle APB, $a + a + b + b = 180°$ because …

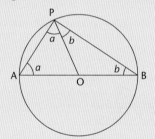

In other words $2(a + b) = 180°$
so angle APB $= a + b = 90°$

- Now use a cylindrical tin, or something similar, to draw a circle.
  Use the fact that the angle in a semicircle is 90° to think of a method for finding the centre of the circle which you have drawn.
  Explain your method.

Notes

(a) You should find that if you repeat the activity enough times the pencil marks at the right-angled corner will trace a circle.

(b) The line joining the two nails (or points) is a diameter.

(c)–(e) If the angle is acute, the points form the major part of a circle.
If the process is continued below the imaginary line joining N1 and N2 the shape formed makes two parts of two equal circles which join but do not make a complete circle.
If the angle is obtuse then a similar result is obtained but from the smaller part of a circle.

The angle in a semicircle is 90°.

You have just demonstrated an important fact!

Exercise 2.2a

In question 1–3, points A and B are at opposite ends of a diameter of the circle with its centre at O.

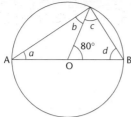

1. (a) Without calculating their values, write down a fact that is true about a and b, and also about c and d.
    (b) Now write down their values, explaining how you worked them out.
    (c) Write down another angle fact that you could use to check that your answer to part (b) is correct.

2. Calculate the value of a.

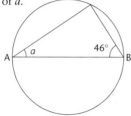

3. (a) Calculate the sizes of the angles marked with letters in this diagram.

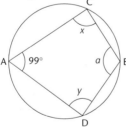

    (b) Why can't the straight line joining C and D be a diameter?

4. APQBRS is a regular hexagon. Prove that AB is a diameter.

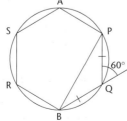

Exercise 2.2b

1. Calculate the size of the angles marked with letters.

    (a)   (b)

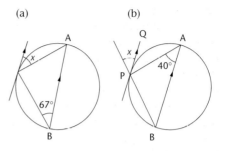

2. If AB is a diameter, what can you say about angles C and D?

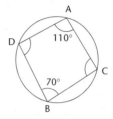

3. These three diagrams show semicircles. Find the sizes of all the angles marked with letters.

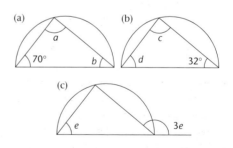

4. Find the sizes of all the angles marked with letters in this diagram, if O is the centre of the circle.

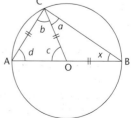

Angles in polygons

Activity 4

- What is the maximum number of internal right angles any particular polygon can have?

  Investigate for polygons with up to eight sides.

- Is there a relationship between the number of sides and the maximum number of right angles?

- Is there a relationship between the number of sides a polygon has and the total of its interior angles?

  > Interior and exterior angles of polygons were explained in Chapter 6 of the Intermediate book.

- Think of some 'What if … ?' questions. Investigate them.

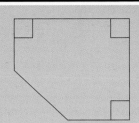

You already know that for any polygon, interior angle + exterior angle = 180°.

This fact can be used to work out the number of sides of a regular polygon, if its interior angle is known.

Example 1

Find the number of sides of a regular polygon with an interior angle of 144°.

If the interior angle = 144° the exterior angle = 36°.

The sum of the exterior angles = 360°.

Therefore the number of sides = 360° ÷ 36° = 10.

Exercise 2.3a

1. Work out the number of sides of the regular polygons with these interior angles.
   (a) 150°   (b) 135°   (c) 140°   (d) 60°
   (e) 156°

2. Is it possible to make a tessellation which has six identical regular polygons fitting round a point?

   (a) If so, what size must the interior angle be?
   (b) How many sides will the polygon have?

3. Calculate the interior angle of a regular polygon with:
   (a) 100 sides   (b) 1000 sides.

Exercise 2.3b

1. The interior angle of a regular polygon is 160°.
    (a) How many sides does it have?
    (b) Will it tessellate?

2. The interior angle of a regular polygon is $13x$ and the exterior angle is $2x$.
    (a) Calculate x.
    (b) Find the number of sides of the polygon.

3. (a) Copy this table for regular polygons, and complete it.

Name of shape	Number of sides	Exterior angle	Interior angle
equilateral triangle	3		
square	4		
pentagon	5		
hexagon	6		
heptagon	7		
octagon	8		
nonagon	9		
decagon	10		
dodecagon	12		

   (b) Draw a graph plotting the interior angle against the number of sides. What do you notice?
   (c) Is it possible to have a regular polygon with $3\frac{1}{2}$ sides?
   (d) Follow these steps and try to draw it. You will need about half a page for the drawing.
       (i) From the graph of interior angle plotted against number of sides, when there are $3\frac{1}{2}$ sides the angle will be about 77°. You could check this by calculation.
       (ii) Follow the sketch below as you read the instructions. Draw a line 10 cm long across the page (line 1). At one end, measure and draw the second line (line 2), also 10 cm long, at an angle of 77° to the first line. Continue drawing lines 3, 4, 5, 6 and 7 in the same way. Line 7 should bring you back to the start.

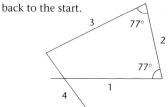

   (e) As an improper fraction, $3\frac{1}{2}$ is $\frac{7}{2}$. Can you see a link with your drawing and the figures 7 and 2?
   (f) Investigate other polygons with fractional numbers of sides. Try a polygon with $2\frac{1}{2}$ sides.

Angles in circles

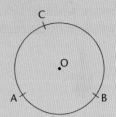

Activity 5

(a) Draw a circle, radius 6 cm. Mark the centre O.

Mark three points, A, B and C, as shown. Join AO, AC, BO, BC.

Measure angle AOB and angle ACB. What do you notice?

Try with other points on the circle.

Suggest two general results.

(b) Now draw a straight line to touch the circle at A. This is a tangent.

Measure the angle between the tangent and the radius at A.

Try this at other points.

Suggest a general result.

(c) Draw another circle.

Mark four points round the circumference, A, B, C and D, join them in order.

Measure angles ABC and CDA. Add them.

Measure angles BCD and DAB. Add them.

Try this for another circle and quadrilateral.

Suggest a general result.

General results

Definitions:
- 'subtended by' means made, or based on

- a cyclic quadrilateral has all its vertices on the circumference of a circle

- The angle subtended by an arc (or chord) of a circle is twice the angle subtended by the same arc at the circumference.
- Angles subtended at the circumference by the same arc (or chord) are equal.
- The angle between a tangent and the radius at the point of contact is 90°.
- The opposite angles of a cyclic quadrilateral add up to 180°.

Exercise 2.4a

Work out the sizes of all the angles marked with letters. In each case, O is the centre of the circle.

1.

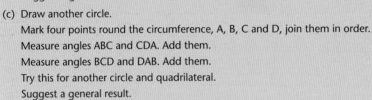

2.

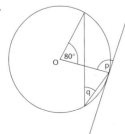
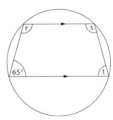

Exercise 2.4b

Work out the sizes of all the angles marked with letters. In each case, O is the centre of the circle.

1.

2.

Angle s = angle t

Key points

- The exterior angle of a triangle is equal to the sum of the interior opposite angles.
- The angle in a semicircle is 90°.
- The exterior angle of an n-sided regular polygon = $360 \div n$.
- Interior angle = 180° – exterior angle.
- The angle subtended by an arc (or chord) of a circle is twice the angle subtended by the same arc at the circumference.
- Angles on the same arc (or chord) are equal.
- The angle between the radius and the tangent at the point of contact is a right angle.
- Opposite angles of a cyclic quadrilateral add up to 180°.

Revision exercise 2a

1. Find the size of the angles marked with letters.

(a)

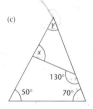

(b)

(c)

2. In each diagram, O is the centre of the circle. Find the size of the angles marked x.

(a)

(b)

(c)

3. Calculate the size of the interior angle of a regular polygon with 20 sides.

4. Calculate the number of sides of a regular polygon with an interior angle of 168°.

5. Find the sizes of the angles marked with letters. In each case, O is the centre of the circle.

Calculating and representing data

Grouped discrete data

When working with large amounts of data, it is often easier to see the pattern of the data if they are grouped. For example, this is a list of goals scored in 20 matches.

1	1	3	2	0	0	1	4	0	2
2	0	6	3	4	1	1	3	2	1

Instead, the information could be set out like this.

Number of goals	Frequency
0	4
1	6
2	4
3	3
4	2
5	0
6	1

Mode

From the table, it is easy to identify the number of goals with the greatest frequency. This is the mode of the data. Here the mode is 1 goal.

Mean

The table can also be used to calculate the mean.

There are: four matches with 0 goals $4 \times 0 = 0$ goals

six matches with 1 goal $6 \times 1 = 6$ goals

four matches with 2 goals $4 \times 2 = 8$ goals

and so on.

To find the total number of goals scored altogether, multiply each number of goals by its frequency and then add the results.

Then dividing by the total number of matches (20) gives the mean.

The working for this is shown in this table.

Number of goals	Frequency	Number of goals × frequency
0	4	0
1	6	6
2	4	8
3	3	9
4	2	8
5	0	0
6	1	6
Totals	20	37

Mean = 37 ÷ 20 = 1.85 goals.

In this example you have been given the original data. Check the answer by adding up the list of goals scored and dividing them by 20!

Examiner's tip

When given a table of grouped data, add an extra column if necessary to help you work out the values multiplied by their frequencies.

Example Work out the mean, mode and range for the number of children in the houses in Berry Road, listed in this table.

Number of children (c)	Frequency (number of houses)	c × frequency
0	6	0
1	4	4
2	5	10
3	7	21
4	1	4
5	2	10
Totals	25	49

Mean = 49 ÷ 25 = 1.96 children
Mode = 3 children
Range = 5 – 0 = 5 children

Exercise 3.1a

1. Ben has counted the number of sweets in ten packets. Here are the results.

   12 11 10 10 12 13 12 11
   12 11

   (a) Make a frequency table for Ben's results.
   (b) What is the mode of his results?
   (c) Use the frequency table to calculate the mean number of sweets.
   (d) Use the original list to calculate the mean, to check your results.

2. Here are some results for the number of crisps in a bag.

Number of crisps	25	26	27	28	29
Frequency	4	9	16	7	4

   (a) How many bags of crisps were counted?
   (b) What was the total number of crisps in these bags?
   (c) What was the mean number of crisps in these bags?

3. (a) What is the mode for the data in question 2?
   (b) What is the range for these data?

4. Find the mean value of x in these data.

x	7	8	9	10	11	12
Frequency	6	0	12	23	8	16

5. Here are the numbers of letters a postman delivered to the houses in Selly Road one morning.

Number of letters	0	1	2	3	4	5	6
Number of houses	4	5	7	2	6	0	2

   (a) How many houses are there in Selly Road?
   (b) What was the mode of the number of letters delivered there?
   (c) What was the mean number of letters delivered there? Give your answer correct to one decimal place.

Exercise 3.1b

1. Jenny counted the numbers of peas in ten pods. Here are the results.

   5 6 4 5 6 5 4 4 3 5

   (a) Make a frequency table for Jenny's results.
   (b) What is the mode of her results?
   (c) Use your frequency table to calculate the mean number of peas.
   (d) Use the original list to calculate the mean, to check your results.

2. Here are some results for the number of matches in a box.

Number of matches	43	44	45	46	47
Frequency	6	8	17	15	4

   (a) How many boxes of matches were counted?
   (b) What was the total number of matches in these boxes?

   (c) What was the mean number of matches in these boxes?

3. (a) What is the mode for the data in question 2?
   (b) What is the range for these data?

4. Find the mean value of x in these data.

x	5	6	7	8	9	10
Frequency	13	9	0	13	24	3

5. In a game, scores from 1 to 10 are possible. Dipta had 60 goes and obtained these scores.

Score	1	2	3	4	5	6	7	8	9	10
Frequency	3	4	8	7	11	9	1	4	5	8

   (a) What was Dipta's modal score?
   (b) Calculate Dipta's mean score.

Representing continuous data

When data involve measurements they are always grouped, even if they don't look like it. For instance, a length L given as 18 cm to the nearest centimetre means $17.5 \leqslant L < 18.5$. Any length between these values will count as 18 cm. Often, however, the groups are larger, to make handling the data easier. For example, when recording the heights, h cm, of 100 students in year 11, groups such as $180 \leqslant h < 185$ may be used.

Bar graph

Continuous data may be represented on a bar graph, using proper scales on both axes. Where the groups are not of the same width, the graph is called a **histogram**, and the **area** of each bar represents the frequency. In this chapter, however, only bars of equal width are considered, and the height of the bars represents the frequency, as with bar charts you have studied before.

 Example 2

Draw a bar graph to represent this information about the heights of students in year 11 at Sandish School.

Height (h cm)	Frequency
$155 \leqslant h < 160$	2
$160 \leqslant h < 165$	6
$165 \leqslant h < 170$	18
$170 \leqslant h < 175$	25
$175 \leqslant h < 180$	9
$180 \leqslant h < 185$	4
$185 \leqslant h < 190$	1

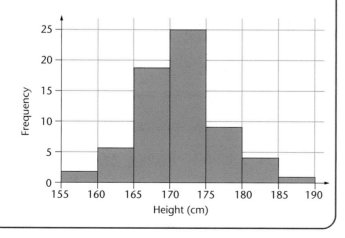

Examiner's tip

Check that you have labelled both scales carefully and that the boundaries of your bars match the boundaries of the groups.

Chapter 3 Representing continuous data

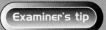

Examiner's tip

To work out the midpoint of a group, add together its boundary values and divide by 2.

Frequency polygons

A frequency polygon may also be used to represent the data. However, in this case, only one point is used to represent each group. The midpoint value of each group is chosen, as it is an average value for the group.

Example 3

Show the heights of the year 11 students in Sandish School in a frequency polygon.

The midpoint of the $155 \leqslant h < 160$ group is
$\dfrac{155 + 160}{2} = 157.5$.

So the points are plotted at h-values of 157.5, 162.5, 167.5 and so on.

Examiner's tip

It can be helpful to add a column to the frequency table, like this.

Height (h cm)	Frequency	Midpoint
$155 \leqslant h < 160$	2	157.5
$160 \leqslant h < 165$	6	162.5
$165 \leqslant h < 170$	18	167.5
$170 \leqslant h < 175$	25	172.5
$175 \leqslant h < 180$	9	177.5
$180 \leqslant h < 185$	4	182.5
$185 \leqslant h < 190$	1	187.5

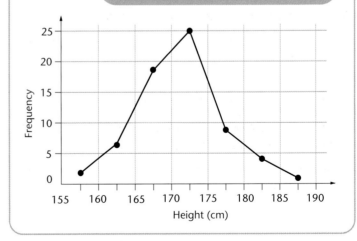

Calculating with grouped continuous data

Finding the mean

When working out the mean of grouped data in a table, you do not know the exact value for each item of data, so again the midpoint value is chosen to represent each group, and this is used to calculate an estimate of the mean. The midpoint is multiplied by the frequency of the group, as in calculating the mean of grouped discrete data.

Examiner's tip

Add two columns to the frequency table to help you work out the mean – one column for the midpoints of each group and one for the midpoints multiplied by their frequencies.

Example 4

Calculate an estimate of the mean height of the students in year 11 at Sandish School.

Height (h cm)	Frequency	Midpoint	Midpoint × frequency
$155 \leqslant h < 160$	2	157.5	315
$160 \leqslant h < 165$	6	162.5	975
$165 \leqslant h < 170$	18	167.5	3015
$170 \leqslant h < 175$	25	172.5	4312.5
$175 \leqslant h < 180$	9	177.5	1597.5
$180 \leqslant h < 185$	4	182.5	730
$185 \leqslant h < 190$	1	187.5	187.5
Totals	65		11 132.5

Mean = 11 132.5 ÷ 65 = 171.3 cm, correct to one decimal place.

Mode and range of grouped continuous data

The **modal class** may be found when data are given as a table, frequency polygon or bar graph. It is the class with the highest frequency.

The **range** cannot be stated accurately from grouped data. For instance, the height of the tallest student in the example might be 189.7 cm or 185.0 cm. As with the mean, the midpoints of the groups are used to estimate the range.

Estimating the median of a grouped continuous distribution is covered in Chapter 7.

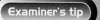
Examiner's tip

When stating the modal class, take care to give its boundaries accurately.

For the heights of the year 11 students in Sandish School,

(a) state the modal class

(b) estimate the range.

(a) The modal class is the one with the largest frequency, which is 170 cm ⩽ height < 175 cm or 170–175 cm.

(b) An estimate of the range is found by finding the difference between the midpoint values of the top and bottom groups in the table. This gives range = 187.5 − 157.5 = 30 cm.

Exercise 3.2a

1. State the boundaries of these intervals.
   (a) 18 cm, to the nearest cm
   (b) 35 m, to the nearest m
   (c) masses to the nearest gram: 5–9, 10–14
   (d) times to the nearest second: 2–3, 4–5

2. State the midpoints of these intervals.
   (a) 10 cm < length ⩽ 20 cm
   (b) 2.0 m ⩽ length ⩽ 2.5 m
   (c) 80 kg ⩽ mass < 85 kg
   (d) masses to the nearest kg: 81–85, 86–90
   (e) times to the nearest second: 31–40, 41–50

3. (a) Calculate an estimate of the mean of these times.

Time (seconds)	0–2	2–4	4–6	6–8	8–10
Frequency	4	6	3	2	7

   (b) Draw a bar graph of this distribution.

4. (a) Calculate an estimate of the mean of these heights.

Height (cm)	50–60	60–70	70–80	80–90	90–100
Frequency	15	23	38	17	7

   (b) Draw a frequency polygon to represent this distribution.

5. Calculate an estimate of the mean of these lengths.

Length (m)	1.0–1.2	1.2–1.4	1.4–1.6	1.6–1.8	1.8–2.0
Frequency	2	7	13	5	3

6. Draw a bar graph to show this information.

Length (y cm)	Frequency
$10 \leqslant y < 20$	2
$20 \leqslant y < 30$	6
$30 \leqslant y < 40$	9
$40 \leqslant y < 50$	5
$50 \leqslant y < 60$	3

7. For the data in question 6:
    (a) state the modal class
    (b) calculate an estimate of the mean.
8. Draw a frequency polygon to show these data.

Mass of tomato (t g)	Frequency
$35 < t \leqslant 40$	7
$40 < t \leqslant 45$	13
$45 < t \leqslant 50$	20
$50 < t \leqslant 55$	16
$55 < t \leqslant 60$	4

9. For the data in question 8:
    (a) estimate the range
    (b) calculate an estimate of the mean.
10. The bar graph shows the masses of a sample of 50 eggs.

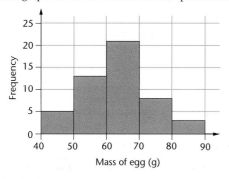

    (a) Make a frequency table for this information.
    (b) Calculate an estimate of the mean mass of these eggs.

Exercise 3.2b

1. State the boundaries of these intervals.
    (a) 20 cm, to the nearest cm
    (b) 41 m, to the nearest m
    (c) masses to the nearest gram: 15–16, 17–18
    (d) times to the nearest second: 11–15, 16–20
2. State the midpoints of these intervals.
    (a) $15\,\text{cm} < \text{length} \leqslant 20\,\text{cm}$
    (b) $12.0\,\text{cm} \leqslant \text{length} < 12.5\,\text{cm}$
    (c) $100\,\text{kg} \leqslant \text{mass} < 105\,\text{kg}$
    (d) masses to the nearest kg: 100–104, 105–109
    (e) times to the nearest second: 24–26, 27–29
3. (a) Calculate an estimate of the mean of these times.

Time (seconds)	0–20	20–40	40–60	60–80	80–100
Frequency	4	9	13	8	6

    (b) Draw a bar graph of this distribution.

4. (a) Calculate an estimate of the mean of these heights.

Height (m)	0–2	2–4	4–6	6–8	8–10
Frequency	12	26	34	23	5

(b) Draw a frequency polygon to represent this distribution.

5. Calculate an estimate of the mean of these lengths.

Length (cm)	3.0–3.2	3.2–3.4	3.4–3.6	3.6–3.8	3.8–4.0
Frequency	3	8	11	5	3

6. Draw a bar graph to show this information.

Mass (w kg)	Frequency
$30 \leqslant w < 40$	5
$40 \leqslant w < 50$	8
$50 \leqslant w < 60$	2
$60 \leqslant w < 70$	4
$70 \leqslant w < 80$	1

7. For the data in question 6:
   (a) state the modal class
   (b) calculate an estimate of the mean.

8. Draw a frequency polygon to show these data.

Length (x cm)	Frequency
$0 < x \leqslant 5$	8
$5 < x \leqslant 10$	6
$10 < x \leqslant 15$	2
$15 < x \leqslant 20$	5
$20 < x \leqslant 25$	1

9. For the data in question 8:
   (a) estimate the range
   (b) calculate an estimate of the mean.

10. The bar graph shows the heights of students in year 9.

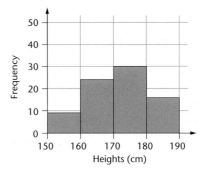

(a) Make a frequency table for this information.
(b) Calculate an estimate of the mean height.

Mean, median or mode?

Each of these terms may be called an average. Sometimes, you need to decide which of them is the best to use in a given situation.

The mean is what most people think of as the average, but it may be 'fairer' to use the mode or median.

Look at these annual wages, for example.

Annual wage (£)	Number of employees
10 000–15 000	2
15 000–20 000	18
20 000–25 000	12
25 000–30 000	4
30 000–35 000	0
35 000–40 000	2

The modal group is £15 000–20 000.

Calculating the mean gives:

Midpoint	Frequency	Midpoint × frequency
12 500	2	25 000
17 500	18	315 000
22 500	12	270 000
27 500	4	110 000
32 500	0	0
37 500	2	75 000
Totals	38	795 000

Mean = 795 000 ÷ 38 = 20 921.0526 = £20 900 to the nearest £100.

Which gives a better idea of the average here, the mean or the mode? It depends on the purpose for which you want to use the average. If you were arguing for a pay rise you would probably use the mode. If you were the management, you would be more likely to use the mean.

If a distribution is quite symmetrical, there is not much difference between the mean, median and mode. If the distribution is weighted to one side (or **skewed**), then it matters much more which is chosen. In this case, the mean may not give the most representative average. Be prepared to give a reason why you have chosen to use a particular average.

Key points

- To find the mean of grouped data, multiply each value by its frequency, add the results, and divide by the sum of the frequencies. For continuous data, use the midpoints of each group as the value for the group.
- For bar graphs of continuous data, label both axes with a scale. Make sure the edges of each bar are at the boundaries of their group.
- To use a frequency polygon to represent continuous data, plot the midpoints of each group.
- To estimate the range of continuous data, subtract the midpoints of the end groups.
- The modal class for continuous data is the group with the largest frequency.

Revision exercise 3a

1. The numbers of matches won by a school's sports teams during one term are shown in this table.

Number of matches won	0	1	2	3	4	5	6	7	8
Number of teams		2	1	0	2	4	6	3	0	2

Calculate the mean number of matches won by the teams.

2. A Biology class counted the number of daisies in 10-cm squares of grass on the field. Here are their results.

Number of daisies	0	1	2	3	4	5	6
Frequency	2	2	5	8	9	3	1

(a) How many 10-cm squares were counted?
(b) What was the total number of daisies found in these squares?
(c) What was the mode?
(d) What was the median?

3. The bar chart shows the results of a survey about the number of videos watched during one week.

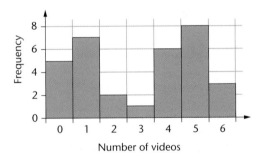

(a) State the mode.
(b) State the range.
(c) Draw up a frequency table to show these results.
(d) Calculate the mean number of videos watched.

4. Sanjit asked some people how many chocolates they had eaten at a party. These are the results.

Number of chocolates	2	3	4	5	6	7	8	9	10
Frequency	1	10	5	4	2	1	0	0	2

   (a) State the mode.
   (b) How many people took part in the survey?
   (c) Find the median.
   (d) Calculate the mean.
   (e) Why does the mean not necessarily give the 'best' average here?

5. Harry picked and measured some runner beans. These were their lengths.

Length (L cm)	Frequency
$10 < L \leqslant 15$	3
$15 < L \leqslant 20$	7
$20 < L \leqslant 25$	11
$25 < L \leqslant 30$	8
$30 < L \leqslant 35$	1

   (a) Draw a bar graph to show this information.
   (b) Estimate the range of the length of these runner beans.

6. Calculate an estimate of the mean length of the runner beans in question 5.

7. Lisa timed her little brother when he was playing with his new toys over Christmas.

Time (t minutes)	Frequency
$0 < t \leqslant 10$	2
$10 < t \leqslant 20$	5
$20 < t \leqslant 30$	7
$30 < t \leqslant 40$	10
$40 < t \leqslant 50$	4

   (a) Draw a frequency polygon for these data.
   (b) Calculate an estimate of the mean of these times.

8. A class held a hopping race and recorded the distances they travelled before putting the other foot down. Here are the results.

Length (x m)	Frequency
$0 < x \leqslant 4$	1
$4 < x \leqslant 8$	4
$8 < x \leqslant 12$	8
$12 < x \leqslant 16$	5
$16 < x \leqslant 20$	2

   For the above data:
   (a) state the modal class
   (b) estimate the range
   (c) calculate an estimate of the mean.

9. Kim and Petra asked their class, 'How much exercise have you had this week?' These were the results.

Time of exercise (h hours)	Number of people
$0 \leqslant h < 1$	3
$1 \leqslant h < 2$	8
$2 \leqslant h < 5$	12
$5 \leqslant h < 10$	5
$h \geqslant 10$	0

   (a) How many people were in the survey?
   (b) What are the midpoints of the classes (i) $2 \leqslant h < 5$ and (ii) $5 \leqslant h < 10$?
   (c) Calculate an estimate of the mean time of exercise.

10. Some batteries were tested to see how long they lasted. Here are the results.

Time (hours)	0–2	2–4	4–6	6–8	8–10
Frequency	4	5	12	16	3

   (a) Calculate an estimate of the mean time these batteries lasted.
   (b) In what circumstances would the mode be a suitable average to use here?

4 Transformations

Drawing reflections

To draw a **reflection** you need an object and a mirror line.

Example 1

Reflect the L-shape in the given mirror line.

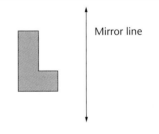

Method 1

For each vertex or corner of the L-shape, use a ruler to measure the perpendicular distance from the mirror line. Then measure the same distance on the other side of the mirror line to find the corresponding image point.

> Remember to keep the ruler at right angles to the mirror line.

Method 2

Using tracing paper, trace the object point and the mirror line. Turn the tracing paper over and line up the tracing of the mirror line with the original mirror line, but with the object on the other side. Using a pin or compass point, prick through the corners of the object onto the paper below. Remove the tracing paper and join up the pinpricks to draw the image.

> Method 2 is often the easier one when the mirror line is sloping, as it is difficult to keep the ruler at right angles to the mirror line.

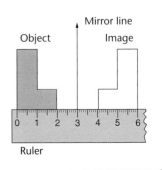

If the mirror line is easy to work with, for example the *x*-axis on a graph, it may be possible to plot the reflection by counting squares. It is still advisable to use tracing paper to check the reflection.

In mathematics all mirror lines are regarded as 'double-sided'. This means that any shape that crosses the mirror line will have part of its reflection on each side of the line.

Recognising reflections

It should be easy to recognise when a transformation is a reflection. If there is any doubt, check that the tracing paper needs to be **turned over** before it will fit on the image. Finding the mirror line can be more difficult.

Describe the transformation that maps shape ABC onto shape PQR.

It should be fairly obvious that the transformation is a reflection but this could be checked using tracing paper.

To find the mirror line, put a ruler between two corresponding points (B and Q) and mark a point halfway between them, at (3, 3).

Repeat this for two other corresponding points (C and R). The midpoint is (4, 4).

Join the two midpoints to find the mirror line. The mirror line is $y = x$.

The transformation is a reflection in the line $y = x$.

Again, the result can be checked using tracing paper.

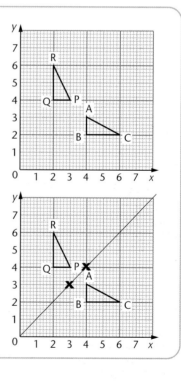

Rotations

A **rotation** involves turning the object about a point, called the **centre of rotation**.

Drawing rotations

Example 3 Rotate triangle ABC through 90° clockwise about C.

Measure an angle of 90° clockwise from the line AC.

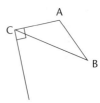

Trace the shape ABC. Put a pencil or pin at C to hold the tracing to the diagram at that point. Rotate the tracing paper until AC coincides with the new line you have drawn. Use another pin or the point of your compasses to prick through the other corners (A and B).

Join up the new points to form the image.

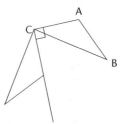

If the centre of rotation is not on the object then the method is slightly more difficult.

Rotate the triangle ABC through 90°
clockwise about the point O.

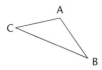

Join O to a point on the object (C).
Measure an angle of 90° clockwise from OC
and draw a line.

Trace the triangle ABC and the line OC.
Rotate the tracing about O until the line
OC coincides with the new line you have
drawn. Use a pin or the point of your
compasses to prick through the corners
(A, B and C). Join up the pin holes to form
the image.

For other angles of rotation (e.g. 120° clockwise), the first angle is
measured as the stated angle (e.g. 120°) instead of 90° but
otherwise the method is the same.

If the centre of rotation is easy to work with, for example the origin,
then you may be able to draw the rotation by counting squares but it
is always best to check using tracing paper.

Recognising rotations

It is usually easy to recognise when a transformation is a
rotation, as it should be possible to place a tracing of the object
over the image without turning the tracing paper over.

To find the angle of rotation, find a pair of sides that correspond
in the object and the image. Measure the angle between them.
You may need to extend both of these sides to do this.

If the centre of rotation is not on the object, its position may not
be obvious. The easiest method to use is trial and error, either by
counting squares or using tracing paper. In a later chapter, you
will learn a method which will find the centre directly, without
trial (or error!).

Examiner's tip

Always remember to state
whether the rotation is
clockwise or anticlockwise.

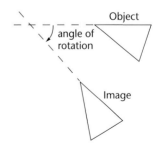

Chapter 4 Rotations

Example 5 Describe fully the transformation that maps flag A onto flag B.

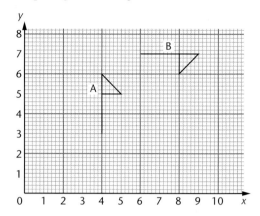

It is clear that the transformation is a rotation and that the angle is 90° clockwise. You may need to make a few trials, using tracing paper and a compass point centred on different points, to find that the centre of rotation is (7, 4).

If you did not spot it, try it now with tracing paper.

Exercise 4.1a

Label the diagrams you draw in this exercise carefully and keep them, as you will need them in a later exercise.

1. Draw a triangle with vertices at (1, 0), (1, −2) and (2, −2). Label it A. Draw the reflection of triangle A in the line $y = 1$. Label it B.

2. On the same grid as for question 1, reflect triangle B in the line $y = x$. Label the new triangle C.

3. On a new grid draw a triangle with vertices at (2, 5), (3, 5) and (1, 3). Label it D. Draw the reflection of triangle in the line $x = \frac{1}{2}$.
   Label it E.

4. On the same grid as for question 3, reflect triangle E in the line $y = -x$. Label the new triangle F.

5. Using graph paper, copy this diagram. Rotate the flag G through 90° clockwise about the point (1, 2). Label the new flag H.

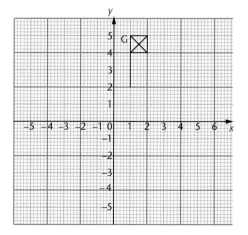

6. On the same grid as for question 5, rotate the flag H through 180° about the point (2, −1). Label the new flag I.

7. Draw a triangle with vertices at (0,1), (0, 4) and (2, 3). Label it J. Rotate triangle J through 90° anticlockwise about the point (2, 3). Label the new triangle K.

8. On the same grid as for question 7, rotate triangle K through 90° clockwise about the point (2, −1). Label the new triangle L.

9. Study the diagram below.

Describe fully the single transformation that maps:

(a) flag a onto flag b
(b) flag a onto flag c
(c) flag b onto flag d

(d) flag b onto flag e
(e) flag e onto flag f
(f) flag f onto flag g.

Exercise 4.lb

For questions 1–6, either use the worksheet or copy the diagrams carefully, making them larger if you wish.

1. Reflect the trapezium in the given mirror line.

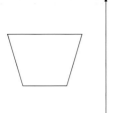

2. Reflect the triangle in the given mirror line.

3. Reflect the triangle in the given mirror line.

4. Rotate the triangle through 180° about the point C.

5. Rotate the triangle through 90° clockwise about the point O.

6. Rotate the triangle through 120° clockwise about the point O.

O×

7. Study the diagram below.

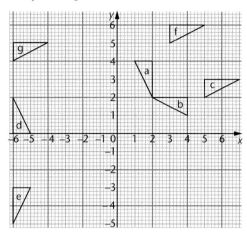

Describe fully the single transformation that maps:

(a) triangle a onto triangle b

(b) triangle a onto triangle c

(c) triangle a onto triangle d

(d) triangle d onto triangle e

(e) triangle e onto triangle f

(f) triangle d onto triangle g.

Translations

In a **translation**, every point of an object moves the same distance in the same direction. The object and the image look identical with no turning or reflection. It looks just as if the object has moved to a different position.

Drawing translations

To draw a translation, all you need to know is how far across the page and how far up the page to move the object.

 Example 6   Translate the shape on the diagram 5 cm to the right and 3 cm down.

The dotted lines show that every point in the object has 'moved' 5 cm to the right and 3 cm down to the corresponding point in the image.

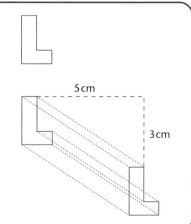

Column vectors

When working with translations, it is usual to work on a grid so it is not necessary to measure the movements.

On a grid, the movements can be described as a movement in the x-direction and a movement in the y-direction. They are written in the form of a **column vector**, for example $\begin{pmatrix} 5 \\ -3 \end{pmatrix}$.

In a column vector:

the top number represents the x-movement
the bottom number represents the y-movement.

The directions are the same as for coordinates.

If the top number is positive, move to the right.

If the top number is negative, move to the left.

If the bottom number is positive, move up.

If the bottom number is negative, move down.

 Example 7

Translate the shape on the grid through the vector $\begin{pmatrix} -3 \\ 4 \end{pmatrix}$.

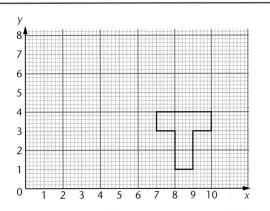

The movement represented by the vector $\begin{pmatrix} -3 \\ 4 \end{pmatrix}$ is 3 units to the left and 4 units up, so every point in the object 'moves' this amount to form the corresponding point in the image.

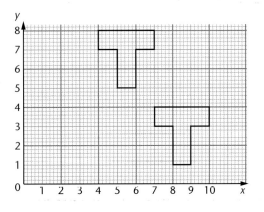

Recognising translations

It should be easy to recognise when a transformation is a translation, as the object and image look identical with no turning or reflecting. Having stated that the transformation is a translation, you need to find the column vector.

Identify a point on the object and its corresponding point on the image. Count:

- how many units left or right and
- how many units up or down

that point has moved. Write these movements as a column vector.

Example 8

Describe fully the transformation that maps triangle ABC onto triangle PQR.

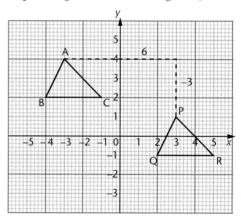

Point A translates on to point P. This is a movement of 6 to the right and 3 down. The transformation is a translation through the vector $\begin{pmatrix} 6 \\ -3 \end{pmatrix}$.

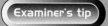

Try not to mix up the words 'transformation' and 'translation'. Transformation is the general name for all the changes made to shapes. Translation is the particular transformation that has been described here.

Enlargements

An **enlargement** produces an image that is exactly similar in
shape to the object, but is larger or smaller.

Drawing enlargements

Example 9

Enlarge the triangle ABC with
scale factor $2\frac{1}{2}$ and centre of
enlargement O, to form
triangle PQR.

Draw lines from O to A, O to
B and O to C and extend them.

Measure the lengths OA, OB
and OC. These are 2.0 cm,
1.5 cm and 2.9 cm respectively.

Multiply these lengths by 2.5
to give OP = 5.0 cm,
OQ = 3.7 cm and OR = 7.2 cm.

Measure these distances
along the extended lines
OA, OB and OC, and
mark P, Q and R.

Join P, Q and R to form the triangle.

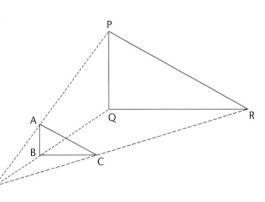

Example 10

Enlarge the shape DEF with scale factor $\frac{1}{2}$
and centre of enlargement O.

The steps are exactly the same as for
Example 9 except that, instead of being
multiplied by 2.5, the distances are
multiplied by 0.5.

Check that OU = $\frac{1}{2}$OD, OV = $\frac{1}{2}$OE and
OW = $\frac{1}{2}$OF.

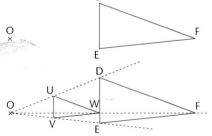

Notice that the length of each side in triangle UVW is half the length of the
corresponding side in triangle DEF. In Mathematics this is still called an enlargement even
though the image is smaller than the object. It just means that the scale factor is less than 1.

Examiner's tip

When you have drawn your enlargement check that the ratio of the sides of the image to the corresponding
sides in the object is equal to the scale factor (in the case of Example 9, $2\frac{1}{2}$). If it is not, you have probably
measured some or all of your distances from the points of the object and not from O.

Chapter 4   Enlargements

Example ⑪ Describe fully the transformation that maps triangle DEF onto triangle STU.

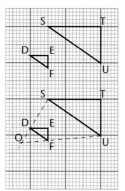

The shapes are similar, so clearly the transformation is an enlargement.

Since the lengths of the sides of triangle STU are 3 times the lengths of the corresponding sides of triangle DEF, the scale factor is 3. All that remains to be found is the centre of enlargement.

Join SD and extend it. Join UF and extend it to cross the extended line SD. The point where the lines cross, O, is the centre of enlargement.

The transformation is an enlargement, scale factor 3, centre of enlargement O.

If you were working on a grid, you would describe the centre of enlargement by stating the coordinates of the point.

Exercise 4.2a

Label the diagrams you draw in this exercise carefully and keep them, as you will need them in a later exercise.

1. Draw a triangle with vertices at (1, 2), (1, 4) and (2, 4). Label it A.
   Draw the translation of triangle A through the vector $\begin{pmatrix} 5 \\ 2 \end{pmatrix}$. Label it B.

2. On the same grid as for question 1, translate triangle B through the vector $\begin{pmatrix} 2 \\ -4 \end{pmatrix}$. Label the new triangle C.

3. On a new grid, draw a triangle with vertices at (0, 2), (1, 4) and (3, 2). Label it D.
   Draw the translation of triangle D through the vector $\begin{pmatrix} -4 \\ 2 \end{pmatrix}$. Label it E.

4. On the same grid as for question 3, translate triangle E through the vector $\begin{pmatrix} 8 \\ 0 \end{pmatrix}$. Label the new triangle F.

   Draw a set of axes. Label the x-axis from 0 to 13 and the y-axis from 0 to 15. Use it to answer questions 5 and 6.

5. Draw a triangle with vertices at (1, 2), (2, 4) and (1, 3). Label it G.
   Draw the enlargement of triangle G with scale factor 2 and centre the origin. Label it H.

6. On the same grid as question 5, draw the enlargement of triangle H with scale factor 3 and centre of enlargement (0, 5). Label it I.

7. Copy the diagram. Enlarge the flag J with scale factor $1\frac{1}{2}$ and centre of enlargement (1, 2). Label the new flag K.

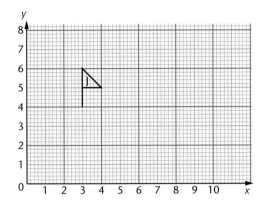

8. On the same grid you drew for question 7 enlarge the flag K with scale factor 2 and centre of enlargement (2, 8). Label the new flag L.

9. Study the diagram below.

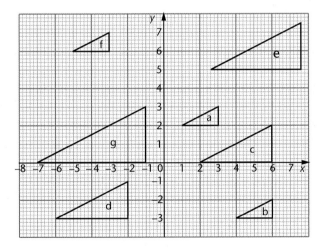

Describe fully the single transformation that maps:
(a) triangle a onto triangle b
(b) triangle a onto triangle c
(c) triangle c onto triangle d
(d) triangle a onto triangle e
(e) triangle a onto triangle f
(f) triangle g onto triangle a.

Chapter 4 Enlargements

For questions 1–6, either use the worksheet or copy the diagrams carefully, making them larger if you wish.

1. Translate flag A through the vector $\begin{pmatrix} -2 \\ -5 \end{pmatrix}$. Label the new flag B.

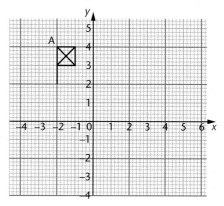

2. On the same grid you drew for question 1, translate flag B through the vector $\begin{pmatrix} 7 \\ 4 \end{pmatrix}$. Label the new flag C.

3. On the same grid as for question 1, translate flag C through the vector $\begin{pmatrix} -5 \\ 1 \end{pmatrix}$. Label the new flag D. What do you notice?

   Try to explain the result.

4. Enlarge the shape with centre O and scale factor 3.

5. Enlarge the shape with centre O and scale factor $\frac{1}{3}$.

6. Enlarge the shape with centre O and scale factor $1\frac{1}{2}$.

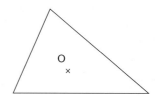

7. Study the diagram below.

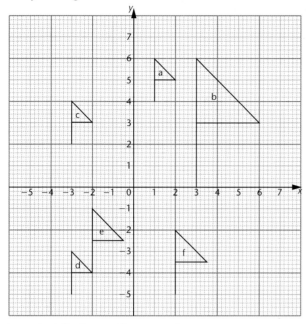

Describe fully the transformation that maps:
(a) flag a onto flag b   (b) flag a onto flag c   (c) flag c onto flag d
(d) flag d onto flag e   (e) flag e onto flag f   (f) flag b onto flag d.

Combining transformations

Sometimes when one transformation is followed by another, the result is equivalent to a single transformation. For example, in the following diagram, triangle A has been translated through the vector $\begin{pmatrix} 2 \\ 5 \end{pmatrix}$ onto triangle B.

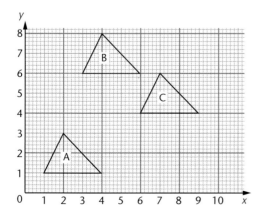

Triangle B has then been translated through the vector $\begin{pmatrix} 3 \\ -2 \end{pmatrix}$ onto triangle C.

Notice that triangle A could have been translated directly onto triangle C through the vector $\begin{pmatrix} 5 \\ 3 \end{pmatrix}$.

So the first transformation followed by the second transformation is equivalent to the single transformation, translation through the vector $\begin{pmatrix} 5 \\ 3 \end{pmatrix}$.

Example 12

Find the single transformation that is equivalent to a reflection in the line $x = 1$, followed by a reflection in the line $y = -2$.

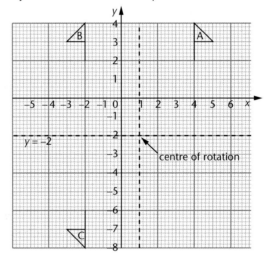

In the diagram, reflecting the object flag A in the line $x = 1$ gives flag B.

Reflecting flag B in the line $y = -2$ gives flag C.

The transformation that maps A directly onto C is a rotation through 180°.

The centre of rotation is $(1, -2)$, which is where the mirror lines cross.

Use tracing paper to check this.

The transformation is a rotation through 180° about the centre of rotation $(1, -2)$.

A rotation of 180° is the only rotation for which you do not need to state the direction, as 180° clockwise is the same as 180° anticlockwise.

Exercise 4.3a

In this exercise you will need some of the diagrams you drew in Exercises 4.1a and 4.2a.

1. Look back at the diagram you drew for questions 1 and 2 of Exercise 4.2a.
   Describe fully the single transformation that is equivalent to a translation through the vector $\begin{pmatrix} 5 \\ 2 \end{pmatrix}$ (A onto B) followed by a translation through the vector $\begin{pmatrix} 2 \\ -4 \end{pmatrix}$ (B onto C).

2. Look back at the diagram you drew for questions 3 and 4 of Exercise 4.2a.
   Describe fully the single transformation that is equivalent to a translation through the vector $\begin{pmatrix} -4 \\ 2 \end{pmatrix}$ (D onto E) followed by a translation through the vector $\begin{pmatrix} 8 \\ 0 \end{pmatrix}$ (E onto F).

3. Look at your answers to the last two questions. Try to make a general statement about the result of translating through the vector $\begin{pmatrix} a \\ b \end{pmatrix}$ followed by translation through the $\begin{pmatrix} c \\ d \end{pmatrix}$ vector.

4. Look back at the diagram you drew for questions 5 and 6 of Exercise 4.2a.
   Describe fully the single transformation that is equivalent to an enlargement scale factor 2, centre the origin (G onto H) followed by an enlargement scale factor 3, centre (0, 5) (H onto I).

5. Look back at the diagram you drew for questions 7 and 8 of Exercise 4.2a.
   Describe fully the single transformation that is equivalent to an enlargement, scale factor $1\frac{1}{2}$, centre the point (1, 2) (J onto K) followed by an enlargement, scale factor 2, centre (2, 8) (K onto L).

6. Look again at the answers to the last two questions. Try to make a general statement about the result of enlarging with scale factor p followed by enlarging with scale factor q.

7. Look back at the diagram you drew for questions 1 and 2 of Exercise 4.1a.
   Describe fully the single transformation that is equivalent to a reflection in the line $y = 1$ (A onto B) followed by a reflection in the line $y = x$ (B onto C).

8. Look back at the diagram you drew for questions 3 and 4 of Exercise 4.1a.
   Describe fully the single transformation that is equivalent to a reflection in the line $x = \frac{1}{2}$ (D onto E) followed by a reflection in the line $y = -x$ (E onto F).

9. Look again at the answers to the last two questions. Try to make a general statement about the result of reflection in a mirror line followed by reflection in an intersecting mirror line.

10. Look back at the diagram you drew for questions 5 and 6 of Exercise 4.1a.
    Describe fully the single transformation that is equivalent to a rotation through 90° clockwise about the point (1, 2) (G onto H) followed by a rotation through 180° about the point (2, −1) (H onto I).

11. Look back at the diagram you drew for questions 7 and 8 of Exercise 4.1a.
    Describe fully the single transformation that is equivalent to a rotation through 90° anticlockwise about the point (2, 3) (J onto K) followed by a rotation through 90° clockwise about the point (2, −1) (K onto L).

Exercise 4.3b

In this exercise, carry out the transformations on a simple object shape of your choice.

1. Describe fully the single transformation that is equivalent to a reflection in the x-axis followed by reflection in the y-axis.

2. Describe fully the single transformation that is equivalent to a reflection in the line $x = 1$ followed by a reflection in the line $x = 5$.

3. Describe fully the single transformation that is equivalent to a reflection in the line $y = 2$ followed by a reflection in the line $y = 6$.

4. Look again at your answers to the last two questions. Try to make a general statement about the result of reflecting in a mirror line followed by a reflection in a parallel mirror line.

5. Describe fully the single transformation that is equivalent to an enlargement, scale factor 2 and centre the origin, followed by a translation through the vector $\begin{pmatrix} 3 \\ 2 \end{pmatrix}$.

6. Describe fully the single transformation that is equivalent to a rotation through 90° clockwise about the origin, followed by a translation through the vector $\begin{pmatrix} 4 \\ 0 \end{pmatrix}$.

7. Describe fully the single transformation that is equivalent to a reflection in the x-axis followed by a rotation through 90° anticlockwise about the origin.

8. Describe fully the single transformation that is equivalent to a reflection in the y-axis followed by a rotation through 90° anticlockwise about the origin.

9. Describe fully the single transformation that is equivalent to a reflection in the line $y = x$ followed by a reflection in the line $y = -x$.

10. Describe fully the single transformation that is equivalent to a rotation through 90° clockwise about the point (2, 1) followed by a rotation through 90° anticlockwise about the point (3, 4).

Key points

- Use tracing paper to carry out or check rotations and reflections.
- When describing transformations, always give the name of the transformation first and then the extra information required.

Name of transformation	Extra information
Reflection	Mirror line
Rotation	Angle, direction, centre of rotation
Translation	Column vector
Enlargement	Scale factor, centre of enlargement

- When asked to describe a single transformation, do not give a combination of transformations.

Revision exercise 4a

1. Draw a triangle with vertices at (1, 4), (1, 6) and (2, 6). Label it A. Reflect triangle A in the line $y = x$. Label it B.

2. On the same grid you drew for question 1, rotate triangle B through 90° anticlockwise about the point (5, 5). Label the new triangle C.

3. Look again at the diagrams you drew for the last two questions. Describe fully the single transformation that is equivalent to reflection in the line $y = x$ followed by a rotation through 90° anticlockwise about the point (5, 5).

4. On a new grid, draw a triangle with vertices at (4, 1) (6, 1) and (4, 2). Label it D. Translate triangle D through the vector $\begin{pmatrix} 2 \\ 3 \end{pmatrix}$. Label it E.

5. On the same grid you drew for question 4, enlarge triangle E with scale factor 2 and centre of enlargement (5, 7). Label the new triangle F.

6. Look again at the diagrams you drew for the last two questions. Describe fully the single transformation that is equivalent to translation through the vector $\binom{2}{3}$ followed by enlargement with scale factor 2 and centre of enlargement (5, 7).

7. Study the diagram below.

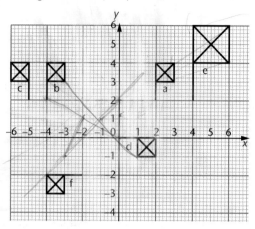

Describe fully the single transformation that maps:

(a) flag a onto flag b

(b) flag b onto flag c

(c) flag a onto flag d

(d) flag d onto flag b

(e) flag e onto flag a

(f) flag a onto flag f.

Calculations

Fractions

In a fraction $\dfrac{a}{b}$, a is called the **numerator** and b is the **denominator**.

Equivalent fractions

These squares can be divided into equal parts in different ways.

The fraction represented by the shaded parts can be thought of as $\frac{1}{4}$ or $\frac{2}{8}$ or $\frac{4}{16}$.

These three fractions are equal in value and are **equivalent**.

You can find equivalent fractions by multiplying or dividing the numerator *and* the denominator by the same number.

Example ①

Fill in the missing numbers in these equivalent fractions.

(a) $\dfrac{1}{2} = \dfrac{2}{\square} = \dfrac{\square}{14}$ (b) $\dfrac{3}{8} = \dfrac{\square}{24} = \dfrac{15}{\square}$

(a) $\dfrac{1}{2} = \dfrac{2}{4} = \dfrac{7}{14}$ Multiply the first fraction by $\frac{2}{2}$, then multiply it by $\frac{7}{7}$.

(b) $\dfrac{3}{8} = \dfrac{9}{24} = \dfrac{15}{40}$ Multiply the first fraction by $\frac{3}{3}$, then multiply it by $\frac{5}{5}$.

You may be asked to write a fraction in its **lowest terms**.

This means finding the smallest possible denominator.

This is sometimes called **cancelling** the fractions.

(Example 2) Write these fractions in their lowest terms.

(a) $\frac{6}{10}$ (b) $\frac{8}{12}$ (c) $\frac{15}{20}$

(a) $\frac{6}{10} = \frac{3}{5}$ Divide the numerator and denominator by 2.

(b) $\frac{8}{12} = \frac{2}{3}$ $\frac{8}{12}$ is also equivalent to $\frac{4}{6}$ but it can be simplified further to $\frac{2}{3}$.

(c) $\frac{15}{20} = \frac{3}{4}$ Divide top and bottom by 5.

Adding fractions

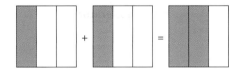

In this diagram, each square is divided into thirds.

The diagram shows $\frac{1}{3} + \frac{1}{3} = \frac{2}{3}$.

Counting squares or columns, 1 column + 1 column = 2 columns. If the denominator is the same in the fractions, just add the numerators.

In this diagram there are 12 small squares in each rectangle.

The diagram shows $\frac{1}{3} + \frac{1}{4}$.

Counting squares, 4 squares + 3 squares = 7 squares or $\frac{7}{12}$

To add two fractions, change them to the same type, so they have the same denominator.

$\frac{1}{3} = \frac{4}{12}$ $\frac{1}{4} = \frac{3}{12}$ $\frac{4}{12} + \frac{3}{12} = \frac{7}{12}$

Example ③

Add the fractions.

(a) $\frac{2}{5} + \frac{1}{5}$ (b) $\frac{1}{5} + \frac{3}{10}$ (c) $\frac{1}{6} + \frac{3}{4}$

(a) $\frac{2}{5} + \frac{1}{5} = \frac{3}{5}$

> They have the same denominator so just add the numerators.

(b) $\frac{1}{5} + \frac{3}{10}$

> They need to be changed so that they both have the same denominator.

$= \frac{2}{10} + \frac{3}{10}$

> Change $\frac{1}{5}$ to $\frac{2}{10}$, so they both have 10 as the denominator.

$= \frac{5}{10} = \frac{1}{2}$

> Write the answer in the lowest terms.

(c) $\frac{1}{6} + \frac{3}{4}$

> This time they both need to be changed, to have the same denominator.

$= \frac{2}{12} + \frac{9}{12} = \frac{11}{12}$ $\frac{1}{6} = \frac{2}{12} = \frac{3}{18} = ..., \frac{3}{4} = \frac{6}{8} = \frac{9}{12} = ...$

Subtracting fractions

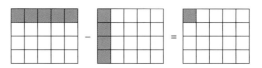

In this diagram there are 20 small squares in each rectangle.

The diagram shows $\frac{1}{4} - \frac{1}{5}$.

5 squares − 4 squares = 1 square = $\frac{1}{20}$

This can be written as $\frac{1}{4} - \frac{1}{5} = \frac{5}{20} - \frac{4}{20} = \frac{1}{20}$

> Change both so that they have the same denominator, as with adding, but then subtract the numerators.

Examiner's tip

When adding or subtracting fractions, change to the same type (same denominator) and add or subtract the numerators. The most common error is to add the denominators and add the numerators.

Example ④

Work these out.

(a) $\frac{3}{5} - \frac{2}{5}$ (b) $\frac{3}{4} - \frac{2}{3}$ (c) $\frac{5}{6} + \frac{1}{4} - \frac{1}{3}$

(a) $\frac{3}{5} - \frac{2}{5} = \frac{1}{5}$

> They have the same denominator so just subtract the numerators.

(b) $\frac{3}{4} - \frac{2}{3} = \frac{9}{12} - \frac{8}{12} = \frac{1}{12}$

> 4 and 3 both divide into 12, so make 12 the denominator for both. Multiply $\frac{3}{4}$ by 3 top and bottom, and $\frac{2}{3}$ by 4 top and bottom.

(c) $\frac{5}{6} + \frac{1}{4} - \frac{1}{3}$

> All the denominators divide into 12.

$= \frac{10}{12} + \frac{3}{12} - \frac{4}{12}$

$= \frac{9}{12} = \frac{3}{4}$

1. Fill in the blanks in these equivalent fractions.
   (a) $\frac{1}{7} = \frac{2}{\square} = \frac{\square}{35}$ (b) $\frac{4}{9} = \frac{16}{\square} = \frac{\square}{72}$

2. Write these fractions in their lowest terms.
   (a) $\frac{6}{8}$ (b) $\frac{12}{15}$ (c) $\frac{12}{24}$ (d) $\frac{12}{54}$

For the rest of the questions, give all answers in their lowest terms.

3. Add these fractions.
   (a) $\frac{2}{3} + \frac{1}{3}$ (b) $\frac{1}{3} + \frac{1}{2}$ (c) $\frac{3}{5} + \frac{1}{4}$ (d) $\frac{1}{6} + \frac{2}{3}$ (e) $\frac{2}{5} + \frac{3}{8}$ (f) $\frac{3}{4} + \frac{1}{6}$

4. Subtract these fractions.
   (a) $\frac{2}{7} - \frac{1}{7}$ (b) $\frac{5}{6} - \frac{1}{3}$ (c) $\frac{2}{3} - \frac{1}{4}$ (d) $\frac{11}{12} - \frac{2}{3}$ (e) $\frac{5}{8} - \frac{1}{3}$ (f) $\frac{7}{9} - \frac{5}{12}$

5. Work these out.
   (a) $\frac{4}{5} + \frac{7}{10} - \frac{3}{5}$ (b) $\frac{3}{5} + \frac{5}{6} - \frac{2}{3}$ (c) $\frac{2}{3} + \frac{3}{4} - \frac{1}{2}$ (d) $\frac{2}{5} + \frac{5}{8} - \frac{3}{4}$
   (e) $\frac{1}{5} + \frac{3}{10} - \frac{1}{2}$ (f) $\frac{3}{7} + \frac{5}{14} - \frac{1}{2}$

Exercise 5.1b

1. Fill in the blanks in these equivalent fractions.
   (a) $\frac{1}{6} = \frac{4}{\square} = \frac{\square}{12}$ (b) $\frac{2}{3} = \frac{\square}{6} = \frac{12}{\square} = \frac{\square}{24}$

2. Write these fractions in their lowest terms.
   (a) $\frac{8}{16}$ (b) $\frac{9}{15}$ (c) $\frac{10}{25}$ (d) $\frac{24}{30}$

For the rest of the questions, give all answers in their lowest terms.

3. Add these fractions.
   (a) $\frac{2}{7} + \frac{4}{7}$ (b) $\frac{1}{3} + \frac{1}{6}$ (c) $\frac{2}{5} + \frac{1}{4}$ (d) $\frac{1}{5} + \frac{3}{4}$ (e) $\frac{3}{8} + \frac{1}{5}$ (f) $\frac{3}{4} + \frac{2}{5}$

4. Subtract these fractions.
   (a) $\frac{3}{4} - \frac{1}{4}$ (b) $\frac{1}{2} - \frac{1}{3}$ (c) $\frac{3}{4} - \frac{3}{5}$ (d) $\frac{3}{4} - \frac{1}{6}$ (e) $\frac{3}{5} - \frac{1}{2}$ (f) $\frac{7}{8} - \frac{2}{3}$

5. Work these out.
   (a) $\frac{3}{5} + \frac{2}{5} - \frac{7}{10}$ (b) $\frac{1}{4} + \frac{3}{8} - \frac{1}{6}$ (c) $\frac{1}{6} + \frac{2}{3} - \frac{1}{4}$ (d) $\frac{5}{8} + \frac{3}{5} - \frac{3}{4}$
   (e) $\frac{3}{4} - \frac{5}{6} + \frac{2}{3}$ (f) $\frac{3}{20} - \frac{2}{5} + \frac{3}{4}$

Mixed numbers

Look at this calculation.

$$\frac{2}{3} + \frac{2}{3} = \frac{4}{3}$$

As you can see the result of this addition is a fraction which is 'top-heavy'. It is usual to write fractions like this as **mixed numbers**.

$$\frac{4}{3} = 1\frac{1}{3}$$

To change a top-heavy fraction to a mixed number, divide the denominator into the numerator and write the remainder as a fraction over the denominator.

Example 5

Change these fractions to mixed numbers.

(a) $\frac{7}{4}$ (b) $\frac{11}{5}$ (c) $\frac{24}{7}$

(a) $\frac{7}{4} = 1\frac{3}{4}$ $7 \div 4 = 1$ with 3 left over.

(b) $\frac{11}{5} = 2\frac{1}{5}$ $11 \div 5 = 2$ with 1 left over.

(c) $\frac{24}{7} = 3\frac{3}{7}$ $24 \div 7 = 3$ with 3 left over.

Mixed numbers can be changed to top-heavy fractions. Just reverse the process.

Example 6

Change these mixed numbers to top-heavy fractions.

(a) $3\frac{1}{4}$ (b) $2\frac{3}{5}$ (c) $3\frac{5}{6}$

(a) $3\frac{1}{4} = 3 + \frac{1}{4} = \frac{12}{4} + \frac{1}{4} = \frac{13}{4}$ Change the whole number to quarters and then add. Another way to think of it is to multiply the whole number by the denominator and add on the numerator. $(3 \times 4 + 1 = 13)$

(b) $2\frac{3}{5} = \frac{13}{5}$ $2 \times 5 + 3 = 13$

(c) $3\frac{5}{6} = \frac{23}{6}$ $3 \times 6 + 5 = 23$

To add or subtract mixed numbers deal with the whole numbers first.

Example 7

Work these out.

(a) $1\frac{1}{6} + 2\frac{1}{3}$ (b) $2\frac{3}{4} + \frac{3}{5}$ (c) $3\frac{2}{3} - 1\frac{1}{6}$ (d) $4\frac{1}{5} - 1\frac{1}{2}$

(a) $1\frac{1}{6} + 2\frac{1}{3} = 3 + \frac{1}{6} + \frac{1}{3}$ Add the whole numbers, then deal with the fractions in the normal way.

$= 3 + \frac{1}{6} + \frac{2}{6}$

$= 3\frac{3}{6} = 3\frac{1}{2}$

(b) $2\frac{3}{4} + \frac{3}{5} = 2 + \frac{15}{20} + \frac{12}{20}$

$= 2 + \frac{27}{20}$ You end up with a top-heavy fraction which you have to change to a mixed number, and then add the whole numbers.

$= 2 + 1 + \frac{7}{20}$

$= 3\frac{7}{20}$

(c) $3\frac{2}{3} - 1\frac{1}{6} = 3 - 1 + \frac{2}{3} - \frac{1}{6}$ Subtract the numbers and then the fractions.

$= 2 + \frac{4}{6} - \frac{1}{6}$

$= 2\frac{3}{6} = 2\frac{1}{2}$

(d) $4\frac{1}{5} - 1\frac{1}{2} = 3 + \frac{2}{10} - \frac{5}{10}$ Working out $\frac{2}{10} - \frac{5}{10}$ gives a negative answer of $\frac{-3}{10}$.

$= 2 + \frac{10}{10} + \frac{2}{10} - \frac{5}{10}$ Change one of the whole numbers into $\frac{10}{10}$, then subtract.

$= 2\frac{7}{10}$

1. Change these top-heavy fractions to mixed numbers.
   (a) $\frac{7}{4}$ (b) $\frac{12}{5}$ (c) $\frac{17}{3}$ (d) $\frac{15}{4}$ (e) $\frac{25}{2}$

2. Change these mixed numbers to top-heavy fractions.
   (a) $1\frac{1}{2}$ (b) $2\frac{3}{5}$ (c) $5\frac{3}{8}$ (d) $2\frac{4}{7}$ (e) $9\frac{1}{4}$

3. Add. Write your answers as simply as possible.
   (a) $1\frac{1}{3} + 3\frac{1}{4}$ (b) $3\frac{1}{5} + \frac{7}{10}$ (c) $1\frac{3}{4} + 4\frac{2}{5}$ (d) $2\frac{5}{6} + 7\frac{4}{9}$
   (e) $\frac{2}{7} + \frac{1}{2} + \frac{5}{14}$ (f) $1\frac{1}{2} + \frac{3}{4} + 2\frac{3}{8}$

4. Subtract. Write your answers as simply as possible.
   (a) $2\frac{4}{5} - 1\frac{3}{5}$ (b) $5\frac{3}{8} - 2\frac{1}{4}$ (c) $3\frac{2}{3} - \frac{1}{2}$ (d) $3\frac{2}{5} - 1\frac{3}{4}$
   (e) $5\frac{1}{6} - 3\frac{2}{3}$ (f) $5\frac{1}{5} - \frac{2}{3}$

5. Work these out. Write the answers as simply as possible.
   (a) $\frac{1}{4} + \frac{2}{3} + \frac{1}{2}$ (b) $2\frac{1}{3} + 2\frac{1}{4} - 1\frac{5}{6}$ (c) $3\frac{3}{5} - \frac{1}{4} + \frac{1}{2}$
   (d) $2\frac{3}{8} - \frac{1}{2} + 3\frac{1}{4}$ (e) $4\frac{1}{5} + 1\frac{3}{10} - \frac{4}{5}$ (f) $2\frac{3}{7} - \frac{1}{2} - 1\frac{2}{7}$

6. Faisal cut two pieces of wood $3\frac{3}{8}$ inches and $5\frac{1}{4}$ inches long from a piece 10 inches long. How long was the piece that was left?

1. Change these top-heavy fractions to mixed numbers.
   (a) $\frac{9}{2}$ (b) $\frac{14}{3}$ (c) $\frac{17}{4}$ (d) $\frac{23}{6}$ (e) $\frac{35}{8}$

2. Change these mixed numbers to top-heavy fractions.
   (a) $5\frac{1}{2}$ (b) $2\frac{3}{10}$ (c) $2\frac{3}{7}$ (d) $4\frac{2}{3}$ (e) $4\frac{5}{6}$

3. Add. Write your answers as simply as possible.
   (a) $1\frac{1}{2} + 2\frac{1}{6}$ (b) $1\frac{4}{5} + 2\frac{1}{10}$ (c) $6\frac{1}{6} + 1\frac{4}{9}$ (d) $2\frac{4}{7} + 1\frac{2}{3}$
   (e) $\frac{4}{5} + 1\frac{3}{4} + 2\frac{1}{2}$ (f) $6\frac{1}{3} + 1\frac{4}{9} + 1\frac{2}{9}$

4. Subtract. Write your answers as simply as possible.
   (a) $2\frac{2}{3} - 1\frac{1}{6}$ (b) $3\frac{5}{8} - 1\frac{1}{4}$ (c) $2\frac{4}{5} - \frac{1}{2}$ (d) $4\frac{2}{5} - 1\frac{1}{4}$
   (e) $8\frac{1}{6} - 5\frac{3}{8}$ (f) $1\frac{1}{4} - \frac{5}{8}$

5. Work these out. Write the answers as simply as possible.
   (a) $2\frac{1}{3} + 3\frac{1}{2} - \frac{5}{6}$ (b) $1\frac{3}{4} - \frac{5}{6} + 2\frac{1}{2}$ (c) $3\frac{1}{6} - 2\frac{1}{8} + \frac{3}{4}$
   (d) $4\frac{1}{3} - \frac{4}{5} + \frac{2}{5}$ (e) $3\frac{3}{4} - 2\frac{1}{2} + 1\frac{5}{8}$ (f) $4\frac{1}{3} - 1\frac{5}{6} - 2\frac{1}{2}$

6. Caroline bought a piece of ribbon 24 inches long.
   She cut off two pieces, each $5\frac{5}{8}$ inches long. How long was the piece she had left?

Multiplying and dividing fractions

Multiplying fractions

> You can think of a fraction as the number 1 multiplied by the numerator and divided by the denominator. For example,
> $\frac{2}{3} = 1 \times 2 \div 3$ or $\frac{1}{1} \times \frac{2}{3} = \frac{1 \times 2}{1 \times 3}$.

To multiply fractions, multiply the numerators and multiply the denominators, then simplify if possible. If the fractions are mixed numbers change them to top-heavy fractions and then multiply.

Examiner's tip

Note: $\frac{1}{2} \times \frac{1}{3} = \frac{1}{6}$
A common error is to multiply 1×1 and get 2.

Examiner's tip

When cancelling, cancel a term in the numerator with one in the denominator.

Example 8   Work these out.

(a) $\frac{3}{5} \times \frac{1}{2}$ (b) $\frac{3}{8} \times \frac{4}{9}$ (c) $1\frac{3}{5} \times 3\frac{3}{4}$

(a) $\frac{3}{5} \times \frac{1}{2} = \frac{3}{10}$

> Multiply the numerators and multiply the denominators. The answer is already in its lowest terms.

(b) $\frac{3}{8} \times \frac{4}{9} = \frac{12}{72} = \frac{1}{6}$

> The answer simplifies to $\frac{1}{6}$ but you could divide by the common factors (cancel) first, for example $\frac{{}^1 3}{{}_2 8} \times \frac{{}^4 1}{{}_9 3} = \frac{1}{2} \times \frac{1}{3} = \frac{1}{6}$ as 3 divides into 3 and 9; 4 divides into 4 and 8.

(c) $1\frac{3}{5} \times 3\frac{3}{4} = \frac{8}{5} \times \frac{15}{4}$

> 5 divides into 5 and 15; 4 divides into 4 and 8.

$= \frac{2}{1} \times \frac{3}{1} = 6$

Remember that, when simplifying or cancelling, you can just cross out the numbers you are cancelling and write in the quotients, for example, $\frac{3}{8} \times \frac{4}{9} = \frac{{}^1 3}{{}_2 8} \times \frac{4^1}{9_3} = \frac{1}{2} \times \frac{1}{3}$.

Dividing fractions

Multiplying by $\frac{1}{2}$ is the same as dividing by 2, so dividing by $\frac{1}{2}$ is the same as multiplying by 2.

This can be extended, for example, $4 \div \frac{2}{3} = 4 \times \frac{3}{2} = \frac{12}{2} = 6$

> When dividing fractions, turn the second fraction upside-down and then multiply.

Example 9 Work these out.

(a) $\frac{4}{5} \div \frac{3}{10}$ (b) $\frac{9}{10} \div \frac{3}{4}$ (c) $2\frac{1}{4} \div 1\frac{1}{2}$

(a) $\frac{4}{5} \div \frac{3}{10} = \frac{4}{5} \times \frac{10}{3}$

Turn the second fraction upside-down and multiply.

$= \frac{4}{1} \times \frac{2}{3} = \frac{8}{3} = 2\frac{2}{3}$

Cancel 10 and 5 by 5, multiply and change to a mixed number.

(b) $\frac{9}{10} \div \frac{3}{4} = \frac{9}{10} \times \frac{4}{3}$

$= \frac{3}{5} \times \frac{2}{1} = \frac{6}{5} = 1\frac{1}{5}$

Cancel 9 and 3 by 3; 4 and 10 by 2.

(c) $2\frac{1}{4} \div 1\frac{1}{2} = \frac{9}{4} \div \frac{3}{2}$

Change to top-heavy fractions.

$= \frac{9}{4} \times \frac{2}{3} = \frac{3}{2} \times \frac{1}{1}$

Cancel 9 and 3 by 3; 2 and 4 by 2.

$= \frac{3}{2} = 1\frac{1}{2}$

Exercise 5.3a

Work these out.

1. $\frac{1}{4} \times \frac{2}{3}$
2. $\frac{2}{3} \times \frac{3}{5}$
3. $\frac{4}{9} \times \frac{1}{2}$
4. $\frac{2}{3} \times \frac{1}{3}$
5. $\frac{4}{5} \div \frac{3}{10}$
6. $\frac{1}{4} \div \frac{3}{8}$

7. $\frac{3}{4} \div \frac{5}{6}$
8. $4\frac{1}{2} \times 2\frac{1}{6}$
9. $1\frac{1}{2} \times 3\frac{2}{3}$
10. $2\frac{1}{3} \div 1\frac{1}{3}$
11. $2\frac{2}{5} \div 1\frac{1}{2}$
12. $1\frac{1}{4} \times 3\frac{3}{5} \div 1\frac{1}{2}$

Exercise 5.3b

Work these out.

1. $\frac{1}{2} \times \frac{5}{6}$
2. $\frac{3}{5} \times \frac{5}{6}$
3. $\frac{2}{3} \times \frac{5}{8}$
4. $\frac{3}{5} \times \frac{5}{12}$
5. $\frac{3}{8} \div \frac{1}{4}$
6. $\frac{2}{3} \div \frac{5}{6}$

7. $\frac{3}{4} \div \frac{3}{8}$
8. $3\frac{1}{3} \times 2\frac{2}{5}$
9. $2\frac{2}{5} \times \frac{3}{4}$
10. $3\frac{1}{8} \div 1\frac{1}{4}$
11. $2\frac{1}{4} \div 3\frac{1}{2}$
12. $3\frac{1}{3} \times 1\frac{1}{4} \div 2\frac{1}{2}$

Adding and subtracting negative numbers

Adding a negative number is the same as subtracting a positive number.

$4 + (-2) = 4 - 2 = 2$

Subtracting a negative number is the same as adding a positive number.

$4 - (-2) = 4 + 2 = 6$

When the numbers to be added are both negative, add them and put the negative sign in front.

$$-4 - 5 = -9$$

If they have different signs, subtract them and give the answer the same sign as the larger number.

$$-4 + 6 = +2$$
$$-5 + 2 = -3$$

When adding or subtracting negative and positive numbers, it is best to:

total the positive numbers
total the negative numbers separately
then find the difference between the two totals,
remembering to give the answer the correct sign.

You can already multiply and divide negative numbers. Now the steps can be combined.

Example 10

Work these out without using a calculator.

(a) $(-3 \times -4) + (-2 \times 3)$

(b) $-5 + 4 - 6 + 7 + 5 + 1 - 3 - 5 - 2$

(c) $\dfrac{5 \times -4 + 3 \times -2}{-6 + 4}$

(a) $(-3 \times -4) + (-2 \times 3) = (+12) + (-6) = 12 - 6 = +6 = 6$

(b) $-5 + 4 - 6 + 7 + 5 + 1 - 3 - 5 - 2 = +17 - 21 = -4$

(c) $\dfrac{5 \times -4 + 3 \times -2}{-6 + 4} = \dfrac{-20 + (-6)}{-2} = \dfrac{-26}{-2} = 13$

Example 11

Use a calculator to work these out, correct to three significant figures.

(a) $(-3.4)^2 - 2 \times 4.6$

(b) $4.7 \times 2.8 + (3 \times -17.1)$

(a) $(-3.4)^2 - 2 \times 4.6 = 11.56 - 9.2 = 2.36$

(b) $4.7 \times 2.8 + (3 \times -17.1) = 13.16 - 51.3$
$$= -38.14 = -38.1 \text{ (to 3 s.f.)}$$

Both of these can be worked out directly on the calculator.

Exercise 5.4a

Work these out without using a calculator.

1. $(-4 \times -3) - (-2 \times +1)$
2. $(-7 \times -2) + (4 \times -2)$
3. $(-15 \div 2) - (4 \times -6)$
4. $-4 + 3 + 2 + 3 + 4 - 5 - 6 - 9 + 1$
5. $\dfrac{-2 + 12}{-5}$
6. $\dfrac{-4 \times -3}{-4 + 3}$

Use a calculator to work these out.

7. $-4.73 + 2.96 - 1.71 + 3.62$
8. $(-4.6 \times 7.2) + (3.1 \times -4.3)$
9. $\dfrac{-4.7 + 2.6}{-5.7}$
10. $\dfrac{7.92 \times 1.71}{-4.2 + 3.6}$

Exercise 5.4b

Work these out without using a calculator.

1. $(-2 \times +3) + (-3 \times +4)$
2. $(-1 \times -4) + (-7 \times -8)$
3. $(24 \div -3) - (-5 \times -4)$
4. $-6 - 2 - 3 + 5 - 7 + 4 - 2 + 8$
5. $\dfrac{-3 + 7}{-2}$
6. $\dfrac{-7 \times -12}{-8 + 4}$

Use a calculator to work these out.

7. $-14.7 + 6.92 - 1.41 - 2.83$
8. $(-1.2 \times -2.4) - (9.2 \times -3.6)$
9. $\dfrac{-4.72}{-1.4} \times \dfrac{8.61}{-7.21}$
10. $\dfrac{3.14 - 8.16}{-8.25 \times 3.18}$

Using a calculator

You already know how to use a calculator to do basic calculations.

In the last exercise you may have answered question 10 by working out the numerator and denominator separately and then dividing them, but you could do it all on your calculator, by using brackets or by various other means.

Calculators vary and you need to practise with yours to see what it can do.

Examiner's tip

Where it is possible to split the question up, it is useful to do so to check, but make sure you do not round the answer too early.

Unless the question states otherwise it is best to give your final answer to 3 s.f.

Example 12

Use a calculator to work these out.

(a) $\dfrac{14.73 + 2.96}{15.25 - 7.14}$ (b) $\sqrt{17.8^2 + 4.3^2}$

(a) $\dfrac{14.73 + 2.96}{15.25 - 7.14} = 2.1812 = 2.18$ (to 2 d.p.)

There are various ways to do this. One is to key in:

1	4	.	7	3	+	2	.	9	6	=
÷	(	1	5	.	2	5	−	7	.	1
4	)	=

(b) $\sqrt{17.8^2 + 4.3^2} = 18.312 = 18.3$ (to 3 s.f.)

Key in:

| (| 1 | 7 | . | 8 | x^2 | + |
| 4 | . | 3 | x^2 |) | √ | = |

Examiner's tip

When using sin, cos, tan, make sure the calculator is in degree mode.

These all need practice.

Some of the more common operations you will be asked to use are powers and roots (using the y^x button and the $\sqrt[x]{\ }$ or $y^{1/x}$ button) and sine (sin), cosine (cos) and tangent (tan) of an angle.

Example 13

Use a calculator to evaluate these.

(a) 4.2^3 (b) $\sqrt[5]{15}$ (c) $\cos 73°$
(d) $\cos^{-1} 0.897$ (e) $(3.7 \times 10^{-5}) \div (8.3 \times 10^6)$

Remember that $\cos^{-1}$ is also called inv cos or arc cos.

(a) $4.2^3 = 74.088 = 74.1$ (to 3 s.f.)

This can be done by keying $4.2 \times 4.2 \times 4.2$, but using the y^x button is quicker.
Key in: | 4 | . | 2 | y^x | 3 | = |

(b) $\sqrt[5]{15} = 1.7187 = 1.72$ (to 3 s.f.)

Key in: | 5 | 2nd F | y^x | 1 | 5 | = |
This may vary, depending on your calculator. $\sqrt[5]{15}$ is the same as $15^{1/5}$.

(c) $\cos 73° = 0.2923 = 0.292$ (to 3 s.f.)

Key in: | cos | 7 | 3 | = |
On some calculators, you need to key in | 7 | 3 | cos |

(d) $\cos^{-1} 0.897 = 26.23° = 26.2°$ (to 3 s.f.)

Key in: | 2nd F | cos | . | 8 | 9 | 7 | = |
On some calculators, you need to key in | . | 8 | 9 | 7 | 2nd F | cos |

(e) $(3.7 \times 10^{-5}) \div (8.3 \times 10^6) = 4.46 \times 10^{-12}$ (to 3 s.f.)

Key in: | 3 | . | 7 | EXP | 5 | +/− | ÷ | 8 | . | 3 | EXP | 6 | = |
This may be different on your calculator.

Work these out.

1. (a) 3.8^4 (b) $31.8^{1/4}$
2. (a) $\sin 46.2°$ (b) $\tan 51.6°$ (c) $\cos 31.6°$
   (d) $\sin 12° - \cos 31°$
3. (a) $\cos^{-1} 0.832$ (b) $\text{inv} \tan 3.60$ (c) $\sin^{-1} 0.910$
   (d) $\sin^{-1} \dfrac{16.3}{43.9}$
4. $43.7^3 + 17.1^2$
5. $\dfrac{3.4 \times \sin 47.1°}{\sin 19.2°}$
6. $4.7 \times 10^5 \times 7.9 \times 10^{-4}$
7. $(9.2 + 15.3)^2$
8. $\dfrac{6.2}{2.6} + \dfrac{5.4}{3.9}$
9. $\dfrac{2.6 + 4.25}{7.8 \times 3.6^2}$
10. $\dfrac{19.4 \times 6.3 - 2.61}{8.1 + 7.94}$

Work these out.

1. (a) 7.31^5 (b) $12.2^{1/5}$
2. (a) $\sin 14.6°$ (b) $\cos 71.3°$ (c) $\tan 15.9°$ (d) $\sin 247°$
3. (a) $\tan^{-1} 3.21$ (b) $\sin^{-1} 0.464$ (c) $\cos^{-1} 0.141$
   (d) $\sin^{-1} \dfrac{\sqrt{3}}{2}$
4. $2.7^2 + 3.6^2 - 2 \times 2.7 \times 3.6 \times 0.146$
5. $3.1 \times 4.2 \times \sin 41.2° \div 2$
6. $\sqrt{6.39^2 - 4.27^2}$
7. $(2.2 \times 10^{-2}) \div (5.3 \times 10^4)$
8. $3 \cos 14.2° - 5 \sin 16.3°$
9. $\left(2.4 \times 3.1 - \dfrac{6.8}{3.4}\right)^2$
10. $\frac{1}{2}(-5 + \sqrt{5^2 + 1200})$

Ratio and proportion

You have already done some work involving simple ratios. This is now extended.

Example 14 Adrian made a fruit drink with 9 parts orange juice, 4 parts lemon juice and 2 parts grapefruit juice. He made 2 litres of fruit drink. How much orange juice did he need?

	orange	:	lemon	:	grapefruit	total
Parts	9		4		2	15
Quantity	x					2000 ml

Using ratios, $x : 9 = 2000 : 15$

$x = \frac{2000}{15} \times 9 = 1200$ ml

Drawing up a table often helps to decide which parts you need to use.

This could have been worked out without a calculator, and you may be asked to do so.

Examiner's tip

A common error, when using a calculator, is to round at too early a stage. In Example 14, if the answer is rounded after dividing by 15 to give 133 and this is then multiplied by 9, the answer comes out as 1197 instead of 1200.

Exercise 5.6a

Answer the first five questions without using a calculator.

1. Split £100 in the ratio 2 : 3 : 5.
2. The angles of a triangle are in the ratio 1 : 2 : 3. What are the sizes of the angles?
3. John and Qasim share £20 in the ratio 2 to 3. How much does John get?
4. Paint is mixed as 3 parts red to 5 parts white. How much of this paint can be made with 2 litres of white?
5. Susan and Chika invest £4000 and £6000 in a business venture and agree to share the profits in the ratio of their investment. They make a profit of £250 in the first year. How much does Chika receive?

For the rest of the questions you can use a calculator.

6. Maureen and Sheena's earnings are in the ratio 3 : 5. They earn £352 all together. How much does Sheena earn?
7. At Carterknowle Church Autumn Bazaar £875 was raised. It was agreed to share the profits between the church and the local charity for the homeless, in the ratio 5 to 1. How much did the charity receive? Give the answer to the nearest pound.

Exercise 5.6a continued

8. To make her own breakfast cereal, Sally mixes bran, currants and wheatgerm in the ratio 8 to 3 to 1 by mass. How much bran, to the nearest 10 grams, does she use to make 500 grams of cereal?

9. David, Michael and Iain employed a gardener and agreed to pay him in the ratio of the time he spent on each garden. He spent 2 hours 20 minutes in David's garden, 3 hours 30 minutes in Michael's garden and 4 hours 10 minutes in Iain's garden. David paid £12.60. How much did the other two pay?

10. In a local election the votes were Labour 1200, Conservative 5312, Lib-Dems 878. Write this ratio in the form $1 : n : m$. Correct n and m to three significant figures.

Exercise 5.6b

Do not use a calculator for the first five questions.

1. Share £75 in the ratio 8 to 7.

2. A firm uses first and second class stamps in the ratio 9 to 1. During a week they used 250 stamps altogether. How many first class stamps did they use?

3. A metal alloy is made up of copper, iron and nickel in the ratio $3 : 4 : 2$. How much copper is there in 450 g of the alloy?

4. Vicki and Inderjit share the winnings from a raffle in the ratio 2 to 3. Vicki received £15. How much did they win altogether?

5. Old 2-stroke scooters used to mix petrol with oil in the ratio 25 to 1. How much oil had to be mixed with 5 litres of petrol?

Use a calculator for the rest of the questions.

6. In a school there are 875 pupils and 41 teachers. Write the pupil : teacher ratio in the form $n : 1$. Express n correct to three significant figures.

7. Shahida spends her pocket money on sweets, magazines and savings in the ratio $2 : 3 : 7$. She receives £15 a week. How much does she spend on sweets?

8. Doreen and Joan invested £5000 and £7500 respectively in a firm. They shared the profits in the ratio of their investment. Doreen received £320. How much did Joan receive?

9. Alec and Pat share a house. They agree to share the rent (to the nearest pound) in the ratio of the area of their bedrooms. The area of Alec's floor is $17\,\text{m}^2$ and the area of Pat's is $21\,\text{m}^2$. The rent is £320 a week. How much do they each pay?

10. In a questionnaire the three possible answers are 'Yes', 'No' and 'Don't know'. The answers from a group of 456 people are in the ratio $10 : 6 : 3$. How many 'Don't knows' are there?

Repeated proportional changes

You already know how to increase or decrease an amount by a percentage or a fraction.

If an amount was increased by 20%, you work out 20% and add it on.

Alternatively, you could multiply by 1.2 (finding 120%).

This second method is vital if you need to deal with successive increases over a number of years.

 Example

Selena invested £4000 and received 5% interest a year which was added on each year. How much had she in total after: (a) 1 year   (b) 6 years?

A 5% increase means that the new amount is $100 + 5 = 105\%$ of the old amount each year.

105% is 1.05, so multiply by 1.05 each year.

(a) After one year the total amount is £4000 $\times$ 1.05 = £4200

(b) After 6 years the total amount is
$4000 \times 1.05 \times 1.05 \times 1.05 \times 1.05 \times 1.05 \times 1.05$
$= 4000 \times (1.05)^6$
$= £5360.38$ (to the nearest penny)

It is the same for fractions. If an amount is increased by $\frac{1}{10}$ each year, the new amount is $1 + \frac{1}{10} = \frac{11}{10}$ of the old amount each year.

Example 16

Andrew said he would increase his giving to charity by $\frac{1}{25}$ each year. He gave £120 at the start. How much did he give at the end of the fifth year?

Each year he gave $\frac{26}{25} \times$ what he gave in the previous year. $(1 + \frac{1}{25} = \frac{26}{25})$

At the end of the fifth year he gave £120 $\times \left(\frac{26}{25}\right)^5$

Key in:

= £145.998
= £146.00 to the nearest penny.

If the change is a decrease, subtract from 100% or 1.

So 'reduce by three per cent' means 'find 97% or multiply by 0.97'
'reduce by one fifth $\left(\frac{1}{5}\right)$' means 'multiply by four fifths $\left(\frac{4}{5}\right)$'.

Example 17

The distance that Patrick can walk in a day is reducing by $\frac{1}{15}$ each year. This year he can walk 12 miles in a day. How far will he be able to walk in five years' time?

The distance reduces by $\frac{1}{15}$ in 1 year, so multiply by $\frac{14}{15}$ for each year.

In five years he will be able to walk $12 \times \left(\frac{14}{15}\right)^5 = 8.499 = 8.50$ miles.

Exercise 5.7a

1. What do you multiply a quantity by if it is increased by:
   (a) 6%   (b) 9%   (c) 17.5%   (d) 1.25%   (e) $\frac{1}{5}$ (f) $\frac{2}{9}$?
2. What do you multiply a quantity by if it is decreased by:
   (a) 6%   (b) 9%   (c) 17.5%   (d) 1.25%   (e) $\frac{1}{5}$ (f) $\frac{2}{9}$?
3. Peter invests £1000 and 5% of the balance is added to the amount each year. How much will be in the account after six years? Give the answer to the nearest pound.
4. A population of bacteria is estimated to increase by 12% every 24 hours. The population was 2000 at midnight on Friday. What was the population (to the nearest whole number) by midnight the following Wednesday?

5. The insurance premium for Della's car was £360. The firm reduced it by 12% for each year she had no claim. What was the cost after six years with no claims? Give the answer to the nearest pound.

6. Mr Costa was offered an 8% rise every year whilst he worked at the same firm. This year he earned £28 500. How much will he earn after four rises? Give the answer to the nearest pound.

7. At Premda department store they said they would reduce the price of goods still not sold by $\frac{1}{3}$ for each day of the sale.
   A coat was offered originally at £65. What was its price after three days, to the nearest penny?

8. An investment firm says it will add $\frac{1}{5}$ to your money each year. If you invested £3000, how much would it amount to after 10 years? Give the answer to the nearest pound.

9. Clement claimed that if you get a 7% increase each year you will double your money after 10 years. Is this true? Show figures to justify your answer.

10. Ambrose invested £3500 in a six-year bond that added 5% to the amount each year for the first three years and 7.5% each year for the next three years. What is the amount in the bond, to the nearest penny:
    (a) after three years   (b) after six years?

Exercise 5.7b

1. What do you multiply a quantity by if it is increased by:
   (a) 4%   (b) 18%   (c) 12.5%   (d) 5.6%   (e) $\frac{1}{6}$ (f) $\frac{3}{5}$?

2. What do you multiply a quantity by if it is decreased by:
   (a) 4%   (b) 18%   (c) 12.5%   (d) 5.6%   (e) $\frac{1}{6}$ (f) $\frac{3}{5}$?

3. Interest of 4% was added to an investment of £1500 each year for four years. How much was it then worth? Give the answer to the nearest pound.

4. Martyn had shares worth £8000. They increased in value by 7.5% each year. What was their value after 10 years? Give the answer to the nearest pound.

5. Cathy said she would withdraw $\frac{1}{5}$ of the money she had in the bank every time she made a withdrawal. She had £187.50 in the bank to start with. How much did she have after three withdrawals?

6. At Patnik shoe shop they offered to decrease the price of a pair of shoes by $\frac{1}{4}$ each day until they were sold. They were priced at £47 to start with. Jean bought them after they had been reduced four times. How much did she pay? Give the answer to the nearest penny.

7. Tony says his narrow boat is increasing in value by 6% a year. It was worth £25 000 in 1999. How much would it be worth, to the nearest hundred pounds, in 2005 (six years later) if he is correct?

8. Sheila joined a keep-fit club that claimed you would reduce your running time by 1% each week. She could run 500 metres in 12 minutes to start with. According to the club, how long would it take her after five weeks? Give the answer to the nearest second.

9. It is claimed that the number of rabbits in Freeshire is increasing by $\frac{1}{12}$ each year. It is estimated that there are 1700 rabbits now. How many will there be after four years if the statement is true? Give the answer to three significant figures.

10. Mordovia has high inflation. In 1999 it was 15% a month for the first six months and 12.5% for the next six months.
    A car cost 78 000 scuds (their unit of currency) in January 1999. How much did it cost:
    (a) after six months   (b) in January 2000?
    Give the answers to the nearest whole number.

Finding the value before a percentage change

If a quantity is increased by 5%, you multiply by 1.05 to get the new amount.

To find the original amount from the new amount just reverse the process and divide by 1.05.

Example 18

Irene paid £38.70 for a skirt in a sale. This was after it had been reduced by 10%.

What was the original price of the skirt?

New price = 0.9 × original price

Original price = new price ÷ 0.9
$$= £38.70 ÷ 0.9 = £43$$

Example 19

Berwyn received an increase of $\frac{1}{5}$ in his salary. After the increase he was earning £31 260 a year. What was his salary before the rise?

New salary = $\frac{6}{5}$ × old salary

Old salary = new salary ÷ $\frac{6}{5}$ = new salary × $\frac{5}{6}$

Old salary = £31 260 × $\frac{5}{6}$ = £26 050

Exercise 5.8a

In this exercise, some of these questions ask for the original amount and some ask for the new amount.

1. A price of £50 is increased by 7.5%. What is the new price?
2. A quantity is decreased by 3%. It is now 38.8. What was it to start with?
3. A coat was advertised at £79. In a sale the price was reduced by 5%. What was the new price?
4. Mr Diffom made a profit of £13 250 in the year 2000. This was an increase of 6% on his profit in 1999. What was his profit in 1999?
5. In a local election in 1997, Labour received 1375 votes. This was increased by 12% in 1998. How many people voted Labour in 1998?
6. Save-a-lot supermarket advertised jam at $\frac{1}{5}$ off. A jar cost £1.80 after the reduction. What did it cost originally?

Exercise 5.8a continued

7. Stephen was given a rise of 7%. His salary after the rise was £28 890. What was it before the rise?

8. Between 1978 and 1979 house prices increased by 12.5%. A house was valued at £27 000 in 1979. What was its value in 1978?

9. A holiday cost £564, including VAT at 17.5%. What was the cost without VAT?

10. At Jack's café all prices were increased by 5% (to the nearest penny).
    (a) A cup of tea cost 75p before the increase. What is the new price?
    (b) The new price of a cup of coffee is £1.30. What did it cost before the increase?

Exercise 5.8b

In this exercise, some of these questions ask for the original amount and some ask for the new amount.

1. A 'best score' of 70 is increased by $\frac{2}{5}$. What is it now?

2. After an increase of 12%, a quantity is 84 tons. What was it before the increase?

3. In a sale everything is reduced by 5%. A pair of shoes costs £47.50 in the sale. How much did they cost before the sale?

4. A newspaper increased its circulation by 3% and the new number sold was 58 195. What was it before the increase?

5. Santos sold his car for £8520. This was 40% less than he paid for it five years before. What did he pay for it?

6. A charity's income has been reduced by $2\frac{1}{2}$%. Its income is now £8580. What was it before the reduction?

7. It was announced that the number of people unemployed had decreased by 3%. The number who were unemployed before the decrease was 2.56 million. How many are now unemployed? Give the answer to three significant figures.

8. The cost of a car, including VAT at 17.5%, is £12 925. What is the cost without VAT?

9. A car firm claims that for its latest model, the number of miles per gallon of fuel has increased by $\frac{1}{5}$. The new model travels 48 miles per gallon. How many miles per gallon did the old model travel?

10. At Percival's sale the price of everything is reduced by $7\frac{1}{2}$%, rounded to the nearest penny.
    (a) A pair of boots cost £94.99 before the sale. What is the price in the sale?
    (b) Delia is charged £13.87 for a blouse in the sale. What was its original price?

Key points

- When adding or subtracting fractions, change both to the same denominator and add or subtract the numerators.
- If mixed numbers are involved, deal with the whole numbers separately.
- When multiplying fractions, multiply the numerators and multiply the denominators and cancel down.
- When dividing fractions, invert the second fraction and multiply.
- If mixed numbers are involved, change to top-heavy fractions before multiplying or dividing.
- When collecting two negative and/or positive numbers:
  - if the signs are the same add the numbers and the answer takes the same sign as both the numbers
  - if the signs are different, subtract the numbers and the answer takes the sign of the bigger number.
- When a quantity is increased by 5% a year for six years, multiply by 1.05^6.
- When a quantity is decreased by 3% a year for four years, multiply by 0.97^4.
- To find the quantity before a 2% increase, divide the new quantity by 1.02.
- To find a quantity before a 4% decrease, divide by 0.96.

Revision exercise 5a

1. Work these out.
   (a) $\frac{1}{2} + \frac{2}{3}$
   (b) $1\frac{2}{5} + 3\frac{1}{4}$
   (c) $\frac{5}{9} - \frac{1}{6}$
   (d) $3\frac{1}{4} - 2\frac{2}{3}$
   (e) $\frac{2}{3} + 4\frac{1}{2} - 2\frac{5}{6}$
   (f) $\frac{2}{3} \times \frac{3}{5}$
   (g) $\frac{3}{8} \div \frac{1}{4}$
   (h) $2\frac{1}{2} \times 3\frac{1}{5}$
   (i) $3\frac{1}{5} \div 2\frac{2}{3}$
   (j) $4\frac{1}{3} \times 1\frac{1}{4} \div 2\frac{1}{6}$

2. To make a frame John uses four pieces of wood: two are $4\frac{1}{4}$ inches long and two are $6\frac{2}{3}$ inches long. He cut them off a piece of wood 24 inches long. How much wood was left?

3. Work these out without using a calculator.
   (a) $(-2 \times -5) + (-6 \times 3)$
   (b) $4 + 6 - 8 - 7 + 1 + 3 - 5 - 6$
   (c) $\frac{-3 \times -2 + 7 \times -2}{-8 + 6}$

4. Use a calculator to work these out. Where answers are not exact, give them correct to three significant figures.
   (a) $-2.73 + 12.6 - 11.91 + 13.2$
   (b) $(-4.5 \times 8.3) + (6.1 \times -4.3)$
   (c) $\frac{-4.7 + 3.6}{-7.5}$
   (d) $\cos 14.2°$
   (e) $\sin^{-1} 0.365$
   (f) $\tan 71.2°$
   (g) 3^9
   (h) $12.3^3 - 2.6^3$
   (i) $\frac{3.2 \sin 12.3°}{\sin 28.2°}$
   (j) $\sqrt{5^2 + 8^2}$
   (k) $\frac{7.92 \times 1.71}{4.2 + 3.6}$
   (l) $(4.1 - 3 \times 2.6)^3$
   (m) $3 \cos 12° - 2 \sin 12°$
   (n) $\tan^{-1} \frac{4.3}{2.9}$
   (o) $(14.6 - 3.2^2)^{\frac{1}{4}}$

5. Kelly, Eileen and Susie share £1500 in the ratio $3:4:5$. How much does Kelly receive?

6. To make 12 scones Maureen uses 5 ounces of flour. How many scones can she make using 8 ounces of flour? Answer to the nearest whole number.

7. The voting in an election was in the ratio $8:4:3$ for Labour, Conservative and Others. If 6328 people voted Labour, how many voted altogether?

8. A bacteria culture is growing at 5% a day. There are 1450 bacteria on Tuesday. How many are there three days later?

9. A paper reported that the number of people taking their main holiday in Britain has reduced by 10% per year over the last five years. There were 560 people from a small town who took their main holiday in Britain five years ago. If the report is true, how many of them do so now? Give the answer to the nearest person.

10. Damien sold his bicycle for £286, at a loss of 45% on what he paid for it. How much did he pay?

11. A magazine sold 1020 copies this month. This is an increase of $\frac{1}{9}$ on the number sold last month. How many were sold last month?

12. At the Star theatre, the seating was changed and the number of seats in the stalls was increased by a third. There are now 312 seats in the stalls. How many were there before the increase?

Equations and manipulation I

You will need to know how to:

- write a simple formula using letters
- collect together simple algebraic terms
- find the nth term of a simple sequence
- expand single brackets
- solve linear equations
- add, subtract, multiply and divide fractions and negative numbers.

Most of these topics were covered in Chapter 3 of the Intermediate book.

Substituting numbers in a formula

Numbers that can be substituted in a formula may be positive, negative, decimals or fractions.

Examiner's tip

Take special care when negative numbers are involved.

Examiner's tip

Remember $5b^2$ means $5 \times b \times b$ not $5 \times b \times 5 \times b$.

Examiner's tip

Work out each term separately and then collect together.

Example 1

If $W = 4p - 5q^2$, find W when:

(a) $p = 2$, $q = -3$

(b) $p = 22.5$, $q = 3.4$

(c) $p = \frac{3}{4}$, $q = \frac{2}{5}$.

(a) $W = (4 \times 2) - (5 \times -3 \times -3)$
$\qquad = 8 - (5 \times 9) = 8 - 45$
$\qquad = -37$

(b) $W = (4 \times 22.5) - (5 \times 3.4 \times 3.4)$
$\qquad = 90 - 57.8$
$\qquad = 32.2$

In part (b) you would use a calculator.

(c) $W = 4 \times \frac{3}{4} - 5 \times \frac{2}{5} \times \frac{2}{5}$
$\qquad = 3 - \frac{4}{5}$
$\qquad = 2\frac{1}{5}$

Example 2

The formula for the surface area of a cylinder is $S = 2\pi rh + 2\pi r^2$.

Find the surface area when $r = 5.7$ and $h = 4.6$.

Give the answer to three significant figures.

$S = (2 \times \pi \times 5.7 \times 4.6) + (2 \times \pi \times 5.7^2)$
$= 164.7\ldots + 204.1\ldots = 368.8\ldots$

$S = 369$ (to 3 s.f.)

Examiner's tip

Use the π key on your calculator. Write down the intermediate values but leave them in your calculator to avoid making errors through rounding too early.

Example 3

If $S = ut + \frac{1}{2}at^2$, find S when $u = 3$, $t = 4$, $a = -5$.

$S = (3 \times 4) + (\frac{1}{2} \times -5 \times 4^2) = 12 - 40 = -28$

Example 4

If $P = ab + 4b^2$, find P when $a = \frac{4}{5}$ and $b = \frac{3}{8}$, giving your answer as a fraction.

$P = (\frac{4}{5} \times \frac{3}{8}) + (4 \times \frac{3}{8} \times \frac{3}{8}) = \frac{3}{10} + \frac{9}{16} = \frac{24}{80} + \frac{45}{80} = \frac{69}{80}$

Exercise 6.1a

Work out each of the formulae in questions 1–7 for the values given.
Do not use a calculator.

1. $V = ab - ac$ when $a = 3$, $b = -2$, $c = 5$
2. $P = 2rv + 3r^2$ when $r = 5$, $v = -2$
3. $T = 5s^2 - 2t^2$ when $s = -2$, $t = 3$
4. $M = 2a(3b + 4c)$ when $a = 5$, $b = 3$, $c = -2$
5. $R = \dfrac{2qv}{q + v}$ when $q = 3$, $v = -4$
6. $L = 2n + m$ when $n = \frac{2}{3}$, $m = \frac{5}{6}$
7. $D = a^2 - 2b^2$ when $a = \frac{4}{5}$, $b = \frac{2}{5}$
8. Use a calculator to find the value of $M = \dfrac{ab}{2a + b^2}$ (correct to three significant figures) when $a = 2.75$, $b = 3.12$.

9. The distance S metres fallen by a pebble is given by the formula $S = \frac{1}{2}gt^2$, where t is in seconds.

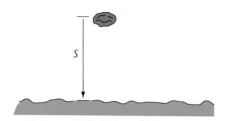

Find S when: (a) $g = 10$, $t = 12$ (b) $g = 9.8$, $t = 2.5$.
Use a calculator in part (b) only.

10. The surface area of a cuboid with sides x, y and z is given by the formula $A = 2xy + 2yz + 2xz$.

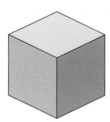

Find the surface area when $x = 5$, $y = 4.5$, $z = 3.5$.

Exercise 6.1b

Work out each of the formulae in questions 1–7 for the values given. Do not use a calculator.

1. $A = a^2 + b^2$ when $a = 5$, $b = -3$
2. $P = 2c^2 - 3cd$ when $c = 2$, $d = -5$
3. $B = p^2 - 3q^2$ when $p = -4$, $q = -2$
4. $T = (4a - 5b)^2$ when $a = -2$, $b = -1$
5. $Q = x(y^2 - z^2)$ when $x = -2$, $y = 7$, $z = -3$
6. $S = ab + 5b^2$ when $a = \frac{3}{4}$, $b = \frac{4}{5}$
7. $R = a + 2b$ when $a = 1\frac{5}{6}$, $b = \frac{2}{3}$
8. The elasticity of an elastic string is given by the formula $E = \dfrac{\lambda x^2}{2a}$.

   Find E (correct to three significant figures) when $\lambda = 3.4$, $x = 5.7$, $a = 2.5$.
9. The area of cross-section of a tree trunk is given by the formula $A = \dfrac{P^2}{4\pi}$ where P is the distance round the trunk.

Find the area of cross-section when $P = 56$ cm. Use $\pi = 3.14$ and give the answer correct to three significant figures.

10. The focal length of a lens is given by the formula $f = \dfrac{uv}{u + v}$. Find the focal length when $u = 6$, $v = -7$.

Collecting like terms and simplifying expressions

Remember that
$$a + a + a = 3a$$
$$4a + 3b + b - a = 3a + 4b$$
$$a \times b = ab$$
$$a \times a \times a = a^3$$

Complicated terms such as ab^2, a^2b and a^3 cannot be collected together unless they are exactly the same type.

Example 5

Simplify these expressions by collecting together the like terms.

(a) $2x^2 - 3xy + 2yx + 3y^2$ (b) $3a^2 + 4ab - 2a^2 - 3b^2 - 2ab$

(c) $3 + 5a - 2b + 2 + 8a - 7b$

(a) $2x^2 - 3xy + 2yx + 3y^2 = 2x^2 - xy + 3y^2$

The two middle terms are like terms because xy is the same as yx.

(b) $3a^2 + 4ab - 2a^2 - 3b^2 - 2ab = a^2 + 2ab - 3b^2$

Here the a^2 terms, the ab terms and the single b^2 term can be collected but they cannot then be combined.

(c) $3 + 5a - 2b + 2 + 8a - 7b = 5 + 13a - 9b$

Here there are three different types which can be collected separately but not together.

Examiner's tip

Errors are often made by trying to go too far, for example $2a + 3b$ cannot be simplified any further.
A further common error is to work out $4a^2 - a^2$ as 4. The answer is $3a^2$.
Remember that ab is the same as ba.

Example 6

Simplify these.

(a) $3(4a - 5) + 2(3a + 2)$ (b) $2x(6x + 2y) - 5y(x - 3y)$

(a) $3(4a - 5) + 2(3a + 2) = 12a - 15 + 6a + 4$ Multiply out the brackets.

$\qquad\qquad\qquad\qquad\qquad = 18a - 11$ Collect like terms.

(b) $2x(6x + 2y) - 5y(x - 3y) = 12x^2 + 4xy - 5xy + 15y^2$ Take care with the signs in the second bracket.

$\qquad\qquad\qquad\qquad\qquad\qquad = 12x^2 - xy + 15y^2$ Collect like terms.

Exercise 6.2a

Simplify where possible.

1. $2a + 3b - 2b + 3a$
2. $4ab - 3ac + 2ab - ac$
3. $a^2 + 3b^2 - 2a^2 - b^2$
4. $2x^2 - 3xy - xy + y^2$
5. $4b^2 + 3a^2 - 2b^2 - 4a^2$
6. $5a^3 + 4a^2 + 3a$
7. $a^3 + 3a^2 + 2a^3 + 4a^2$
8. $9abc + 4cab - 5bca + 6cba$
9. $3x^3 - 2x^2 + 4x^2 - 3x^3$
10. $a + 3b - b + 2a - 3a - 2b$
11. $2(a - 2) + 3(a + 4)$
12. $3(3x + 7) + 5(2x - 6)$
13. $4(2b + 5) - 2(3b + 2)$
14. $3(2x - 3) - (3x - 8)$
15. $2x(x + y) + 3y(x - 4y)$

Exercise 6.2b

Simplify where possible.

1. $3a - 4b + 2a - 2b$
2. $9a^2 - 3ab + 5ab - 6b^2$
3. $4ab + 2bc - 3ba - bc$
4. $2p^2 - 3pq + 4pq - 5p^2$
5. $3ab + 2ac + ad$
6. $9ab - 2bc + 3bc - 7ab$
7. $a^3 + 3a^3 - 6a^3$
8. $3ab^2 - 4ba^2 + 7a^2b$
9. $8a^3 - 4a^2 + 5a^3 - 2a^2$
10. $abc + cab - 3abc + 2bac$
11. $2(c - 4) + 5(2c + 3)$
12. $3(x - y) + 4(2x - 3y)$
13. $2(2x + 4) - 3(x + 2)$
14. $5(x + 7) - 2(2x - 1)$
15. $a(a - 2b) - b(2a + 4b)$

Examiner's tip

Most errors are made in multiplying out the second bracket when the sign in front is negative.

Examiner's tip

Apart from multiplying out the brackets, you may sometimes be asked to simplify, expand or remove the brackets, which all mean the same thing.

Multiplying out two brackets

Expressions such as $a(3a - 2b)$ can be multiplied out to give
$a(3a - 2b) = (a \times 3a) - (a \times 2b) = 3a^2 - 2ab$.

This can be extended to working out expressions such as $(2a + b)(3a + b)$.

Each term of the first bracket must be multiplied by each term of the second bracket.

$(2a + b)(3a + b)$
$= 2a(3a + b) + b(3a + b)$ Expanding the first bracket.
$= 6a^2 + 2ab + 3ab + b^2$
$= 6a^2 + 5ab + b^2$ Notice that the middle two terms are **like terms** and so can be collected.

Example 7

Multiply out the brackets.

(a) $(2a + 3)(a - 1)$ (b) $(5a - 2b)(3a - b)$ (c) $(2a - b)(a + 2b)$

(a) $(2a + 3)(a - 1) = 2a(a - 1) + 3(a - 1) = 2a^2 - 2a + 3a - 3$
$= 2a^2 + a - 3$ Be careful with the signs.

(b) $(5a - 2b)(3a - 2b) = 5a(3a - b) - 2b(3a - b)$
$= 15a^2 - 5ab - 6ab + 2b^2$
$= 15a^2 - 11ab + 2b^2$ Note that it is $-2b$ times the bracket.

(c) $(2a - b)(a + 2b) = 2a(a + 2b) - b(a + 2b)$
$= 2a^2 + 4ab - ab - 2b^2$
$= 2a^2 + 3ab - 2b^2$ Note that it is $-b$ times the bracket.

In each of examples 6 and 7, the two brackets have resulted in three terms.

There are two other types of expansions of two brackets that you need to know.

Example 8

Expand the brackets.

(a) $(2a - 3b)^2$ (b) $(2a - b)(2a + b)$

(a) $(2a - 3b)^2 = (2a - 3b)(2a - 3b)$

$$= 2a(2a - 3b) - 3b(2a - 3b) = 4a^2 - 6ab - 6ab + 9b^2$$

$$= 4a^2 - 12ab + 9b^2 \quad \boxed{\text{Note that } -6ab - 6ab = -12ab}$$

(b) $(2a - b)(2a + b) = 2a(2a + b) - b(2a + b) = 4a^2 + 2ab - 2ab - b^2$

$$= 4a^2 - b^2$$

Note that we only get two terms here because the middle terms cancel each other out. This type is known as the difference of two squares because: $(A - B)(A + B) = A^2 - B^2$

Examiner's tip

Take care with the negative signs.

Examiner's tip

The important thing in Example 8a is to make sure that you write the brackets separately and that you end up with three terms.

Examiner's tip

Some people can multiply out two brackets without writing down anything. However, you are more likely to make an error by missing steps and so it is worth showing every step in an examination.

Exercise 6.3a

Multiply out the brackets.

1. $(x + 2)(x + 3)$
2. $(a + 4)(a + 3)$
3. $(a + 2)(a + 1)$
4. $(x - 2)(2x + 1)$
5. $(2x - 3)(x + 2)$
6. $(3a + b)(2a - 2b)$
7. $(4a - b)(a + 2b)$
8. $(3a - 2b)(2a - 3b)$
9. $(4a - 3b)(2a - 3b)$
10. $(4 - 3b)(5 + 2b)$
11. $(2a - b)(3a - b)$
12. $(7a + 3b)(2a + b)$
13. $(a + 2)^2$
14. $(4x - 3y)^2$
15. $(3x - y)^2$
16. $(a - 2)(a + 2)$
17. $(3a + b)(3a - b)$
18. $(5x - 2y)(5x + 2y)$
19. $(4a + 3b)(a - b)$
20. $(5a + 4b)(2a - b)$

Multiply out the brackets.

1. $(x + 1)(x + 3)$
2. $(a + 3)(a + 3)$
3. $(a + 2)(a + 1)$
4. $(x - 2)(x + 1)$
5. $(5x - 3y)(x + 2y)$
6. $(3a + b)(a - 2b)$

7. $(a - b)(3a + 2b)$
8. $(5a - 2)(a - 3)$
9. $(7 - 3b)(1 - 3b)$
10. $(a - 3b)(2a + b)$
11. $(6a - b)(3a - 2b)$
12. $(a + 3b)(2a + b)$
13. $(a - b)^2$

14. $(2x - 1)^2$
15. $(x + 4)^2$
16. $(a - 5)(a + 5)$
17. $(2a + b)(2a - b)$
18. $(3x - 2y)(3x + 2y)$
19. $(5a + 4b)(2a - b)$
20. $(7a - 5b)(a - b)$

Simplifying expressions using indices

Remember that: $a \times a \times a = a^3$ and $a \times a \times a \times a \times a = a^5$.

This can be extended: $a^3 \times a^5 = (a \times a \times a) \times (a \times a \times a \times a \times a) = a^8$

which is the same as: $a^3 \times a^5 = a^{3+5} = a^8$

This suggests a general rule for indices.

$$a^m \times a^n = a^{m+n}$$

Similarly: $a^5 \div a^3 = (a \times a \times a \times a \times a) \div (a \times a \times a)$

$$= \frac{a \times a \times a \times a \times a}{a \times a \times a} = a \times a = a^2$$

Cancelling $a \times a \times a$ top and bottom.

This is the same as $a^5 \div a^3 = a^{5-3} = a^2$

which suggests another general rule for indices.

$$a^m \div a^n = a^{m-n}$$

Now $(a^2)^3 = a^2 \times a^2 \times a^2 = a^6$ By the first rule.

This is the same as $(a^2)^3 = a^{2 \times 3} = a^6$

and this suggests yet another rule.

$$(a^n)^m = a^{n \times m}$$

$$a^3 \div a^3 = a^{3-3} = a^0 \qquad \text{but} \qquad a^3 \div a^3 = 1$$

This gives another rule.

$$a^0 = 1$$

You can use these rules, together with the algebra you have already learnt, to simplify a number of different algebraic expressions.

Example 9

Simplify these.

(a) $3a^2 \times 4a^3$ (b) $\dfrac{6a^5}{2a^3}$ (c) $(a^3)^4 \times a^3 \div a^5$

(a) $3a^2 \times 4a^3 = 12a^5$ The numbers are just multiplied and the indices are added.

(b) $\dfrac{6a^5}{2a^3} = 3a^2$ The numbers are divided and the indices are subtracted.

(c) $(a^3)^4 \times a^3 \div a^5 = a^{12} \times a^3 \div a^5$
$$= a^{15} \div a^5$$
$$= a^{10} \quad \text{Use the three rules.}$$

Example 10

Simplify where possible.

(a) $4a^2b^3 \times 3ab^2$ (b) $\dfrac{12ab^3 \times 3a^2b}{2a^3b^2}$ (c) $4a^2 + 3a^3$

(a) $4a^2b^3 \times 3ab^2 = 12a^3b^5$ The numbers are multiplied and the indices are added for each letter. Note that a is the same as a^1, so $a^2 \times a = a^{2+1} = a^3$.

(b) $\dfrac{12ab^3 \times 3a^2b}{2a^3b^2} = 18b^2$ The numbers combine as $12 \times 3 \div 2 = 18$, $a \times a^2 \div a^3 = a^{1+2-3} = a^0 = 1$, $b^3 \times b \div b^2 = b^{3+1-2} = b^2$.

(c) $4a^2 + 3a^3$ This cannot be simplified. The two terms are different and cannot be added.

Exercise 6.4a

Simplify where possible.

1. $3a^2 \times 4a^3$

2. $\dfrac{12a^5}{6a^3}$

3. $(3a^3)^2$

4. $2a^2b \times 3a^3b^2$

5. $4a^2b - 2ab^2$

6. $\dfrac{15a^2b^3 \times 3a^2b}{9a^3b^2}$

7. $\dfrac{9p^2q \times (2p^3q)^2}{12p^5q^3}$

8. $\dfrac{4abc \times 3a^2bc^3}{6a^2bc^2}$

9. $\dfrac{12t^3}{(2t)^2}$

10. $2a^2b \times 3ab^2 - 4a^3b^3$

Exercise 6.4b

Simplify where possible.

1. $\dfrac{a^5 \times a^3}{a^6}$

2. $3a^2 \times 4a^2$

3. $(2c)^3$

4. $3a^2b^3 \times 2a^3b^4$

5. $12a^2 \times 3b^2$

6. $2a^2 + 3a^3$

7. $8a^2b^3 \times 2a^3b \div 4a^4b^2$

8. $\dfrac{(3a^2b^2)^3}{(a^3b)^2}$

9. $4a^2 \times 2b^3 - a \times 3b \times ab^2$

10. $6a^2 \times (2ab^2)^2 \div 12b^2a$

Finding the *n*th term of a sequence

The *n*th term of a sequence, where the rule is linear, can be found by looking at the first differences, which are constant.

If the rule is not linear, for example a quadratic containing n^2, the first differences will not be constant. Find the second differences.

Example 11

Work out the *n*th term for this sequence.

$$4 \quad 7 \quad 12 \quad 19 \quad 28$$

Look at the differences.

Sequence:		4		7		12		19		28
First differences:			3		5		7		9	
Second differences:				2		2		2		

The second differences are constant.

> The rule for the *n*th term in sequences like this one will involve n^2 and the coefficient of n^2 will be half the second difference.

In the sequence above, dividing 2 by 2 gives 1, so the *n*th term must include $1n^2$ or just n^2.

Now compare the original sequence with the sequence n^2.

Sequence:	4	7	12	19	28
n^2:	1	4	9	16	25
Subtract n^2:	3	3	3	3	3

The *n*th term is $n^2 + 3$.

Example 12

Work out the *n*th term for this sequence.

$$2 \quad 11 \quad 26 \quad 47 \quad 74$$

Look at the differences.

Sequence:		2		11		26		47		74
First differences:			9		15		21		27	
Second differences:				6		6		6		

Dividing 6 by 2 gives 3, so the *n*th term will include $3n^2$.
Subtract $3n^2$ from each term.

Sequence:	2	11	26	47	74
$3n^2$:	3	12	27	48	75
Subtract:	−1	−1	−1	−1	−1

So the *n*th term is $3n^2 - 1$.

Most of the sequences you will have to deal with will be like the two above, but you may be asked to find the nth term of sequences that include n^2, n and a number.

Example B

Work out the nth term for this sequence.

2   7   14   23   34

Sequence:	2		7		14		23		34
First differences:		5		7		9		11	
Second differences:			2		2		2		

Dividing 2 by 2 gives 1 so the nth term will include n^2.

Subtract n^2 from the sequence.

Sequence:	2	7	14	23	34
n^2:	1	4	9	16	25
Subtract	1	3	5	7	9

This sequence is like those you dealt with earlier.

The difference is 2 so the nth term will include $2n$.

When $n = 1$, $2n$ is 2, but the term is 1 so the nth term is $2n - 1$ for this sequence.

The nth term for the main sequence is therefore $n^2 + 2n - 1$.

Exercise 6.5a

Find the nth term of each of these sequences.

1.	2	5	10	17	26
2.	1	7	17	31	49
3.	5	8	13	20	29
4.	6	15	30	51	78

5.	−1	2	7	14	23
6.	7	16	31	52	79
7.	1	13	33	61	97
8.	4	9	16	25	36
9.	2	8	16	26	38
10.	2	6	12	20	30

Exercise 6.5b

Find the nth term of each of these sequences.

1.	3	6	11	18	27
2.	4	13	28	49	76
3.	6	9	14	21	30
4.	6	12	22	36	54

5.	1	10	25	46	73
6.	8	14	24	38	56
7.	1	16	41	76	121
8.	1	5	11	19	29
9.	0	5	12	21	32
10.	−2	−2	0	4	10

Factorising algebraic expressions

Factors are numbers or letters which will divide into an expression.

The factors of 6 are 1, 2, 3 and 6.

The factors of b^3 are 1, b, b^2 and b^3.

Remember that multiplying or dividing by 1 leaves a number unchanged, so 1 is not a useful factor and it is ignored.

To factorise an expression, look for common factors, for example, the common factors of $2a^2$ and $6a$ are 2, a and $2a$.

Example 14

Factorise these fully.

(a) $4p + 6$ (b) $2a^2 - 3a$ (c) $15ab^2 + 10a^2b^2$ (d) $2a - 10a^2 + 6a^3$

(a) $4p + 6 = 2(2p + 3)$ The only common factor is 2 and $2 \times 2p = 4p$, $2 \times 3 = 6$.

(b) $2a^2 - 3a = a(2a - 3)$ The only common factor is a and $a \times 2a = 2a^2$, $a \times -3 = -3a$.

(c) $15ab^2 + 10a^2b^2 = 5ab^2(3 + 2a)$ 5, a and b^2 are common factors and $5ab^2 \times 3 = 15ab^2$, $5ab^2 \times +2a = 10a^2b^2$.

(d) $2a - 10a^2 + 6a^3 = 2a(1 - 5a + 3a^2)$ 2 and a are common factors and $2a \times 1 = 2a$, $2a \times -5a = -10a^2$ and $2a \times 3a^2 = 6a^3$.

Exercise 6.6a

Factorise these fully.

1. $2a + 8$
2. $3a + 5a^2$
3. $2ab - 6ac$
4. $5a^2b + 10ab^2$
5. $2x^2y^2 - 3x^3y$
6. $3a^2b - 6ab^2$
7. $12x - 6y + 8z$
8. $9ab + 6b^2$
9. $4a^2c - 2ac^2$
10. $15xy - 5y$
11. $6a^3 - 4a^2 + 2a$
12. $3a^2b - 9a^3b^2$
13. $5a^2b^2c^2 - 10abc$
14. $2a^2b - 3a^2b^3 + 7a^4b$
15. $4abc - 3ac^2 + 2a^2b$

Exercise 6.6b

Factorise these fully.

1. $3x - 12$
2. $4a + 5ab$
3. $4ab - 2a^2$
4. $3ab - 2ac + 3ad$
5. $5x^2 - 15x + 15$
6. $4a^2b - 3ab^2$
7. $9x^2y - 6xy^2$
8. $14a^2 - 8a^3$
9. $21x^2 - 14y^2$
10. $12x^2y + 8xy - 4xy^2$
11. $14s^2t - 7st^2$
12. $10z^3 - 15z^2 + 5z$
13. $5abc - 15a^2b^2c^2$
14. $3a^2bc - 6ab^2c + 9abc^2$
15. $7a^3b^3c^2 - 14a^2b^3c^3$

Factorising expressions of the type $x^2 + ax + b$

Expressions where the last sign is positive

The expression $(x + 2)(x + 3)$ can be simplified to give $x^2 + 5x + 6$. Therefore, $x^2 + 5x + 6$ can be factorised as a product of two brackets, by reversing the process. Look at your answers for Exercises 6.3.

Example 15

Factorise $x^2 + 7x + 12$.

This will factorise into two brackets with x as the first term in each.

$$x^2 + 7x + 12 = (x \quad)(x \quad)$$

As both the signs are positive, both the numbers will be positive.
You need to find two numbers that multiply to give 12 and add to give 7.

These will be $+3$ and $+4$.

So $x^2 + 7x + 12 = (x + 3)(x + 4)$ or
$\qquad x^2 + 7x + 12 = (x + 4)(x + 3)$

The order you write the brackets does not matter.

If the middle sign is negative and the last sign is positive, the two numbers will be negative.

Example 16

Factorise $x^2 - 3x + 2$.

You need to find two negative numbers that multiply to give $+2$ and add to -3.
They are -2 and -1.

$$x^2 - 3x + 2 = (x - 2)(x - 1).$$

Examiner's tip

If the last sign is positive $(+)$, both the signs in the brackets must be the same as the sign before the x term.

Exercise 6.7a

Factorise these expressions.

1. $x^2 + 5x + 6$
2. $x^2 + 6x + 5$
3. $x^2 + 6x + 8$
4. $x^2 + 5x + 4$
5. $x^2 + 2x + 1$
6. $x^2 - 7x + 6$
7. $x^2 - 7x + 10$
8. $x^2 - 4x + 3$
9. $y^2 - 9y + 14$
10. $x^2 - 6x + 8$
11. $a^2 + 8a + 12$
12. $a^2 - 6a + 9$
13. $b^2 - 12b + 32$
14. $x^2 + 11x + 24$
15. $x^2 - 9x + 20$

Exercise 6.7b

Factorise these expressions.

1. $x^2 + 7x + 10$
2. $x^2 + 4x + 3$
3. $x^2 + 8x + 15$
4. $x^2 + 9x + 20$
5. $x^2 + 7x + 6$
6. $x^2 - 9x + 18$
7. $x^2 - 7x + 12$
8. $a^2 - 2a + 1$
9. $b^2 - 10b + 24$
10. $c^2 - 4c + 3$
11. $a^2 + 15a + 36$
12. $x^2 - 12x + 27$
13. $b^2 - 10b + 25$
14. $x^2 + 14x + 24$
15. $x^2 - 15x + 56$

Expressions where the last sign is negative

Example 17

Factorise $x^2 - 3x - 10$.

As the last sign is negative, you need two numbers, with opposite signs, that multiply to give -10 and add to give -3.
The numbers are -5 and $+2$.

$x^2 - 3x - 10 = (x - 5)(x + 2)$

Examiner's tip

Remember that if the last sign is negative the two numbers have different signs and the larger number has the sign of the *x* term.
It is easy to make a mistake when factorising. Always check by multiplying out the brackets.

Example 18

Factorise $x^2 + 4x - 12$.

The last sign is negative, so you need two numbers, with opposite signs, that multiply to give -12 and add to give $+4$.
The numbers are $+6$ and -2.

$x^2 + 4x - 12 = (x + 6)(x - 2)$

Exercise 6.8a

Factorise these expressions.
1. $x^2 - 2x - 8$
2. $x^2 + 4x - 5$
3. $x^2 - x - 6$
4. $x^2 + 5x - 6$
5. $x^2 + 2x - 3$
6. $x^2 - 3x - 18$
7. $x^2 - 9x - 10$
8. $x^2 + 9x + 14$
9. $y^2 + 9y - 22$
10. $x^2 + x - 12$
11. $a^2 + 8a - 20$
12. $a^2 - 6a - 27$
13. $b^2 + 12b + 20$
14. $x^2 - 25$
15. $x^2 - 49$

Exercise 6.8b

Factorise these expressions.
1. $x^2 + 2x - 3$
2. $x^2 + 3x - 10$
3. $x^2 - x - 12$
4. $x^2 + 5x - 14$
5. $x^2 - 2x - 15$
6. $x^2 - 3x - 28$
7. $x^2 - 17x + 30$
8. $x^2 + 4x - 32$
9. $a^2 + 9a - 36$
10. $x^2 + x - 20$
11. $y^2 + 19y + 48$
12. $a^2 - 6a - 16$
13. $b^2 - 15b + 36$
14. $x^2 - 4$
15. $x^2 - 144$

Rearranging formulae

Formulae can be treated in the same way as equations. This means they can be rearranged, to change the subject.

Example

Rearrange these formulae to make the letter in brackets the subject.

(a) $a = b + c$ (b) (b) $a = b + cx^2$ (x)
(c) $n = m - 3s$ (s) (d) $p = r + a(a - r)$ (r)
(e) $s = 3(a + b)$ (b)

(a) $a = b + c$
$\quad a - c = b$ Subtract c from both sides.
$\quad b = a - c$ Reverse to get b on the left.

(b) $a = b + cx^2$
$\quad a - b = cx^2$ Subtract b from both sides.
$\quad x^2 = \dfrac{a - b}{c}$ Swap and divide both sides by c.
$\quad x = \dfrac{\sqrt{a - b}}{c}$ Take square roots of both sides.

(c) $n = m - 3s$
$\quad n + 3s = m$ Add $3s$ to both sides.
$\quad 3s = m - n$ Subtract n from both sides.
$\quad s = \dfrac{m - n}{3}$ Divide both sides by 3.

Example 19

continued

(d) $p = r + a(a - r)$

$p = r + a^2 - ar$	Multiply out the bracket.
$p - a^2 = r(1 - a)$	Rearrange and take out r.
$r(1 - a) = p - a^2$	Reverse to get r on the left.
$r = \dfrac{p - a^2}{1 - a}$	Divide both sides by $(1 - a)$.

(e) $s = 3(a + b)$

$s = 3a + 3b$	Multiply out the brackets.
$s - 3a = 3b$	Subtract $3a$ from both sides.
$\dfrac{s - 3a}{3} = b$	Divide both sides by 3.
$b = \dfrac{s - 3a}{3}$	Reverse to get b on the left.

Exercise 6.9a

Rearrange each formula to make the letter in the brackets the subject.

1. $a = b - c$ (b)
2. $3a = wx + xy$ (x)
3. $v = u + at$ (t)
4. $A = \dfrac{T}{H}$ (T)
5. $C = P - 3T$ (T)
6. $P = \dfrac{u + v}{2}$ (u)
7. $C = 2\pi r$ (r)
8. $A = p(q^2 + r)$ (q)
9. The formula for finding the perimeter P of a rectangle with sides of length x and y is $P = 2(x + y)$.
   Rearrange the formula to make x the subject.

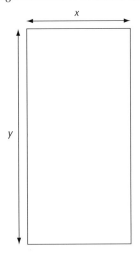

10. The cost (£C) of catering for a wedding reception is given by the formula $C = A + 32n$, where A is the cost of the room and n is the number of guests.
    (a) Rearrange the formula to make n the subject.
    (b) Work out the number of guests when A is £120 and the total cost C is £1912.

Rearrange each formula to make the letter in the brackets the subject.

1. $p = q + 2r$ (q)
2. $B = s + 5r^2$ (r)
3. $s = 2u - t$ (t)
4. $m = \dfrac{pqr}{s}$ (q)
5. $L = 2G - 2FG$ (G)
6. $F = \dfrac{m + 4n}{t}$ (n)
7. $T = \dfrac{S}{2a}$ (S)
8. $A = t(x - 2y)$ (y)
9. The formula for the volume V of a cone of height h and base radius r is $V = \frac{1}{3}\pi r^2 h$.

   Rearrange the formula to make h the subject.

10. The cost ($£C$) of a minibus to the airport is given by the formula

    $$C = 20 + \frac{d}{2}$$

    where d is the distance in miles.

    (a) Rearrange the formula to make d the subject.

    (b) Work out the distance when it costs £65 to go to the airport.

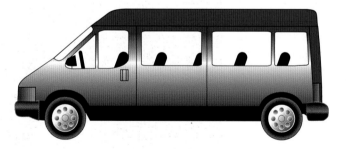

Inequalities

$a < b$ means a is less than b.
$a \leqslant b$ means a is less than or equal to b.
$a > b$ means a is greater than b.
$a \geqslant b$ means a is greater than or equal to b.

Expressions involving these signs are called **inequalities**.

Example 20

Find the integer (whole number) values of x when:

(a) $-3 < x \leqslant -1$ (b) $1 \leqslant x < 4$.

(a) If $-3 < x \leqslant -1$, then $x = -2$ or -1.

> Note that -3 is not included but -1 is.

(b) If $1 \leqslant x < 4$, then $x = 1, 2$ or 3.

> Note that 1 is included but 4 is not.

In equations, if you always do the same thing to both sides the equality is still valid.

The same is true for inequalities, except in one case.

Consider the inequality $5 < 7$.

Add 2 to each side:	$7 < 9$	Still true.
Subtract 5 from each side:	$2 < 4$	Still true.
Multiply each side by 3:	$6 < 12$	Still true.
Divide each side by 2:	$3 < 4$	Still true.
Multiply each side by -2:	$-6 < -12$	No longer true.
But reverse the inequality sign:	$-6 > -12$	Now true.

> If an inequality is multiplied or divided by a negative number, the **inequality sign must be reversed**.

Otherwise inequalities can be treated in the same way as equations.

Example 21

Solve these inequalities.

(a) $3x + 4 < 10$ (b) $2x - 5 \leqslant 4 - 3x$
(c) $x + 4 > 3x - 2$

(a) $3x + 4 < 10$

$3x < 6$	Subtract 4 from each side.
$x < 2$	Divide each side by 2.

(b) $2x - 5 \leqslant 4 - 3x$

$2x \leqslant 9 - 3x$	Add 5 to each side.
$5x \leqslant 9$	Add $3x$ to each side.
$x \leqslant \frac{9}{5} \, (= 1\frac{4}{5})$	Divide each side by 5.

(c) $x + 4 > 3x - 2$

$x > 3x - 6$	Subtract 4 from both sides.
$-2x > -6$	Subtract $3x$ from both sides.
$x < 3$	Divide each side by -2 and change the $>$ to $<$ (when dividing by -2).

Chapter 6   Equations and manipulation

1. Write down the integer values of x when:
   (a) $-4 \leqslant x < 0$
   (b) $1 < x \leqslant 5$.

Solve these inequalities.

2. $x - 3 \leqslant 4$
3. $x + 7 > 9$
4. $2x - 3 < 5$
5. $3x + 4 \leqslant 7$
6. $2x \geqslant x + 5$
7. $5x > 3 - x$
8. $2x + 1 < 7$
9. $4x > 2x + 5$
10. $3x - 6 \geqslant x + 2$
11. $2(x + 3) < 1 - 3x$
12. $3(2x - 1) \geqslant 11 - x$
13. $x + 4 > 2x$
14. $2x - 5 < 4x + 1$
15. $3(x - 4) > 5(x + 1)$

1. Write down two possible values of x for the inequality $x < -2$.
2. Write down the integer values of x when:
   (a) $1 < x \leqslant 4$
   (b) $-5 < x \leqslant -1$.

Solve these inequalities.

3. $x - 2 < 5$
4. $2x + 3 > 6$
5. $3x - 4 \leqslant 8$
6. $3x \geqslant x - 2$
7. $4x + 2 < 3$
8. $5a - 3 > 2a$
9. $2x - 3 < x + 1$
10. $3x + 2 \geqslant x - 1$
11. $x - 2 < 2x + 4$
12. $2x - 1 > x - 4$
13. $3(x + 3) \geqslant 2x - 1$
14. $\frac{1}{2}x + 4 < 5$
15. $3(2x - 4) < 5(x - 6)$

Forming equations and inequalities

Everyday problems can often be solved by forming equations or inequalities and solving them.

 Example 22

The length of a rectangle is 4 cm longer than its width, which is x cm.

(a) Write down an expression in terms of x for the perimeter of the rectangle.

(b) The perimeter is 32 cm.
   (i) Write down an equation in x and solve it.
   (ii) What are the length and width of the rectangle?

(a) The length is 4 cm longer than the width, so it is $x + 4$ cm.

   Perimeter $= x + x + 4 + x + x + 4 = 4x + 8$

(b) (i) The perimeter is 32 cm, so:
$$4x + 8 = 32$$
$$4x = 24$$
$$x = 6$$

   (ii) The width is $x = 6$ cm.
   The length is $x + 4 = 10$ cm.

Example 23

John is having a party but he has only £60 to spend on it. He has to pay £10 to hire the room and £4 for every person at the party. How many people can he invite to his party?

Let the number of people be n. Write down an inequality involving n and solve it to find the largest number that can go to the party.

Cost of party $\leqslant$ £60.
Therefore $10 + 4n \leqslant 60$
$$4n \leqslant 50$$
$$n \leqslant 12.5$$
So the largest number of people who can be at the party is 12.

Exercise 6.11a

1. Erica is x years old and Jayne is three years older than Erica. Their ages add up to 23. Write down an equation in x and solve it to find out their ages.

2. Two angles of a triangle are the same and the other is 15° bigger. Call the two equal angles a. Write down an equation and solve it to find the angles.

3. A man is papering a room. It takes him 30 minutes to prepare his paste and 20 minutes to cut and hang a length of paper. He is working for 4 hours and hangs x lengths.

Write down an inequality in x and solve it to find the largest number of lengths he can hang in the time.

4. In Devonshire School there are 28 more girls than boys. There are 616 pupils in the school. Let the number of boys be x. Write down an equation in x and solve it. Write down the number of boys and girls in the school.

5. To hire a bus the charge is £60 and £2 a mile. The bus company will only hire the bus if they take at least £225. Let the number of miles be x.
   (a) Write down an inequality and solve it for x.
   (b) What is the smallest distance that the bus can be hired to go?

6. It costs £x to hire a bike for an adult, and it is £2 cheaper for a child's bike. Mr Newton hires bikes for two adults and three children.

   (a) Write down an expression in x for the cost of the bikes.
   (b) The cost is £19.
       (i) Write down an equation and solve it to find x.
       (ii) How much did each bike cost?

7. Ameer has 40 metres of fencing, in one-metre lengths that cannot be split. He wants to use as much of it as he can to mark out a rectangle that is twice as long as it is wide.
   (a) Call the width of the rectangle x and write down an inequality.
   (b) Solve it to find the length and width of the biggest rectangle that he can make.

8. Mark, Patrick and Iain all collect matchbox cars. Mark has four more than Patrick. Iain has three more than Mark. They have 41 altogether. Set up an equation and solve it to find how many matchbox cars each boy has.

1. Mrs Pippard and her daughter go shopping. Mrs Pippard spends £x and her daughter spends twice as much. The spend £45 altogether. Set up an equation and solve it to find how much each spends.

2. A pentagon has two angles of 150°, two of x° and one of $(x + 30)$°. The sum of the angles in a pentagon is 540°.
   (a) Write down an equation in x and solve it.
   (b) State the size of each of the angles.

3. Sara is x years old; Mary is ten years older than Sara. The sum of their ages is less than 50.
   (a) Write down an inequality and solve it.
   (b) What is the oldest Sara can be?

4. On a school trip to France, there are 15 more girls than boys. Altogether 53 pupils go.
   (a) If the number of boys is x, write down an equation in x and solve it.
   (b) How many boys and how many girls go on the trip?

5. Paul goes to the shop and buys two chocolate bars at 30p each and x cans of cola at 45p each. He has £2 and wants to buy as many cans as possible.
   (a) Write down an inequality in x and solve it.
   (b) What is the largest number of cans he can buy?

6. In the Oasis café a cup of tea costs x pence; a cup of coffee costs 10 pence more than tea. David bought three teas and two coffees and spent £1.20.
   (a) Write down an equation in x and solve it.
   (b) What do tea and coffee cost at the Oasis café?

7. A firm employs 140 people, of whom x are men. There are ten fewer women than men.
   Use algebra to find how many men and women work for the firm.

8. It costs £5 for each person to go skating. Skates can be hired for £2. Ten friends went skating and n of them hired skates.
   (a) Write down an expression in pounds for the amount they spent.
   (b) They spent £62. Write down an equation in n and solve it to find how many hired skates.

Key points

- Terms can only be added or subtracted if they are of exactly the same type.
  ab and $2ab$ can be added but a^2 and $2a$ cannot.
- When multiplying two brackets , multiply every term in the first bracket by every term in the second.
- When multiplying or dividing algebraic expressions involving powers, add or subtract the indices.
- To find the nth term of a quadratic sequence, look at the second difference and divide by 2 to find the coefficient of the n^2 term.

- When finding common factors make sure you factorise fully.
- To factorise $x^2 + ax + b$:
  - if b is positive find two numbers that multiply to give b and add up to a
  - if b is negative find two numbers that multiply to give b and have a difference of a.
- To solve inequalities treat them like equations, except when multiplying or dividing by a negative number, when you *must reverse* the inequality sign.
- To solve a problem using algebra, set up an equation for the unknown quantity, then solve it.

Revision exercise 6a

1. If $h = 7a - 2bc$, find h when:
   - (a) $a = 2$, $b = 3$, $c = -1$
   - (b) $a = \frac{1}{4}$, $b = \frac{1}{2}$, $c = \frac{3}{4}$
   - (c) $a = 3.6$, $b = 7.4$, $c = 2.5$.

2. The formula for finding the area of the surface of a sphere is $A = 4\pi r^2$.
   Find the area when $r = 4.2$ cm, giving the answer correct to three significant figures.

3. Simplify these by collecting like terms.
   - (a) $3a + 4b + 2a - 4b$
   - (b) $5ab^2 - 2a^2b + 3a^2b - 4ab^2$
   - (c) $2ab + 3ac - 4ad + 2ab + 4ad - ac$
   - (d) $x^2 - 2xy + 3yx + 3x^2$

4. Take out the brackets and collect like terms.
   - (a) $5(x + 3) + 2(x - 5)$
   - (b) $2(3x + 1) - 2(x + 4)$
   - (c) $3(a + 4) + 2(2 - a)$
   - (d) $3(2x - 2) - 2(x - 5)$
   - (e) $2(x + 1) + (2x - 3)$
   - (f) $3x(x - 2y) - 4y(3x - y)$

5. Multiply out these brackets.
   - (a) $(x + 7)(x + 1)$
   - (b) $(a - 3)(a + 5)$
   - (c) $(2y - 4)(y + 1)$
   - (d) $(x - 5)(2x + 1)$
   - (e) $(4a + b)(a - b)$

   - (f) $(2 - c)(3 - 2c)$
   - (g) $(x - 5)(x + 5)$
   - (h) $(x + 2y)^2$
   - (i) $(7x - 5y)(2x + 3y)$

6. Simplify these.
   - (a) $2a^2 \times a^3$
   - (b) $10a^2 \div 2a$
   - (c) $(a^3)^2 \times a^3 \div a^4$
   - (d) $12a^2b \times 2a^2b^3$
   - (e) $6x^2y^2z^2 \div 2xy^2z$
   - (f) $\dfrac{8a^2b \times 3abc}{6ab^2}$

7. Find the nth term of the following sequences.
   - (a) 4 7 12 19 28
   - (b) 3 9 19 33 51
   - (c) 4 8 14 22 32

8. Factorise each of these fully.
   - (a) $3a + 6b - 12c$
   - (b) $2a + 3ab$
   - (c) $a^2b - 3ab^2$
   - (d) $2x^2y - 6xy$
   - (e) $7abc + 14a^2b$
   - (f) $9a^2 + 3b^2 - 6c^2$
   - (g) $5pq - 10$
   - (h) $2a - 4a^2 + 6a^3$
   - (i) $100abc - 50ac$

9. Factorise these.
   (a) $x^2 + 5x + 4$
   (b) $x^2 - 6x + 8$
   (c) $x^2 - 10x + 16$
   (d) $x^2 + 8x + 15$
   (e) $x^2 - 6x - 7$
   (f) $x^2 - 3x - 10$
   (g) $x^2 - 8x + 12$
   (h) $x^2 - 2x - 15$
   (i) $x^2 - 3x - 70$
   (j) $x^2 + 16x + 48$
   (k) $x^2 - 7x - 18$
   (l) $16 - x^2$

10. Rearrange the following formulae to make the letter in brackets the subject.
    (a) $x = y - 3b$ (y)
    (b) $t = \dfrac{u + v}{2}$ (u)
    (c) $P = 2b - a$ (a)
    (d) $p = qx + m$ (q)
    (e) $I = \dfrac{PTR}{100}$ (P)
    (f) $v^2 = u^2 + 2as$ (s)

11. Solve the inequalities.
    (a) $2x > 5$
    (b) $x + 3 \leqslant 5$
    (c) $2x - 4 \geqslant x + 2$
    (d) $4x - 3 < 7 - x$
    (e) $4x - 9 \leqslant 2x + 7$
    (f) $2(3x - 1) \leqslant 3x + 5$
    (g) $2x - 3 < 3x - 1$
    (h) $x + 2 > 3x + 1$
    (i) $3(2x - 3) > 2(x - 5)$

12. David has two brothers. One brother is two years younger than him and the other brother is five years older than him.
    (a) Let David be x years old and write down an expression for the sum of their ages.
    (b) The sum of their ages is 39. Write down an equation and solve it to find x.
    (c) What are their ages?

13. Angela has £5 to spend. She spends £3.20 on her lunch and decides to buy as many packets of crisps as possible at 24p each with the rest.
    (a) If the number of packets she buys is x, write down an inequality in x and solve it.
    (b) How many packets of crisps does she buy?

14. A quadrilateral has angles $x°$, $3x°$, $90°$ and $(x + 20)°$.
    (a) Write down an equation in x and solve it.
    (b) What are the sizes of the angles?

Questionnaires and cumulative frequency

You will need to know:

- how to calculate mode, median, mean and range.

Questionnaires

Planning and collecting data

The first part of this unit is about the design of **questionnaires** or **experiments** to test a **hypothesis**.

> A hypothesis is a statement which may be true but for which you have no proof.

Questionnaires are designed to find out, for example, people's opinions. Questionnaires are used a lot. Their findings are often shown on TV or in newspapers, for example:

- 63% of the people asked would vote Labour
- Eight out of ten owners who expressed a preference said their cats preferred fresh fish.

Experiments are tests intended to find out if something is true; for example an experiment could be carried out to see if people are better at catching a ball with their 'writing' hand or with their 'non-writing' hand.

After you have thought of a task, challenge or a question to answer, or had one set for you, there are several important issues for you to consider as you plan how you are going to find the information you need.

Think about and discuss the following three topics.

Hypothesis: Boys are better at mathematics than girls are.

How could you prove it?

You might decide to change the statement into a question which you could then test, for example,

Do boys get higher marks than girls in mathematics tests?

but then you will need to think about issues such as:

- Does age or year group matter? Is it true for boys and girls in year 11, but not for year 7?
- Does the type of test matter?
- Does the topic matter?
  Are the results for algebra the same as for shape and space?
- How will you define 'higher' marks?
  - Will you use the actual highest mark or the average mark?
  - Should the average be the mean, the median or the mode?

- How will you actually get the results?
  - Write a test?
  - Ask your teachers?
  - Use the results from the KS3 tests?
- How will you analyse and show the information?
  - Will the questions you ask help you?
  - Should you be asking different questions?
- Will your results be fair or biased?
  Will you consider a cross-section of students or just those in a particular set?

You must consider bias or fairness when you are trying to find information to prove a hypothesis. If you wanted to find out if people like hamburgers, would you expect to get a fair or unbiased response if you only asked teenagers who were going into or out of a hamburger restaurant?

Survey: What do people eat for breakfast?

You might ask:

'Do you have breakfast?'

What sort of answers might you get?

'yes', 'no', 'sometimes', 'only on a school day' …

- Ask some members of your class and see what they say.

Or you might ask:

'Do you have cereal or toast?'

How would you analyse an answer of 'yes'?

Does it mean toast **or** cereal, or toast **and** cereal?

Are there better questions, or a better way to find out what people had for breakfast?

You might consider setting out your questions like this:

Breakfast survey

Please tick if you have:

Fruit juice	☐	Fruit	☐	Cereal	☐
Tea	☐	Coffee	☐	Toast	☐
Bread	☐	Cooked	☐		

What other questions could you ask?

• Write them down and discuss them.

You might want to ask people other than students at school.

Perhaps you could sort the answers by age, but be careful! It would be tactless to ask, 'How old are you?' so you need to think of an alternative approach. It would be much better to ask people to tick a box from a range of possibilities, for example:

Please tick the appropriate age group (in years):

5–10	☐	11–16	☐	17–20	☐
21–30	☐	31–40	☐	41–60	☐
over 60	☐				

Clearly it is easier to analyse responses to questions that can be ticked or which have a 'yes' or 'no' answer. These are **closed** questions.

Activity 3

How will you know if the questions are good ones?

A quick and simple way is to ask about ten people to answer your questions, and see how they 'work'.

• Can the questions be answered clearly?
• Can you analyse the answers?

This is called a **pilot survey**.

Now think of a question of your own, or choose one of the following:

• Do you think too much homework is set?
• Do tall people have bigger heads than shorter people do?
• Do boys spend more time than girls watching TV?
• Make three sets of ten cards:
  – one set with the numbers 0–9
  – one set with the letters A–J
  – one set with the letters Q–Z

Read the following three questions and then ask your volunteers to sort the cards in each set into order, recording the results appropriately. Shuffle each set before carrying out the experiment, each time.

– Are people quicker to put numbers in order, or letters?
– Are people quicker to put numbers or letters in order using their 'writing' hand or their 'non-writing' hand?
– Are people quicker with the first ten letters or the last ten letters of the alphabet?

Remember:

• write down what questions you will ask
• write down who you will ask, making sure that you ask a cross-section of people.

Try to justify what you do.

• Now carry out the survey or experiment you have chosen.

After you have produced the data you will have to analyse it.

Analysing data

This section suggests one way of analysing data. There are others, including calculating the mean or the mode.

Activity 4

Cumulative frequency tables and diagrams

A plant grower wants to find out if one sort of compost is better than another. He sows equal numbers of seeds, from the same packet, in each compost and measures the height, to the nearest centimetre, of 60 plants which grow in each.

Compost A

22	13	33	31	51	24	37	83	39	28	31	64
23	35	9	34	42	26	68	38	63	34	44	77
37	15	38	54	34	22	47	25	48	38	53	52
35	45	32	31	37	43	37	49	24	17	48	29
57	33	30	36	42	36	43	38	39	48	39	59

Compost B

33	43	17	50	37	59	21	58	45	78	36	34
45	77	52	42	79	38	63	48	47	71	63	49
8	53	47	66	49	69	55	33	54	28	40	68
55	67	36	76	27	86	29	67	57	47	64	55
48	65	58	41	35	57	44	39	59	23	64	36

This gives a total of 120 results (60 for each compost), which is a lot to analyse.

In cases like this it is better to group the results in intervals. A sensible interval for the heights in this case would be 10 cm.

This is like sorting the results into 'bins'.

	13	22 24 28	33 31 37 39		and so on.
$0 \leqslant h < 10$	$10 \leqslant h < 20$	$20 \leqslant h < 30$	$30 \leqslant h < 40$	$40 \leqslant h < 50$	

Remember that $\leqslant$ means 'less than or equal to' and $<$ means 'less than' so $30 \leqslant h < 40$ means all the heights between 30 and 40, including 30 but excluding 40.

Here are the figures for compost A, grouped into a frequency table.

Height h (cm)	Frequency	Height h (cm)	Cumulative frequency
$0 \leqslant h < 10$	1	$h < 10$	1
$10 \leqslant h < 20$	3	$h < 20$	4
$20 \leqslant h < 30$	9	$h < 30$	13
$30 \leqslant h < 40$	25	$h < 40$	38 $\leftarrow 38 = 1 + 3 + 9 + 25$
$40 \leqslant h < 50$	11	$h < 50$	49
$50 \leqslant h < 60$	6	$h < 60$	55
$60 \leqslant h < 70$	3	$h < 70$	58
$70 \leqslant h < 80$	1	$h < 80$	59
$80 \leqslant h < 90$	1	$h < 90$	60

The cumulative frequency in the last column gives the running total. In this case it is the number of plants less than a certain height, for example there are 38 plants less than 40 cm high. Make sure you can see how the cumulative frequency values are obtained.

> The values for cumulative frequency can be plotted to give a cumulative frequency diagram.

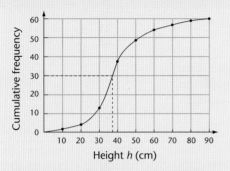

Note that the cumulative frequency values are plotted at the upper value of each interval i.e. at 10, 20, 30 and so on.

You can use a cumulative frequency diagram to estimate the median value.

There are 60 results so the median will be the halfway value, which is the 30th.

> **Note:** If you were using a list of numbers, then for an even number of numbers the median is halfway between the two middle values.

Find 30 on the vertical scale and look across the graph until you reach the curve. Read off the corresponding value on the horizontal scale (see the dotted line on the graph).

The median height is about 37 cm – check you agree.

It is also possible to calculate the **quartiles**. As the name suggests these are quarters – the cumulative frequency is divided into four equal parts. The median is the middle quartile. The lower quartile will be at $\frac{1}{4}$ of 60, which is the 15th value, giving a height of 31 cm. The upper quartile is at $\frac{3}{4}$ of 60, which is the 45th value, giving a height of 45 cm.

The difference between these two values is called the **interquartile range**.

Interquartile range = 45 cm − 31 cm = 14 cm

> The interquartile range shows how widely the data are spread out. Half the data are within the interquartile range, and if that range is small then the data are bunched together.

You can also use the cumulative frequency graph to estimate how many plants were taller than a given height, such as 55 cm. From the graph, a height of 55 cm corresponds to cumulative frequency 52, so the number of plants that were taller than 55 cm is 60 − 52 = 8.

- Now construct a grouped frequency table and find the cumulative frequency for the plant heights for compost B.

- Copy the cumulative frequency diagram for compost A. Using the same axes, draw the cumulative frequency diagram for compost B and calculate the median value and the interquartile range.

- Compare the results for the two composts, writing down what you notice.

- Now repeat this process for the results from the survey or experiment you chose to do above.

In a cumulative frequency diagram, you can join the points with straight (ruled) line segments instead of a curve.

Chapter 7 Analysing data

Writing up your findings

There are several things you need to remember when you are writing up your work. Look back at the table and reread the advice given in chapter 1.

You need to:

- show evidence of the planning that you did
- show how you found the information, who you asked and how you chose them

- include ideas for extending the task, for example suggesting other questions that you could ask
- present the information clearly
- explain or state what you wanted to find out
- state what you notice, how your analysis supports this and try to explain why the results occur.

Box-and-whisker plots

As you have seen in this chapter, data which have been ordered and/or presented in a cumulative frequency table or graph can be divided into four equal parts called **quartiles**. This example illustrates the use of quartiles.

Example

Here are the examination results for a class.

80 62 53 76 76 41 59 78 84

66 71 50 79 69 87 64 56 65

58 78 75 60 51 73 74

These can be shown in a frequency table like this... and plotted like this.

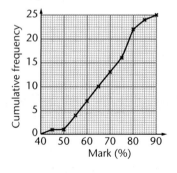

Mark m	Frequency		Cumulative frequency
$40 \leqslant m < 45$	/	1	1
$45 \leqslant m < 50$			1
$50 \leqslant m < 55$	///	3	4
$55 \leqslant m < 60$	///	3	7
$60 \leqslant m < 65$	///	3	10
$65 \leqslant m < 70$	///	3	13
$70 \leqslant m < 75$	///	3	16
$75 \leqslant m < 80$	ЖHT /	6	22
$80 \leqslant m < 85$	//	2	24
$85 \leqslant m < 90$	/	1	25

There are 25 values so the median is the middle, the 13th. The lower quartile is one-quarter of the way up, in this case in the $0.25 \times 25 = 6.25$th position. The upper quartile is three-quarters of the way up, in this case in the $0.75 \times 25 = 18.75$th position.

Reading from the graph, the lower quartile is 59, the median is 70 and the upper quartile is 77.

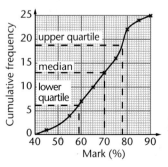

An alternative method of showing the quartiles and the range is with a **box-and-whisker plot**. These plots are produced to allow people to compare data quickly – they are not always useful for accurate work.

The left-hand side of the box is at the point corresponding to the value of the lower quartile. The right-hand side of the box is at a point corresponding to the upper quartile. The median is also drawn in the box.

The left-hand whisker extends from the lower quartile to the minimum value, the right-hand whisker extends from the upper quartile to the maximum value.

The box itself shows the location of the middle 50% of the data, the whiskers show how the data are spread out.

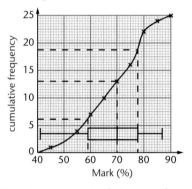

It is not necessary to draw cumulative frequency graphs to find or show quartiles before constructing box-and-whisker plots.

For example, the data below give the numbers of fish caught over a period of 11 days.

$$0 \ 3 \ 4 \ 5 \ 0 \ 3 \ 5 \ 7 \ 8 \ 7 \ 6$$

Rearranging these data into order gives:

$$0 \ 0 \ 3 \ 3 \ 4 \ 5 \ 5 \ 6 \ 7 \ 7 \ 8$$

With a small amount of data, it is easy to find the quartiles as follows.

- The median is 5.
- The median splits the data into a lower half: 0 0 3 3 4 and an upper half: 5 6 7 7 8.
- Find the median for each of these halves: the lower quartile is 3 and the upper quartile is 7.

You can now draw a box-and-whisker plot, knowing that the lowest value is 0 and the highest is 8.

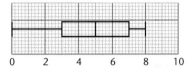

If you have to draw a box and whisker plot for grouped data when you are not given the actual minimum or maximum values the whiskers should be drawn to the minimum value of the lowest group and to the maximum value of the highest group. For example, if you were given a table of examination marks grouped $0 \leqslant M < 10$, $10 \leqslant M < 20$, $20 \leqslant M < 30$, ... $90 \leqslant M < 100$, the whiskers would be drawn to 0 and to 100.

Exercise 7.1a

1. Two policemen did separate traffic surveys at different locations. Each policeman recorded the speeds of 50 cars that passed him. Their findings are recorded in this table.

Speed v (km/h)	Policeman A	Policeman B
$10 \leqslant v < 30$	6	2
$30 \leqslant v < 50$	12	4
$50 \leqslant v < 70$	12	4
$70 \leqslant v < 90$	13	19
$90 \leqslant v < 110$	4	19
$110 \leqslant v < 130$	3	2

(a) Draw a cumulative frequency graph for each set of data and find the median and quartiles.
(b) Show these on box-and-whisker plots.
(c) Compare the results. Can you draw any conclusions about the two locations?

2. Draw box-and-whisker plots for each of these sets of data.
   (a) 8 3 15 8 13 1 20 5 16
   (b) 8.6 3.8 1.5 6.8 4.7 7.6 10.3 5.4 1.6

Exercise 7.1b

1. A sample of 200 potatoes was weighed and sorted into groups, as shown in this table.

Weight w (g)	Frequency	Cumulative frequency
$10 \leqslant w < 30$	12	
$30 \leqslant w < 50$	37	
$50 \leqslant w < 70$	63	
$70 \leqslant w < 90$	52	
$90 \leqslant w < 110$	31	
$110 \leqslant w < 130$	5	

(a) Copy the cumulative frequency table and complete it.
(b) Draw a cumulative frequency graph and use it to find the lower and upper quartiles and the median of the samples.
(c) Draw a box-and-whisker plot for the data.

2. A gardener measured the heights of 170 plants he was growing and produced this table.

Height h (cm)	Frequency	Cumulative frequency
$0 \leqslant h < 6$	5	
$6 \leqslant h < 10$	11	
$10 \leqslant h < 14$	57	
$14 \leqslant h < 18$	52	
$18 \leqslant h < 22$	27	
$22 \leqslant h < 26$	18	

(a) Copy the cumulative frequency table and complete it.
(b) Draw a cumulative frequency graph.
(c) Show the information on a box-and-whisker plot.

Key points

- Questionnaires and experiments can be used to prove or disprove a hypothesis.
- Questionnaires should be designed to avoid bias.
- Closed questions, which have a 'yes' or 'no' answer are easier to analyse for a questionnaire.
- A pilot survey is a small survey carried out with a few people to see if the planned questions 'work'.

- Grouped data are used when there are a lot of results to analyse.
- Cumulative frequency diagrams are useful for estimating the interquartile range and the median of a set of data.
- Findings should be written up clearly, to explain what has been done and why.
- Box-and-whisker plots show the quartiles, the median and the range of a set of data.

Revision exercise 7a

1. In 1970, a small factory employed 200 people. The frequency table shows their annual earnings.

Earnings (£E)	$400 < E \leqslant 600$	$600 < E \leqslant 800$	$800 < E \leqslant 1000$	$1000 < E \leqslant 1200$	$1200 < E \leqslant 1400$
Frequency	50	55	63	27	5

(a) Draw a cumulative frequency curve of the data.
(b) Use your graph to find:
   (i) the median earnings
   (ii) the interquartile range
   (iii) the number of employees who earned more than £900.

2. This table shows the numbers of marks obtained by candidates in an examination.

Mark	10	20	30	40	50	60	70	80	90	100
Number of candidates obtaining less than this mark	7	16	36	64	102	130	151	162	168	170

   (a) Draw a cumulative frequency curve of the data.
   (b) Use your graph to find:
      (i) the median mark
      (ii) the interquartile range
      (iii) the number of candidates who obtained at least 55 marks
      (iv) the mark achieved by at least 60% of the candidates.

3. A new treatment is tested on 50 young apple trees. When the fruit was picked, these were the results.

Yield y (kg)	$0 \leqslant y < 2$	$2 \leqslant y < 4$	$4 \leqslant y < 6$	$6 \leqslant y < 8$	$8 \leqslant y < 10$	$10 \leqslant y < 12$
Frequency	0	1	2	25	18	4

   (a) Draw a cumulative frequency curve of the data and use your graph to find:
      (i) the median yield
      (ii) the interquartile range.
   These are the individual yields, in kilograms, for 50 similar trees that were not treated.

6	1	8	3	6	5	7	8	4	3
5	7	7	8	7	8	2	9	5	7
8	4	5	6	1	5	3	6	7	5
5	7	8	7	4	6	6	5	8	9
8	6	8	5	5	3	7	7	8	6

   (b) Compare the yields from the two samples. Was the treatment effective?

4. The table shows the age distribution (in millions) for males in England and Wales for two years.

Age	1881	1966
under 15	4.7	5.6
15 and under 30	3.4	4.9
30 and under 45	2.3	4.4
45 and under 60	1.4	4.4
60 and under 75	0.7	0.7
75 and under 90	0.1	0.7

   Draw cumulative frequency diagrams for the two years and use the medians, interquartile ranges and the numbers over 65 to compare the distributions.

5. A local theatre monitored the size of audience on Wednesday and Thursday evenings during one year. The results are shown in the table.

Audience size	50–99	100–199	200–299	300–399	400–499	500–599
Number of Wednesdays	11	20	10	6	4	1
Number of Thursdays	3	3	18	19	5	4

   (a) Draw cumulative frequency graphs to compare the data.
   (b) From these curves draw box-and-whisker plots to show the data.

8 Solving problems and checking results

Checking answers by rounding to one significant figure

It is important to be able to check calculations quickly, without using a calculator. One way to do this is to round the numbers to one significant figure, which was discussed in Chapter 1.

Examiner's tip

In a calculation it may be possible to round one number up and another number down. This might give an answer close to the exact answer.

Example ①

Find an approximate answer to the calculation 5.13×3.83.

$5.13 \times 3.83 \approx 5 \times 4$

Rounding 5.13 and 3.83 each to 1 s.f. to give a much simpler calculation

$= 20$

Exercise 8.1a

1. Find approximate answers to these calculations by rounding each number to one significant figure.
   (a) $31.3 \div 4.85$ (b) 113.5×2.99
   (c) $44.669 \div 8.77$ (d) $3.6 \times 14.9 \times 21.5$
   Now use a calculator to see how close your approximations are to the correct answers.

2. Find approximate answers to these calculations by rounding each number to one significant figure.
   (a) $\dfrac{14.56 \times 22.4}{59.78}$ (b) $\dfrac{4.9^2 \times 49.3}{96.7}$
   (c) $\sqrt{4.9 \times 5.2}$
   Now use a calculator to see how close your approximations are to the correct answers.

3. Find approximate answers to these calculations by rounding each number to one significant figure.
   (a) $(0.35 \times 86.3) \div 7.9$
   (b) $\sqrt{103.5} \div \sqrt{37.2}$
   (c) 9.87×0.0657
   (d) $0.95 \div 4.8$

4. Make up some multiplication and division calculations of your own to test this statement:
   'In multiplication and division calculations, rounding each number to one significant figure will always give an answer which is correct to one significant figure'.

Exercise 8.1b

1. Find approximate answers to these calculations by rounding each number to one significant figure.
   (a) 48.67×12.69 (b) 0.89×5.2 (c) 61.33×11.79
   (d) $(1.8 \times 2.9) \div 3.2$
   Now use a calculator to see how close your approximations are to the correct answers.

2. Find approximate answers to these calculations by rounding each number to one significant figure.
   (a) $\dfrac{3.99}{0.8 \times 1.64}$ (b) $198.5 \times 63.1 \times 2.8$ (c) $\dfrac{\sqrt{8.1 \times 1.9}}{1.9}$
   Now use a calculator to see how close your approximations are to the correct answers.

3. Find approximate answers to these calculations by rounding each number to one significant figure.
   (a) $32 \times \sqrt{124}$ (b) $\dfrac{62 \times 9.7}{10.12 \times 5.1}$ (c) 0.246×0.789
   (d) $44.555 \div 0.086$

Compound interest

Compound interest is different from simple interest. At the end of each year the interest is added to the amount. The interest at the end of the next year is calculated on this new figure.

 Example 2

Helen puts £500 into the bank, which pays interest at 8% per annum (written as p.a.). How much money will she have at the end of three years?

Interest at the end of 1st year = 8% of £500
$$= 0.08 \times £500$$
$$= £40$$

Amount at the end of 1st year = £500 + £40 = £540

> This amount can be found easily if you remember that the new amount will be $(100 + 8)\% = 108\%$ of the previous amount. £500 × 1.08 = £540

Amount at the end of the 2nd year = £540 × 1.08
$$= £583.20$$

Amount at the end of the 3rd year = £583.20 × 1.08
$$= £629.856$$

Chapter 8   Compound interest

Examiner's tip

If you are asked to find the compound interest rather than the total amount, make sure you subtract the original investment from the final balance.

Exercise 8.2a

1. Calculate the compound interest on these amounts.
    (a) £300 invested for two years at 5%
    (b) £1000 invested for four years at 4%
    (c) £450 invested for three years at 3%
    (d) £5000 invested for two years at 8%
    (e) £30 000 invested for four years at 7%
2. Is it better to invest £1000 for five years at 8% or for four years at 9%?

Exercise 8.2b

1. Calculate the compound interest on these amounts.
    (a) £250 invested for two years at 3.5%
    (b) £100 000 invested for three years at 2.5%
    (c) £50 invested for six years at 1.7%
    (d) £2000 invested for four years at 6.1%
    (e) £800 invested for five years at 3.4%
2. Find the difference in interest earned by investing £500 for three years at 12% simple interest or for three years at 10% compound interest.
3. I invest £500 at 7% compound interest. How many years must I leave it, before it doubles in value?

Insurance

Motor insurance

Everyone who drives a car needs to insure it. Each year they will have to pay an insurance company a certain amount, called the **insurance premium**. Then the insurance company will pay for the car to be repaired if it is stolen or if it is damaged in an accident or a fire, and they will also pay some medical expenses for people injured in the crash.

If the car driver doesn't make any claims for a year, the insurance company will give a discount called a no-claim bonus the following year. The discount could be a 20% reduction in the premium for every year (up to three years) without a claim, then from the fourth year a maximum reduction of 65% would apply (see the table on next page). If the driver makes a claim, the no-claim bonus may be reduced. Usually, a driver loses a year's no-claim bonus for making a claim, for example, a driver who makes a claim in the third year would find that the no-claim bonus is reduced from 60% to 40%.

Years with no claim	No-claim bonus
0	0%
1	20%
2	40%
3	60%
more than 3	65%

Example 3

Jackie drives a 1997 Ford Escort 1.8. The basic premium for this type of car is £350. How much would she have to pay if she had completed three years of driving and had never claimed?

From the table, the no-claim bonus = 60%. Therefore she pays 100% − 60% = 40% of the premium.

40% of £350 = 0.4 × £350 = £140

Therefore Jackie must pay £140.

Health insurance

Some people take out health insurance which will give them some money if they are ill and unable to work. Insurance companies work out how much people have to pay depending upon factors such as their age, whether or not they smoke, whether they are male or female.

A simplified table that an insurance company might use is given below.

Age (years)	Cost per month (£)	
	Female	Male
under 16	19.50	20.30
16–25	18.20	18.90
26–35	19.80	20.70
36–45	20.50	21.40
46–55	21.70	22.60
56–65	25.50	26.40
over 65	28.90	31.30

Add 15% for smokers.

Exercise 8.3a

Refer to the table for motor insurance to calculate how much each of the following motorists will have to pay.

1. Tariq, basic premium £480, driving for four years, never made a claim.
2. Claire, basic premium £530, driving for three years, no claims.

Refer to the table for health insurance to work out the insurance premiums per month for the following people.

3. A 55 year old male who smokes.
4. A 36 year old female, non-smoker.
5. A 66 year old female who smokes.

Exercise 8.3b

Refer to the table for motor insurance to calculate how much each of the following motorists will have to pay.

1. Bill, basic premium £654, driving for three years, one claim.
2. David, basic premium £686, driving for two years, one claim.

Refer to the table for health insurance to work out the insurance premiums per month for the following people.

3. A 22-year-old male who smokes.
4. A married couple:
   (a) the man is aged 29 and a non-smoker
   (b) the woman is aged 25 and a smoker.

Compound measures

Speed

Speed is an example of a compound measure, because it is calculated from two other measurements: distance and time.

For a journey, the average speed is $\dfrac{\text{total distance travelled}}{\text{total time taken}}$.

Speed is written as 'distance per time', for example 30 km/h.

Example 4 Calculate the average speed of a car that travels 80 km in 2 hours.

$$\text{Average speed} = \frac{\text{total distance travelled}}{\text{total time taken}} = \frac{80}{2} = 40 \text{ km/h}$$

The formula for speed can be rearranged to find the distance travelled or the time taken for a journey.

$$\text{distance} = \text{speed} \times \text{time} \qquad \text{time} = \frac{\text{distance}}{\text{speed}}$$

Density

Another example of a compound measure is **density**, which is linked to mass and volume.

The density of a substance $= \dfrac{\text{mass}}{\text{volume}}$.

It is measured in units such as grams per cubic centimetre (g/cm^3).

Example 5 The density of gold is 19.3 g/cm^3. Calculate the mass of a gold bar with a volume of 30 cm^3.

$$\text{density} = \frac{\text{mass}}{\text{volume}}$$

$$\text{so mass} = \text{density} \times \text{volume}$$

The mass of the gold bar $= \text{density} \times \text{volume} = 19.3 \times 30 = 579 \text{ g}$.

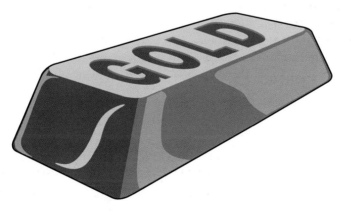

Population density

Population density is another example of a compound measure. It gives an idea of how heavily populated an area is. It is measured as the number of people per square kilometre.

Chapter 8 Compound measures

Exercise 8.4a

1. A train covers a distance of 750 metres in a time of 12.4 seconds. Calculate its average speed.
2. Paula jogs at a steady speed of 7 miles per hour. How far does she run in 90 minutes?
3. How long will it take a boat sailing at 6 km/h to travel 45 km?
4. Look at these three different packets of washing powder.

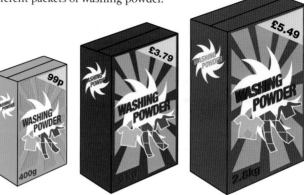

   Calculate the price per kilogram for each size.
5. The density of aluminium is 2.7 g/cm^3. What is the volume of a block of aluminium with a mass of 750 g?
6. Calculate the population density of Africa, if the population is
   7.43×10^8 and its area is 3.03×10^7 km^2.

Exercise 8.4b

1. Calculate the density of a 5 cm^3 block of copper with a mass of 35 g.
2. Brian's car travels 120 miles in 4 hours. Calculate his average speed.
3. A car is travelling at 25 m/s. Find how long it will take to travel:
   (a) 1 m   (b) 1 km   (c) 1 mile (1 mile is about 1.6 km).
4. The petrol tank of Nick's car has a capacity of 100 litres. She weighs 100 cm^3 of petrol and finds it has a mass of 80 g. What is the mass of petrol in the tank when it is full?
5. Which is better value?

6. Calculate the population density of Europe, if the population is 4.95×10^8 and the land area is 4.94×10^6 km^2.

Working to a reasonable degree of accuracy

Measurements and calculations should always be expressed to a suitable degree of accuracy. For example, it would be silly to say that a car journey took 4 hours 46 minutes and 13 seconds, but reasonable to say that it took four and three-quarter hours, or about five hours. In the same way, saying that the distance the car travelled was 93 kilometres 484 metres and 78 centimetres would be giving the measurement to an unnecessary degree of accuracy. It would more sensibly be stated as 93 km.

As a general rule the answer you give after a calculation should not be given to a greater degree of accuracy than any of the values used in the calculation.

> **Example 6**
>
> Ben measured the length and width of a table as 1.8 m and 1.3 m. He calculated the area as $1.8 \times 1.3 = 2.34 \, \text{m}^2$. How should he have given the answer?
>
> Ben's answer has two places of decimals (2 d.p.) so it is more accurate than the measurements he took. His answer should be $2.3 \, \text{m}^2$.

Exercise 8.5a

Write down sensible values for each of these measurements.

1. 3 minutes 24.8 seconds to boil an egg.
2. 2 weeks, 5 days, 3 hours and 13 minutes to paint a house.

Work these out and give the answers to a reasonable degree of accuracy.

3. Find the length of the side of a square field with area $33 \, \text{m}^2$.
4. Three friends win £48.32. How much will each receive?
5. It takes 12 hours to fly between two cities, if the aeroplane is travelling at 554 km/h. How far apart are the cities?
6. The length of a strip of card is 2.36 cm and the width is 0.041 cm, each measured to two significant figures. Calculate the area.

Exercise 8.5b

Write down sensible values for each of these measurements.

1. A book weighing 2.853 kg.
2. The height of a door as 2 metres 12 centimetres and 54 millimetres.

Work these out and give the answers to a reasonable degree of accuracy.

3. The length of a field is 92 m correct to two significant figures and the width is 58.36 m correct to four significant figures. Calculate the area of the field.
4. A book has 228 pages and is 18 mm thick. How thick is Chapter 1 which has 35 pages?
5. The total weight of 13 people in a lift is 879 kg. What is their average weight?
6. Last year a delivery driver drove 23 876 miles. Her van travels an average of 27 miles to the gallon. Diesel costs 72p per litre. If one gallon equals 4.55 litres, calculate the cost of the fuel used.

- Check answers to calculations by rounding numbers to one significant figure.
- Find the amount after compound interest at $x\%$ per annum by multiplying by $(100 + x)\%$ for each year.
- Compound measures such as speed and density are found by dividing one unit by another.
- The degree of accuracy in measurement depends on the purpose of the measurement.

Revision exercise 8a

1. Find approximate answers to these.
   (a) 63.9×14.9
   (b) $\sqrt{143} \times \sqrt{170} \times \sqrt{80}$
   (c) $(6.32 + 5.72) \times (\sqrt{16.1} + \sqrt{48.9})$

2. Calculate the compound interest on £1800 invested for three years at 4.8% p.a.

3. Tom invests £560 in the bank for three years at a rate of interest of 7.5% p.a. How much more interest will he earn than if he had invested the same amount at a rate of 7.5% simple interest?

4. A car travels 158 miles in 3.5 hours. What is its average speed?

5. A car travels an average of 22.6 miles per gallon of fuel. Petrol costs £2.95 per gallon. About how much will fuel for a journey of 500 miles cost?

6. The population of a city is 543 861. The population is expected to grow by 6% next year. What will the population be then?

7. A tap takes 13.5 minutes to fill a 70 litre tank. Calculate the flow rate in litres per minute. How long would it take to fill the same tank from a tap with a flow rate of 18.2 litres/minute?

8. Which of these is better value?

99p for 500g

63p for 200g

9. The volume of the Earth is approximately $1.4 \times 10^{27} \, \text{m}^3$. The mass of the Earth is approximately $2 \times 10^{30} \, \text{kg}$. Calculate the density of the Earth.

10. The diameter of a circle is 3.5 m correct to two significant figures. Calculate the circumference of the circle. Take $\pi = 3.141\,593$.

11. Light travels at approximately $3 \times 10^5 \, \text{km/s}$. If light takes about 8 minutes to reach the Earth from the sun, how far is the Earth from the sun, in kilometres?

12. The mean weight of eight men is 78.7 kg. A ninth man joins them. His weight is 48.6 kg. What is the mean weight of all nine men?

Pythagoras' theorem and trigonometry

Pythagoras' theorem

This is a square drawn on dotty paper.

Its area is 4 square units.

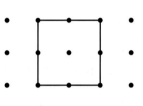

Here is a tilted square.

Calculating its area is more difficult. There are two methods you could use.

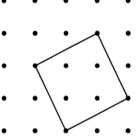

(a) Calculate the area of the large square drawn round the outside and subtract the area of the shaded triangles:

$9 - 1 - 1 - 1 - 1 = 5$ square units

or

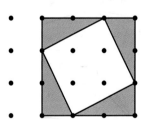

(b) Add together the area of the four shaded triangles and the area of the middle square:

$1 + 1 + 1 + 1 + 1 = 5$ square units

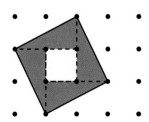

Activity 1

- Using either method (a) or method (b) calculate the area of the squares in the diagram below.

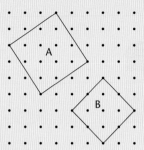

You should have found that the area of square A is 13 square units and the area of square B is 8 square units.

- Draw some more tilted squares of your own on dotty paper and find their areas.

  Look at all the tilted squares.

  Code the tilt by drawing a triangle at the base and writing down the length of its sides, like this.

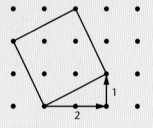

In this diagram the code is (2, 1).

In the diagram on the left, square A has a code of (3, 2) and square B has a code of (2, 2). Check that you agree.

- Code the squares you have drawn and write the codes and the areas of the squares in a table.

  Include the square from the beginning of this chapter. Its code is (2, 0) and its area is 4 square units. Include all the other squares you have already studied.

Code	Area
2, 0	4
2, 1	5
3, 2	13
2, 2	8

- Look at the codes and their areas. See if you can find a rule linking them together.

You will have found that squaring each code number and then adding the squares together gives the area:

$$3^2 + 2^2 = 9 + 4 = 13$$
$$2^2 + 2^2 = 4 + 4 = 8$$
$$2^2 + 1^2 = 4 + 1 = 5$$

The rule linking them together is called **Pythagoras' theorem**.

Squaring the numbers in the code and adding them is the same as squaring the lengths of the sides of the triangle.

Here is square A again.

Can you see that you can calculate the area of the largest square by adding together the areas of the smaller squares?

The largest square will always be on the longest side of the triangle – this is called the **hypotenuse** of the triangle.

Thus Pythagoras' theorem can be stated as:

The area of the square on the hypotenuse = the sum of the areas of the squares on the other two sides

but it is normally abbreviated to:

The square on the hypotenuse = the sum of the squares on the other two sides.

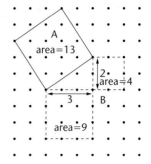

Activity 2

- Calculate the missing area in each of these diagrams.

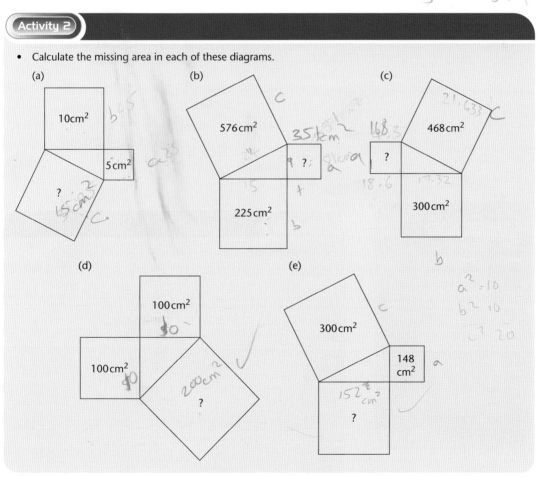

(a)

10cm²

5cm²

?

(b)

576cm²

225cm²

(c)

468cm²

300cm²

(d)

100cm²

100cm²

?

(e)

300cm²

148 cm²

?

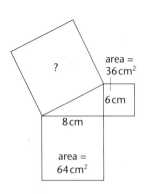

If you know the lengths of two sides of a right-angled triangle you can use Pythagoras' theorem to find the length of the third side.

The unknown area = $64 + 36 = 100\,\text{cm}^2$

This means that the length of the sides of the unknown square is 10 cm.

When using Pythagoras' theorem, you don't need to draw the squares − you can simply use the rule.

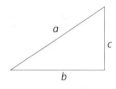

$$a^2 = b^2 + c^2$$

Thus:

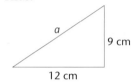

$$a^2 = 9^2 + 12^2 = 81 + 144 = 225$$
$$a = \sqrt{225} = 15\,\text{cm}$$

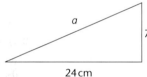

$$a^2 = 7^2 + 24^2 = 49 + 576 = 625$$
$$a = \sqrt{625} = 25\,\text{cm}$$

Examiner's tip

You can use Pythagoras to find the distance between two points on a coordinate diagram.

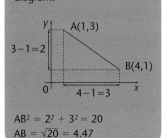

$$AB^2 = 2^2 + 3^2 = 20$$
$$AB = \sqrt{20} = 4.47$$

Activity 3

- Find the length of the hypotenuse in each of these triangles:

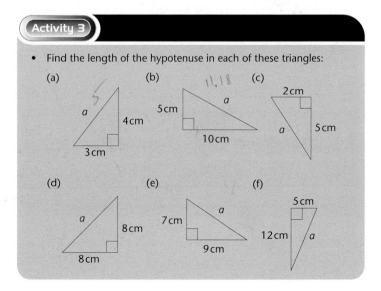

(a)
(b)   (c)
(d)   (e)   (f)

If you know the length of the hypotenuse and the length of one other side you can find the length of the third side.

(a)

8 cm

6 cm

c

$$a^2 = b^2 + c^2$$
$$8^2 = 6^2 + c^2$$
$$64 = 36 + c^2$$
$$c^2 = 64 - 36 = 28$$
$$c = \sqrt{28} = 5.29 \text{ cm (to 2 d.p.)}$$

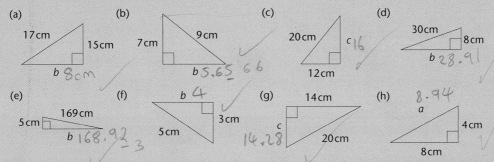

Activity 4

- Calculate the length of the third side in each of these triangles. Give your answers correct to two decimal places.

(a)

17 cm 15 cm b 8 cm

(b)

7 cm 9 cm b 5.65 66

(c)

20 cm 12 cm c 16

(d)

30 cm 8 cm b 28.91

(e)

5 cm 169 cm b 168.92 — 3

(f)

5 cm 3 cm b 4

(g)

14 cm 20 cm c 14.28

(h)

a 8.94 4 cm 8 cm

- Solve these problems.

(a) A rectangular field is 225 m long and 110 m wide. Find the length of the diagonal path across it.   250.4

(b) A rectangular field is 250 m long. A footpath 38.0 m long crosses the field diagonally. Find the width of the field.   247.095

(c) A ladder is 7 m long. It is resting against a wall, with the top of the ladder 5 m above the ground. How far from the wall is the base of the ladder?   4.8989

(d) Harry is building a kite for his sister. This is his diagram of the kite. The kite is 30 cm wide.

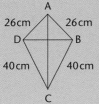

A
26 cm   26 cm
D   B
40 cm   40 cm
C

Harry needs to buy some cane to make the struts AC and DB. What length of cane does he need to buy?

(e) This is the side view of a shed. Find the length of the sloping roof.

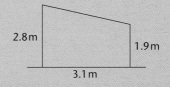

2.8 m   1.9 m
3.1 m

Examiner's tip

It is a good idea to draw a sketch if a diagram isn't given. Try to draw it roughly to scale and mark on it any lengths you know. It may help you see any errors in your working.

Trigonometry

You will need a protractor and a ruler for this section.

The hypotenuse is the longest side of a right-angled triangle. It is the side opposite the right angle.

The other sides are named according to the angle under consideration.

For *a*:   For *b*:

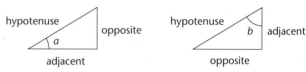

In this activity you will need to draw triangles and identify the sides, like this:

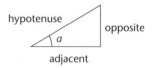

Activity 5

- Draw six different triangles. Use these values for *a* but make the **adjacent** side 5 cm long each time.

  (a) 10°   (b) 20°   (c) 30°   (d) 40°
  (e) 50°   (f) 60°

  a is the angle between the adjacent and the hypotenuse.

  For each triangle, measure the length of the **opposite side** and divide this by the length of the adjacent side (5 cm). Record your results in a table like this one. Round each ratio to one decimal place.

Angle *a* (°)	Adjacent (cm)	Opposite (cm)	opposite adjacent
10	5		
20	5		
30	5		
40	5		
50	5		
60	5		

Now draw two more triangles. Keep the angle fixed at 30° but change the length of the adjacent side to 10 cm and then 15 cm.

Record your results in a table like this.

Angle *a* (°)	Adjacent (cm)	Opposite (cm)	opposite adjacent
30	5		
30	10		
30	15		

What do you notice?

What do you think the length of the opposite side would be, if you drew another triangle with *a* = 30° and the adjacent side 20 cm long?

Estimate your answer and then check by drawing and measuring.

- What do you think the length of the adjacent side would be, if you drew another triangle with *a* = 30° and the opposite side 8 cm long?

Estimate your answer and check by drawing and measuring.

The ratio $\dfrac{\text{opposite}}{\text{adjacent}}$ is called the **tangent** (ratio).

The value of the tangent has been calculated for all angles and is one of the functions on a scientific calculator.

- Now look back at all the triangles you have drawn and for each one measure the length of the hypotenuse.

Copy this table and complete it.

Write the ratios correct to one decimal place.

Angle (°)	Adjacent (cm)	Opposite (cm)	Hypotenuse (cm)	$\dfrac{\text{opposite}}{\text{hypotenuse}}$	$\dfrac{\text{adjacent}}{\text{hypotenuse}}$
10	5				
20	5				
30	5				
40	5				
50	5				
60	5				
30	5				
30	10				
30	15				

What do you notice?

The ratio $\dfrac{\text{opposite}}{\text{hypotenuse}}$ is called the **sine** (ratio)   The ratio $\dfrac{\text{adjacent}}{\text{hypotenuse}}$ is called the **cosine** (ratio)

Use the tangent ratio to calculate the missing side or angle in a right-angled triangle.

Example 1

Calculate the value of x.

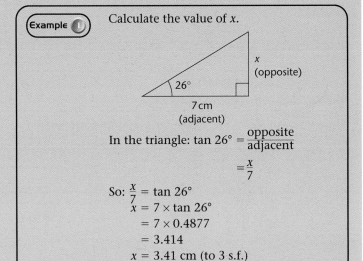

In the triangle: $\tan 26° = \dfrac{\text{opposite}}{\text{adjacent}}$

$= \dfrac{x}{7}$

So: $\dfrac{x}{7} = \tan 26°$

$x = 7 \times \tan 26°$

$= 7 \times 0.4877$

$= 3.414$

$x = 3.41 \text{ cm (to 3 s.f.)}$

Example 2

Find the size of the angle marked a.

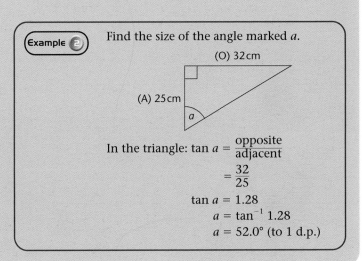

In the triangle: $\tan a = \dfrac{\text{opposite}}{\text{adjacent}}$

$= \dfrac{32}{25}$

$\tan a = 1.28$

$a = \tan^{-1} 1.28$

$a = 52.0° \text{ (to 1 d.p.)}$

- Find the length of the side marked *x* in each of these triangles.

(a)

5.5 cm

68°

x

(b)

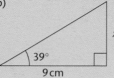

39°

9 cm

x

(c)

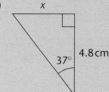

x

37°

4.8 cm

(d)

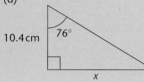

10.4 cm

76°

x

(e)

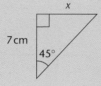

x

7 cm

45°

(f)

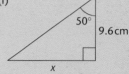

50°

9.6 cm

x

- Find the size of the angle marked *a* in each of these triangles.

(a)

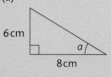

6 cm

8 cm

a

(b)

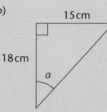

15 cm

18 cm

a

(c)

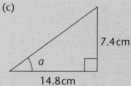

7.4 cm

a

14.8 cm

(d)

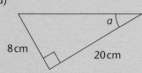

8 cm

a

20 cm

(e)

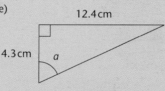

12.4 cm

4.3 cm

a

Use the sine or cosine ratios to calculate the missing side or angle in a right-angled triangle.

Example 3 Calculate the value of *x*.

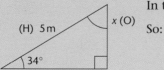

(H) 5 m

x (O)

34°

In the triangle: $\sin 34° = \dfrac{\text{opposite}}{\text{hypotenuse}}$

So: $\sin 34° = \dfrac{x}{5}$

$x = 5 \times \sin 34°$

$x = 2.80 \text{ cm (to 2 d.p.)}$

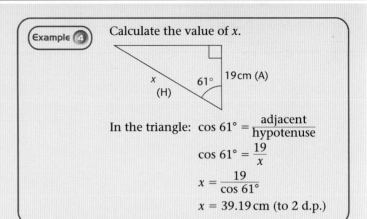

Calculate the value of x.

Example 4

Examiner's tip

Take care when you are finding the hypotenuse. Remember to multiply by x and divide by cos 61°.

In the triangle: $\cos 61° = \dfrac{\text{adjacent}}{\text{hypotenuse}}$

$$\cos 61° = \frac{19}{x}$$

$$x = \frac{19}{\cos 61°}$$

$$x = 39.19 \text{ cm (to 2 d.p.)}$$

• Find the length of the side marked x, or the size of the angle marked a, in each of these triangles.

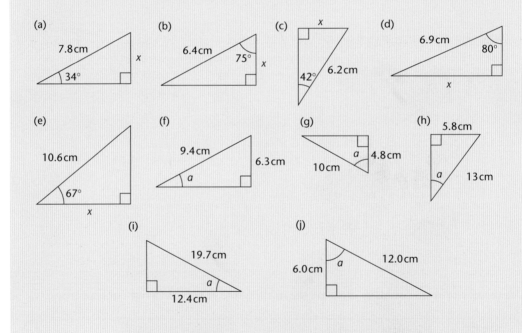

Examiner's tip

Follow these three steps.
Step 1 Draw and label a diagram.
Step 2 Label the two appropriate sides as O, A or H.
Step 3 Write down the formula to be used and calculate the answer.

Use trigonometry to solve problems.

Example 5 A kite flies at the end of a string 20 m long. The string is straight and it makes an angle of 47° with the horizontal. How high is the kite from the ground?

Step 1

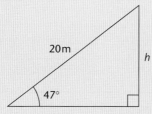

Step 2

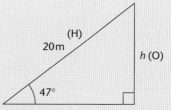

Step 3 In the triangle: $\sin 47° = \dfrac{O}{H} = \dfrac{h}{20}$

So $h = 20 \times \sin 47°$

$h = 14.6\,\text{m}$ (1 d.p.)

- Use trigonometric ratios to solve these problems.

(a) A ladder of length 4.8 m rests against a vertical wall so that the base of the ladder is 1.8 m from the wall. Calculate the angle between the ladder and the ground.

(b) A ladder of length 5 m rests against a vertical wall. The angle between the ladder and the wall is 62°. How far up the wall does the ladder reach?

(c) From a distance of 25 m, the angle of elevation from the ground to the top of a tower is 37°. How high is the tower?

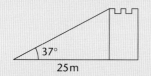

(d) A ship is due south of a lighthouse. It sails on a bearing of 065° until it is due east of the lighthouse.

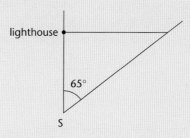

If the ship is now 40 km away from the lighthouse, how far has it sailed?

(e) An isosceles triangle has sides of length 8 cm, 8 cm and 5 cm. Find the angle between the equal sides.

(f) Find the acute angle between the diagonals of a rectangle with sides of 5 cm and 8 cm.

(g) A path slopes up a hill at 12° from the horizontal. The path is 2.8 km long. How high is the hill?

(h) A ship sails for 70 km on a bearing of 130°. How far south and east of its starting point is it?

Example 6 Find the length of AC and the value of cos 45°.

$$AC^2 = \left(\tfrac{1}{2}\right)^2 + \left(\tfrac{1}{2}\right)^2 = \tfrac{1}{4} + \tfrac{1}{4} = \tfrac{2}{4}$$

$$AC = \frac{\sqrt{2}}{2}$$

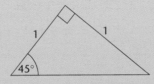

$$\cos 45° = \frac{\tfrac{1}{2}}{\tfrac{\sqrt{2}}{2}} = \frac{1}{\sqrt{2}}$$

Multiply top and bottom by 2.

Expressions like these, which include square roots ($\sqrt{\ }$) are called **surds**.

- Use Pythagoras' theorem and trigonometry to work these out.
  Do not use a calculator. Leave surds in your answer.

  (a) Find the length of the hypotenuse.

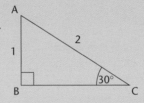

  (b) Find: (i) the length of BC
           (ii) the values of sin 30° and cos 30°.

  (c) Find: (i) the length of the hypotenuse
           (ii) the values of sin 45° and cos 45°.

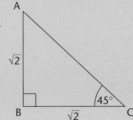

Examiner's tip

You could be asked to use Pythagoras' theorem and trigonometry without a calculator. If so, leave any square roots in your answer.

Chapter 9 · Pythagoras' theorem and trigonometry

Key points

- For a right-angled triangle, Pythagoras' theorem states that $a^2 = b^2 + c^2$

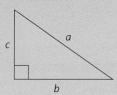

- In a right-angled triangle, for angle x:

$$\tan x = \frac{O}{A}$$

$$\sin x = \frac{O}{H}$$

$$\cos x = \frac{A}{H}$$

Revision exercise 9a

1. Calculate the value of x in each triangle.

   (a)

   4 cm, 6 cm, x

   (b)

   x, 14.9 cm, 8 cm

   (c)

   12.1 cm, 10 cm, x

2. Calculate the length of the diagonal of a rectangle with length 22 cm and width 12 cm.

3. A ship sails 20 km due north and then 30 km due west. How far is it from its starting point?

4. Calculate the lengths or angles marked with letters. (All lengths are in cm.)

   (a) 23, a, 40

   (b) 8, a, 7

   (c) 7, a, 12

   (d) x, 14, 37°

   (e) 50°, x, 9

   (f) 48°, 13, x

5. A boy is flying a kite with a string of length 45 m. If the string is straight and it makes an angle of 75° with the ground, how high is the kite? Ignore the height of the boy.

6. The sides of a triangle are 5 cm, 5 cm and 7 cm. Calculate the angles of the triangle.

7. A ramp for disabled people must slope at not more than 10°. If the height of the ramp has to be 0.8 m, how long must the ramp be?

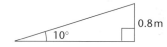

   10°, 0.8 m

8. A man sails for 5 km on a bearing of 285° from a harbour.

   (a) How far north and west of the harbour is he?

   He then sails 3 km due north.

   (b) Find the bearing on which he needs to sail to return to the harbour, and how far he needs to sail.

9. Find the length of PQ.

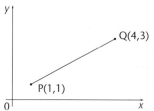

   Q(4,3), P(1,1)

10 Equations and manipulation 2

> ## You will need to know how to:
>
> - write a formula using letters
> - collect together algebraic expressions
> - expand brackets
> - form and solve simple linear equations
> - form and solve simple inequalities
> - factorise quadratic expressions
> - draw graphs of linear, square and cubic equations.

Solving harder linear equations

Some linear equations you may be asked to solve may include decimals or have the unknown in the denominator.

Example 1

Solve $2(5x - 4) = 3(x + 2)$.

$10x - 8 = 3x + 6$	Multiply out the brackets.
$[10x - 8 + 8 = 3x + 6 + 8]$	Add 8 to each side.
$10x = 3x + 14$	
$[10x - 3x = 3x + 14 - 3x]$	Subtract $3x$ from each side.
$7x = 14$	
$x = 14 \div 7 = 2$	Divide by 7.

The lines in square brackets are often missed out.

Example 2

Solve $\dfrac{x}{3} = 2x - 3$.

$x = 3(2x - 3)$	Multiply each side by 3.
$x = 6x - 9$	Multiply out the bracket.
$6x - 9 = x$	Reverse the equation to put the x-term with the larger positive coefficient on the left.
$[6x - 9 + 9 = x + 9]$	Add 9 to each side.
$6x = x + 9$	
$[6x - x = x + 9 - x]$	Subtract x from each side.
$5x = 9$	
$x = 9 \div 5 = 1\frac{4}{5}$	Divide each side by 5.

Example 3

Solve the equation $\dfrac{400}{x} = 8$.

$400 = 8x$ Multiply each side by x.

$400 \div 8 = x$ Divide each side by 8.

$x = 50$

Example 4

Solve the equation $3.6x = 8.7$.

$x = 8.7 \div 3.6$ Divide each side by 3.6.

$x = 2.416\,666\,6$ Use a calculator and give the
$ = 2.42$ answer to three significant
                     figures unless you are told
                     otherwise.

Examiner's tip

A common error when multiplying through by a number or letter is to multiply just the first term. Use brackets to make sure. Another common error in the above example would be to give the answer as $\frac{5}{9}$ rather than $\frac{9}{5}$.
It is helpful to swap the sides if necessary to make the coefficient of x greater on the left-hand side.

Exercise 10.1a

Solve these equations.

1. $5(x - 2) = 4x$
2. $3(2x + 3) = 9$
3. $4(2x - 3) = 3(x + 1)$
4. $2(4x - 5) = 2x + 6$
5. $10(x + 2) = 3(x - 5)$
6. $3(2x - 1) = 2(x + 4)$
7. $\dfrac{x}{2} = 3x - 10$
8. $\dfrac{2x}{3} = x - 2$

9. $\dfrac{3x}{2} = 7 - 2x$
10. $\dfrac{5x}{3} = 4x - 2$
11. $\dfrac{50}{x} = 2$
12. $\dfrac{300}{x} = 15$
13. $\dfrac{75}{2x} = 3$

Now give the answers to the remaining questions correct to three significant figures.

14. $3.5x = 9.6$
15. $5.2x = 25$
16. $4.6x = 7.5$
17. $\dfrac{x}{1.4} = 2.6$
18. $2.1(x - 3.2) = 4.4$
19. $2.2(2x + 5.1) = 4.9$
20. $\dfrac{2.3}{x} = 4.5$

Exercise 10.1b

Solve these equations.

1. $2(3x - 5) = 14$
2. $4(3x - 1) = 10x$
3. $3(2x + 1) = 7x + 1$
4. $5(2x - 2) = 2(x + 3)$
5. $3(4x + 3) = 2(x + 6)$
6. $5(x + 2) = 3(4 - x)$
7. $5(x + 2) = 3(2x + 1)$
8. $\dfrac{x}{3} = x - 4$
9. $\dfrac{2x}{5} = x - 3$

10. $\dfrac{3x}{5} = 4 - x$
11. $\dfrac{2x}{3} = 4x - 5$
12. $\dfrac{200}{x} = 4$
13. $\dfrac{25}{2x} = 5$
14. $\dfrac{15}{2x} = 3$

Give the answers to the remaining questions correct to three significant figures.

15. $2.4x = 9.7$
16. $22x = 7.55$
17. $4.2x = 9.3$
18. $2.1(3x - 6.4) = 9.2$
19. $\dfrac{x}{3.4} = 2.5$
20. $\dfrac{3.5}{x} = 1.6$

Chapter 10   Solving harder linear equations

Solving inequalities

The inequalities in earlier chapters had only one answer. These are more complicated.

Example 5 Solve the inequality $x^2 < 9$.

Since $3^2 = 9$, one answer is $x < 3$, but remember that $(-3)^2$ also gives an answer of 9. The inequality has two solutions, since 9 has two possible square roots. $x > -3$ also satisfies the inequality.

Take square roots on both sides but if you take the negative value you must reverse the inequality sign.

$x < 3$ or $x > -3$

This can be written as $-3 < x < 3$.

Examiner's tip

Take care with the direction of the inequality when taking the square root. It is useful to check. In Example 6, the answer is $x \leqslant -3$ so check by putting in a value of x such as $x = -4$. This gives $x^2 - 3 = 16 - 3 = 13$ and $13 \geqslant 6$ as required.

Example 6 Solve the inequality $x^2 - 3 \geqslant 6$.

$x^2 \geqslant 9$ Add 3 to each side.

$x \leqslant -3$ or $x \geqslant 3$ Again change the inequality for the negative answer. These cannot be combined.

Exercise 10.2a

Solve these inequalities.

1. $2x + 3 < 5$
2. $5x - 4 > 10 - 2x$
3. $3(2x - 1) > 15$
4. $4(x - 4) \geqslant x - 1$
5. $\dfrac{x}{2} > 3$

6. $x^2 \geqslant 4$
7. $x^2 < 25$
8. $x^2 \geqslant 1$
9. $x^2 - 2 \leqslant 14$
10. $x^2 + 6 < 22$

Exercise 10.2b

Solve these inequalities.

1. $4n - 2 > 6$
2. $2n + 6 < n + 3$
3. $4n - 9 \geqslant 2n + 1$
4. $3(x - 1) \geqslant 6$
5. $2(3x - 1) > 4x + 6$

6. $x^2 < 1$
7. $x^2 \leqslant 9$
8. $x^2 > 36$
9. $x^2 - 5 \leqslant 4$
10. $x^2 + 8 > 33$

Forming equations and inequalities

Simple problems can be solved using equations and inequalities.

Example 7

The length of a rectangle is a cm, the width is 15 cm shorter. The length is three times the width.

Write down an equation in a and solve it to find the length and width of the rectangle.

a

$a - 15$

If the length = a, the width = $a - 15$

and the length = $3 \times$ width = $3(a - 15)$.

The equation is $a = 3(a - 15)$.

$a = 3a - 45$	Multiply out the brackets.
$3a - 45 = a$	Swap sides to write them the other way round.
$[3a - 45 + 45 = a + 45]$	Add 45 to each side.
$3a = a + 45$	
$[3a - a = a + 45 - a]$	Subtract a from each side.
$2a = 45$	
$a = 22.5$	

So the length = 22.5 cm and the width = 7.5 cm.

Example 8

£400 was shared by n people and each received £16.

Set up an equation and find how many people there were.

The equation is $\dfrac{400}{n} = 16$

$400 = 16n$ Multiply each side by n.

$n = 400 \div 16 = 25$

There were 25 people.

Examiner's tip

When you are asked to set up an equation and solve it you will not score any marks if you just give the answer without the equation.

1. Two angles in a triangle are x and $2x - 30$. The first angle is twice the size of the second. Set up an equation and solve it to find the size of the two angles.

2. The width of a rectangle is $3\,cm$ and the length is $x + 4\,cm$. The area is $27\,cm^2$. Set up an equation and solve it to find x.

3. In a class of 32 pupils, x are girls. There are three times as many girls as boys. Set up an equation and solve it to find out how many boys and how many girls there are.

4. A greengrocer sells potatoes at x pence per kilogram. He paid $\frac{2x}{3}$ per kilogram for them. This is 20p less than x. Set up an equation and solve it to find x.

5. Stephen thinks of a number. If he doubles the number and then subtracts 5, he gets the same answer as if he subtracts 2 from the number and then multiplies by 3. Let the number be n. Set up an equation and solve it to find n.

6. On a bus trip each child pays £p and each adult pays £12 more than each child. There are 28 children and four adults on the bus. The same amount of money is collected from all the children as from all the adults. Set up an equation and solve it to find how much each child and each adult pays.

7. At Joe's Diner one-course meals cost £x. Two-course meals cost £2 more. A group of eight people bought three one-course meals and five two-course meals. They paid £38. Set up an equation and solve it to find the cost of a one-course meal.

8. The square of a number is less than 36. Set up an inequality and find the possible values for the number.

1. Two angles of a pentagon are $x°$ and the other three are each $(2x - 20)°$. The total of all the angles is 540°. Write down an equation and solve it to find the size of the angles.

2. A triangle has a base of $x\,cm$ and a height of $5\,cm$. The area is $30\,cm^2$. Set up an equation in x and solve it to find the length of the base.

3. The cost per person of a flight from Sheffield Airport is the charge by the airline plus £40 tax. Four people flew from Sheffield to Cairo and the total they had to pay was £1640. Let the charge by the airline be £x. Write down an equation in x and solve it to find the charge by the airline.

4. A 32-year-old man has three children who are x, $2x$ and $2x + 4$ years old. The man is four times as old as his eldest child. Set up an equation and solve it to find the ages of the children.

5. Jane thinks of a number. Her number divided by three gives the same answer as taking the number away from sixteen. Let the number be n. Set up an equation and solve it to find what the number was.

6. At Deno's Pizza Place, a basic pizza costs £x and extra toppings are 50p each. Bernard and four of his friends each have pizzas with two extra toppings. They pay £25.50. Set up an equation and find the cost of a basic pizza.

7. Ahmed had £x. He spent £4 on books and still had three-fifths of his money left. Write down an equation in x and solve it to find how much he had to start with.

8. Timothy squares a number and gets an answer greater than 49. Set up an inequality and find the values that the number can take.

Simultaneous equations

An equation in two unknowns does not have a unique solution. For example, the graph of the equation $x + y = 4$ is a straight line. Every point on the line will have coordinates that satisfy the equation.

When you are given two equations in two unknowns, such as x and y, they usually have common solutions where the two lines meet in a point. These are called **simultaneous equations**.

Solving by the method of elimination

Example 9

Solve the simultaneous equations $x + y = 4$ and $2x - y = 5$.

$$x + y = 4 \qquad ①$$
$$2x - y = 5 \qquad ②$$

Write the two equations, one under the other, and label them.

Look to see if either of the unknowns (x or y) has the same coefficient in both equations. In this case there is $1y$ in equation ① and $1y$ in equation ②. As their signs are different, the two y-terms will be eliminated (cancel each other out) if the two equations are added.

$$x + 2x + y + (-y) = 4 + 5 \qquad \text{Adding } 1 + 2.$$
$$3x = 9$$
$$x = 3$$

To find the value of y, substitute $x = 3$ in equation ①.

$$3 + y = 4 \qquad \text{Replacing } x \text{ by } 3.$$
$$y = 1$$

So the solution is $x = 3$ and $y = 1$.

Check in equation ②: The left-hand side is $2x - y = 6 - 1 = 5$ which is correct.

Example 10

Solve the simultaneous equations $2x + 5y = 9$ and $2x - y = 3$.

$$2x + 5y = 9 \qquad ① \qquad \text{Set out in line.}$$
$$2x - y = 3 \qquad ②$$

This time $(+)2x$ appears in each equation, so subtract to eliminate the x-terms.

$$2x - 2x + 5x - (-y) = 9 - 3 \qquad ①-② \text{ Take care with the signs. } 5y - (-y) = 5y + y.$$
$$6y = 6$$
$$y = 1$$
$$2x + 5 = 9 \qquad \text{Substitute in } ①. \; 5y \text{ is replaced by } 5 \times 1 = 5.$$
$$2x = 4$$
$$x = 2$$

The solution is $x = 2$, $y = 1$.

Check in equation ②: The left-hand side is $2x - y = 4 - 1 = 3$ which is correct.

When eliminating, if the signs of the letter to be eliminated are the same, subtract. If they are different, add.

When subtracting, take great care with the signs. This is where most errors are made. If your check is wrong, see if you have made an error with any signs.

Examiner's tip

When subtracting equations, you can use ①–② or ②–①. It is better to make the letter positive.

Always write down clearly what you are doing.

Example 11

Solve the simultaneous equations $x + 3y = 10$, $3x + 2y = 16$.

$$x + 3y = 10 \quad ① \quad \boxed{\text{Set out in line.}}$$
$$3x + 2y = 16 \quad ②$$

This time the coefficients of x and y are different in both equations.

Multiply ① by 3 to make the coefficient of x the same as in equation ②.

$$3x + 9y = 30 \quad ③ \quad \boxed{①\times 3}$$
$$3x + 2y = 16 \quad ②$$

Now $(+)3x$ appears in both equations, so subtract.

$$3x - 3x + 9y - 2y = 30 - 16 \quad \boxed{③-②}$$
$$7y = 14$$
$$y = 2$$
$$x + 6 = 10 \quad \boxed{\text{Substitute in ①.}}$$
$$x = 4$$

The solution is $x = 4$, $y = 2$.

Check in equation ②: The left-hand side is $3x + 2y = 12 + 4 = 16$ which is correct.

There is no need to write as much detail as in the last example. The next example shows what is required. The commentary can be omitted.

Example 12

Solve simultaneously $4x - y = 10$ and $3x + 2y = 13$.

$$4x - y = 10 \quad ① \quad \boxed{\text{Set out in line.}}$$
$$3x + 2y = 13 \quad ②$$
$$①\times 2: \quad 8x - 2y = 20 \quad ③ \quad \boxed{\text{To get } 2y \text{ in each equation.}}$$
$$②+③: \quad 8x + 3x + 2y + (-2y) = 13 + 20 \quad \boxed{\text{To eliminate } y.}$$
$$11x = 33$$
$$x = 3$$

Substitute in ①: $12 - y = 10$
$$-y = -2$$
$$y = 2$$

The solution is $x = 3$, $y = 2$.

Check in ②: LHS $= 3x + 2y = 9 + 4 = 13$ which is correct.

Exercise 10.4a

Solve these simultaneous equations.

1. $x + y = 5$
   $2x - y = 7$

2. $3x + y = 9$
   $2x + y = 7$

3. $2x + 3y = 11$
   $2x + y = 5$

4. $2x + y = 7$
   $4x - y = 5$

5. $2x + 3y = 13$
   $3x - 3y = 12$

6. $2x + 3y = 14$
   $5x + 3y = 26$

7. $3x + y = 7$
   $2x + 3y = 7$

8. $2x - 3y = 0$
   $3x + y = 11$

9. $2x + 3y = 13$
   $x + 2y = 8$

10. $3x + 2y = 13$
    $x + 3y = 16$

11. $2x + 3y = 7$
    $3x - y = 5$

12. $x + y = 4$
    $4x - 2y = 7$

13. $2x + 2y = 7$
    $4x - 3y = 7$

14. $4x - 2y = 14$
    $3x + y = 8$

15. $2x - 2y = 5$
    $4x - 3y = 11$

Exercise 10.4b

Solve these simultaneous equations.

1. $x + y = 3$
   $2x + y = 4$

2. $2x + y = 6$
   $2x - y = 2$

3. $2x - y = 7$
   $3x + y = 13$

4. $2x + y = 12$
   $2x - 2y = 6$

5. $3x - y = 11$
   $3x - 5y = 7$

6. $2x + y = 6$
   $3x + 2y = 10$

7. $x + 3y = 9$
   $2x - y = 4$

8. $x + 2y = 19$
   $3x - y = 8$

9. $x + 2y = 6$
   $3x - 3y = 9$

10. $2x + y = 14$
    $3x + 2y = 22$

11. $2x + y = 3$
    $3x - 2y = 8$

12. $2x + 4y = 11$
    $x + 3y = 8$

13. $2x - y = 4$
    $4x + 3y = 13$

14. $2x - 4y = 2$
    $x + 3y = -9$

15. $x + y = 0$
    $2x + 4y = 3$

Further simultaneous equations

Sometimes the letters in the equations are not in the same order, so the first thing to do is to rearrange them.

Example 13

Solve simultaneously the equations $y = 3x - 4$, $x + 2y = -1$.

$$-3x + y = -4 \quad ① \qquad \text{Rearrange the equation.}$$
$$x + 2y = -1 \quad ②$$

This can be solved in two ways, either ①$\times 2$ and subtract or ②$\times 3$ and add. It is normally easier to add.

$$②\times 3 \quad 3x + 6y = -3 \quad ③$$
$$-3x + y = -4 \quad ① \qquad ① \text{ is copied down.}$$

$$③+① \quad 3x + (-3x) + 6y + y = -3 + (-4)$$
$$7y = -7$$
$$y = -1$$

Substitute in ①: $-3x - 1 = -4 \qquad \text{Replace } y \text{ by } -1.$
$$[-3x - 1 + 1 = -4 + 1]$$
$$-3x = -3$$
$$x = 1$$

The solution is $x = 1$, $y = -1$.

Check in ②: LHS $= x + 2y = 1 - 2 = -1$ which is correct.

Sometimes each of the equations needs to be multiplied by a different number.

Example 14

Solve the equations $3y = 4 - 4x$, $6x + 2y = 11$.

$$4x + 3y = 4 \quad ① \qquad \text{Rearrange the first equation.}$$
$$6x + 2y = 11 \quad ②$$

To eliminate x multiply ① by 3 and ② by 2 and subtract, or to eliminate y multiply ① by 2 and ② by 3 and subtract.

$$①\times 3 \quad 12x + 9y = 12 \quad ③ \qquad \text{Eliminate } x.$$
$$②\times 2 \quad 12x + 4y = 22 \quad ④$$
$$③-④ \quad 5y = -10$$
$$y = -2$$

Substitute in ①: $4x - 6 = 4 \qquad 3y \text{ is replaced by } -6.$
$$[4x - 6 + 6 = 4 + 6]$$
$$4x = 10$$
$$x = 2\frac{1}{2}$$

The solution is $x = 2\frac{1}{2}$ and $y = -2$.

Check in ②: LHS $= 6x + 2y = 15 - 4 = 11$ which is correct.

Solve these simultaneous equations.

1. $y = 2x - 1$
   $x + 2y = 8$
2. $y = 3 - 2x$
   $3x - 3y = 0$
3. $3y = 11 - x$
   $3x - y = 3$
4. $3x + 2y = 7$
   $2x - 3y = -4$
5. $3x - 2y = 3$
   $2x - y = 4$
6. $2x + 3y = 7$
   $7x - 4y = 10$
7. $3x + 4y = 5$
   $2x + 3y = 4$
8. $4x - 3y = 1$
   $5x + 2y = -16$
9. $3x + 2y = 5$
   $2x + 3y = 10$
10. $4x - 2y = 3$
    $5y = 23 - 3x$

Examiner's tip

If there is a choice whether to add or subtract it is normally easier to add.

Exercise 10.5b

Solve these simultaneous equations.

1. $3y = 5 - x$
   $2x + y = 5$
2. $5y = x + 1$
   $2x + 2y = 10$
3. $y = 3x - 3$
   $2x + 3y = 13$
4. $4x - y = 2$
   $5x + 3y = 11$
5. $3x - 2y = 11$
   $2x + 3y = 16$
6. $2x - 3y = 5$
   $3x + 4y = 16$
7. $2x + 3y = 4$
   $3x - 2y = -7$
8. $4x + 3y = 1$
   $3x + 2y = 0$
9. $y = x + 2$
   $2x - 4y = -9$
10. $2y = 4x - 5$
    $3x - 5y = 9$

Solving quadratic equations

For any two numbers, if $A \times B = 0$, then either $A = 0$ or $B = 0$.

If $(x - 3)(x - 2) = 0$ then either $(x - 3) = 0$ or $(x - 2) = 0$.

To solve a quadratic equation, factorise it into two brackets and then use this fact.

Remember: to factorise $x^2 + ax + b$:
- if b is positive find two numbers with product b and sum a
  the signs in the bracket are both the same as a
- if b is negative find two numbers with product b and difference a
  the signs in the bracket are different
  the bigger number in the bracket has the same sign as a.

Chapter 10 Solving quadratic equations

Example 15

Solve the equation $x^2 - 4x + 3 = 0$.

$(x - 3)(x - 1) = 0$ | Factorising: both signs are negative, $1 \times 3 = +3$ and $1 + 3 = 4$.

$x - 3 = 0$ or $x - 1 = 0$

The solution is $x = 3$ or $x = 1$.

Example 16

Solve the equation $x^2 + 5x + 6 = 0$.

$(x + 3)(x + 2) = 0$ | Factorising: both signs are positive, $2 \times 3 = 6$ and $2 + 3 = 5$.

$x + 3 = 0$ or $x + 2 = 0$

The solution is $x = -3$ or $x = -2$.

Example 17

Solve the equation $x^2 - 3x - 10 = 0$.

$(x - 5)(x + 2) = 0$ | Factorising: the signs are different, $5 \times 2 = 10$ and $5 - 2 = 3$.

$x - 5 = 0$ or $x + 2 = 0$

The solution is $x = 5$ or $x = -2$.

If an equation is written as $x^2 - 2x = 15$ or $x^2 = 2x - 15$, first rearrange it so that all three terms are on the same side.

Example 18

Solve the equation $x^2 = 4x - 4$ by factorisation.

$x^2 - 4x + 4 = 0$ | Rearrange so that all three terms are on the same side.

$(x - 2)(x - 2) = 0$ | Factorising: the signs are both negative, $2 \times 2 = 4$, $2 + 2 = 4$.

$x - 2 = 0$ or $x - 2 = 0$

The solution is $x = 2$ (twice).

There are always two answers, so if they are both the same write 'twice'.

Solve these equations by factorisation.

1. $x^2 - 5x + 6 = 0$
2. $x^2 - 6x + 5 = 0$
3. $x^2 + 6x + 8 = 0$
4. $x^2 + 5x + 4 = 0$
5. $x^2 + 2x + 1 = 0$
6. $x^2 - 7x + 6 = 0$
7. $x^2 - 7x + 10 = 0$
8. $x^2 - 4x + 3 = 0$
9. $x^2 - 9x + 14 = 0$
10. $x^2 - 6x + 8 = 0$
11. $x^2 - 2x - 8 = 0$
12. $x^2 + 4x - 5 = 0$
13. $x^2 - x - 6 = 0$
14. $x^2 + 5x - 6 = 0$
15. $x^2 + 2x - 3 = 0$
16. $x^2 - 3x - 18 = 0$
17. $x^2 - 9x - 10 = 0$
18. $x^2 + 9x + 14 = 0$
19. $x^2 + 9x - 22 = 0$
20. $x^2 + x - 12 = 0$

Exercise 10.6b

Solve these equations by factorisation.

1. $x^2 - 7x + 10 = 0$
2. $x^2 - 4x + 3 = 0$
3. $x^2 - 8x + 15 = 0$
4. $x^2 + 9x + 20 = 0$
5. $x^2 + 7x + 6 = 0$
6. $x^2 - 9x + 18 = 0$
7. $x^2 + 7x + 12 = 0$
8. $x^2 - 2x + 1 = 0$
9. $x^2 - 10x + 24 = 0$
10. $x^2 + 4x + 3 = 0$
11. $x^2 + 2x - 3 = 0$
12. $x^2 + 3x - 10 = 0$
13. $x^2 - x - 12 = 0$
14. $x^2 + 5x - 14 = 0$
15. $x^2 - 2x - 15 = 0$
16. $x^2 - 3x - 28 = 0$
17. $x^2 - 17x + 30 = 0$
18. $x^2 + 4x - 32 = 0$
19. $x^2 + 9x - 36 = 0$
20. $x^2 + x - 20 = 0$

Graphical methods of solving equations

One way to solve simultaneous linear, quadratic and cubic equations is to use a graph. The point(s) where the lines or curves meet will give the solution.

Example

Solve the simultaneous equations

$y = 2x - 4$ and
$3y = 12 - 2x$

graphically. Use values of x from 0 to 6.

Three points for equation ① are $(0, -4)$, $(3, 2)$, $(6, 8)$.

Three points for equation ② are $(0, 4)$, $(3, 2)$, $(6, 0)$.

The two lines cross at $(3, 2)$ so the solution is $x = 3$, $y = 2$.

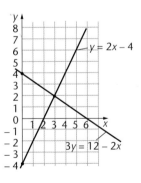

Example 20

(a) Draw the graph of $y = x^2 - 2x - 8$ for values of x from -3 to $+5$.

(b) Solve the equation $x^2 - 2x - 8 = 0$.

(a)

x	-3	-2	-1	0	1	2	3	4	5
x^2	9	4	1	0	1	4	9	16	25
$-2x$	6	4	2	0	-2	-4	-6	-8	-10
-8	-8	-8	-8	-8	-8	-8	-8	-8	-8
$y = x^2 - 2x - 8$	7	0	-5	-8	-9	-8	-5	0	7

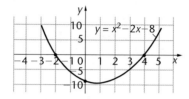

(b) The solution of $x^2 - 2x - 8 = 0$ is when $y = 0$, where the curve cuts the x-axis. The solution is $x = -2$ or $x = 4$.

 Example 21

(a) Draw the graph of $y = x^3 - 4x + 1$, for values of x from -3 to $+3$.

(b) Solve the equation $x^3 - 4x + 1 = 0$.

(a)

x	-3	-2	-1	0	1	2	3
x^3	-27	-8	-1	0	1	8	27
$-4x$	12	8	4	0	-4	-8	-12
1	1	1	1	1	1	1	1
$y = x^3 - 4x + 1$	-14	1	4	1	-2	1	16

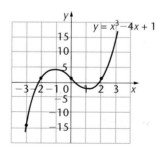

(b) The solution is when $y = 0$, where the curve cuts the x-axis. The solution is $x = -2.2$, $x = 0.2$ or $x = 1.9$.

Solve the simultaneous equations in questions 1–4 graphically.

1. $y = 2x$ and $y = 8 - 2x$. Use **values of** x **from** -1 to 4.
2. $y = 3x + 5$ and $y = x + 3$. Use **values of** x **from** -3 to $+2$.
3. $y = 5 - x$ and $y = 2x - 7$. Use **values of** x **from** -1 to $+5$.
4. $2y = 2x + 1$, $2y + x = 7$. Use **values of** x **from** 0 to 7.
5. (a) Draw the graph of $y = x^2 - 7x + 10$ for values of x from 0 to 7.
   (b) Solve the equation $x^2 - 7x + 10 = 0$.
6. (a) Draw the graph of $y = x^2 - x - 2$ for values of x from -2 to $+3$.
   (b) Solve the equation $x^2 - x - 2 = 0$.
7. (a) Draw the graph of $y = x^2 - 8$ for values of x from -3 to $+3$.
   (b) Solve the equation $x^2 - 8 = 0$.
8. (a) Draw the graph of $y = x^2 + x - 3$ for values of x from -3 to $+2$.
   (b) Solve the equation $x^2 + x - 3 = 0$.
9. (a) Draw the graph of $y = x^3 - 3x$ for values of x from -3 to $+3$.
   (b) Solve the equation $x^3 - 3x = 0$.
10. (a) Draw the graph of $y = x^3 - 5x + 3$ for values of x from -3 to $+3$.
    (b) Solve the equation $x^3 - 5x + 3 = 0$.

Solve the simultaneous equations in questions 1–4 graphically.

1. $y = 3x$ and $y = 4x - 2$. Use values of x from -1 to $+4$.
2. $y = 2x + 3$ and $y = 4x + 1$. Use values of x from -2 to $+3$.
3. $y = x + 4$ and $4x + 3y = 12$. Use values of x from -3 to $+3$.
4. $y = 2x + 8$ and $y = -2x$. Use values of x from -5 to $+1$.
5. (a) Draw the graph of $y = x^2 - 4x + 3$ for values of x from -1 to $+5$.
   (b) Solve the equation $x^2 - 4x + 3 = 0$.
6. (a) Draw the graph of $y = x^2 - 3x$ for values of x from -2 to $+5$.
   (b) Solve the equation $x^2 - 3x = 0$.
7. (a) Draw the graph of $y = x^2 - 5$ for values of x from -3 to $+3$.
   (b) Solve the equation $x^2 - 5 = 0$.
8. (a) Draw the graph of $y = x^2 - 3x - 2$ for values of x from -2 to $+5$.
   (b) Solve the equation $x^2 - 3x - 2 = 0$.
9. (a) Draw the graph of $y = x^3 - 6x$ for values of x from -3 to $+3$.
   (b) Solve the equation $x^3 - 6x = 0$.
10. (a) Draw the graph of $y = x^3 - 8x - 2$ for values of x from -3 to $+3$.
    (b) Solve the equation $x^3 - 8x - 2 = 0$.

Chapter 10   Graphical methods of solving equations

Make sure you give the
x-value (not the value on the
right-hand side of the
equation) to the required
accuracy.

Solving cubic equations by trial and improvement

Questions 9 and 10 in the previous exercises show that solving a cubic equation by a graphical method is not very accurate. In fact, it is difficult to be accurate even to one decimal place. A more accurate method is **trial and improvement**.

Example 22

A solution of the equation $x^3 - 4x + 1 = 0$ lies between 1 and 2. Use trial and improvement to find the solution correct to one decimal place.

For the first trial try 1: $1^3 - 4 \times 1 + 1 = -2$ Too small.

Try 1.5: $1.5^3 - 4 \times 1.5 + 1 = -1.625$ Too small, try solutions between 1.5 and 2.0.

Try 1.8: $1.8^3 - 4 \times 1.8 + 1 = -0.368$ Too small.

Try 1.9: $1.9^3 - 4 \times 1.9 + 1 = 0.259$ Too big.

The solution lies between 1.8 and 1.9.

To find which is nearer, try 1.85:

$1.85^3 - 4 \times 1.85 + 1 = -0.0684$ Too small.

So the solution lies between 1.85 and 1.9. It is nearer to 1.9 than 1.8.

The solution is $x = 1.9$ correct to one decimal place.

You should be able to find the solution within about five or six trials.

Example 23

A solution of $x^3 - 3x = 6$ lies between 2 and 3. Find it correct to one decimal place.

Try 2: $2^3 - 3 \times 2 = 2$ Too small.

Try 2.5: $2.5^3 - 3 \times 2.5 = 8.125$ Too big, try solutions between 2 and 2.5.

Try 2.3: $2.3^3 - 3 \times 2.3 = 5.267$ Too small, try solutions between 2.3 and 2.5.

Try 2.4: $2.4^3 - 3 \times 2.4 = 6.624$ Too big, try solutions between 2.3 and 2.4.

Try 2.35: $2.35^3 - 3 \times 2.35 = 5.928$ Too small, the solution is between 2.35 and 2.4.

The solution is $x = 2.4$ correct to one decimal place.

Find the two values between which the answer lies to the required degree of accuracy and then try midway values.

Exercise 10.8a

Use trial and improvement to find the solutions.

1. A solution of $x^3 = 5$ lies between 1 and 2. Find it correct to one decimal place.
2. A solution of $x^3 - 8x = 0$ lies between 2 and 3. Find it correct to one decimal place.
3. A solution of $x^3 - 5x = 8$ lies between 2 and 3. Find it correct to one decimal place.
4. A solution of $x^3 - x = 90$ lies between 4 and 5. Find it correct to one decimal place.
5. A solution of $x^3 - x^2 = 30$ lies between 3 and 4. Find it correct to one decimal place.
6. A solution of $x^3 = 12$ lies between 2 and 3. Find it correct to two decimal places.
7. A solution of $x^3 + 50 = 0$ lies between -4 and -3. Find it correct to one decimal place.
8. A solution of $x^3 + 4x + 25 = 0$ lies between -3 and -2. Find it correct to one decimal place.
9. A solution of $x^3 - 2x^2 = 4$ lies between 2 and 3. Find it correct to two decimal places.
10. A solution of $x^3 + 3x^2 + x = 0$ lies between -3 and -2. Find it correct to two decimal places.

Exercise 10.8b

Use trial and improvement to find the solutions.

1. A solution of $x^3 = 15$ lies between 2 and 3. Find it correct to one decimal place.
2. A solution of $x^3 - 2x = 0$ lies between 1 and 2. Find it correct to one decimal place.
3. A solution of $x^3 - 7x = 25$ lies between 3 and 4. Find it correct to one decimal place.
4. A solution of $x^3 + 2x = 2$ lies between 0 and 1. Find it correct to one decimal place.
5. A solution of $x^3 - x^2 = 1$ lies between 1 and 2. Find it correct to one decimal place.
6. A solution of $x^3 = 56$ lies between 3 and 4. Find it correct to two decimal places.
7. A solution of $x^3 + 12 = 0$ lies between -3 and -2. Find it correct to one decimal place.
8. A solution of $x^3 - 2x + 6 = 0$ lies between -3 and -2. Find it correct to one decimal place.
9. A solution of $x^3 - 4x^2 + 9 = 0$ lies between 2 and 3. Find it correct to one decimal place.
10. A solution of $x^3 - 5x^2 + 2x = 0$ lies between 0 and 1. Find it correct to two decimal places.

Problems that lead to simultaneous or quadratic equations

Example 24 In a café two cups of tea and three cups of coffee cost £5.30. Three cups of tea and a cup of coffee cost £4.10.

Let a cup of tea cost t pence and a cup of coffee cost c pence.

(a) Write down two equations in t and c.

(b) Solve them to find the cost of a cup of tea and a cup of coffee.

(a) $2t + 3c = 530$ ①   Working in pence.
    $3t + c = 410$ ②

(b) ②× 3 $9t + 3c = 1230$ ③
                         $2t + 3c = 530$ ①

   ③−① $7t = 700$
                                 $t = 100$

Substitute in ①: $200 + 3c = 530$
                           $3c = 330$
                            $c = 110$

So tea costs £1 a cup, coffee costs £1.10 a cup.

Check in the problem: 2 teas + 3 coffees cost £2 + £3.30 = £5.30
                          and 3 teas + 1 coffee cost £3 + £1.10 = £4.10.

Example 25 A rectangle has width x cm and length $x + 4$ cm. The area is 21 cm².

Write down an equation in x and solve it to find the dimensions of the rectangle.

$x(x + 4) = 21$ Form the equation.

$x^2 + 4x = 21$ Expand the brackets.

$x^2 + 4x - 21 = 0$ Take all the non-zero terms to the left-hand side.

$(x + 7)(x - 3) = 0$ Solve the equation.

The solution is $x = -7$ or $x = 3$.   From $x + 7 = 0$ or $x - 3 = 0$.

Lengths must be positive, so the width is 3 cm, the length is $3 + 4 = 7$ cm.
Check: $3 \times 7 = 21$.

Exercise 10.9a

1. Two numbers x and y have a sum of 47 and a difference of 9.
   (a) Write down two equations in x and y.
   (b) Solve them to find the numbers.

2. Cassettes cost £c each and compact discs cost £d each. John bought two cassettes and three discs and paid £27.50. Shahida bought three cassettes and one disc and paid £18.50.
   (a) Write down two equations in c and d.
   (b) Solve them to find the cost of a cassette and a disc.

3. Paint is sold in small and large tins. Peter needs 13 litres and he buys one small and two large tins.
   Gamel needs 11 litres and he buys two small and one large tin. Both have exactly the correct amount.
   Let the small tin hold s litres and the large tin hold b litres.
   (a) Write down two equations in s and b.
   (b) Solve them to find the amount each tin holds.

4. A coach journey cost each adult £a and each child £c. Tickets for one adult and two children cost £31. Tickets for two adults and three children cost £54. Use algebra to find the cost of each ticket.

5. Two consecutive odd numbers x and $x + 2$ have a product of 63. Set up a quadratic equation and solve it to find the two numbers.

Exercise 10.9b

1. Two numbers x and y have a sum of 86 and a difference of 16.
   (a) Write down two equations in x and y.
   (b) Solve them to find the two numbers.

2. At Turner's corner shop beans cost b pence a tin and spaghetti costs s pence a tin. Three tins of beans and two tins of spaghetti cost £1.37. Two tins of beans and a tin of spaghetti cost 81p.
   (a) Write down two equations in b and s.
   (b) Solve them to find the cost of each tin.

3. Orange juice is sold in cans and bottles. Cans hold c ml and bottles hold b ml. Three cans and four bottles contain 475 cl altogether. Four cans and three bottles hold 400 cl altogether. Use algebra to find how much each holds.

4. The entry fees for Barford museum are £a for adults and £c for children. Mr Ekebussi paid £25 for two adults and five children. Mrs Taylor paid £14 for one adult and three children. Use algebra to work out the cost of each ticket.

5. Joan is x years old and her mother is 25 years older. The product of their ages is 306.
   (a) Write down a quadratic equation in x.
   (b) Solve the equation to find Joan's age.

Showing regions on graphs

It is often possible to show the area on a graph that satisfies an inequality.

Example 26

Write down the inequality that describes the region shaded in each graph.

(a)

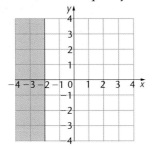

(b)

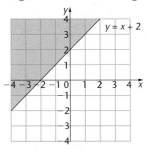

(a) $x < -2$

> The line drawn is $x = -2$. This line divides the graph into two regions $x < -2$ and $x > -2$. The shaded region is $x < -2$. Check by testing any point in the region.

(b) $y > x + 2$

> The line is $y = x + 2$ and it divides the graph into two regions $y < x + 2$ and $y > x + 2$. To decide which side is shaded choose any point not on the line and test it, for example, $(0, 0)$. Here $x + 2 = 2$, and $y = 0$, so $y < x + 2$ at $(0, 0)$ and $(0, 0)$ is not in the region. So the shaded region is $y > x + 2$.

Example 27

On separate grids shade the regions: (a) $y > 2$ (b) $y < 2x - 3$.

(a)

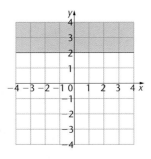

(b)

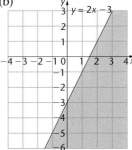

> It is clear that $y > 2$ is above the line $y = 2$.

> Draw the line $y = 2x - 3$. Then the two regions are $y > 2x - 3$ and $y < 2x - 3$. To test which side is wanted, choose any point not on the line, for example $(0, 0)$. Here $y = 0$ and $2x - 3 = -3$, so $y > 2x - 3$ at $(0, 0)$. Therefore $(0, 0)$ is not in the region required. Shade the other region.

In the previous examples the region required has been shaded. If more that one region is required, then it is best to shade out the regions not required and leave blank the required region.

Examiner's tip

When testing a region, if possible use (0, 0). If the line goes through (0, 0) choose a positive number to test the region.

Examiner's tip

Either shading in or shading out is acceptable, but indicate the required region by labelling it clearly.

Example 28

Show by shading the region where $x > 0$, $y > 0$ and $x + 2y < 6$.

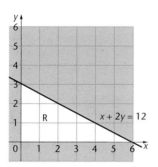

Shade out the regions $x < 0$ and $y < 0$.
Draw the line $x + 2y = 6$ and test (0, 0);
$x + 2y = 0 < 6$ so (0, 0) is in the region
$x + 2y < 6$, which is the required region.
So shade out the region not containing (0, 0).
R is the region required.

Exercise 10.10a

For questions 1–4, write down the inequality that describes the region shaded.

1.

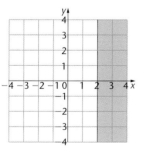

3.

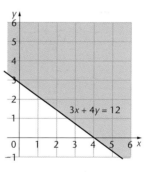

2.

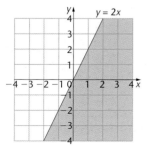

4.

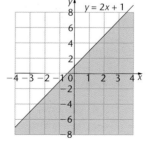

5. Draw a set of axes and label them from −4 to +4 for x and y. Shade the region $y > -3$.

6. Draw a set of axes and label them from −3 to +6 for x and from −3 to +5 for y. Shade the region $2x + 5y < 10$.

7. Draw a set of axes and label them from 0 to 5 for x and y. Show by shading the region where $y > 0$, $x > 0$ and $3x + 5y < 15$.

8. Draw a set of axes and label them from −3 to +3 for x and from −6 to +10 for y. Show by shading the region where $x > 0$, $y < 8$ and $y > 2x$.

Exercise 10.10b

For questions 1−4, write down the inequality that describes the region shaded.

1.

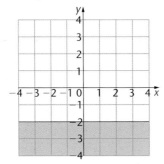

2.

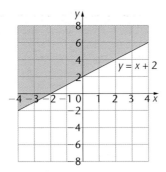

3.

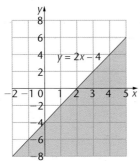

4.

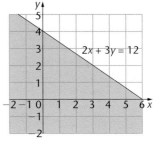

5. Draw a set of axes and label them from −4 to +4 for x and y. Shade the region $x > -1$.

6. Draw a set of axes and label them from −2 to 6 for x and from −2 to +5 for y. Shade the region $4x + 5y < 20$.

7. Draw a set of axes and label them from 0 to 12 for x and from 0 to 8 for y.
Show by shading the region where $y > 0$, $x > 0$ and $3x + 5y < 30$.

8. Draw a set of axes and label them from −3 to +3 for x and from −6 to +10 for y.
Show by shading the region where $x > 0$, $3x + 8y > 24$ and $5x + 4y < 20$.

Rearranging formulae

All the formulae that have been studied so far included the new subject only once, and the subject was not raised to a power. The following examples show how to deal with these situations.

Example 29   Rearrange the formula $A = \pi r^2$ to make r the subject.

$A = \pi r^2$

$\dfrac{A}{\pi} = r^2$ Divide both sides by π.

$r^2 = \dfrac{A}{\pi}$ Change sides to get terms involving r on the left-hand side.

$r = \sqrt{\dfrac{A}{\pi}}$ Take the square root of both sides.

Example 30   Rearrange the formula $V = \tfrac{4}{3}\pi r^3$ to make r the subject.

$V = \tfrac{4}{3}\pi r^3$

$3V = 4\pi r^3$ Multiply both sides by 3.

$r^3 = \dfrac{3V}{4\pi}$ Swap sides and divide both sides by 4π.

$r = \sqrt[3]{\dfrac{3V}{4\pi}}$ Take the cube root of both sides.

Example 31   Rearrange the formula $a = x + \dfrac{cx}{d}$ to make x the subject.

$a = x + \dfrac{cx}{d}$

$ad = dx + cx$ Multiply both sides by d.

$dx + cx = ad$ Change sides to get all the x-terms to the left-hand side.

$x(d + c) = ad$ Factorise the left-hand side, taking out the factor x.

$x = \dfrac{ad}{d + c}$ Divide both sides by the term in the bracket, $(d + c)$.

Example 32   Rearrange the equation $ax + by = cy - ad$ to make a the subject.

$ax + by = cy - ad$

$ax + ad = cy - by$ Rearrange to get all the terms involving a on the left-hand side and all the other terms on the right-hand side (adding ad to both sides, subtracting by from both sides).

$a(x + d) = cy - by$ Factorise the left-hand side, taking out the factor a.

$a = \dfrac{cy - by}{x + d}$ Divide both sides by the term in the bracket $(x + d)$.

For each question, make the letter in brackets the subject.

1. $s = at + 2bt$ (t)

2. $P = t - \dfrac{at}{b}$ (t)

3. $A = \pi r^2$ (r)

4. $ab - cd = ac$ (a)

5. $ab - cd = ac$ (c)

6. $s - 2ax = b(x - s)$ (s)

7. $s - 2ax = b(x - s)$ (x)

8. $a = \dfrac{t}{b} - st$ (t)

9. $a = b + c^2$ (c)

10. $A = P + \dfrac{PRT}{100}$ (P)

For each question, make the letter in brackets the subject.

1. $s = ab - bc$ (b)

2. $v^2 = u^2 - 2as$ (u)

3. $3(a + y) = by + 7$ (y)

4. $2(a - 1) = b(1 - 2a)$ (a)

5. $\dfrac{a}{b} - 2a = b$ (a)

6. $s = 2r^2 - 1$ (r)

7. $a(b + d) = c(b - d)$ (d)

8. $a(b + d) = c(b - d)$ (b)

9. $V = 5ab^2 + 3c^2$ (c)

10. $s = \dfrac{uv}{u + v}$ (v)

Key points

- If a problem asks you to use algebra to solve it, you must start with an equation.
- To solve simultaneous equations, make the coefficient (number) of one of the letters the same in both equations. If they are the same sign, subtract. If different signs, add.
- To solve quadratic equations, factorise and then put each bracket equal to zero.
- To solve linear simultaneous equations graphically, draw the lines on a graph and find where they cross.

- To solve quadratic or cubic equations graphically, draw the curve and find where it cuts the x-axis.
- To solve a cubic equation by trial and improvement, find the two values between which it lies, to the required degree of accuracy and then test the midway point.
- When representing inequalities on a graph, if there is more than one region it is best to shade out the regions not required, leaving the region required clear.

1. Solve these equations.
   (a) $3(x - 2) = x$
   (b) $5(2x + 3) = 55$
   (c) $4(x - 3) = 3(x - 2)$
   (d) $2(3x - 4) = 4(x + 1)$
   (e) $\frac{x}{2} = 3x - 10$
   (f) $\frac{x}{3} = 3 - 2x$
   (g) $\frac{500}{x} = 20$
   (h) $\frac{300}{x} = 60$

2. Solve these inequalities.
   (a) $2x - 1 < 5$
   (b) $3x + 4 \leqslant 16$
   (c) $5x - 2 > 3 + 4x$
   (d) $x^2 \leqslant 49$
   (e) $x^2 \geqslant 16$
   (f) $x^2 - 5 < 31$

3. A number x divided by 3 is the same as 3 times the number minus 24. Write down an equation and solve it to find the number.

4. An ice-lolly costs x pence and an ice-cream costs 20 pence more.
   (a) Write down the cost of an ice-cream in terms of x.
   Jon buys three ice-lollies and two ice-creams and pays £3.40.
   (b) Write down an equation in x and solve it to find the cost of an ice-lolly and of an ice-cream.

5. Marcia is x cm tall and her friend Carole is 25 cm shorter.
   (a) Write down Carole's height in terms of x.
   Carole is $\frac{4}{5}$ as tall as Marcia.
   (b) Write down an equation in x and solve it to find Marcia's height.

6. Solve these simultaneous equations.
   (a) $x + y = 15$
   $2x + y = 22$
   (b) $2x + 3y = 13$
   $3x - y = 3$
   (c) $2x - 3y = 3$
   $4x + 5y = 17$
   (d) $3x - 6y = 3$
   $2x + 3y = 16$

   (e) $x + 2y = 3$
   $3x + 3y = 3$
   (f) $y = x + 5$
   $2x + 3y = 5$
   (g) $2x + 3y = 8$
   $5x - 2y = 1$
   (h) $x + y = 3$
   $5x + 3y = 10$
   (i) $6x + 5y = -2$
   $4x - 3y = 5$

7. Solve the quadratic equations.
   (a) $x^2 - 6x + 8 = 0$
   (b) $x^2 + 5x + 6 = 0$
   (c) $x^2 - 2x - 3 = 0$
   (d) $x^2 - 3x - 10 = 0$
   (e) $x^2 - 5x + 4 = 0$
   (f) $x^2 + 7x + 10 = 0$
   (g) $x^2 - 5x - 14 = 0$
   (h) $x^2 + 17x + 30 = 0$
   (i) $x^2 - 9x + 20 = 0$
   (j) $x^2 + 4x + 3 = 0$
   (k) $x^2 - 9x - 36 = 0$
   (l) $x^2 + 7x - 18 = 0$

8. Solve these simultaneous equations graphically.
   (a) $y = x + 3$ and $y = 6 - 2x$. Use values of x from -1 to $+3$.
   (b) $y = 2x - 1$ and $3x + 2y = 12$. Use values of x from 0 to 4.

9. (a) Draw the graph of $y = x^2 + 2x$ for values of x from -4 to $+2$.
   (b) Solve the equation $x^2 + 2x = 0$ from your graph.

10. (a) Draw the graph of $y = x^2 - 5x + 5$ for values of x from 0 to $+5$.
    (b) Solve the equation $x^2 - 5x + 5 = 0$ from your graph.

11. (a) Draw the graph of $y = x^3 - 7x$ for values of x from -3 to $+3$.
    (b) Solve the equation $x^3 - 7x = 0$ from your graph.

12. Find a solution for each of these by trial and improvement, giving your answer correct to one decimal place.
    (a) $x^3 - 7x = 0$ between 2 and 3
    (b) $x^3 - 35 = 0$ between 3 and 4
    (c) $x^3 - 2x = 5$ between 2 and 3
    (d) $x^3 + 40 = 0$ between -4 and -3

13. A packet of crisps costs c pence and a can of apple juice costs a pence.
    Three packets of crisps and two cans of apple juice cost £1.39.
    Two packets of crisps and one can of apple juice cost 81p.
    Write down two equations in c and a and solve them to find the cost of the crisps and the cans.

14. Packets of detergent are sold in medium and large packets. A medium packet holds x grams and a large holds y grams. A large packet holds 200 grams more than a medium.
    Joan buys three medium and two large and has 2400 grams of detergent.
    Write down two equations in x and y and solve them to find how much each holds.

15. Write down the inequality satisfied by the shaded region in each diagram.
    (a)

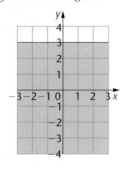

    (b)

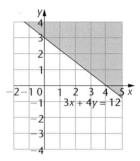

16. Draw sets of axes and label them from -4 to $+4$ for x and y. Shade these regions.
    (a) $x < 1$
    (b) $2y < 3x + 2$

17. Draw a set of axes and label them from -1 to $+8$ for x and y. Show, by shading, the region where $x > 0$, $y > 0$, $x < 8$, $y < x - 1$.

18. Draw a set of axes and label x from -1 to $+8$ and y from -1 to 6. Show, by shading, the region where $x > 0$, $y > 0$, $y < x + 2$, $3x + 7y < 21$.

Measurement and compound units

Estimating measurements

Sometimes you may be asked to estimate measures with which you are not familiar. For example, you may know how much a bag of sugar weighs, but what about a hen's egg? Would it be 5 g, 50 g or 500 g?

Here are some ideas.

- Know your own height, in metric and imperial units, such as 5 ft 7 in or 170 cm.
- Know how much you weigh, in metric and imperial units, such as 9 st 10 lb or 62 kg.
- Occasionally pick up a kilogram bag of sugar to remind yourself how heavy it feels.
- Measure your handspan. Knowing what it is (for example, 20 cm) enables you to measure the width of a table quickly in handspans, for instance, and then estimate the width in centimetres.
- Draw a 10 cm line and look at it carefully, to see how long it is. Practise drawing lines of given lengths without measuring them and see how close you can get to the correct length.
- For a 100 metre distance, think of the length of the 100 m race on an athletics track.

When comparing, ask yourself questions such as:

- Is it the same as … ?
- Is it twice as long as … ?
- Is it much heavier than … ?
- How many of these would weigh the same as … ?
- How many of these laid end to end would be the same length as … ?

Example ①

Choose the most suitable value, from this list, for the mass of the telephone directory for Guildford and West Surrey.

10 g   100 g   1000 g   10 000 g

A telephone directory is quite a large book. A mass of 10 g is quite small. Change the larger masses in the list to kilograms.

1000 g = 1 kg
10 000 g = 10 kg

A mass of 10 kg is too much to carry easily, but 1 kg is about right.

Checking with the smaller masses, 100 g is a small pack of cheese, for instance, and this would be too light in comparison.

So the answer is 1000 g.

Exercise II.Ia

1. Estimate the length of this line.

_____

2. Estimate the size of this angle.

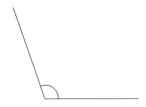

3. Estimate the height of this tower.

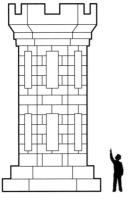

4. Which of these is closest to the mass of a tablespoon of sugar?
   2.5 g   25 g   250 g

5. Which of the masses below is likely to be how much Sarah is carrying in one of these shopping bags?
   40 g   400 g   4 kg   40 kg

Exercise 11.1b

1. Estimate the length of this line.

2. Estimate the size of this angle.

3. Estimate the length of this trailer.

4. Choose the most appropriate of these measurements for the length of a sports hall.

   7 m   70 m   700 m   7000 m

5. When a large jug is full, it holds enough water to fill six tumblers. Choose the most likely measurement from the list for the capacity of the jug.

   0·02 litres   0.2 litres   2 litres   20 litres

Discrete and continuous measures

Discrete measures can be counted. They can only take particular values.

Continuous measures include length, time and mass. They cannot be measured exactly.

Look at this table of some data for a bicycle.

Number of wheels	2
Number of gears	15
Diameter of wheel	66 cm
Frame size	66 cm
Price	£99.99

In the table, the discrete measures are: number of wheels
number of gears
price

The continuous measures are: diameter of wheel
frame size.

Accuracy

Although the table above does not make this clear, the frame size is given to the nearest centimetre. A less accurate measurement, such as to the nearest 10 cm, would not give enough information about the size of the bicycle. Someone wanting to buy a bicycle would not be able to tell whether it would be the right size for them. A more accurate measurement would be unnecessary in the context.

Similarly, giving a person's height to the nearest millimetre would not be sensible, since a person's height varies by more than a millimetre during the day.

When solving problems, the accuracy of your answer is limited by the accuracy of the data available. The answer cannot be accurate to more significant figures than the data. It is often accurate to one fewer significant figure.

Examiner's tip

When giving the answers to practical situations, think what would be an appropriate degree of accuracy to use. Where there are no practical considerations, answers requiring rounding are usually given to three significant figures.

Example 2

Bryn is asked to calculate the hypotenuse of a right-angled triangle, for which the other two sides are given as 2.8 cm and 5.1 cm. To what accuracy should he give his answer?

The data are given to two significant figures, so his answer should be accurate within one or two significant figures. An accuracy of one significant figure would give the answer to the nearest centimetre, which may not be sufficiently accurate. He should round to two significant figures, which is to the nearest millimetre.

Exercise 11.2a

In questions 1 and 2, look at the descriptions from catalogues. For each measurement, identify whether the data are discrete or continuous.

1. Prestige 20 cm polyester golf bag, 6-way graphite-friendly top, 2 accessory pockets
2. Black attaché case, 2 folio compartments, 3 pen holders, size (H) 31.5 cm, (W) 44.5 cm, (D) 11.5 cm

Read this extract from a newspaper article.

> Andy James has now scored 108 goals in just 167 games, making him the Town's most prolific scorer ever. In Saturday's game a penalty brought his first goal after 30 minutes, with Pete Jeffreys having been fouled. Six minutes later, James volleyed into the net again, after a flick on from Neil Matty, five yards outside the penalty box.

3. Give two examples of discrete data in the article above.
4. Give three examples of continuous data in the article above.

5. Write a description including two discrete measurements and three continuous measurements.
6. What is the appropriate degree of accuracy for the length of a line that could be drawn on this page?
   (a) to the nearest cm
   (b) to the nearest 10 cm
   (c) to the nearest mm
   (d) to the nearest 0.1 mm
7. To what degree of accuracy would a field be measured?
8. What is the usual degree of accuracy on road signs:
   (a) on motorways
   (b) on country lane signposts?
9. For teenagers, what is the usual degree of accuracy for giving their age?
10. What is the usual degree of accuracy for measuring flour in cake recipes?

Exercise 11.2b

In questions 1 and 2, look at these descriptions from catalogues. For each measurement, identify whether it is discrete or continuous.

1. 16 piece dinner set, 4 dinner plates (dia. 24.5 cm), side plates and bowls
2. Food blender, 1.5 litre working capacity, 3 speed settings, 400 watt

Read this extract from a newspaper article.

> Lightning killed two people in Hyde Park yesterday as storms swept the south-east, where 1.75 in of rain fell in 48 hours. In Pagham, winds of up to 120 mph damaged more than 50 houses and bungalows and several boats. One catamaran was flung 100 ft into the air and landed in a tree.

3. Give two examples of discrete data in the article above.
4. Give three examples of continuous data in the article above.

5. Write a description including three discrete measurements and two continuous measurements.
6. What is the appropriate degree of accuracy for a waist measurement?
   (a) to the nearest cm
   (b) to the nearest 10 cm
   (c) to the nearest mm
   (d) to the nearest 0.1 mm
7. To what degree of accuracy is the length of a garden usually given?
8. To what degree of accuracy is: (a) a baby's (b) an adult's mass usually given?
9. To what degree of accuracy would the time for the winner of a 50 m swimming race normally be given?
10. To what degree of accuracy is body temperature usually given?

Bounds of measurement

Suppose a measurement is given as 26 cm 'to the nearest centimetre'. This means the next possible measurements on either side are 25 cm and 27 cm. Where does the boundary between these measurements lie?

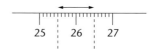

Any measurement that is nearer to 26 cm than to 25 cm or 27 cm will be counted as 26 cm. This is the marked interval on the number line above.

The boundaries of this interval are 25.5 cm and 26.5 cm. These values are exactly halfway between one measurement and the next. Usually when rounding to a given number of decimal places or significant figures, you would round 25.5 up to 26 and 26.5 up to 27.

So this gives:

> the interval for 26 cm to the nearest centimetre is m cm where $25.5 \leqslant m < 26.5$.

25.5 cm is called the **lower bound** of the interval

26.5 is called the **upper bound** of the interval (although it is not actually included in the interval).

Example 3

Simon won the 200 m race in his year in a time of 24.2 s, to the nearest tenth of a second.
Complete the sentence below:
Simon's time was between … s and … s.

As the measurement is stated to the nearest tenth of a second, the next possible times are 24.1 s and 24.3 s.

Simon's time was between 24.15 s and 24.25 s.

Exercise 11.3a

Give the upper and lower bounds of the measurements in questions 1–5.

1. Given to the nearest centimetre:
   (a) 27 cm (b) 30 cm (c) 128 cm
2. Given to the nearest 10 cm:
   (a) 10 cm (b) 30 cm (c) 150 cm
3. Given to the nearest millimetre:
   (a) 5.6 cm (b) 0.8 cm (c) 12.0 cm
4. Given to the nearest centimetre:
   (a) 1.23 m (b) 0.45 m (c) 9.08 m
5. Given to the nearest hundredth of a second:
   (a) 10.62 s (b) 9.81 s (c) 48.10 s

Complete the sentences in questions 6–10.

6. A mass given as 57 kg to the nearest kilogram is between … kg and … kg.
7. A height given as 4.7 m to two significant figures is between … m and … m.
8. A volume given as 468 ml (to the nearest ml) is between … ml and … ml.
9. A winning time given as 34.91 s to the nearest hundredth of a second is between … s and … s.
10. A mass given as 0.634 kg to the nearest gram is between … kg and … kg.

Exercise 11.3b

Give the upper and lower bounds of the measurements in questions 1–5.

1. Given to the nearest centimetre:
   (a) 34 cm (b) 92 cm (c) 210 cm
2. Given to the nearest 10 cm:
   (a) 20 cm (b) 60 cm (c) 210 cm
3. Given to the nearest millimetre:
   (a) 2.7 cm (b) 0.2 cm (c) 18.0 cm
4. Given to the nearest centimetre:
   (a) 8.17 m (b) 0.36 m (c) 2.04 m
5. Given to the nearest hundredth of a second:
   (a) 15.61 s (b) 12.10 s (c) 54.07 s

Complete the sentences in questions 6–10.

6. A mass given as 57 kg to the nearest kilogram is between … kg and … kg.
7. A height given as 8.3 m to two significant figures is between … m and … m.
8. A volume given as 234 ml (to the nearest ml) is between … ml and … ml.
9. A winning time given as 27.94 s to the nearest hundredth of a second is between … s and … s.
10. A mass given as 0.256 kg to the nearest gram is between … kg and … kg.

Compound units

Some measures depend on others, which means you need to multiply or divide other measures.

One important example of this is:

$$\text{average speed} = \frac{\text{total distance travelled}}{\text{total time taken}}$$

The units of your answer will depend on the units you begin with.

 Example 4
Find the average speed of an athlete who runs 100 m in 20 s.

$$\text{average speed} = \frac{100 \, \text{m}}{20 \, \text{s}} = 5 \, \text{m/s}$$

Example **5** Find the average speed of a delivery driver who travelled 45 km in 30 minutes.

The average speed $= \dfrac{45\,\text{km}}{30\,\text{minutes}} = 1.5\,\text{km/minute}$

However, the speed here is more likely to be needed in kilometres per hour. To find this, first change the time into hours.

So the average speed $= \dfrac{45\,\text{km}}{0.5\,\text{h}} = 90\,\text{km/h}$

You may also be able to see other ways of obtaining this result.

Other examples of compound units are:

- density $= \dfrac{\text{mass}}{\text{volume}}$ with units such as g/cm^3.

- population density $= \dfrac{\text{population}}{\text{area}}$ with units such as number of people/km^2.

Exercise 11.4a

1. Find the average speed of a car which travels 75 miles in one and a half hours.
2. Find the average speed of a runner who covers 180 m in 40 s.
3. Calculate the density of a stone of mass 350 g and volume 40 cm^3.
4. Waring has a population of 60 000 in an area of 8 square kilometres. Calculate its population density.
5. A motorbike travels 1 mile in 3 minutes. Calculate its average speed, in miles per hour.

6. A bus travels at 5 m/s on average. How many kilometres per hour is this?
7. A foam plastic ball with volume 20 cm^3 has density 0.3 g/cm^3. What is its mass?
8. A town has a population of 200 000. Its population density is 10 000 people per square mile. What is the area of the town?
9. A runner's average speed in a 80 m race is 7 m/s. Find the time he takes for the race, to the nearest 0.1 seconds.
10. A car travels 15 km in 12 minutes. What is the average speed in km/h?

Exercise 11.4b

1. Find the average speed of a car which travels 63 miles in one and a half hours.
2. Find the average speed of a runner who goes 180 m in 48 s.
3. Calculate the density of a stone of mass 690 g and volume 74 cm^3. Give your answer to a suitable degree of accuracy.
4. Trenton has a population of 65 000 in an area of 5.8 square kilometres. Calculate its population density, correct to two significant figures.
5. A cyclist rides 0.6 mile in 3 minutes. Calculate her average speed, in miles per hour.

6. A bus travels at 6.1 m/s on average. How many kilometres per hour is this?
7. A rubber ball with volume 28.3 cm^3 has density 0.7 g/cm^3. What is its mass?
8. A town has a population of 276 300. Its population density is 9800 people per square mile. What is the area of the town?
9. A runner's average speed in a 200 m race is 5.3 m/s. Find the time he takes for the race, to the nearest 0.1 seconds.
10. A car travels 15 km in 14 minutes. What is the average speed, in km/h?

- When estimating measures in unfamiliar contexts, try to compare them with measures you do know.
- Discrete measures can be counted. They can only take particular values.
- Continuous measures include length, time, mass etc. They cannot be measured exactly.
- When giving the answers to practical situations, think what is an appropriate degree of accuracy to use. Where there

are no practical considerations, answers requiring rounding are usually given to three significant figures.
- A time of 5.47 s to the nearest one hundredth of a second lies between 5.465 s and 5.475 s.
- Some compound units are average speed (such as m/s), density (such as g/cm^3) and population density (such as population/km^2).

Revision exercise 11a

1. Estimate the height of this work-top.

2. Walking at a normal pace, it takes Yasmin five minutes to walk from home to school.
   Estimate how far her school is from her home.

3. Name: (a) three discrete (b) three continuous measurements that could be used in describing a car.

4. Jeni and Suni were trying to draw a line 10 cm long. Jenny said hers was 0.102 m long. Suni said his was 9.68 cm long.
   (a) Whose line was more accurate?
   (b) Comment on the units and degree of accuracy they were using.

5. To what degree of accuracy are the lengths of CD tracks usually given?

6. The dimensions of a picture frame were given as 17 cm by 28 cm. Assuming these were to the nearest centimetre, what is the least these dimensions can be?

7. A length is stated as being between 6.805 cm and 6.815 cm.
   (a) What measurement would be recorded?
   (b) What is its degree of accuracy?

8. Sasha runs a 100 m race in 13.58 s. Calculate her average speed. Give your answer to a suitable degree of accuracy.

9. A cyclist travels 5 km in 20 minutes. Calculate her speed in kilometres per hour.

10. A metal weight has mass 200 g and density $25\,g/cm^3$. What is its volume?

Interpreting graphs

Story graphs

Examiner's tip

When drawing a graph, don't forget to label the axes.

Some graphs tell a story – they show what happened in an event. To find out what is happening, first look at the labels on the axes. They tell you what the graph is about.

Look for important features on the graph. For instance, does it increase or decrease at a steady rate (a straight line) or is it curved?

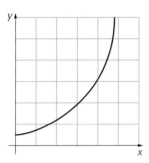

The rate of change is increasing.

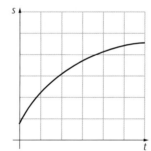

The rate of change is decreasing.

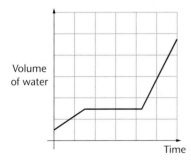

A flat part of the graph – no change for the variable on the vertical axis.

Example 1

This graph shows the noise levels at a football stadium one afternoon.

The boxes describe what may have caused the change in shape of the graph at certain points.

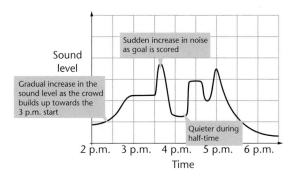

Example 2

John ran the first two miles to school at a speed of 8 mph. He then waited 5 minutes for his friend. They walked the last mile to school together, taking 20 minutes.

The graph for this story has been started. Finish the graph. (The different line on the graph shows where this has been done.)

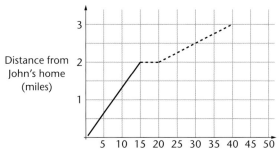

The first part of this graph is steeper than the last part. This shows that John went faster in the first 15 minutes than he did in the last 20 minutes. The flat part of the graph shows where John stayed in the same place for 5 minutes.

Chapter 12 Story graphs

1. This graph shows the volume of water in a bath.

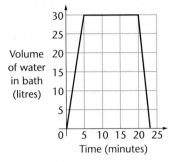

Time (minutes)

(a) How long did the bath take to fill?
(b) How much water was in the bath when the taps were turned off?
(c) How many litres per minute went down the plughole when the bath was emptied?

2. This graph shows the number of people at a theme park one bank holiday.

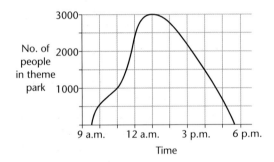

Time

(a) When did the park open?
(b) During which hour did most people go into the park?

3. At a rock concert, the gates opened at 5 p.m. People came in fairly slowly at first, but then quite steadily from 5.45 until the start at 7 p.m. There were then 50 000 people in the stadium. The concert lasted until 10 p.m. At the end people left quickly and the stadium was almost empty by 10.30 p.m.
Sketch a graph to show how the number of people in the stadium for this rock concert changed.

4. This graph shows the cost of hiring a car for a day.

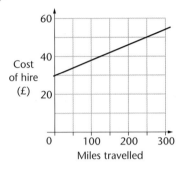

Miles travelled

(a) Pedro travelled 150 miles. How much did he pay for his car hire?
(b) Jane paid £48 for her car hire. How many miles did she travel?
(c) What was:
   (i) the basic hire charge
   (ii) the charge per mile?

5. Water is poured at a steady rate into this conical glass until it is full, Sketch a graph to show how the depth of water in the glass changes with time.

1. This graph shows the amount of fuel in a car's petrol tank.

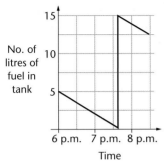

   (a) How many litres were used between 6 and 7 p.m?
   (b) Describe what happened between 7.30 and 8 p.m.

2. The speed of a car at the start of a journey is shown on this graph.

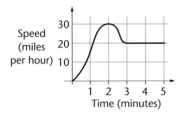

   (a) What is happening on the flat portion of the graph?
   (b) Between which times is the car slowing down?

3. Jane ran hot water into a bath for 4 minutes at a rate of 15 litres per minute. She then turned on the cold tap too so that the bath filled at 20 litres a minute for another 2 minutes.
   (a) Draw a graph to show how the volume of water in the bath changed.
   (b) How much water was there in the bath at the end of this time?

4. This graph shows the monthly bill for a mobile phone for different amounts of minutes used.

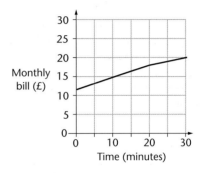

   (a) How many minutes have been used if the bill is £15?
   (b) There are two line segments on the graph. What do they show?

5. A water company charges £8 each quarter for a meter, then 50p per cubic metre for the first 100 cubic metres used, and 70p per cubic metre for water used above this amount.
   Draw a graph to show the total bill for different amounts of water used, up to 200 cubic metres.

> **Examiner's tip**
>
> If you are asked to describe a story graph, try to include numerical information. For example, instead of 'stopped' write 'stopped at 10.14 p.m. for 6 minutes'.

Gradient

The **gradient** of a graph is the mathematical way of measuring its **steepness** or **rate of change**.

$$\text{gradient} = \frac{\text{increase in } y}{\text{increase in } x}$$

Examiner's tip

Choose two points far apart on the graph, so that the x-distance between them is an integer. If possible choose points where the graph crosses gridlines. This makes reading values and dividing easier.

To find the gradient of a line, mark two points on the graph, then draw in the horizontal and the vertical to form a triangle as shown.

$$\text{gradient} = \frac{6}{2} = 3$$

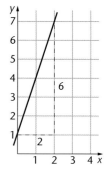

Here the gradient $= \dfrac{-8}{2}$ or $\dfrac{8}{-2}$.

Both give the answer -4.

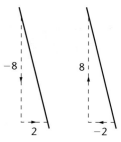

Examiner's tip

Check you have the correct sign, positive or negative, for the slope of the line.

Lines with a **positive gradient** slope forwards /.

Lines with a **negative gradient** slope backwards \.

Flat lines — have a gradient of zero.

Example 3 Find the gradient of the line joining the points (3, 5) and (8, 7).

Increase in $x = 5$ Subtract $8 - 3 = 5$.

Increase in $y = 2$ Subtract $7 - 5 = 2$. Remember to subtract in the same order.

Gradient $= \frac{2}{5} = 0.4$

You can do this type of example without drawing a diagram, as shown above, but draw a sketch to help you, if you prefer, so that you can see the triangle.

When interpreting graphs about physical situations, the gradient tells you the rate of change.

Example 4 For a distance-time graph the gradient gives the speed.

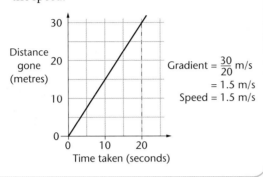

Gradient = $\frac{30}{20}$ m/s

= 1.5 m/s

Speed = 1.5 m/s

Exercise 12.2a

1. Find the gradient of each of these lines.

(a)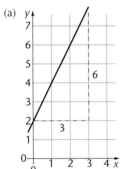

(b)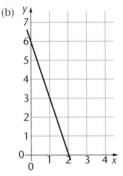

(c)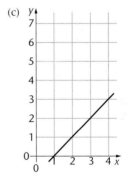

2. Find the gradient of each of these lines.

(a)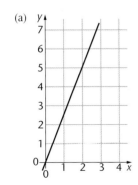

(b)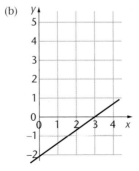

(c)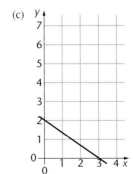

Chapter 12 Gradient

175

3. Calculate the gradients of the lines joining each of these pairs of points.
   (a) (3, 2) and (4, 8)
   (b) (5, 3) and (7, 3)
   (c) (0, 4) and (2, −6)
   (d) (−1, 1) and (3, 2)

4. Calculate the gradients of the lines joining each of these pairs of points.
   (a) (1, 8) and (5, 6)
   (b) (−3, 0) and (−1, 5)
   (c) (3, −1) and (−1, −5)
   (d) (2.5, 4) and (3.7, 4.9)

5. A ball bearing rolls in a straight groove. The graph shows its distance from a point P in the groove. Find the gradient of the line in this graph. What information does it give?

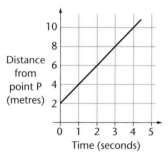

6. Find the gradient of each of the sides of triangle ABC.

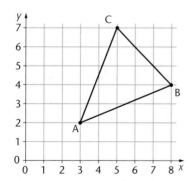

7. The table shows the cost of x minutes of calls on a mobile phone.

Number of minutes (x)	5	12	20	23
Cost (£C)	1.30	3.12	5.20	5.98

Find the gradient of the graph of C against x, and say what this gradient represents.

8. Draw, on the same diagram, the graphs of:
   (a) y = 3x
   (b) y = 3x + 2 and find their gradients.

9. Draw a graph for each of these straight lines and find their gradients.
   (a) y = 2x + 1
   (b) y = 5x − 2
   (c) y = 4x + 3

10. Draw a graph for each of these straight lines and find their gradients.
    (a) y = −2x + 1
    (b) y = −3x + 2
    (c) y = −x

1. Find the gradient of each of these lines.

(a)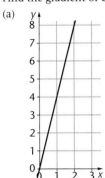

(b)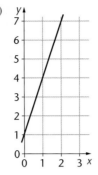

(c)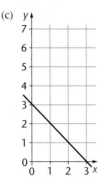

2. Find the gradient of each of these lines.

(a)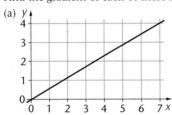

(b)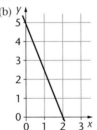

(c)

3. Calculate the gradient of the lines joining each of these pairs of points.

   (a) (4, 0) and (6, 8)   (b) (−1, 4) and (7, 2)

   (c) (1, 5) and (3, 5)   (d) (−2, 6) and (0, 4)

4. Calculate the gradients of the lines joining each of these pairs of points.

   (a) (2, 10) and (10, 30)

   (b) (−3, 6) and (−1, −2)

   (c) (0.6, 3) and (3.6, −9)

   (d) (2.5, 7) and (4, 2.2)

5. Find the gradient of the line in this graph. What information does it give?

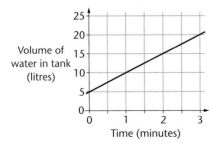

6. Find the gradient of each of the sides of triangle ABC.

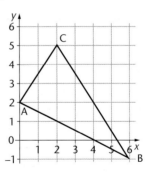

7. The table gives the cost when x metres of ribbon are sold.

Number of metres (x)	0.25	0.5	1.75	3.00
Cost (C pence)	21	42	147	252

Find the gradient of the graph of C against x and say what this gradient represents.

8. Draw, on the same diagram, the graphs of:
   (a) $y = 2x$ (b) $y = 2x + 1$
   and find their gradients.

9. Draw a graph for each of these straight lines
   and find their gradients.
   (a) $y = x + 1$ (b) $y = 2x - 3$
   (c) $y = 4x$

10. Draw a graph for each of these straight lines
    and find their gradients.
    (a) $y = -x + 3$ (b) $y = -3x$
    (c) $y = -2x - 5$

Straight-line graphs

If you did the last two questions in the exercises on gradients,
you may have noticed a connection between the equation of a
line and its gradient.

> When the equation is written in the form $y = mx + c$, where
> m and c are numbers, then:
> m is the gradient of the line
> c is the value of y where the graph crosses the y-axis. In other words,
> the graph passes through $(0, c)$.

Using these facts means that:

- you can work out the equation of a line from its graph
- if you know the equation of a line you can easily find its
  gradient and where it crosses the y-axis.

Example 5

Find the equation of this straight line.

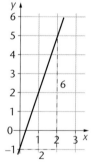

The gradient is $\dfrac{6}{2} = 3$.

The line passes through $(0, -1)$.

So the equation is $y = 3x - 1$.

The equation of a straight line is $5x + 2y = 10$. Find its gradient.

Rearranging the equation: $2y = -5x + 10$
$$y = -2.5x + 5$$

So the gradient is -2.5.

Equations of curved graphs

You are expected to know the shapes of the graphs of some types of equation and be able to sketch them. These include curved graphs, and you have already plotted some of them.

Here is a reminder.

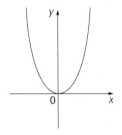

$y = ax^2$
a is positive

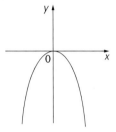

$y = ax^2$
a is negative

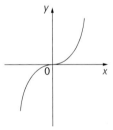

$y = ax^3$
a is positive

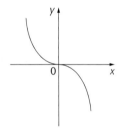

$y = ax^3$
a is negative

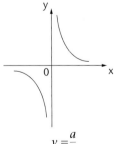

$y = \dfrac{a}{x}$
a is positive

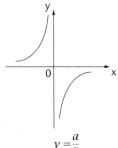

$y = \dfrac{a}{x}$
a is negative

Examiner's tip

These last two graphs each have two separate curves, since any number divided by zero is infinity.

Chapter 12 Equations of curved graphs

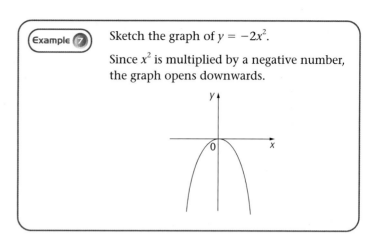

Example 7   Sketch the graph of $y = -2x^2$.

Since x^2 is multiplied by a negative number, the graph opens downwards.

Exercise 12.3a

1. Write down the equations of the straight lines:
   (a) with gradient 3 and passing through (0, 2)   (b) with gradient -1 and passing through (0, 4)
   (c) with gradient 5 and passing through (0, 0).
2. Find the equations of these lines.

(a)

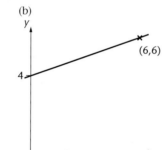

(b)

(c)

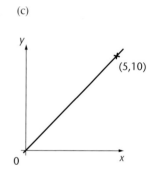

3. Find the equations of these lines.

(a)

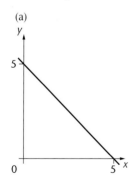

(b)

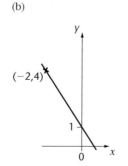

(c)

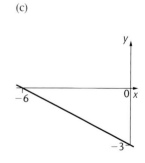

4. Find the gradient of these lines and where they cross the y-axis.
   (a) $y = 3x - 2$
   (b) $y = 2 + 5x$
   (c) $y = 7 - 2x$
5. Find the gradient of these lines and where they cross the y-axis.
   (a) $y + 2x = 5$
   (b) $4x + 2y = 7$
   (c) $6x + 5y = 10$
6. Find an equation for the cost ($£C$) of travelling m miles for the car hire in question 4, Exercise 12.1a.
7. The table shows the cost of x minutes of calls on a mobile phone (as in Exercise 12.2a, question 7).

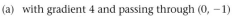

Number of minutes (x)	5	12	20	23
Cost ($£C$)		1.30	3.12	5.20 5.98

   Find an equation connecting x and C.
8. On the same diagram, sketch the graphs of these three equations.
   (a) $y = 2x + 1$
   (b) $y = 2x - 3$
   (c) $y = -4x + 1$

9. Match each of these sketch graphs with the correct equation.
   (a) 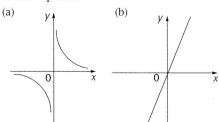 (b)

   (c)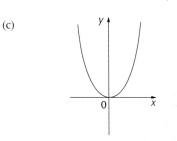

   (i) $y = 3x$
   (ii) $y = -\dfrac{3}{x}$
   (iii) $y = 3x^2$
10. Sketch these graphs.
   (a) $y = 3x - 2$ (c) $y = -x^2$
   (b) $y = -\dfrac{2}{x}$ (d) $y = 3x^3$

1. Write down the equations of the straight lines:
   (a) with gradient 4 and passing through $(0, -1)$
   (b) with gradient -2 and passing through $(0, 5)$
   (c) with gradient 3 and passing through the origin.
2. Find the equations of these lines.
   (a)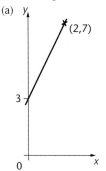

   (b)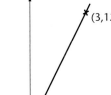

   (c)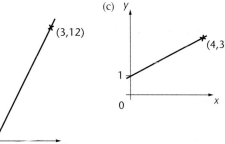

3. Find the equations of these lines.

(a)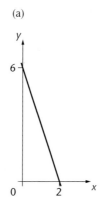

(b)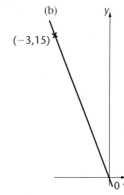

(c)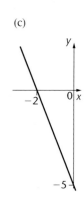

4. Find the gradient of these lines and where they cross the y-axis.
   (a) $y = 5x - 3$ (b) $y = 7 + 2x$
   (c) $y = 9 - 3x$

5. Find the gradient of these lines and where they cross the y-axis.
   (a) $y - 5x = 1$ (b) $3x + 2y = 8$
   (c) $2x + 5y = 15$

6. Using the diagram for question 6 in Exercise 12.2b, find the equations of the sides of triangle ABC.

7. The table gives the cost when x metres of ribbon are sold (as in Exercise 12.2b question 7).

Number of metres (x)	0.25	0.5	1.75	3.00
Cost $(C$ pence)	21	42	147	252

Find an equation connecting x and C.

8. On the same diagram, sketch the graphs of these questions:
   (a) $y = 3x + 2$ (b) $y = 3x - 2$
   (c) $y = -x + 2$

9. Match each of these sketch graphs with the correct equation.

(a)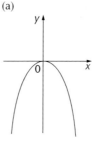

(b)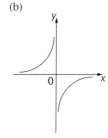

(c)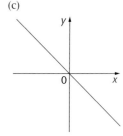

(i) $y = -2x$ (ii) $y = -2x^2$ (iii) $y = -\dfrac{3}{x}$

10. Sketch these graphs.
    (a) $y = 4x - 1$ (b) $y = -\dfrac{2}{x}$ (c) $y = 3x^2$ (d) $y = -2x^3$

Key points

Story graphs
- The labels on the axes tell you what a graph is about.
- Each feature on the graph is part of the story. For instance, does it increase or decrease at a steady rate (a straight line) or is it curved?

Gradient of straight lines
- $\text{Gradient} = \dfrac{\text{increase in } y}{\text{increase in } x}$
- Lines with a positive gradient slope forwards /.
- Lines with a negative gradient slope backwards \.

- Flat lines —— have a gradient of zero.
- Gradient gives the rate of change in graphs about physical situations.

Equation of a straight-line graph
- The equation of a line can be written as $y = mx + c$, where m and c are numbers. m is the gradient of the line and c is the value of y where the graph crosses the y-axis. In other words, the graph passes through $(0, c)$.

Shapes of graphs
- Learn the shapes of graphs such as $y = x^2$, $y = x^3$, $y = \dfrac{1}{x}$.

Revision exercise 12a

1. The distance travelled by a train between two stations is shown on this graph.

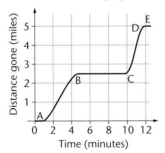

   (a) How far is it between the stations?
   (b) What was happening on section BC of the graph?
   (c) What was happening on section DE of the graph?
   (d) On which section did the train travel at the greatest speed?

2. A kite was launched and gained height, slowly at first but then more quickly, until it was 30 m up after about 10 s. It flew at this height for 30 s, then came down 20 m very quickly. It descended the remaining 10 m more gently, landing 50 s after it started.
   Draw a graph to show this information.

3. Find the gradient of the lines joining these pairs of points.
   (a) (2, 4) and (4, 9)
   (b) (2, 4) and (6, 0)
   (c) (−1, 2) and (5, 2)

4. Plot and join the points A(3, 1), B(−3, 4) and C(5, 6). Calculate the gradients of the sides of triangle ABC.

5. State the gradients of these lines, and the coordinates of their intersection with the y-axis.
   (a) $y = 2x − 3$
   (b) $x = 2y$
   (c) $3y = x + 2$
   (d) $2x + 5y = 10$

6. (a) Plot a graph for these data for the distance (d km) of a car from a motorway junction at time t minutes.

t	2	4	8	15
d	5.0	7.4	12.2	20.6

   (b) What was the speed of the car, in km per minute?
   (c) How far was the car from the junction when t was zero?
   (d) Write an equation connecting d and t.

7. Find an equation for each of these lines.

(a)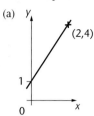

(b)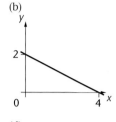

(c)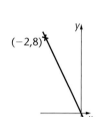

(d)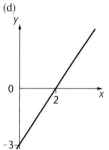

8. Sketch the graphs of these straight lines.
    (a) $y = 3x - 2$
    (b) $y = -3x + 1$
    (c) $x = 2y$
    (d) $x = 2$

9. Sketch the graphs of these curves.
    (a) $y = x^3$
    (b) $y = -\dfrac{12}{x}$
    (c) $y = 4x^2$

10. Match each of these graphs with the correct equation.

(a)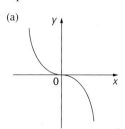

(b)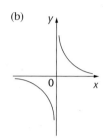

(c)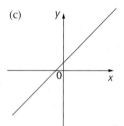

(d)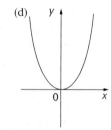

(i) $y = 2x^2$ (ii) $y = 2x + 1$

(iii) $y = -2x^3$ (iv) $y = \dfrac{2}{x}$

- probabilities are expressed as fractions, decimals or percentages
- all probabilities lie on a scale of 0 to 1 (0 to 100%)
- how to find probability from a set of equally likely outcomes
- the probability of an outcome happening is 1 − the probability of the outcome **not** happening
- what mutually exclusive events are
- if events A, B and C are mutually exclusive and cover all possible outcomes then
  P(A) + P(B) + P(C) = 1
- how to add and subtract simple fractions.

Covering all the possibilities

To find the probability of an event happening it is essential to consider all the possible outcomes. There are various ways to set out the work, to ensure that none of the outcomes is overlooked.

Each method is introduced in the context of tossing two coins to see whether they come up heads or tails.

List of equally likely outcomes

When looking at the outcomes for tossing two coins it is tempting to say that the possible outcomes are:

two heads   two tails   one of each.

However, the simple practical experiment of tossing two coins a large number of times should show that 'one of each' comes up approximately twice as often as 'two heads' or 'two tails'. This is because to throw either 'two heads' or 'two tails' both coins must come up the same, whereas to throw 'one of each' it does not matter which way the first coin comes up as long as the second one comes up the other way.

So the correct list of equally likely outcomes is:

| head, head | head, tail | tail, head | tail, tail |

and therefore $P(2 \text{ heads}) = \frac{1}{4}$ $\quad$ $P(2 \text{ tails}) = \frac{1}{4}$

but $P(1 \text{ head and } 1 \text{ tail}) = \frac{2}{4} = \frac{1}{2}$

The main disadvantage of this method is immediately obvious. It is all too easy to miss possible outcomes.

Another disadvantage is that listing outcomes can be very time-consuming, especially if there are very many possible outcomes. For example, if you are throwing two dice, there are 36 possible outcomes since for every one of six possibilities for the first die there are six possibilities for the second.

Table of outcomes

This method is useful for organising the list of outcomes, and reduces the chance of leaving some out. The table for the above example is on the right. The probabilities can be found exactly as before.

The disadvantage of a table is that again it can be time-consuming if there are many possible outcomes.

Showing outcomes on a grid (a possibility space)

In this method the outcomes for the first trial are listed on the *x*-axis and the outcomes for the second trial are listed on the *y*-axis. The outcomes for the combination of trials are then represented by crosses on the grid. The outcomes for two coins are shown like this. Again the probabilities can now easily be found.

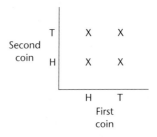

The advantages of this method are:

- it is a very quick way of showing the outcomes when there are very many possibilities, for example it is a very good way to show all 36 outcomes for throwing two dice
- if the outcomes are numerical, the crosses can be replaced by the numerical result. For example, if you are interested in the total score when you throw two dice, you can replace the X for (3, 4) by 7 and the X for (5, 6) by 11 etc.

A disadvantage is that it cannot be extended for a third or subsequent trial. It is difficult to draw a three-dimensional graph but it is easy to add a third column to a table.

Examiner's tip

When filling in a table of outcomes, always try to work logically changing one thing at a time. If you choose outcomes haphazardly you may miss some or repeat some.

First coin	Second coin
head	head
head	tail
tail	head
tail	tail

Tree diagrams

In this method 'branches' are drawn from a starting point to show the possibilities for the first trial. From the end of each of the first branches, further branches are drawn showing each of the possibilities for the second trial, and so on.

The tree diagram for tossing two coins looks like this.

The advantages of a tree diagram are:

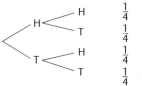

- it can easily be extended for a third and subsequent trials
- it can also be used when the outcomes are not equally likely. (This is covered later in the chapter.)

The main disadvantage of a tree diagram is that it can look very messy if there are too many possibilities. For example it is difficult to organise for the example of throwing two dice. However, if there are only two or three possible outcomes for each trial it is often the best method.

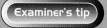

When drawing a tree diagram:
1. allow plenty of space on the page
2. always line up the possibilities for each trial underneath each other
3. for the first trial, draw the branches to points approximately $\frac{1}{4}$ way from the top of your space to $\frac{1}{4}$ way from the bottom of your space.

Fatima throws an ordinary die and tosses a coin. Show the possible outcomes in a table and find the probability that:

(a) Fatima scores a head and a 6

(b) Fatima scores a tail and an odd number.

(a) P(head and 6) $= \frac{1}{12}$

(b) P(tail and odd number) = P[(T, 1) or (T, 3) or (T, 5)] $= \frac{3}{12} = \frac{1}{4}$

This question could also have been answered using a grid.

```
        T │ X  X  X  X  X  X
Coin
        H │ X  X  X  X  X  X
          └─────────────────
            1  2  3  4  5  6
                  Die
```

Choose the outcomes logically, changing the number on the die first.

Die	Coin
1	head
2	head
3	head
4	head
5	head
6	head
1	tail
2	tail
3	tail
4	tail
5	tail
6	tail

Therefore there are 12 possible outcomes.

Example 2

Gareth tosses two dice. Show the outcomes on a grid (possibility space) and use the grid to find the probability that:

(a) Gareth scores a double

(b) Gareth scores a total of 11.

From the grid, there are 36 possible outcomes.

(a) $P(\text{double}) = \frac{6}{36} = \frac{1}{6}$

(b) $P(\text{score of } 11) = \frac{2}{36} = \frac{1}{18}$

The grid could also have been drawn with the total scores replacing the Xs.

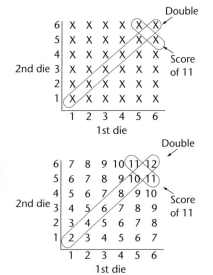

Example 3

Rachel is selecting a main course and a sweet from this menu.

MENU

Main course	Sweet
Sausage & Chips	Apple Pie
Ham Salad	Fruit Salad
Vegetable Lasagne	

Draw a tree diagram to show Rachel's possible selections. If she is equally likely to select any of the choices, what is the probability that she selects Vegetable Lasagne and Apple Pie?

Therefore there are six possible outcomes.

P(Vegetable Lasagne and Apple Pie) $= \frac{1}{6}$

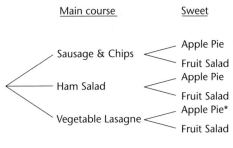

*Rachel's Selection

1. Jamil has brown socks, red socks and green socks in his drawer. He selects two socks at random from the drawer. Copy the table and complete it to show the possible outcomes.

First sock	Second sock

2. In tennis one player must win, a draw is not possible. Alex plays three games of tennis against Meiling. Copy the table and complete it to show the possible winner of each game. The first entry has been done for you

First game	Second game	Third game
Alex	Alex	Alex

3. Mr and Mrs Green plan to have three children. Draw a table to show the possible sexes for the first, second and third child. Assuming that all the outcomes are equally likely, what is the probability that Mr and Mrs Green will have:
   (a) all girls   (b) two boys and a girl?

4. The picture shows a fair spinner. Claire spins the spinner twice and records the total score.

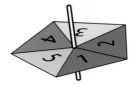

   Draw a grid, with each of the axes marked 1−5, to show the possible outcomes.
   Find the probability that Claire scored:
   (a) 10   (b) 5.

5. There are four suits in a set of playing cards: hearts (H), spades (S), diamonds (D) and clubs (C). There are equal numbers of each. Hearts and diamonds are red, spades and clubs are black.
   David chooses a card from a set of playing cards. He records the suit, replaces the card and then chooses another. Draw a grid with the axes labelled H, S, D and C to show the possible outcomes for his two cards.
   What is the probability that David chooses:
   (a) two spades   (b) two red cards?

6. Soraya chooses a card from a pack of playing cards and records its suit. She then throws a fair die. Draw a grid showing the possible outcomes. What is the probability that Soraya scores:
   (a) a club and a 5
   (b) a red card and a 6
   (c) a heart and an even number?

7. Fiona chooses a playing card, records its suit and tosses a coin. Copy the tree diagram below and complete it.

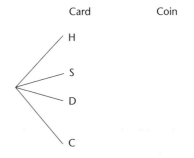

   Find the probability that Fiona scores:
   (a) a club and a head
   (b) a red card and a tail.

8. Lisa is choosing from this menu.
   Draw a tree diagram to show her possible choices.
   You could use the initial letters e.g. OB to save you writing the names out in full.
   Assuming she is equally likely to choose any of the items, find the probability that she chooses Onion Bhaji and Lamb Madras.

STARTER AND MAIN COURSE   £6

MENU

Starters	Main Course
Onion Bhaji	Chicken Tikka
Sheek Kebab	Lamb Madras
	Vegetable Bhuna

1. Robbie tosses three coins together. Copy the table and complete it to show all the possible outcomes. The first has been done for you.

First coin	Second coin	Third coin
head	head	head

Find the probability that Robbie tosses:
(a) two heads and a tail
(b) at least one head.

2. Anne plays a game. She tosses a coin to see whether to pick up a number or a letter card at random. If she tosses a head she picks a number card: 1, 2 or 3. If she tosses a tail she picks a letter card: A, B or C. Copy the table and complete it to show her possible outcomes.

Coin	Card

What is the probability that she picks:
(a) card C
(b) a card with an odd number on it?

3. In a game, Bobbie spins both of the spinners. Make a table showing all the possible outcomes. What is the probability of getting a B and a 3?

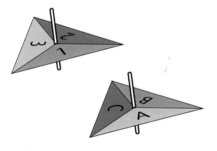

4. Draw a grid showing all the outcomes when two dice are thrown. What is the probability of scoring:
(a) a double six   (b) a total score of 9?

5. In the game of Monopoly, you throw two dice and your score is the total. Use the grid you drew for question 4 to answer these questions.

(a) To buy Park Lane, Hamish needs to score 11. What is the probability that Hamish can buy Park Lane after his next go?
(b) To get out of jail, Sylvia needs to throw a double. What is the probability that Sylvia gets out of jail on her next go?
(c) If Sanjay scores 7, he lands on Regent Street. What is the probability that Sanjay does **not** land on Regent Street?

6. Mr Ahmed is choosing his new company car. He can choose a Rover or a Peugeot. He can choose red, blue or black. Copy the tree diagram and complete it to show his possible choices.

Make   Colour

Rover

Peugeot

If he chooses completely randomly, what is the probability that he will choose:
(a) a blue Peugeot   (b) a black car?

7. Nicola and John are doing their Maths coursework. They can choose 'Billiard tables', 'Stacking cans' or 'Number trees'. Copy and complete the tree diagram to show their possible choices.

Nicola   John

BT

SC

NT

8. Gary and Salma are going out on Saturday night. They can go bowling, to the cinema or to the fair. After that they can either go for a meal or go dancing. Since they cannot agree what to do they decide to choose randomly.
Draw a tree diagram to show their possible choices. Find the probability that they go bowling and then on for a meal.

Probability of event A or event B happening

Look again at the grid for throwing two dice.

Suppose Louise needs a score of 8 or 11. Out of a total of 36 possible outcomes, there are seven that give 8 or 11.

The probability of scoring 8 or 11 is therefore $\frac{7}{36}$.

But the probability of scoring 8 is $\frac{5}{36}$ and the probability of scoring 11 is $\frac{2}{36}$

and $\frac{5}{36} + \frac{2}{36} = \frac{7}{36}$

So   P(8 **or** 11) = P(8) + P(11)

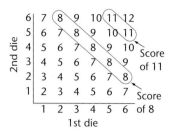

If the two events are 'scoring a double' or 'scoring 8' the situation is different.

There are ten outcomes that give a double or a score of 8 and therefore:

P(double **or** 8) = $\frac{10}{36}$ P(double) = $\frac{6}{36}$ P(8) = $\frac{5}{36}$

and $\frac{6}{36} + \frac{5}{36}$ does not equal $\frac{10}{36}$.

So P(double **or** 8) does **not** equal P(double) + P(8).

This is because the events 'scoring a double' and 'scoring 8' are not mutually exclusive events. It is possible to do both by throwing a double 4.

The addition rule only applies to mutually exclusive events.

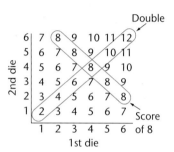

> If events A and B are mutually exclusive then P(A **or** B) = P(A) + P(B)

Independent events

If two coins are tossed, the way the first one lands cannot possibly affect the way the second one lands.

Similarly, if two dice are thrown, the way the first one lands cannot possibly affect the way the second one lands.

If there are six red balls and four black balls in a bag, and one is selected and replaced before a second one is selected, the probability of getting a red ball is exactly the same on the second choice as on the first: $\frac{6}{10}$.

When an event is unaffected by what has happened in another event, the events are said to be **independent**.

In the example of six red balls and four black ones, if the first ball is not replaced then the probability of getting a red ball on the second draw is no longer $\frac{6}{10}$ as there are fewer balls in the bag. In this case the events are **dependent**.

Probability of event A and event B happening

In Example 1 Fatima tossed a coin and threw a die. Since there were 12 equally likely outcomes, and scoring a head and a 6 was one of them, it was concluded that:

P(head and a 6) = $\frac{1}{12}$

Now P(head) = $\frac{1}{2}$ and P(6) = $\frac{1}{6}$

But $\frac{1}{2} \times \frac{1}{6} = \frac{1}{12}$ so P(head and a 6) = P(head) $\times$ P(6)

In the first example in this chapter, tossing two coins, it was concluded that:

P(2 heads) = $\frac{1}{4}$

Now P(head) = $\frac{1}{2}$

But $\frac{1}{2} \times \frac{1}{2} = \frac{1}{4}$ so P(2 heads) = P(head) $\times$ P(head)

These results are only true because the events are independent. If they were dependent events, the second probability in the multiplication sum would be different.

For independent events P(A **and** B) = P(A) $\times$ P(B)

Clearly it is more of a coincidence to throw two heads than one, so it is to be expected that the probability will be less. Multiplying fractions and decimals less than one gives a smaller answer, whereas adding them gives a bigger answer.

The result for events A and B extends to more than two events. For example in Exercise 10b, Question 1 you should have found that when tossing three coins, the probability of getting all three heads = $\frac{1}{8}$.

P(head) $\times$ P(head) $\times$ P(head) = $\frac{1}{2} \times \frac{1}{2} \times \frac{1}{2} = \frac{1}{8}$

So included in the multiply rule are words such as 'both' and 'all'.

Examiner's tip

It is very common for examination candidates to add probabilities when they should have multiplied. If you get an answer to a probability question that is more than 1 you have almost certainly added instead of multiplied.

Example 4

The probability that the school hockey team will win their next match is 0.4. The probability that they draw their next match is 0.3. What is the probability that they will win or draw their next match?

The events are mutually exclusive, since they cannot both win and draw their next match, so:

P(win **or** draw) = P(win) + P(draw) = 0.3 + 0.4 = 0.7

Example 5

Matt spins the fair spinner shown in the picture twice.

What is the probability that Matt scores a 4 on both his spins?

The events are independent, since the second spin cannot be affected by the first.

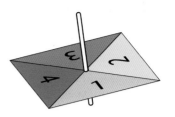

$P(4 \textbf{ and } 4) = P(4) \times P(4) = \frac{1}{4} \times \frac{1}{4} = \frac{1}{16}$

Example 6

There are six red balls and four black balls in a bag. Gina selects a ball, notes its colour and replaces it. She then selects another ball. What is the probability that Gina selects:

(a) two red balls

(b) one of each colour?

Since Gina replaces her first ball before choosing the second the events are independent.

(a) $P(2 \text{ reds}) = P(\text{red}) \times P(\text{red}) = \frac{6}{10} \times \frac{6}{10} = \frac{36}{100} = \frac{9}{25}$

(or in decimals $0.6 \times 0.6 = 0.36$)

(b) Before doing this question it is important to think about what the outcomes are.

Gina requires first ball red **and** second ball black
or   first ball black **and** second ball red.

Both the add and multiply rules are needed.

$P(\text{one of each colour}) = (\frac{4}{10} \times \frac{6}{10}) + (\frac{6}{10} \times \frac{4}{10}) = \frac{24}{100} + \frac{24}{100} = \frac{48}{100} = \frac{12}{25}$

(or in decimals $(0.4 \times 0.6) + (0.6 \times 0.4) = 0.24 + 0.24 = 0.48$)

Questions like part (b) of example 6, which require both rules, are clearly more difficult. Later in the chapter, you will see that these can often be more easily tackled using tree diagrams.

Exercise 13.2a

1. There are five green balls, three red balls and two yellow balls in a bag. If a ball is selected at random, find the probability that it is green or red.

2. Craig is choosing his next holiday. The probability that he will choose Ibiza is 0.4, the probability that he will chose Corfu is 0.35 and the probability that he will choose Tenerife is 0.25. Find the probability that Craig chooses Ibiza or Corfu.

3. There are four kings and four queens in a pack of 52 playing cards. Salim chooses a card at random from the pack. What is the probability that it is a king or queen?

4. There are five green balls, three red balls and two yellow balls in a bag. Ian chooses a ball at random, notes its colour and puts it back in the bag. He then does this a second time. Find the probability that both Ian's choices are red.

5. The probability that I take sandwiches for dinner is 0.4. The probability that I have a school lunch is 0.6. Assuming the events are independent, what is the probability that I have sandwiches on Monday and a school lunch on Tuesday?

6. What is the probability that I get a multiple of 3 when I throw a single fair die?
   If I throw the die twice, what is the probability that both throws give a multiple of 3?

7. There are four kings in a pack of 52 playing cards. Roger selects a card at random from the pack, returns it to the pack, shuffles the pack and then selects another. Find the probability that both Roger's selections were kings.

8. Alice and Carol are choosing clothes to go out. The probability that Alice chooses jeans is 0.6. The probability that Carol chooses jeans is 0.5. Assuming that their choices are independent, find the probability that they both choose jeans. Explain why this assumption may not be true.

Exercise 13.2b

1. The probability that the school hockey team will win their next game is 0.3. The probability that they draw the next game is 0.45. What is the probability that they will not lose their next game? (That is, they win or draw the game.)

2. If the results of the hockey team are independent, use the probability given in question 1 to find the probability they win both their next two games.

3. Janine travels to school by bus, cycle or car. She says that the probability that she travels by bus is 0.25, by cycle is 0.1 and by car is 0.6. Why must she be incorrect?

4. Rachel is selecting a main course and a sweet from this menu.

MENU

Main course	Sweet
Sausage & Chips (0.35)	Apple Pie (0.4)
Ham Salad (0.4)	Fruit Salad (0.6)
Vegetable Lasagne (0.25)	

The numbers next to the items are the probabilities that Rachel chooses those items.
   (a) Find the probability that Rachel chooses Ham Salad or Vegetable Lasagne for her main course.
   (b) Assuming her choices are independent, find the probability that Rachel chooses Vegetable Lasagne and Fruit Salad.

5. There are 12 picture cards in a pack of 52 playing cards. Ubaid picks a card at random. He then replaces the card and chooses another.
   (a) Find the probability, as a fraction in its lowest terms, that Ubaid's first card is a picture card.
   (b) Find the probability that both Ubaid's cards are picture cards.

6. The weather forecast says 'there is a 40% chance of rain tomorrow'.
   (a) Write 40% as a decimal.
   (b) Assuming the probability that it rains on any day is independent of whether it rained or not the previous day, find the probability that it rains on two successive days.
   (c) State why the assumption made in (b) is unlikely to be correct.

7. There is an equal likelihood that someone is born on any day of the week. What is the probability that Gary and Rushna were both born on a Monday?

8. Sally spins this five-sided spinner three times.

What is the probability that all Sally's spins landed on 1?

Using tree diagrams for unequal probabilities

In the first section, tree diagrams were used as a way of organising work on probability when the outcomes were equally likely. It is possible to use them when outcomes are not equally likely.

Look again at Rachel's choices on the menu, from question 4 in the last exercise. These can be shown on a tree diagram with the probabilities written on the branches.

Main Course   Sweet

```
                        0.4      Apple Pie    0.35 × 0.4
          Sausage &
0.35      Chips         0.6      Fruit Salad  0.35 × 0.6
   0.4                  0.4      Apple Pie    0.4  × 0.4
          Ham Salad
                        0.6      Fruit Salad  0.4  × 0.6
0.25      Vegetable     0.4      Apple Pie    0.25 × 0.4
          Lasagne
                        0.6      Fruit Salad  0.25 × 0.6
```

MENU

Main course   **Sweet**
Sausage & Chips (0.35)   Apple Pie (0.4)
Ham Salad (0.4)   Fruit Salad (0.6)
Vegetable Lasagne (0.25)

So the probability of choosing Sausage & Chips and Fruit Salad
= 0.35 × 0.6 = 0.21

and the probability of choosing Ham Salad and Apple Pie is
0.4 × 0.4

and so on.

As you go along the 'branches' of any route through the tree, **multiply** the probabilities. Now look at Example 6 in a different way.

Examiner's tip

If you are going along the 'branches' of a tree diagram **multiply** the probabilities. At the end, if you want more than one route through the tree, **add** the probabilities.

Example 7

There are six red balls and four black balls in a bag. Gina selects a ball, notes its colour and replaces it. She then selects another ball. What is the probability that Gina selects:

(a) two red balls

(b) one of each colour?

A tree diagram can be drawn to show this information.

Notice that at each stage the probabilities add up to 1 and at the end all four probabilities add up to 1.

```
              1st ball    2nd ball
                          0.6   R   0.6 × 0.6 = 0.36
              0.6    R
                          0.4   B   0.6 × 0.4 = 0.24
                          0.6   R   0.4 × 0.6 = 0.24
              0.4    B
                          0.4   B   0.4 × 0.4 = 0.16
```

(a) Probability of red followed by red = 0.6 × 0.6 = 0.36.

(b) For one of each colour, Gina needs either the second route **or** the third route through the tree diagram.

So P(one of each colour) = (0.6 × 0.4) + (0.4 × 0.6) = 0.24 + 0.24 = 0.48.

Exercise 13.3a

1. There are seven red balls and three yellow balls in a bag. Lee chooses a ball at random, notes its colour and replaces it. He then chooses another. Copy and complete the tree diagram to show Lee's choices.

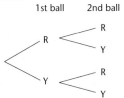

   1st ball   2nd ball

   What is the probability that Lee chooses:
   (a) two red balls
   (b) a red ball and then a yellow ball
   (c) a yellow ball and then a red ball
   (d) a red ball and a yellow ball in either order?

2. Li is choosing a starter and main course from this menu. The probabilities of each of her choices are in brackets next to the items.

   MENU

   Starter
   Soup (0.3)
   Spring Rolls (0.7)

   Main course
   Chicken Fried Rice (0.3)
   Beef Satay (0.2)
   Sweet & Sour Pork (0.5)

   (a) Draw a tree diagram to show Li's choices.
   (b) Calculate the probability that Li chooses:
      (i) Spring Roll and Beef Satay
      (ii) Soup and Sweet & Sour Pork.

3. The probability that Aftab wakes up when his alarm goes off is 0.8. Copy the tree diagram and complete it for the first two days of the week.

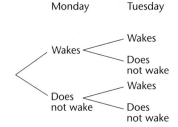

   Monday   Tuesday

   Calculate the probability that Aftab:
   (a) wakes on both days
   (b) wakes on one of the two days.

4. There are five red balls, two blue balls and three yellow balls in a bag. Susan chooses a ball at random, notes its colour and replaces it. She then chooses another.
   (a) Draw a tree diagram to show the results of Susan's choices.
   (b) Calculate the probability that Susan chooses:
      (i) two red balls
      (ii) two balls of the same colour.

5. Mr and Mrs Jones plan to have three children. Assuming there is an equal chance of a boy and girl, draw a tree diagram to show the possible sexes of the three children.
   Calculate the probability that Mr and Mrs Jones have:
   (a) three girls
   (b) two girls and a boy.

Exercise 13.3b

1. On any day the probability that Sarah's bus is late is 0.2. Copy the tree diagram and complete it for two days.

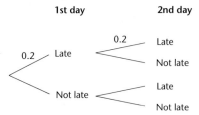

   1st day   2nd day

   Calculate the probability that Sarah's bus is:
   (a) late on both days
   (b) late on one of the two days.

2. In an experiment a drawing pin falls point up 300 times in 500 throws.

(a) Write down, as a fraction in its lowest terms, the probability of the pin landing point up.

(b) Draw a tree diagram to show the result of two throws, and the pin landing point up or point down.

(c) Find the probability that the pin lands point up on:
   (i) both throws
   (ii) one of the two throws.

3. Extend the tree diagram you drew for question 2 to show the results of three throws.
   Find the probability that the pin lands point up on:
   (a) all three throws
   (b) one of the three throws.

4. There are ten red balls, three blue balls and seven yellow balls in a bag. Waseem chooses a ball at random, notes its colour and replaces it. He then chooses another.
   (a) Draw a tree diagram to show the results of Waseem's choices.
   (b) Calculate the probability that Waseem chooses:
      (i) two blue balls
      (ii) two balls of the same colour
      (iii) two balls of different colours. (Look for the quick way of doing it.)

5. Brian drew this tree diagram for the results of choosing coloured balls from a bag.

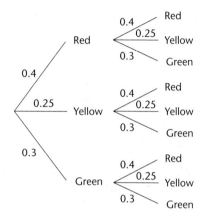

Explain why Brian must have made a mistake.

Key points

- Events can be shown using:

Tables	Advantage	Easy to read for probabilities of equally likely events	
	Disadvantages	Lengthy, cannot be used if events are not equally likely	
Grids	Advantage	Easy to read for probabilities of equally likely events	
	Disadvantages	Lengthy, cannot be used if events are not equally likely	
		Cannot be used for more than two successive events.	
Tree diagrams	Advantages	Can be used for more than two successive events	
		Can be used when events are not equally likely	
	Disadvantage	Can be messy when there are more than three outcomes.	

- If events A and B are mutually exclusive then P(A or B) = P(A) + P(B)
- For independent events P(A and B) = P(A) × P(B)
- The multiply rule should also be used for words like 'both' and 'all'.

1. The probability that Brenda goes to school by bus is 0.4. The probability that she goes by car is 0.15. What is the probability that she goes by bus or by car?

2. If Brenda's choices of travel are independent, use the probabilities in question 1 to find the probability that she travels by bus on Monday and by car on Tuesday.

3. A fairground game offers a bottle of champagne if the fair spinner lands on the shaded section twice in succession. What is the probability of winning the champagne?

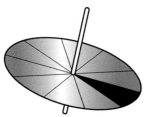

4. The probability of the school football team winning any of their games is 0.2. What is the probability that they do **not** win either of their next two games?

5. Salma throws two dice and records the result of multiplying the two scores together.
   Draw a grid to show all the possible outcomes.
   Find the probability that Salma's result is:
   (a) 36   (b) 12   (c) 4.

6. Colin throws two dice. He is not interested in all the individual results, just whether he gets a six or not.
   Copy the tree diagram and complete it for the results of Colin's two throws.

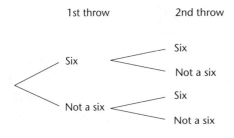

Find the probability that Colin throws:
(a) two sixes   (b) at least one six.

7. The probability that the school netball team will win any match is 0.4. The probability that they draw any match is 0.1. Draw a tree diagram to show the outcomes of their next two matches. Find the probability that the team:
   (a) loses both matches
   (b) does not lose both matches
   (c) wins one of the two matches and draws the other.

8. The probability that it rains on 15 July is 0.1. The probability that it rains on 16 July is also 0.1.
   Find the probability that it:
   (a) rains on both days
   (b) rains on one of the two days.

9. The whole of year 9 take tests in English, Maths and Science. The probability that a randomly-chosen pupil passes English is 0.8, Maths is 0.7 and Science is 0.9.
   Copy the tree diagram and complete it for the three subjects. Assume these events are independent.

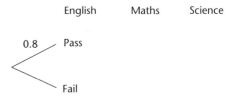

Calculate the probability that a randomly chosen Year 9 pupil:
(a) passes all three subjects
(b) passes two subjects.

Length, area and volume 14

You will need to know:

- common metric units for length, area, and volume
- how to find the area of a rectangle and a triangle
- how to find the volume of a cuboid
- how to find the circumference and area of a circle
- how to find lengths using Pythagoras' theorem and trigonometry
- how to round answers to a suitable degree of accuracy.

Area of a parallelogram

A parallelogram may be cut up and rearranged to form a rectangle or two congruent triangles.

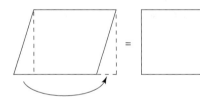

Area of a rectangle =
base × height

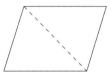

Area of a triangle $= \frac{1}{2} \times$ base × height

Both these ways of splitting a parallelogram show:

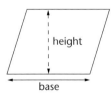

Area of a parallelogram = base × height

Examiner's tip

Make sure you use the perpendicular height and not the sloping edge when finding the area of a parallelogram.

Find the area of this parallelogram.

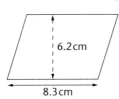

Area of a parallelogram = base × height

= 8.3 × 6.2 cm²

= 51.46 cm²

= 51.5 cm² to three significant figures

Examiner's tip

Don't forget to give your final answer to a suitable degree of accuracy, but don't use rounded answers in your working.

Exercise 14.1a

1. Find the area of each of these parallelograms.

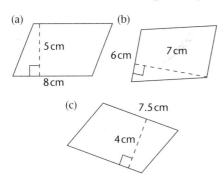

(a)

5 cm

8 cm

(b)

6 cm

7 cm

(c)

7.5 cm

4 cm

2. Find the area of each of these parallelograms. The lengths are in centimetres.

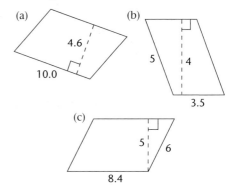

(a)

4.6

10.0

(b)

5

4

3.5

(c)

5

6

8.4

3. Measure the base and height and calculate the area of each of these parallelograms.

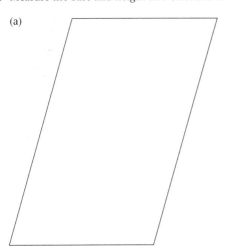

(a)

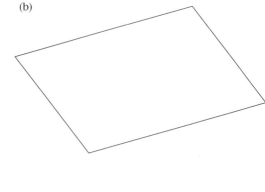

(b)

(c)

4. Find the values of x, y and z.

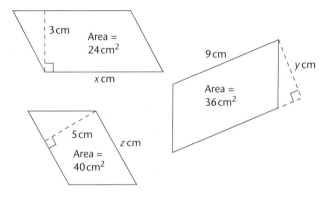

5. This rectangle and parallelogram have the same area. Calculate the height of the parallelogram.

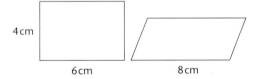

Exercise 14.1b

1. Find the area of each of these parallelograms.

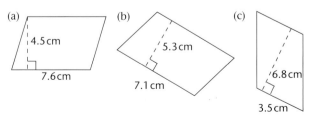

2. Find the area of each of these parallelograms. The lengths are in centimetres.

(a)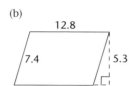

(b)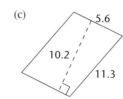

(c)

3. Measure the base and height and calculate the area of each of these parallelograms.

(a) (b)

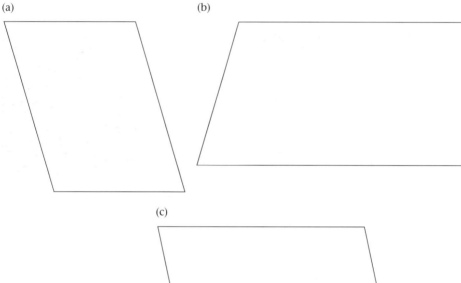

(c)

4. Find the values of x, y and z.

(a)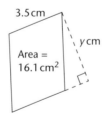

Area = 25.2 cm² 4.2 cm

x cm

(b)

3.5 cm

y cm

Area = 16.1 cm²

(c)

Area = 35.1 cm² z cm

7.8 cm

5. This triangle and parallelogram have the same area. Calculate the height of the parallelogram.

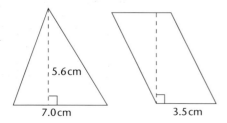

5.6 cm

7.0 cm

3.5 cm

Area of a trapezium

A trapezium has one pair of opposite sides parallel. A trapezium can also be split into two triangles.

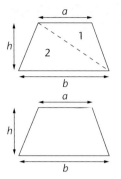

Area of triangle 1 $= \frac{1}{2} \times a \times h$

Area of triangle 2 $= \frac{1}{2} \times b \times h$

Area of trapezium $= \frac{1}{2} \times a \times h + \frac{1}{2} \times b \times h = \frac{1}{2} \times (a + b) \times h$

Area of a trapezium $= \frac{1}{2} \times (a + b)h$

In words, a useful formula to remember is:

Area of a trapezium = half the sum of the parallel sides × the height.

Examiner's tip

When finding the area of a parallelogram or a trapezium, don't try to split the shape up. Instead, learn the area formulae and use them as it is quicker.

Example 2 Calculate the area of this trapezium.

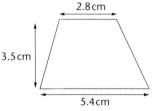

Area of trapezium $= \frac{1}{2}(a + b)h$
$= \frac{1}{2}(2.8 + 5.4) \times 3.5\,\text{cm}^2$
$= 14.35\,\text{cm}^2$
$= 14.4\,\text{cm}^2$ to three significant figures.

Example 3 Without using a calculator, find the area of this trapezium.

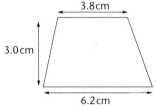

Area of a trapezium $= \frac{1}{2}(a + b)h$
$= \frac{1}{2}(3.8 + 6.2) \times 3\,\text{cm}^2$
$= \frac{1}{2} \times 10 \times 3\,\text{cm}^2$
$= 15\,\text{cm}^2$

Examiner's tip

When finding the area of a trapezium, an efficient method is to use the brackets function on your calculator. Without a calculator, work out the brackets first.

1. Find the area of each of these trapezia.

(a)

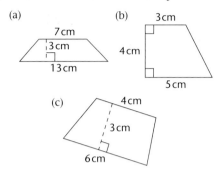

(b) 3cm

(c)

2. Find the area of each of these trapezia.

(a)

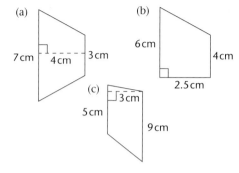

(b)

(c)

3. Measure the lengths you need and calculate the area of each of these trapezia.

(a)

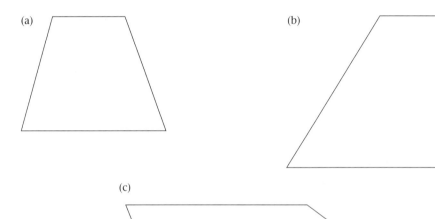

(b)

(c)

4. Find the values of a, b and c in these trapezia.

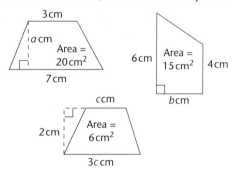

3cm

a cm

Area = 20 cm²

7cm

6cm Area = 15 cm² 4cm

b cm

c cm

2cm Area = 6 cm²

$3c$ cm

5. A trapezium has height 4 cm and area 28 cm². One of its parallel sides is 5 cm long. How long is the other parallel side?

1. Find the area of each of these trapezia.

(a)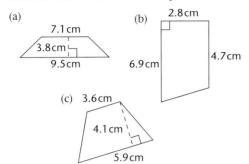
7.1 cm
3.8 cm
9.5 cm

(b)
2.8 cm
6.9 cm
4.7 cm

(c) 3.6 cm
4.1 cm
5.9 cm

2. Find the area of each of these trapezia.

(a)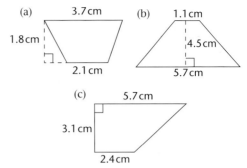
3.7 cm
1.8 cm
2.1 cm

(b)
1.1 cm
4.5 cm
5.7 cm

(c)
5.7 cm
3.1 cm
2.4 cm

3. Measure the lengths you need and calculate the area of each of these trapezia.

(a)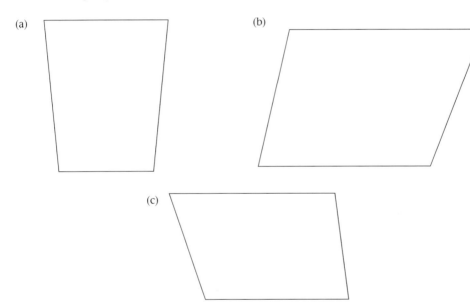

(b)

(c)

4. Find the values of a, b and c in these trapezia.

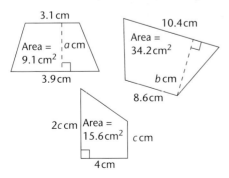
3.1 cm
Area = 9.1 cm^2
a cm
3.9 cm

10.4 cm
Area = 34.2 cm^2
b cm
8.6 cm

2c cm
Area = 15.6 cm^2
c cm
4 cm

5. A trapezium has height 6.6 cm and area 42.9 cm^2. One of its parallel sides is 5 cm long. How long is the other parallel side?

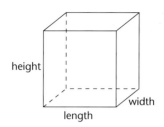

height

length width

Volume of a prism

You should remember how to find the volume of a cuboid.

> Volume of a cuboid = length × width × height

It may also be thought of as:

> Volume of a cuboid = area of cross-section × height

This is an example of a general formula for the volume of a prism. When laid on its side, along its length:

> Volume of a prism = area of cross-section × length

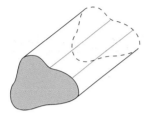

Another important prism is the cylinder. Its cross-section is a circle, which has area πr^2.

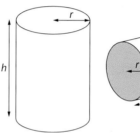
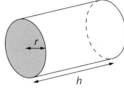

> Volume of a cylinder = $\pi r^2 h$

Example 4

Calculate the volume of a cylinder with base diameter 15 cm and height 10 cm.

Radius of base $= \frac{15}{2} = 7.5$ cm

Volume of a cylinder $= \pi r2h$
$$= \pi \times 7.5^2 \times 10 \, \text{cm}^3$$
$$= 1770 \, \text{cm}^3 \text{ to three significant figures}$$

Example 5

A chocolate box is a prism with a trapezium as cross-section, as shown. Calculate the volume of the prism.

Area of a trapezium $= \frac{1}{2}(a + b)h$
$$= \frac{1}{2}(20 + 16) \times 6 \, \text{cm}^2$$
$$= 108 \, \text{cm}^2$$

Volume of a prism = area of cross-section × length
$$= 108 \times 25 \, \text{cm}^3$$
$$= 2700 \, \text{cm}^3$$

16 cm
25 cm
6 cm
20 cm

Example 6 A cylinder has volume 100 cm³ and is 4.2 cm high. Find the radius of its base. Give your answer to the nearest millimetre.

$$\text{Volume of cylinder} = \pi r^2 h$$
$$100 = \pi \times r^2 \times 4.2$$
$$r^2 = \frac{100}{\pi \times 4.2}$$
$$= 7.578\ldots$$
$$r = \sqrt{7.578\ldots}$$
$$= 2.8 \text{ cm to the nearest mm}$$

Exercise 14.3a

1. Calculate the volume of a cylinder with base radius 5.6 cm and height 8.5 cm.

2. A cylindrical stick of rock is 12 cm long and has radius 2.4 cm. Find its volume.

3. A cylinder has diameter 8 cm and height 8 cm. Calculate its volume.

4. Calculate the volume of prisms each 15 cm long, with these cross-sections.

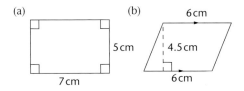

(a)

(b)   6 cm

5 cm   4.5 cm

7 cm   6 cm

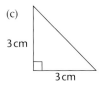

(c)

3 cm

3 cm

5. A chocolate bar is in the shape of a triangular prism. Calculate its volume.

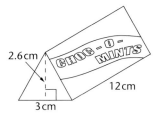

2.6 cm   CHOC-O-MINTS   12 cm

3 cm

6. A pencil-box is a prism with a trapezium as its cross-section, as shown. Calculate the volume of the box.

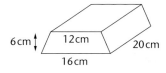

6 cm   12 cm   20 cm

16 cm

7. The area of cross-section of a prism is 75 cm². Its volume is 1200 cm³. Calculate its length.

8. The volume of a cylinder is 800 cm³. Its radius is 5.3 cm. Calculate its length.

9. A cylinder has volume 570 cm³ and height 7 cm. Find its base radius. Give your answer to the nearest millimetre.

10. The volume of a cylindrical tank is 600 m³. Its height is 4.6 m. Calculate the radius of its base.

Chapter 14   Volume of a prism

1. Calculate the volume of a cylinder with base radius 4.3 cm and height 9.7 cm.

2. A cylindrical water tank is 4.2 m high and has radius 3.6 m. Find its volume.

3. A cylinder has diameter 9 cm and height 12 cm. Calculate its volume.

4. Calculate the volume of prisms each 12 cm long, with these cross-sections.

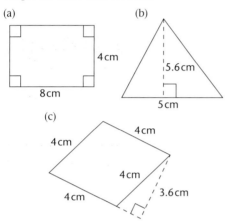

(a)

4 cm

8 cm

(b)

5.6 cm

5 cm

(c)

4 cm

4 cm

4 cm

4 cm

3.6 cm

5. A gift box is a prism with a triangular base. Calculate its volume.

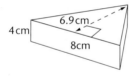

6.9 cm

4 cm

8 cm

6. A vase is a prism with a trapezium as its base. The internal measurements are as shown. How much water can the vase hold? Give your answer in litres. (1 litre = 1000 cm³)

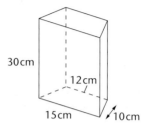

30 cm

12 cm

15 cm

10 cm

7. The area of cross-section of a prism is 90 cm². Its volume is 1503 cm³. Calculate its length.

8. The volume of a cylinder is 1500 cm³. Its radius is 7.5 cm. Calculate its length. Give your answer to the nearest millimetre.

9. A cylinder has volume 620 cm³ and height 8 cm. Find its base radius. Give your answer to the nearest millimetre.

10. The volume of a cylinder is 1100 cm³. Its length is 10.8 cm. Calculate its radius, giving your answer to the nearest millimetre.

Dimensions

You can tell whether a formula gives length, area or volume by looking at its dimensions.

The area of a circle is πr^2...

...or is it $2\pi r$?

number × length = length   [1 dimension]
length + length = length   [1 dimension]
length × length = area   [2 dimensions]
length × length × length = volume   [3 dimensions]

So which circle formula is for area?

$2\pi r$ = number × length = length   [the circumference of a circle]

πr^2 = number × length × length
= length × length
= area [the area of a circle]

Thinking about the number of dimensions also helps you to sort out what units you should be using. For example:

length = m   [1 dimension]
area = m^2 [2 dimensions]
volume = m^3 [3 dimensions]

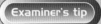

Examiner's tip

For practice, check the dimensions of formulae you know.

Example 7

If a, b and h are lengths, does the expression $\frac{1}{2}(a + b)h$ represent a length, area or volume, or none of these?

$a + b$ = length

so $\frac{1}{2}(a + b)h$ = number × length × length = length × length = area

Exercise 14.4a

Throughout this exercise, letters in algebraic expressions represent lengths.

1. State whether each of these expressions represents a length, area or volume.
   (a) $r + h$ (b) rh (c) $2\pi rh$

2. Which of these expressions represents a length?
   (a) $\frac{1}{2}bh$ (b) $3b$ (c) $b + 2h$

3. Which of these expressions represents an area?
   (a) xy (b) xy^2 (c) $x(x + y)$

4. Which of these expressions represents a volume?
   (a) r^3 (b) $\pi r^2 h$ (c) $r^2(r + h)$

5. State whether each expression represents length, area, volume or none of these.
   (a) $r(r^2 + h)$ (b) $(3 + \pi)h$ (c) $4\pi r^2$

Exercise 14.4b

Throughout this exercise, letters in algebraic expressions represent lengths.

1. State whether each of these expressions represents a length, area or volume.
   (a) $a + 2b$ (b) $2ab$ (c) a^2b

2. Which of these expressions represents a length?
   (a) $a + 2b + c$ (b) $3a + 2a^2$ (c) $a(2a + b)$

3. Which of these expressions represents an area?
   (a) $4a^2$ (b) $x(x + 2y)$ (c) $\pi r^2 + 2\pi rh$

4. Which of these expressions represents a volume?
   (a) πab (b) $\frac{4}{3}\pi r^3$ (c) $h^2(a + b)$

5. State whether each expression represents length, area, volume or none of these.
   (a) $\frac{1}{3}\pi r^2 h$ (b) $2a^2b(a + b)$ (c) $a(3 + \pi)$

Key points

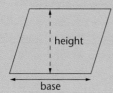

- Area of a parallelogram = base × height

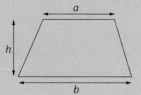

- Area of trapezium = $\frac{1}{2}(a + b)h$

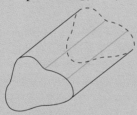

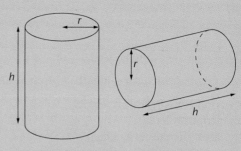

- Volume of a cylinder = $\pi r^2 h$
- Dimensions help to distinguish between formulae for length, area and volume:

  number × length
  = length   [1 dimension]

  length + length
  = length   [1 dimension]

  length × length = area   [2 dimensions]

  length × length × length
  = volume   [3 dimensions]

- Volume of a prism
  = area of cross-section × length

Revision exercise 14a

1. Calculate the area of each of these parallelograms.

   (a)   (b)

   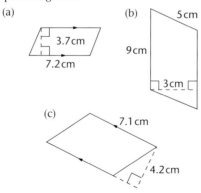

   (c)

2. Calculate the area of each trapezium.

   (a)   (b)

   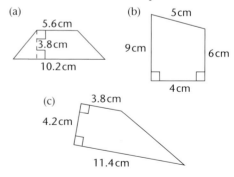

   (c)

3. A prism, 25 cm long, has this L-shape as its cross-section. Calculate the volume of the prism.

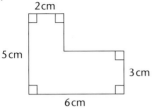

4. A cylindrical vase has internal radius 5.6 cm and height 22.5 cm. Calculate how many litres of water this vase can hold.

5. A large cylindrical can of baked beans has volume 3000 cm^3 and base radius 7.9 cm. Calculate the height of the can.

6. In these expressions, r and h are lengths. State which of length, area and volume is represented by each of these expressions.
(a) $\pi r h + \pi r^2$
(b) $\frac{1}{2}(r + h)$
(c) $3r^2 h$

7. Find the missing powers in these formulae.
(a) volume $= \frac{1}{3}\pi r^2 h$
(b) area $= 6r^?$
(c) length $= \dfrac{r^?}{h^2}$

8. The diagram shows a full-size net for a triangular prism. Use measurements from the drawing to calculate:
(a) the surface area
(b) the volume of the prism.

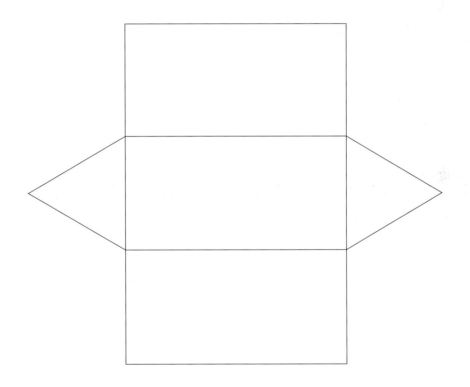

9. Calculate the areas of this parallelogram and trapezium.

    (a)

    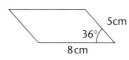

    (b)

    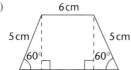

10. The diagram shows the cross-section of a prism which is 8 cm long. Calculate:

    (a) the height of the trapezium
    (b) the volume of the prism.

    (c)

    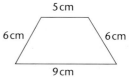

Properties of transformations

Patterns from transformations

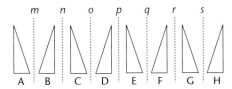

Triangle A is reflected in the mirror line m to give triangle B,

triangle B is reflected in the mirror line n to give triangle C,

triangle C is reflected in the mirror line o to give triangle D,

and so on to form a continuous pattern.

Within patterns like this, there are often other transformations.
For example, triangle A maps onto triangle C by a translation.

 Example ①

Triangle P has vertices at (1, 1), (2, 1) and (1, 3).

Triangle P is reflected in the line $x = 3$ to give triangle Q.

Triangle Q is reflected in the line $x = 7$ to give triangle R.

(a) Draw triangles P, Q and R on the same diagram and label them.

(b) Describe fully the transformation that will map triangle P onto triangle R.

Example ①
continued

(a)

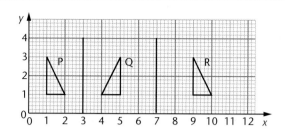

(b) Triangle P is mapped onto triangle R by a translation through the vector $\begin{pmatrix}8\\0\end{pmatrix}$.

Congruence

If two shapes are identical in shape and size they are **congruent**.

The shapes need not be the same way round. If a tracing of one can be placed exactly over the other, even if it has to be turned over, the shapes are still congruent.

If a shape is rotated, reflected or translated, the new shape is congruent to the original shape, since all these transformations leave the original size and shape unchanged.

Example ②

Explain why triangle ABC is congruent to triangle DEF.

Since the triangle DEF is a reflection of the triangle ABC in the mirror line, m, the two triangles are congruent.

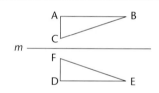

Examiner's tip

When describing congruent shapes using the letters labelling the vertices, always put the points in corresponding order.
For instance, in Example 2, having put A first in the first triangle, you should put D first in the second triangle because it corresponds to A. Similarly, having put B in second place in the first triangle, you should put the corresponding point, E, second in the second triangle and so on. You can spot which points are corresponding by looking at the angles, for example angle A = angle D = 90°.

Tessellations

Look at the diagram, which is made up of three regular hexagons.

The interior angle of a regular hexagon is 120°.

Since 360° is exactly divisible by 120°, giving an answer of 3, the hexagons fit together exactly at the point O.

The pattern can be continued by joining another hexagon at the point P and so on.

When shapes fit together exactly to fill up the plane they are said to **tessellate**.

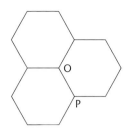

Example 3

With the help of a diagram, explain why regular pentagons will not tessellate.

The interior angle of a regular pentagon is 108°.

Since $3 \times 108 = 324$, there is a gap of 36° that is not filled by the pentagons.

This means that regular pentagons will not tessellate.

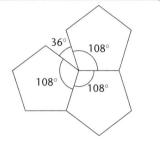

Exercise 15.1a

1. Draw a set of axes with x-values from 0 to 14 and y-values from 0 to 4.
   Repeat Example 1, starting with the same triangle P but this time using the mirror lines $x = 4$ and $x = 10$.
   Look at the answers to this question and Example 1. What conclusions can you draw?

For Questions 2, 3 and 4, refer to the diagram below.

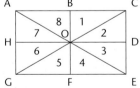

2. Describe fully the transformations that will map triangle:
   (a) 1 onto 2 (b) 2 onto 3 (c) 3 onto 4
   (d) 4 onto 5 (e) 5 onto 6 (f) 6 onto 7
   (g) 7 onto 8.

3. Describe fully the transformations that will map triangle:
   (a) 2 onto 6 (b) 2 onto 5
   (c) 2 onto triangle CEG.

4. Explain why triangle 1 is congruent to:
   (a) triangle 4 (b) triangle 6.

5. Explain why quadrilaterals A, B and C are all congruent to each other.

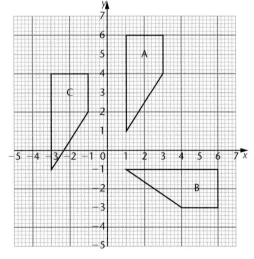

6. (a) Find the interior angle of a regular decagon.
   (b) With the help of a diagram, explain why regular decagons will not tessellate.

1. Draw a set of axes with *x*-values from –6 to +6 and *y*-values from –6 to +6.
   (i) (a) Draw the triangle with vertices at (0, 0), (2, 2) and (6, 0). Label it A.
       (b) Reflect triangle A in the *x*-axis. Label the new triangle B.
       (c) Rotate triangle B through 90° clockwise about the origin. Label the new triangle C.
       (d) Rotate triangle C through 180° about the origin. Label the new triangle D.
       (e) Reflect triangle D in the line *y* = –*x*. Label the new triangle E.
       (f) Rotate triangle E through 90° anti-clockwise about the origin. Label the new triangle F.
   (ii) Describe fully the transformations that will map F onto G and G onto H to complete a shape with rotational symmetry order 4.

2. Explain why these shapes are not congruent.

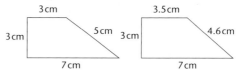

3. Explain why triangles A, B and C are congruent to each other.

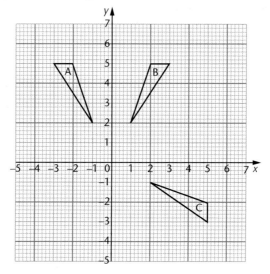

4. With the help of a diagram, explain why trapeziums of this shape will tessellate.

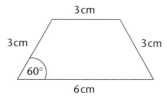

5. (a) Calculate the interior angle of a regular octagon.
   (b) With the help of a diagram, explain why regular octagons will not tessellate.
   (c) Suggest another shape which could be combined with regular octagons to make a tessellating pattern. Draw a diagram which shows how this tessellation would work. You only need a few of the shapes.

Enlargements

Scale drawings

Example 4

The diagram shows a garden shed.

(a) Make a scale drawing of the front of the shed, using a scale factor of $\frac{1}{20}$.

(b) Find the length of the sloping side of the roof.

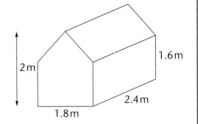

(a) First divide each of the lengths by 20.
1.6 m = 160 cm, 160 ÷ 20 = 8 cm
1.8 m = 180 cm, 180 ÷ 20 = 9 cm
2 m = 200 cm, 200 ÷ 20 = 10 cm

Now draw the shape.

Mark the distance 9 cm along the bottom. Then draw the two sides 8 cm high, at right angles to the first line. To find the top point, mark the middle of the base line and measure up 10 cm at right angles to the base line (the dotted line in the diagram). Then draw the two sloping sides.

(b) The sloping side measures 4.9 cm.

On the actual shed this length will be 4.9 × 20 = 98 cm or 0.98 m.

When making a scale drawing of a larger object, the first thing to do is decide on a scale factor. In examination questions this will usually be given to you.

If the units are the same, this scale factor can be given as a simple fraction or ratio.

The scale factor used above could be written $\frac{1}{20}$ or 1 to 20 or 1 : 20.

Another way of writing the same scale is 1 cm to 0.2 m since 20 cm = 0.2 m.

Once the scale factor has been established, all the lengths on the scale drawing can be calculated. Then the drawing can be made. It is, of course, important to make sure that the angles are the same on the scale drawing as on the actual object.

Maps

Maps are scale drawings of what is actually on the ground. Because the area of the land is very large compared with the area of the piece of paper on which the map is drawn, the scale factor is usually a very small fraction.

Ordnance Survey Outdoor Leisure maps are drawn to a scale of $\frac{1}{25\,000}$ or 1 : 25 000.

Example 5

Find the distance on an Ordnance Survey Outdoor Leisure map which represents a distance of 1 km on the ground.

1 km = 1000 m = 100 000 cm

100 000 ÷ 25 000 = 4

So the distance on the map is 4 cm.

Another way of writing the scale would be **4 cm to 1 km**.

Similar shapes

In Mathematics the word 'similar' has a very exact meaning. It does **not** mean 'roughly the same' or 'alike'.

For two shapes to be similar each shape must be an exact enlargement of the other. For example look at these two rectangles.

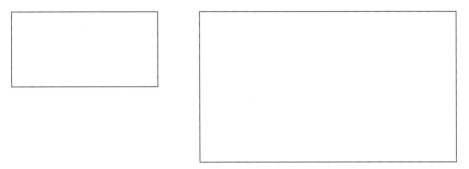

The first rectangle is 2 cm wide by 4 cm long.

The second rectangle is 4 cm wide by 7 cm long.

The rectangles are **not** similar because although the width of the large one is twice the width of the small one, the length of the large one is **not** twice the length of the small one. If the length of the large one were 8 cm then the rectangles would be similar.

Now look at these two shapes.

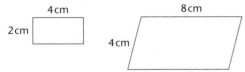

Although the scale factor for both pairs of sides is 2, the shapes are not similar because corresponding angles are not the same.

> For two shapes to be similar:
> * all corresponding sides must have proportional lengths
> * all corresponding angles must be equal.

Similar triangles

If all the sides of a triangle are known the shape of the triangle is fixed. You can demonstrate this, using drinking straws. Take three straws and make a triangle by squeezing the end of one straw and pushing it into the open end of the next. Even if the straws are only loosely jointed, the triangle will be rigid.

This is not the case with a quadrilateral or other polygon, as the angles may change. Make a quadrilateral with drinking straws. It is easy to push opposite angles and make the shape deform into a different quadrilateral.

Because the lengths of three sides define a unique triangle, for two triangles to be similar only one of the tests on the previous page needs to be made.

If you can establish that the angles are the same, you can conclude that the triangles are similar and carry out calculations to find lengths of sides.

Calculations of lengths of similar shapes

The rectangles ABCD and PQRS are similar. Find the length of PQ.

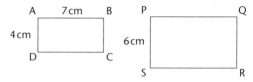

Since the widths of the rectangles are 6 cm and 4 cm, the scale factor is 6 ÷ 4 = 1.5.

The length of PQ = 7 × 1.5 = 10.5 cm.

In the triangle, angle ABC = angle BDC = 90°, AB = 6 cm, BC = 8 cm and BD = 4.8 cm.

(a) Explain why triangles ABC and BDC are similar.

(b) Calculate the length of DC.

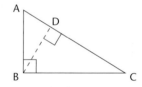

(a) In the triangles ABC and BDC, angle ABC = angle BDC = 90°.

The angle C is in both triangles.

Since the angle sum of a triangle is 180°, the third angles must be equal.

So, since all the corresponding angles are equal, the triangles are similar.

(b) First redraw the triangles so they are the same way round as each other.

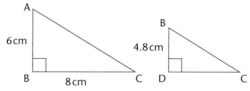

Since AB = 6 cm and BD = 4.8 cm the scale factor = 4.8 ÷ 6 = 0.8.

CD = 8 × 0.8 = 6.4 cm

1. A scale model of a jumbo jet is made to a scale of $\frac{1}{500}$.
   (a) The length of the real aircraft is 70 m. What is the length of the model, in cm?
   (b) The wingspan of the model is 12 cm. What is the wingspan of the real aircraft, in m?

2. The diagram shows a plan of a garden. It is not drawn to scale.

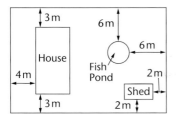

   The garden is 30 m × 20 m.
   The house is 14 m × 8 m.
   The shed is 2.4 m × 1.8 m.
   The fish pond has a diameter of 4 m.
   Draw a scale drawing of the garden, using a scale of $\frac{1}{200}$ or 1 cm to 2 m.

3. The scale of a map is 1 : 50 000.
   (a) A road is 2.5 km long. How long is the road on the map?
   (b) The distance between two villages on the map is 7 cm. What is the real distance between the villages?

4. A road map is drawn to a scale of 1 : 200 000.
   (a) How far, in kilometres, is 200 000 cm?
   (b) The distance from London to Cambridge is 87 km. How far is it on the map, in cm?
   (c) The distance from Exeter to Newcastle on the map is 293 cm. How far is the actual distance, in kilometres?

5. You need an A4 sheet of paper.
   (a) Measure the length and width of the paper.
   (b) Fold the paper in two (along the dotted line).

   This size of paper is called A5.
   Measure the length and width of this paper.
   Divide the length of the A4 sheet by the length of the A5 piece. Do the same for the widths.
   Is A4 paper similar to A5 paper? If so, what is the scale factor?
   (c) Fold the paper in two again. This size of paper is called A6.
   Repeat part (b) for A5 and A6 paper. What do you notice?
   (d) All the A-series of paper sizes work in the same way. What is the size of A3 paper?

6. The two rectangles in the diagram are similar. Find the length of the larger rectangle.

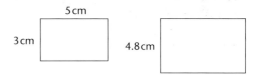

7. The line PQ is parallel to the line CD. The line QR is parallel to the line DE. Explain why the pentagons ABCDE and ABPQR are not similar.

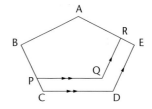

8. The triangles ABC and PQR are similar. Calculate the lengths of PQ and PR.

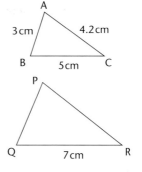

9. The triangles DEF and UVW are similar. Calculate the lengths UV and UW.

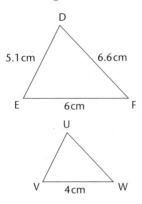

10. The lines PQ and BC are parallel.

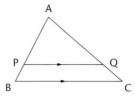

   (a) Explain why triangles ABC and APQ are similar.
   (b) If AB = 6 cm, BC = 8 cm and AP = 4.7 cm, calculate the length of PQ. Give your answer correct to three significant figures.

Exercise 15.2b

1. A toy car is a scale model of a real car, on a scale of $\frac{1}{50}$.
   (a) The length of the real car is 3.8 m. What is the length of the toy car, in cm?
   (b) The height of the toy car is 2.8 cm. What is the height of the real car, in m?

2. The diagram is a plan of Aftab's bedroom. It is not drawn to scale.

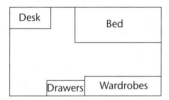

   The room is 3.4 m × 2.5 m.
   The bed is 2 m × 0.9 m.
   The wardrobes are 1.8 m × 0.6 m.
   The desk is 1.2 m × 0.6 m.
   The drawers are 0.8 m × 0.45 m.
   Draw a scale drawing of Aftab's bedroom using a scale of $\frac{1}{25}$.

3. A map is drawn to a scale of 1 : 25 000.
   (a) Two farms are 650 m apart. How far apart, in cm, are they on the map?
   (b) Lesley measures the distance she has walked in a day on the map. It measures 64 cm. How far has she actually walked, in kilometres?

4. A map of Europe is drawn to a scale of 1 : 15 000 000.
   On this map Britain measures approximately 6 cm, north to south. Estimate the actual distance, in kilometres, from the north of Britain to the south of Britain.

5. These two parallelograms are similar. Find the length of PQ.

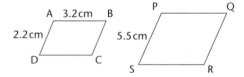

6. Explain why these quadrilaterals are **not** similar.

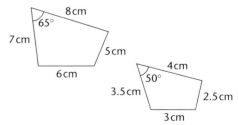

7. The triangles ABC and PQR are similar. Calculate the lengths of PQ and QR.

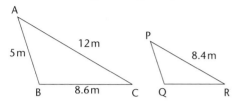

8. In the diagram, DE is parallel to BC, AB = 4.5 cm, BC = 6 cm and DE = 10 cm. Calculate the length BD.

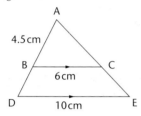

9. In the diagram, angle BAC = angle ADC = 90°, AD = 3 cm and DC = 5 cm.

(a) Explain why triangles ADC and BDA are similar.

(b) Calculate the length BD.

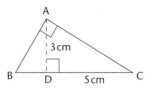

10. ABCD is a trapezium. The diagonals meet at O, and AB = 5 cm, DC = 8 cm and OD = 6 cm.

(a) Explain why triangles OAB and OCD are similar.

(b) Calculate the length of OB.

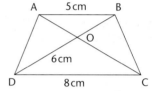

Key points

- Shapes are congruent if they are identical in size and shape.
- If one shape can be mapped onto another by a reflection, rotation or translation then the shapes are congruent.
- If shapes can fit together to fill the plane around a point, with no gaps, then the shapes are said to tessellate.

- Scales for maps and drawings can be given as, for example, $\frac{1}{200}$ or $1 : 200$ or 1 cm to 2 m.
- For shapes to be similar:
  - all corresponding sides must have proportional lengths
  - all corresponding angles must be equal.
- For similar triangles if one of the above conditions is true, the other must be.

Revision exercise 15a

1. Draw a set of axes with x-values from −4 to +4 and y-values from −4 to +4.
   (a) Draw triangle PAB with vertices at P(1, 1), A(1, 3) and B(3, 1).
   (b) Draw triangle QCD, the image of triangle PAB after it has been rotated through 90° clockwise about the origin.
   (c) Carry out the same transformation on triangle QCD. Label the new triangle REF.
   (d) Carry out the same transformation on triangle REF. Label the new triangle SGH.
   (e) How many lines of symmetry has the octagon ABCDEFGH?
   (f) Is the octagon regular? Give your reasons.

2. Look again at your diagram for question 1. Explain why trapezium ABCD is congruent to trapezium GHAB.

3. Using a parallelogram of your choice, draw a diagram to see whether it will tessellate. Will all parallelograms tessellate?

4. Sasha's bedroom is a rectangle which measures 3.1 m by 3.6 m. Her bed measures 1.9 m by 0.9 m. Sasha makes a scale drawing of the plan of her bedroom. She uses a scale of $\frac{1}{40}$.
   (a) What are the length and width of the bedroom on Sasha's scale drawing?
   (b) What are the length and width of the bed on Sasha's scale drawing?

5. A map is drawn to a scale of 1 : 25 000.
   (a) What length on the map represents 1 km on the ground?
   (b) The distance between two churches on the map is 18 cm. How far apart are they on the ground?

6. The two rectangles are similar. Calculate the height of the smaller rectangle.

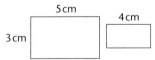

7. Are these rectangles similar? Show a calculation to explain your answer.

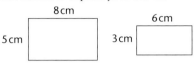

8. (a) Explain why triangles ABC and PQR are similar.

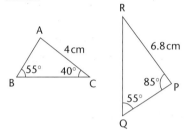

   (b) What is the scale factor?

9. Triangle PQR is similar to triangle ABC. Calculate the lengths PR and QR.

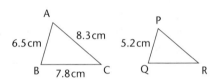

10. BC is parallel to DE, AB = 6.3 m, BD = 2.7 m and DE = 10.2 m. Calculate the length of BC.

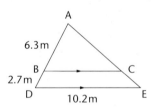

You will need to know:

- how to calculate the mean, median and mode for grouped and ungrouped data
- how to calculate the range
- how to find the median and interquartile range from a cumulative frequency graph.

Comparing data

Comparing sizes of sets of data

If there are two (or more) sets of data it is often necessary to make comparisons between them. For instance, if the information below gives the marks obtained by John and Aisha in their last five Maths tests, the question may arise as to who is better at Maths.

John	7	8	10	4	6
Aisha	8	9	7	8	6

One way to compare the two sets of figures is to calculate the mean of their scores.

John's mean $= 35 \div 5 = 7$
Aisha's mean $= 38 \div 5 = 7.6$

This would suggest that Aisha is better at Maths than John.

Whilst the mean is often a reliable way of comparing sets of data it is unwise to draw too many conclusions from such a small amount of data. It may be that the topics tested were just more suited to Aisha and, in any case, the difference is not large.

The three measurements of 'average', the mean, median and mode, can all be used to compare the sets of data.

Usually the mean, which takes into account all the data, is the most reliable but there are circumstances where this is not so. One or two very large or very small figures can distort a mean and give a false impression.

When comparing relative sizes of data always try to interpret the information in the question. For example in John and Aisha's case, say that Aisha is better at Maths rather than Aisha's mean is higher than John's. In the case of house prices, state that Area B's houses are more expensive, not that their modal class is higher.

Here are John and Aisha's score in the last ten Maths tests.

John	7	8	10	4	6	3	8	5	9	8
Aisha	8	9	7	8	6	9	8	7	6	9

Who is better at Maths?

John's mean = 68 ÷ 10 = 6.8

Aisha's mean = 77 ÷ 10 = 7.7

These figures suggest that Aisha is better at Maths and, since we now have more evidence, the conclusion is likely to be more reliable than before.

The tables below give the sale prices of houses in two areas. Which area has the higher house prices?

Area A		Area B	
Price in pounds (£)	Number of houses	Price in pounds (£)	Number of houses
40 000–59 999	5	40 000–59 999	0
60 000–79 999	17	60 000–79 999	16
80 000–99 999	64	80 000–99 999	27
100 000–119 999	11	100 000–119 999	47
120 000–139 999	3	120 000–139 999	10

The modal class of Area A is £80 000–£99 999.

The modal class of Area B is £100 000–£119 999.

This suggests that the houses are more expensive in Area B.

Comparing spread of sets of data

When comparing sets of data, it is generally not sufficient to know that values in one set are, on average, 'bigger' than those in the other. It is also helpful to know whether one set of data is more spread out than the other.

The two measurements of spread that have been covered so far are the **range** and the **interquartile range**.

Look again at John and Aisha's scores in the last ten Maths tests.

John's range is 10 – 3 = 7   Aisha's range is 9 – 6 = 3

These figures show that John's spread of scores is greater than Aisha's.

Another way of stating the conclusion is to say that Aisha is more **consistent** than John.

The cumulative frequency graphs below are for the house prices in Example 2.

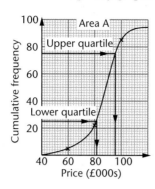

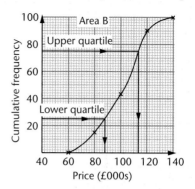

Use the interquartile ranges to compare the spread of the house prices in the two areas.

The interquartile range for area A = £95 000 – £82 000 = £13 000

The interquartile range for area B = £114 000 – £88 000 = £26 000

So the spread of house prices is greater in area B than in Area A.

The median, range and interquartile range of distributions can be compared visually, by means of a box plot.

For the houses in the example above, the median in Area A is £89 000 and the median in Area B is £104 000. The box plots for the two areas look like this.

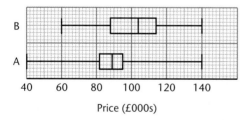

These box plots assume minimum prices of £40 000 and £60 000 and a maximum price of £139 999 for both areas. In fact, there is a strong likelihood that, for example, the maximum price in Area A is below £139 999.

Usually the interquartile range is the more reliable of the two measures of spread, since one or two very low or very high values can greatly distort the range. The interquartile range disregards extreme values.

Chapter 16 Comparing data

It is sometimes possible to compare spreads of distributions if there is a marked difference in the shape of the frequency diagrams.

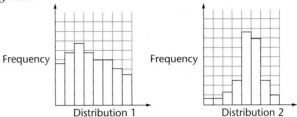

Looking at these frequency diagrams, you can see that the data in Distribution 1 are much more spread out than the data in Distribution 2.

Exercise 16.1a

1. In golf the lowest score is the best. Colin's mean score in this season's golf rounds is 71. His lowest score is 63 and his highest is 88. Vijay's mean score is 73. His lowest score is 66 and his highest score is 82. Make two comparisons of the two players' scores.

2. The table below shows the results of an investigation into costs of dental treatment in two towns.

	Median cost	Interquartile range
Town A	£19.25	£4.20
Town B	£16.50	£5.30

Make two comparisons of the cost of dental treatment in the two towns.

3. Here is a set of nine numbers.

   8   6   7   3   12   6   11   5   8

   Write down another set of nine numbers with the same median but a larger range.

4. The table below shows the amounts of rainfall, in millimetres, in twelve months in Moralia and Sivarium.

	J	F	M	A	J	J	A	S	O	N	D
Moralia	25	23	21	18	16	15	14	18	17	22	27
Sivarium	5	6	8	12	78	70	21	7	4	3	2

Find the mean and range for each of the places and state your conclusions.

5. Here are Tara's and Justin's marks in their last five English homeworks.

Tara	14	15	17	13	15
Justin	10	18	11	19	20

Calculate the mean and range of each of the two pupils' scores and state your conclusions.

Why might these conclusions be somewhat unreliable?

6. The numbers of letters delivered to the houses in two roads are shown in this table.

| Number of letters | Number of houses | |
	Jubilee Road	Riverside Road
0	2	0
1	27	5
2	18	16
3	11	29
4	5	18
5	3	5
6	1	4
7	0	3
8	0	2
9	0	1

Find the mode and range of the numbers of letters delivered in the two roads and state your conclusions.

7. The table shows how much pocket money (to the nearest pound) is received by pupils in Class 9a.

Amount of pocket money in pounds (£)	Number of pupils
2	1
3	5
4	10
5	7
6	4

(a) Calculate an estimate for the mean and range of the amounts of pocket money received.

(b) In class 9b the mean amount of pocket money is £3.80 and the range is £8. Compare the amounts of pocket money in the two classes.

8. The cumulative frequency diagrams below show the times of response to 100 alarm calls for two fire brigades.

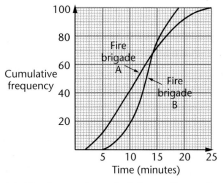

(a) Use the graphs to find the median and interquartile range of the response times for each fire brigade.

(b) Draw box plots to compare the results for each fire brigade.

(c) Comment on your results.

9. Panesh is buying light bulbs. Britelite have a mean life of 300 hours with a range of 200 hours. Lightglo have a mean life of 280 hours and a range of 20 hours. Which would you advise Panesh to buy? Explain why.

Exercise 16.1b

1. The median age of the Ribchester hockey team is 24 years 9 months and the range is 8 years 2 months. The median age of Sillington hockey team is 22 years 5 months and the range is 5 years 4 months. Make two statements to compare the ages of the two teams.

2. The lengths of time in minutes spent on homework by Gareth and Salima on five days in a week are listed below.

	M	Tu	W	Th	F
Gareth	50	60	45	80	70
Salima	20	80	100	30	55

Find the mean and range of the two pupils' times. State your conclusions.

3. The table shows the mean and interquartile range of the price of a 'standard basket of shopping' in two regions of the country.

	Mean	Interquartile range
Region A	£43.52	£3.54
Region B	£46.54	£1.68

Compare the prices in the two regions.

4. The table shows the amounts spent on Christmas presents by the 120 pupils in year 10.

Amount of money in pounds (£)	Number of pupils
0.00–4.99	3
5.00–9.99	14
10.00–14.99	36
15.00–19.99	50
20.00–24.99	13
25.00–29.99	4

(a) Draw a cumulative frequency diagram and use it to find the median and interquartile range for the money spent.

(b) The median amount spent by Year 11 pupils was £19, the lower quartile was £17 and the upper quartile was £21.50. The minimum was £5 and the maximum £31. Draw a box plot for each of the years.

(c) Compare the distributions of money spent by Year 10 and Year 11 pupils.

5. The frequency diagrams show the number of children per family, in two classes.

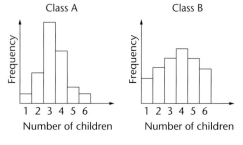

Use the modes and the shapes of the diagrams to compare the distributions.

6. These are the weekly earnings, in pounds, of the employees at a small firm.

96	120	120	125	137	145
157	190	200	220	590	

State, with reasons, which measurement of spread you would use to compare this firm with another, similar, small firm.

7. The lengths of 100 leaves from an ash tree in a park in a city centre are shown in the table. The lengths are measured to the nearest centimetre.

Length of leaf (cm)	Frequency
9	12
10	15
11	33
12	19
13	13
14	8

(a) Calculate an estimate for the mean length of leaf and estimate the range.

(b) Leaves from an ash tree from a country area have a mean length of 12.7 cm and a range of 4.2 cm. Compare the distributions of the leaves from the two different areas.

8. The table shows the means and interquartile ranges of two batsmen's scores in their last 20 innings.

	Mean	Interquartile range
Mike	43.4	6.4
Alec	47.8	15.2

Which batsman would you select? Explain why.

Correlation

The table below shows the amount of ice-cream sold by an ice-cream seller in ten days last summer.

Number of hours of sunshine	3	6	11	2	0	7	2	12	7	5
Number of ice-creams sold	120	200	360	100	50	250	150	470	330	230

The graph below shows this information plotted on a scatter diagram or scatter graph.

The number of hours of sunshine is plotted as the *x*-coordinate and the number of ice-creams sold is plotted as the *y*-coordinate.

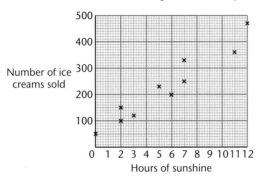

From the graph, it can be seen that, in general, the **more** hours of sunshine there were, the **more** ice-creams were sold.

This is an example of **positive correlation**.

Although the points are not exactly in a straight line, nevertheless there is a trend that the further to the right on the graph the higher the point is.

In graphs such as these the nearer the graph is to a straight line, the better the correlation is.

Examples of graphs showing positive correlation

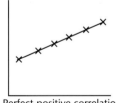

Perfect positive correlation

Strong positive correlation

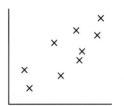

Weak positive correlation

If there is no correlation the scatter diagram looks like this.

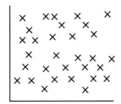

A shopkeeper in the same town as the ice-cream seller noted how many umbrellas were sold in the same ten days. This is the table.

Number of hours of sunshine	3	6	11	2	0	7	2	12	7	5
Number of umbrellas sold	6	5	2	9	11	4	8	0	5	7

The scatter diagram for this information looks like this.

The number of hours of sunshine is plotted as the x-coordinate and the number of umbrellas sold is plotted as the y-coordinate.

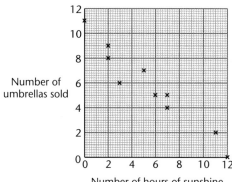

Number of umbrellas sold

Number of hours of sunshine

Here the trend is the other way round. In general, although the points are not exactly in a straight line, the **more** hours of sunshine there are the **fewer** umbrellas are sold.

This is an example of **negative correlation**.

Examples of graphs showing negative correlation

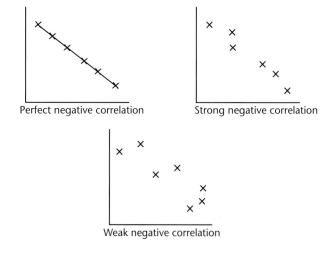

Perfect negative correlation

Strong negative correlation

Weak negative correlation

Examiner's tip

When commenting on a scatter diagram it is better (and quicker) to use the correct terms such as 'strong positive correlation' rather than using phrases like 'the more hours of sunshine, the more ice-creams are sold'.

Lines of best fit

Look again at the graph for ice-cream and hours of sunshine.

A straight line has been drawn on it, passing through the cluster of points. There are as many points above the line as there are below it. This is the 'best' straight line that can be drawn to show the trend of the points. It is called the **line of best fit**.

It should ignore any points that obviously do not fit the trend. These are called **outliers**. A line of best fit should **not** be attempted if there is little or no correlation.

The line of best fit can be used to estimate values that are not in the original table. For example, you could estimate that for 5 hours of sunshine 210 ice-creams would be sold.

If the line of best fit is used to estimate values it must be recognised that:

- if the correlation is not good the estimate will probably not be a very good one
- estimates should **not** be made too far beyond the range of the given points. For example, in the above case, estimates should not be made for 15 hours of sunshine.

Examples of bad 'lines of best fit'

Fault: Slope about right but does not have the same number of points on either side.

Fault: Same number of points either side but slope wrong.

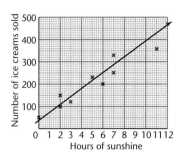

The line of best fit should reflect the slope of the points and have approximately the same number of points on either side.

Exercise 16.2a

1. The scatter diagram below shows the number of sunbeds hired out and the hours of sunshine at Brightsea.

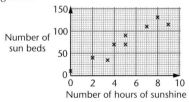

Comment on the results shown by the scatter graph.

2. A firm noted the number of days 'sick-leave' taken by its employees in a year, and their ages. The results are shown in the graph.

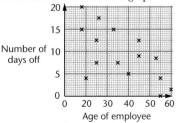

Comment on the results shown by the scatter graph.

Exercise 16.2a continued

3. The table below shows the Maths and Science marks of eight pupils in their last examination.

Pupil	A	B	C	D	E	F	G	H
Maths mark	10	20	96	50	80	70	26	58
Science mark	30	28	80	55	62	70	38	48

(a) Draw a scatter graph to show this information, with the Maths score on the x-axis.

(b) Comment on the graph.

(c) Draw a line of best fit.

(d) Use your line of best fit to estimate:
   (i) the mark in Science of a pupil who scored 40 in Maths
   (ii) the mark in Maths of a pupil who scored 75 in Science.

4. The table below shows the amount of petrol left in the fuel tank after the number of miles travelled.

Number of miles	50	100	150	200	250	300
Number of gallons	7	5.2	4.2	2.6	1.2	0.4

(a) Draw a scatter graph to show this information, with the number of miles on the x-axis.

(b) Comment on the graph.

(c) Draw a line of best fit.

(d) Use your line of best fit to estimate the number of gallons left after 170 miles.

5. In Kim's game 20 objects are placed on a table and you are given a certain time to look at them. They are removed or covered up and you then have to recall as many as possible. The table shows the amount of time given to nine people and the number of items they remembered.

Time in seconds	20	25	30	35	40	45	50	55	60
Number of items	9	8	12	10	12	15	13	16	18

(a) Draw a scatter graph to show this information, with the amount of time on the x-axis.

(b) Comment on the graph.

(c) Draw a line of best fit.

(d) Use your line of best fit to estimate the number of items remembered if 32 seconds are allowed.

(e) Why should the graph not be used to estimate the number of items remembered in three seconds?

6. Sanjay thinks that the more time he spends on his school work, the less money he will spend. Sketch a scatter graph that shows this.

Exercise 16.2b

1. A teacher thinks that there is a correlation between how far back in class a pupil sits and how well they do at Maths. To test this she plotted their last Maths grade against the row they sit in. Here is the graph she drew.

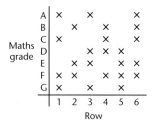

Was the teacher right? Give your reasons.

2. The scatter graph below shows the positions of football teams in the league and their mean crowd numbers, in thousands.

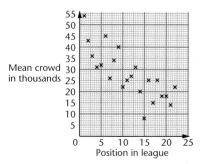

Comment on the graph.

3. The scatter graph shows the ages of people and the numbers of lessons they took before they passed their driving tests.

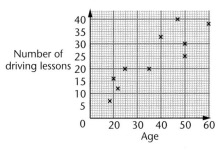

Comment on the graph.

4. In Jane's class a number of pupils have part-time jobs. Jane thinks that the more time they spend on their jobs, the worse they will do at school. She asked ten of them how many hours a week they spend on their jobs, and found their mean marks in the last examinations. Her results are shown in the table.

Pupil	A	B	C	D	E	F	G	H	I	J
Time on part-time job (hours)	9	19	13	3	15	20	5	17	6	22
Mean mark in examination	50	92	52	70	26	10	80	36	74	24

(a) Plot a scatter graph to show Jane's results, with time in hours on the *x*-axis.
(b) Do the results confirm Jane's views? Are there any exceptions?
(c) Draw a line of best fit for the relevant points.
(d) Estimate the mean score of a pupil who spent 12 hours on their part-time job.

5. In an experiment, Tom's reaction times are tested after he has undergone vigorous exercise. The table shows Tom's reaction times and the amounts of time spent in exercise.

Amount of exercise (minutes)	0	10	20	30	40	50
Reaction time	0.34	0.46	0.52	0.67	0.82	0.91

(a) Draw a scatter graph to show this information, with the number of minutes of exercise on the *x*-axis.
(b) Comment on the graph.
(c) Draw a line of best fit.
(d) Use your line of best fit to estimate Tom's reaction time after 35 minutes' exercise.

6. Fiona thinks that the more she practises, the more goals she will score at hockey. Sketch a scatter graph to show this.

Time series

The table below shows the value, in thousands of pounds, of an ice-cream company's quarterly sales for 1995 to 1998.

	First quarter	Second quarter	Third quarter	Fourth quarter
1995	145	256	328	258
1996	189	244	365	262
1997	190	266	359	250
1998	201	259	401	265

The graph illustrates these figures.

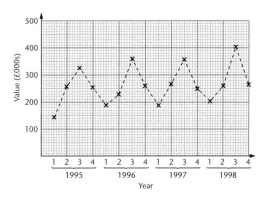

Note that the points have been joined, in order, by dotted lines. In general, points on graphs should only be joined up when it makes sense to read information between the points. Here, since the figures are total sales it does not really make sense to do so. However it is often useful to join the points with dotted lines to show the **trend**.

The figures and the graph are an example of a **time series**. You can see there are **peaks** at each third quarter and **troughs** at each first quarter. With a repeating pattern or **cyclical** effect like this it is sometimes difficult to see trends.

Other examples of figures that may be cyclical are monthly or seasonal rainfall, or monthly or seasonal unemployment figures in certain areas.

Moving averages

Moving averages can help you see trends in figures that are cyclical. They are calculated as follows.

Look at the figures for the first four quarters above.

The mean = (145 + 256 + 328 + 258) ÷ 4 = 246.75

Then find the mean for the second group of consecutive quarters.

(256 + 328 + 258 + 189) ÷ 4 = 257.75

Notice that 1995's first quarter is omitted and 1996's first quarter is included.

Now find the next mean by omitting the 256 and including the next quarter, 244, that is:

(328 + 258 + 189 + 244) ÷ 4 = 254.75

The next mean is (258 + 189 + 244 + 365) ÷ 4 = 264

Continue until the last quarter is included, each time omitting the first figure and picking up the next one in the table.

If all the quarters' figures are put in order and numbered as below, the lines underneath move along one each time and indicate the numbers that should be used.

1	2	3	4	5	6	7	8	9	10	11	12	13	14	15	16
145	256	328	258	189	244	365	262	190	266	359	250	201	259	401	265

and so on.

Check that you agree with this complete list.

Quarters	1–4	2–5	3–6	4–7	5–8	6–9	7–10
Moving average	246.75	257.75	254.75	264	265	265.25	270.75

Quarters	8–11	9–12	10–13	11–14	12–15	13–16
Moving average	269.25	266.25	269	267.25	277.75	281.5

These points are now plotted on the graph, at the middle of each interval of points, for example at 2.5 for quarters 1 to 4, at 3.5 for the next four quarters and so on.

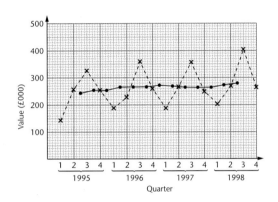

You can see that plotting the moving averages flattens out the peaks and troughs and gives a fairly flat graph, with possibly a slight overall increase.

Using four figures to find a moving average, as in the case in quarterly figures, gives a **four-quarter moving average**. If the figures varied monthly, 12-month moving averages may be found using the means of 12 consecutive months.

Exercise 16.3a

1. The table below shows the gross Accident and Health Insurance premiums (in millions of euros) paid in the Netherlands for the four quarters of 1997 to 1999.

	1st quarter	2nd quarter	3rd quarter	4th quarter
1997	43	17	15	15
1998	47	19	18	18
1999	57	26	22	13

(a) Plot these figures in a graph. Use a scale of 1 cm to each quarter on the horizontal axis and 2 cm to 10 million euros on the vertical axis.
(b) Calculate the four-quarter moving averages.
(c) Plot the moving averages on your graph.
(d) Comment on the general trend and the quarterly variation.

2. The table below shows the total sales (in megawatts) of Danish wind turbines in the years 1995 to 1998.

	1st quarter	2nd quarter	3rd quarter	4th quarter
1995	96.6	125.8	122.9	229.1
1996	74.1	143.1	173.0	335.9
1997	216.2	234.2	234.5	282.6
1998	168.8	239.7	282.1	525.4

(a) Plot these figures in a graph. Use a scale of 1 cm to each quarter on the horizontal axis and 2 cm to 100 megawatts on the vertical axis.
(b) Calculate the four-quarter moving averages.
(c) Plot the moving averages on your graph.
(d) Comment on the general trend and the quarterly variation.

Exercise 16.3a continued

3. The table below shows a company's quarterly sales (in £000s) of raincoats in the years 1996–99.

	1st quarter	2nd quarter	3rd quarter	4th quarter
1996	154	121	63	134
1997	132	106	72	108
1998	115	111	58	97
1999	110	93	47	82

(a) Plot these figures in a graph. Use a scale of 1 cm to each quarter on the horizontal axis and 2 cm to £20 000 on the vertical axis.
(b) Calculate the four-quarter moving averages.
(c) Plot the moving averages on your graph.
(d) Comment on the general trend and the quarterly variation.

4. The table below shows the daily audiences for a four-week Christmas pantomime season.

	Mon	Tues	Wed	Thurs	Fri	Sat
Week 1	256	312	324	452	600	580
Week 2	297	367	382	538	600	600
Week 3	248	327	325	495	570	583
Week 4	192	219	287	306	490	572

(a) Plot these figures in a graph. Use a scale of 1 cm to each day on the horizontal axis and 2 cm to 100 people on the vertical axis. Turn your graph paper to make the graph fit well.
(b) Calculate the six-day moving averages.
(c) Plot the moving averages on your graph.
(d) Comment on the general trend and the daily variation.

Exercise 16.3b

1. The table below shows a household's quarterly expenditure (in pounds) on fuel and light in the years 1995–98.

	1st quarter	2nd quarter	3rd quarter	4th quarter
1995	380	272	264	371
1996	432	285	207	272
1997	298	192	158	285
1998	310	208	182	291

(a) Plot these figures in a graph. Use a scale of 1 cm to each quarter on the horizontal axis and 2 cm to £100 on the vertical axis.
(b) Calculate the four-quarter moving averages.
(c) Plot the moving averages on your graph.
(d) Comment on the general trend and the quarterly variation.
(e) During this period, major insulation work was carried out on the house. When do you think that was?

2. The table below shows the number of bankruptcies in Auckland by quarters from 1995 to 1998.

	1st quarter	2nd quarter	3rd quarter	4th quarter
1995	60	61	72	57
1996	83	75	90	66
1997	62	96	99	79
1998	72	63	79	65

(a) Plot these figures in a graph. Use a scale of 1 cm to each quarter on the horizontal axis and 2 cm to 20 bankruptcies on the vertical axis.

(b) Calculate the four-quarter moving averages.

(c) Plot the moving averages on your graph.

(d) Comment on the general trend and the quarterly variation.

3. The table below shows the daily sales (in £000) of a shop over a three-week period.

	Mon	Tues	Wed	Thurs	Fri	Sat	Sun
Week 1	7.3	8.8	9.2	10.3	15.5	16.2	12.8
Week 2	6.7	7.8	10.1	11.8	14.7	17.9	11.3
Week 3	7.1	6.3	8.2	10.9	12.9	16.6	11.6

(a) Plot these figures in a graph. Use a scale of 1 cm to each day on the horizontal axis and 2 cm to £2000 on the vertical axis. Turn your graph paper to make the graph fit well.

(b) Calculate the seven-day moving averages.

(c) Plot the moving averages on your graph.

(d) Comment on the general trend and the quarterly variation.

4. The table below shows the monthly number (in hundred thousands) of US Citizens flying to Europe from 1997 to 1998.

	Jan	Feb	Mar	Apr	May	Jun
1997	5.8	5.4	7.6	7.5	10.3	11.8
1998	6.3	5.9	8.9	8.5	11.0	12.8
1999	6.4	6.2	10.3	9.3	11.5	13.2

	Jul	Aug	Sep	Oct	Nov	Dec
1997	10.9	9.9	10.2	8.0	6.8	7.0
1998	12.0	10.3	10.8	8.8	7.1	7.4
1999	12.5	11.0	11.1	9.4	8.2	7.5

(a) Plot these figures in a graph. Use a scale of 1 cm to two months on the horizontal axis and 1 cm to 100 000 citizens on the vertical axis.

(b) Calculate the 12-month moving averages.

(c) Plot the moving averages on your graph.

(d) Comment on the general trend and the monthly variation.

Key points

- The mean, median and mode can be used to compare distributions.
- The range and interquartile range can be used to compare the spread of distributions.
- The interquartile range disregards extreme values.
- Scatter graphs show the correlation between two variables.
- If there is reasonable correlation, a line of best fit can be drawn.
- The line of best fit should reflect the slope of the points and should have approximately the same number of points on either side.
- The line of best fit can be used to estimate values of one variable if the other is known.
- The line of best fit can only be used to estimate values within the range of the given data.
- A time series shows the variation of sets of figures over periods of time. These periods can be quarterly, daily, monthly, etc. These are usually displayed on a graph.
- To calculate a moving average, for example for quarterly figures, first calculate the mean for the first four quarters. Then omit the first quarter and include the fifth quarter and find the new mean. Then omit the second quarter and include the sixth, and so on.
- The moving averages are plotted at the middle of the interval.

Perfect positive correlation

Perfect negative correlation

Strong positive correlation

Strong negative correlation

Weak positive correlation

Weak negative correlation

No correlation

Revision exercise 16a

1. Over the last month, David's mean journey time to work has been 43 minutes, with an interquartile range of 7 minutes. Angie's mean time is 32 minutes with an interquartile range of 12 minutes. Make two comparisons of David and Angie's journey times.

2. Eleven members of 10g and eleven members of 10f are given a Maths problem to solve. The times they took to solve the problem are shown in the table.

10f	17	15	11	9	6	27	18	21	6	19	8

10g	4	13	15	11	32	7	9	12	6	10	14

Find the median and range for each class and comment on the results. Why might the inter-quartile range be a better measurement to use?

3. The table shows the prices of a sample of 100 houses in the north-west of England.

Price (£000)	Number of houses
$20 < x \leqslant 40$	4
$40 < x \leqslant 60$	15
$60 < x \leqslant 80$	27
$80 < x \leqslant 100$	41
$100 < x \leqslant 120$	10
$120 < x \leqslant 140$	3

Use mid-interval values of £30 000, £50 000, £70 000, £90 000, £110 000 and £130 000 to estimate the mean house price in the sample. A similar sample in the south-east gave a mean of £107 000 and a range of £150 000. Compare the two areas.

4. A survey on 50 adults in each of England and France studied the amount of wine consumed in a year. The table shows the mean and interquartile range of the number of bottles consumed in each country. Compare the two countries.

	Mean	Interquartile range
England	21	9
France	46	8

5. These cumulative frequency diagrams show the marks obtained in examinations in French and English by 200 pupils in year 8.

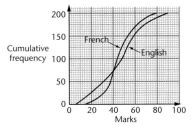

(a) Draw box plots for each of the languages.
(b) Use the median and interquartile range for each subject to compare the results.

6. The scatter graphs show heights and weights of ten boys and ten girls. Compare the two graphs, noting any differences and any similarities.

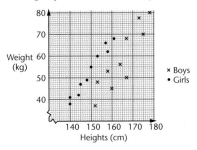

7. Brian thinks that the more he practises, the lower his golf score will be. State the type of correlation of which this is an example.

8. The table shows marks given, out of 30, by two judges for eight cats for quality of their coats.

Cat	A	B	C	D	E	F	G	H
Judge 1	17	23	15	28	22	18	27	14
Judge 2	7	23	9	27	13	15	25	4

(a) Draw a scatter diagram to show the judges' scores, with Judge 1 on the *x*-axis.

(b) Comment on the relationship between the two judges' scores.
(c) Draw a line of best fit.
(d) Judge 2 gave a ninth cat 18 marks. Estimate the marks that Judge 1 would give the same cat.

9. Market research predicts that the possible prices for replica shirts would lead to sales as in the table below.

Price (£)	20	25	30	35	40	45	50
Number of shirts	7600	7400	6800	5600	5400	4500	3600

(a) Draw a scatter graph for this information.
(b) Comment on the relationship between price and predicted sales.
(c) Draw a line of best fit.
(d) Estimate the sales of shirts if the price were fixed at £33.
(e) Why would it be wrong to predict the sales if the price were fixed at £65?

10. A survey is carried out at the checkout of a supermarket. It investigates the total cost of bills and the number of items bought. Sketch what you think the scatter diagram would look like, with number of items on the *x*-axis and total cost of the bill on the *y*-axis.

11. The table shows the number of unemployed people at the end of each quarter in Devon, to the nearest 100. The months indicate the end of the quarter for which the figures are given.

	January	April	July	October
1996	41 700	38 300	35 600	33 100
1997	33 800	28 500	24 600	23 500
1998	26 600	24 000	22 200	21 100
1999	23 800	20 900	18 900	17 700

(a) Plot these figures in a graph. Use a scale of 1 cm to each quarter on the horizontal axis and 2 cm to 10 000 people on the vertical axis.
(b) Calculate the four-quarter moving averages.
(c) Plot the moving averages on your graph.
(d) Comment on the general trend and the quarterly variation.

Locus

Identifying a locus

The locus of a point is the path or the region that the point covers as it moves according to a particular rule.

The plural of locus is loci.

The locus of a point 3 cm from A is a circle, centre A, radius 3 cm.

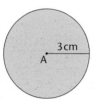

The locus of a point less than (<) 3 cm from A is the region inside a circle centre A, radius 3 cm.

The locus of a point greater than (>) 3 cm from A is the region outside a circle centre A, radius 3 cm.

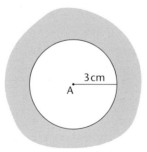

You need to know some other basic loci.

The locus of a point 2 cm from a straight line is a pair of lines parallel to that line, 2 cm away from it on either side.

	locus
2 cm ↕	given line
2 cm ↕	locus

The locus of a point that stays an equal distance from two points is the perpendicular bisector of the line joining the two points.

The locus of a point that stays an equal distance from two intersecting lines is the pair of lines that bisect the angles between the lines. Can you see why this is so?

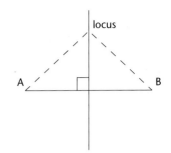

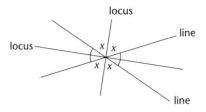

Drawing the perpendiculars to the lines from a point on the locus creates two congruent triangles.

Sketching loci

When you sketch a locus, draw it as accurately as you can but not to size or with accurately constructed bisectors. You must mark all the distances and angles that are equal.

Examiner's tip

The locus of the points equidistant from two lines is a pair of lines, but normally you only require one.

Example 1

A line is 6 cm long. Sketch the locus of all points that are 2 cm from the line.

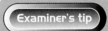

The locus is two parallel lines with a semicircle joining them at each end.

Examiner's tip

Even if you are asked to sketch a locus, use a ruler and draw the angles as near to the required size as you can.

Example 2

Two towns A and B are 6 miles apart. Make a sketch and shade the region that is nearer to B than A.

Draw the perpendicular bisector of the line AB and shade the region on B's side of the line. The shading could go past B and up or down the page further.

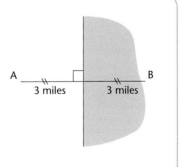

The two parts of the line AB need to be shown as 3 miles each, and the 90° angle must be indicated.

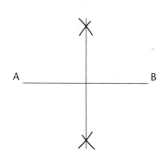

Constructing loci

You need to know two constructions.

1. The perpendicular bisector of a line

This is the locus of a point that moves so that it is equidistant from two points.

Draw the line AB.
Open the compasses to a radius that is more than half the length of AB.
Put the compass point at A and draw an arc above and below the line.
Keep the compasses set to the same radius.
Put the compass point at B and draw an arc above and below the line.
Join the two points where the arcs meet.

2. The bisector of an angle

This is the locus of a point that moves so that it is equidistant from two lines.

Draw an angle and mark the vertex (corner) A.
Put the point of the compasses at A and draw an arc to cut the lines forming the angle at B and C.
Put the point at B and draw an arc in the angle.
Keep the compasses set to the same radius.
Put the point at C and draw an arc in the angle to cut the arc just drawn.
Draw a straight line through A and the point where the arcs cut.
The bisector could be continued to the left of A. If the lines are extended, another bisector could be drawn, perpendicular to the first one.

Use these constructions, and what you already know, to draw various loci.

Examiner's tip

A similar method can be used to draw the perpendicular from a point P to a line I. Start with an arc, centre P. Use the points A and B as before.

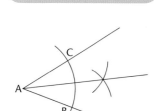

Examiner's tip

These methods are more accurate that just using measurement.

Example B Draw a triangle ABC with sides AB = 5 cm , AC = 4 cm and A = 50°.

Use compasses to bisect angle A. Shade in the locus of the points inside the triangle that are nearer to AB than AC.

This diagram is half-size.

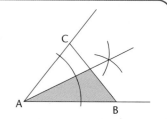

Exercise 17.1a

1. Draw a circle, centre A, radius 5 cm. Shade the locus of the points that are less than 5 cm from A.
2. Draw a rectangle 4 cm by 5 cm. Sketch the locus of the points that are 1 cm from the perimeter of the rectangle, outside the rectangle.
3. Draw a rectangle ABCD with AB = 6 cm and BC = 4 cm. Sketch the locus of the points inside the rectangle that are nearer to A than B.
4. Draw two parallel lines across the page, 4 cm apart. Draw the locus of the points that are 1 cm from the top line and 3 cm from the bottom line.
5. A fox never travels more than 5 miles from its den or earth. Draw a sketch to show the region where it travels.
6. Draw a line 7 cm long. Construct the perpendicular bisector of the line.
7. Draw an angle of 70°. Construct the bisector of the angle.
8. Construct a triangle ABC with AB = 8 cm, AC = 7 cm and BC = 5 cm. Use compasses and a ruler to bisect angle A. Shade the locus of the points inside the triangle that are nearer to AB than AC.
9. Draw a square ABCD with side 6 cm. Construct the locus of the points that are equidistant from A and C. What do you notice about the locus?
10. Draw triangle ABC with AB = 8 cm, A = 90° and B = 40°. Do a construction to find the locus of the points inside the triangle that are nearer to AC than BC.

Examiner's tip

In most cases you will be asked to construct a locus either to size or to scale. Draw it as accurately as you can. Do not stop the line of a construction at the intersection of the arcs. Draw it through the intersection. When you do a construction, leave in your construction lines.

Exercise 17.1b

1. Show, by shading, the locus of the points that are more than 4 cm from a fixed point A.
2. Draw a line 6 cm long. Show, by shading in a sketch, the locus of the points that are less than 2 cm from the line.
3. Draw an angle of 80°. Construct the bisector of the angle.
4. Draw a line AB 6 cm long. Construct the perpendicular bisector of AB.
5. Draw a square with side 4 cm. Label one corner A. Show the locus of the points inside the square that are less than 3 cm from A.
6. Draw a rectangle ABCD with sides AB = 7 cm and BC = 5 cm. Use compasses to construct the line equidistant from AB and AC.
7. Construct the triangle ABC with A = 30°, B = 50° and AB = 10 cm. Construct the locus of the points equidistant from A and B.
8. Two towns Bimouth and Tritown are 10 miles apart. Phoebe wants to live nearer to Bimouth than Tritown. Using a scale of 1 cm : 2 miles, make a scale drawing and show, by shading, the region where she can live.
9. Draw a triangle ABC with AB = 7 cm, A = 50° and B = 40°. Show, by shading, the locus of the points within the triangle that are nearer to AC than BC.
10. Sonia has a 20 metre flex on her lawnmower and the socket is in the middle of the back wall of her house. The back of the house is 12 m wide and her garden is a rectangle the same width as the house, stretching 24 m from the house. Using a scale of 1 cm : 4 m, make a drawing of her garden and show, by shading, the region she can reach with the mower.

Chapter 17 Identifying a locus

245

Problems involving intersection of loci

Combining all you know about loci, you can answer more complicated questions involving more than one locus.

 Example 4

Construct triangle ABC with AB = 7 cm, AC = 6 cm and BC = 4 cm. By using constructions, find the point that is equidistant from all three vertices. Mark this point D.

This diagram is not to scale

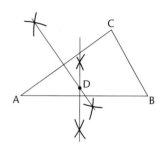

> First you need the line equidistant from two vertices. If you choose AB you need to construct the perpendicular bisector of AB. Then you need to construct the perpendicular bisector of another side. Where they cross is the required point.

> You could also bisect the third side and that line would also pass through the same point.

 Example 5

Two points A and B are 4 cm apart. Show, by shading, the locus of the points that are less than 2.5 cm from A, and nearer to B than A.

> You need to draw a circle, radius 2.5 cm and centre A. You also need to draw the bisector of the line AB. The region you require is inside the circle and on the B side of the bisector. Here the region required is shaded.

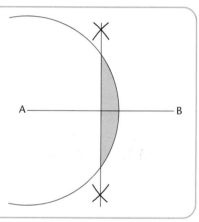

 Example 6

Erica wants to put a rocking chair in her room. She wants the chair more than 0.5 m from a wall and less than 2 m from corner A. This is a sketch of her room. Using a scale of 1 cm : 1 m, make a scale drawing of the room and show, by shading, the region where the chair can be placed.

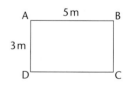

> Draw the rectangle and then add lines 0.5 cm from each side. Draw a circle, centre A radius 2 cm. In this diagram the regions not required are shaded, leaving the blank region where the chair can be placed.

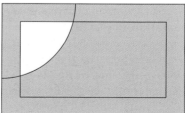

Example 7 Find the centre of the rotation that maps triangle ABC onto triangle A'B'C'.

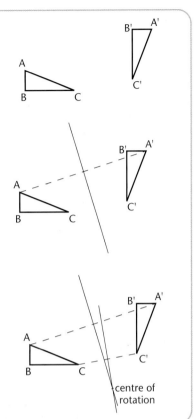

> The centre of rotation must be equidistant from A and A'. It will be on the perpendicular bisector of AA'. Arcs have been omitted to make the diagram clearer.

> The centre must also be equidistant from C and C'. The centre of rotation will be the point where the two perpendicular bisectors meet.
> The centre must also be equidistant from B and B'. Construct the perpendicular bisector of BB' to check.

Exercise 17.2a

Draw all of these accurately.

1. Two points A and B are 5 cm apart. Show, by shading, the region that is less than 3 cm from A and more than 4 cm from B.

2. A rectangle ABCD has sides AB = 5 cm and BC = 4 cm. Draw the rectangle and show, by shading, the region inside the rectangle that is nearer to AB than CD, and less than 3.5 cm from B.

3. Draw a triangle ABC with AB = 6 cm, A = 60° and B = 55°. Use constructions to find the point D that is equidistant from all three sides.

4. Draw a rectangle ABCD with sides AB = 4 cm and BC = 3 cm. Show the points that are equidistant from AB and BC and 3.5 cm from A.

5. Draw a triangle ABC with sides AB = 9 cm, BC = 6 cm and AC = 5 cm. Show, by shading, the region inside the triangle that is nearer to AB than BC and more than 3 cm from C.

6. Two towns, Hilldon and Baton are 20 miles apart. It is proposed to build a new shopping centre within 15 miles of Hilldon but nearer to Baton than Hilldon. Using a scale of 1 cm : 5 miles, make a drawing and show the region where the shopping centre can be built.

7. Richard's bedroom is rectangular with sides 4 m and 6.5 m. He wants to put a desk within 1 metre of a longer wall and within 2.5 m of the centre of the window in the middle of one of the shorter walls. Using a scale of 1 cm : 1 m, make a scale drawing and show, by shading, the region where the desk can be placed.

Examiner's tip

You can either shade the region required or shade the regions not required. It is often easier to do the latter if the regions are at all complicated.

Chapter 17 Problems involving intersection of loci

8. Kirsty has a triangular patio with sides 6 m, 4 m and 5 m. She wants to put a plant pot on the patio more than 2 m from any corner. Using a scale of 1 cm : 1 m, make a drawing and show, by shading, where she can put the plant pot.

9. This is a sketch of a plot of land that Arun wants to use for camping.

He wants to put a tap in the field within 35 m of the gate, G, which is at the middle of one of the shorter sides. He also wants to it to be within 25 m of his farm which is at corner F. Using a scale of 1 cm : 10 m, make a scale drawing of the land. Show, by shading, the position where the tap can be placed.

10. A field is in the shape of a quadrilateral ABCD with AB = 25 m, BC = 30 m, A = 90°, B = 106° and C = 65°. The farmer wants to put the scarecrow within 15 m of corner A and nearer to CD than CB. Using a scale of 1 cm to 5 m, draw the field and show, by shading, the region where the scarecrow can be placed.

1. Show, by shading, the locus of the points that are more than 2 cm from a point A and less than 3 cm from point A.

2. Two points A and B are 4 cm apart. Show, by shading, the locus of all the points that are less than 2.5 cm from A and more than 3 cm from B.

3. Draw a triangle ABC with AB = 6 cm, A = 40° and B = 35°. Use constructions to find the point D that is equidistant from A and B and 4 cm from C.

4. Draw a square with side 4 cm. Show, by shading, the region within the square that is more than 2 cm from ever vertex.

5. Draw a triangle ABC with AB = 6 cm, AC = 5 cm and A = 55°. Bisect the angle A. Draw the perpendicular bisector of AB. Show, by shading, the region that is inside the triangle, nearer to AB than AC and nearer to B than A.

6. Dave and Clare live 7 miles apart. They set out on bikes to meet. They ride directly towards each other. When they meet, Dave has ridden less than 5 miles and Clare less than 4 miles. Using a scale of 1 cm : 1 mile, make a scale drawing showing where they could have met.

7. Tariq's garden is a rectangle ABCD with AB = 10 m and BC = 4 m. He wants to put a rotary washing line in the garden. It must be more than 4 m from corner C and more than 1 m from side AB. Using a scale of 1 cm : 1 m,

make a scale drawing of the garden and show where he can put the rotary washing line.

8. The distances between three towns Arbridge, Beaton and Ceborough are AB = 25 miles, AC = 40 miles and BC = 30 miles. A new garage is to be built as near as possible to all three towns. Use a scale of 1 cm : 5 miles and make constructions to find the point D where the garage should be placed.

9. Sasha has a rectangular garage 2 m by 5 m. It has a door at one end. She wants to put a hook in the ceiling. It must be midway between the two longer sides, less than 3.5 m from the door end and less than 2.5 m from the other end. Make a scale drawing of the ceiling using a scale of 1 cm : 1 m. Show by shading the region where the hook can be fixed.

10. This is a sketch of the playing field in Towbridge.

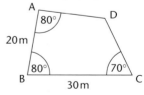

A new swing is to be placed in the field. It must be within 15 m of A and nearer to AB than AD. Use a scale of 1 cm : 5 m to make a drawing and show the region where the swing can be placed.

Key points

- A locus is the path or region where a point can move according to a rule.
- The locus of a point x cm from point A is a circle centre A, radius x cm.
- The locus of a point equidistant from two points A and B is the perpendicular bisector of the line AB.
- The locus of a point equidistant from two parallel lines is a line parallel to the two lines and midway between the lines.
- The locus of a point equidistant from two non-parallel lines is the bisector(s) of the angle(s) between the lines.

Revision exercise 17a

1. Draw an angle of 65° and construct the bisector of the angle.

2. Draw a line AB, 5 cm long. Construct the perpendicular bisector of AB.

3. Draw a triangle ABC with AB = 6 cm, A = 40° and B = 60°. Find the point D that is equidistant from A and B and also equidistant from AB and AC. Show your construction lines.

4. Two points A and B are 6 cm apart. Show, by shading, the locus of the points that are less than 5 cm from A and more than 5 cm from B.

5. Draw a rectangle ABCD with sides AB = 4 cm and BC = 3 cm. Show the locus of the points outside the rectangle that are within 2 cm of the sides of the rectangle.

6. Draw a triangle ABC with AB = 8 cm, A = 47° and AC = 5 cm. Show the locus of the points inside the triangle that are nearer to AB than BC.

7. This diagram shows the position of three schools.

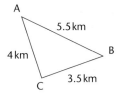

It is decided to build a swimming pool for the three schools. It must not be more than 3.5 km from any of the schools. Using a scale of 2 cm : 1 km, make a scale drawing and show the region where the pool can be located.

8. Carterknowle Church hall is rectangular with sides AB = 12 m and BC = 5 m. The main door is at corner C. A spotlight is to be fixed on the ceiling, more than 6 m from the main door, more than 5 m from the opposite corner and nearer to AB than AD. Using a scale of 1 cm : 1 m, make a scale drawing of the hall and show the region where the light can be fitted.

9. This is a plan of the floor area of a shop.

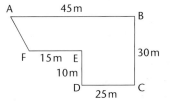

All the corners are 90° except A and F. A heat detector is placed at A and another at D. They both have a range of 20 m and do not work round corners. Using a scale of 1 cm : 5 m, make a scale drawing of the plan and show, by shading, the region that is not covered by heat detectors.

10. This is a sketch of Sanjay's patio.

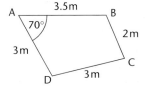

He wants to place a plant pot on the patio, within 1 metre of AB, nearer AB than AD, and no more than 2 metres from A. Using a scale of 2 cm : 1 m, make a scale drawing of the patio and show the region where the pot can be placed.

18 Proportion and variation

You will need to know:

- how to find and use multipliers
- simple algebraic manipulation of formulae and substitution.

You have met **proportion** before. Look at this example.

A car uses 12 litres of petrol to travel 100 km.
How many litres will it use to travel 250 km?

This is an example of **direct proportion**. As the distance increases so does the amount of petrol used.

The distance has been increased by multiplying by a factor of $\frac{250}{100} = 2.5$.

Increase the amount of petrol by multiplying by the same factor.
Amount of petrol = 12 × 2.5 = 30 litres.

In this example, if the distance is x km and the amount of petrol is y litres, then y is directly proportional to x.
In other words, y varies in the same way as x: if you double x, you also double y.
It is possible to express this in symbols:

$$y \propto x,$$

which is read as 'y varies as x' or 'y is proportional to x'.
Now look at this example.

It takes 4 men 10 days to dig a hole.
How long will it take 20 men?

This is an example of **inverse proportion**. As the number of men increases the time taken will decrease.

The number of men has increased by multiplying by a factor of $\frac{20}{4} = 5$.

Decrease the time by dividing by the same factor.
Number of days = 10 ÷ 5 = 2.
(Of course, this does assume that there will be room for all the men in the hole!)

This time, if the number of men is x and the number of days y, then y is inversely proportional to x. In other words, y varies inversely as x: if you double x, you halve y. This is the same as y varies as $\frac{1}{x}$, so in symbols:

$$y \propto \frac{1}{x}$$

Examiner's tip

You can easily tell whether the proportion is direct or inverse: in direct proportion both variables change in the same way, either up or down; in inverse proportion, when one variable goes up the other goes down.

Exercise 18.1a

Describe the variation in each of these, using the symbol $\propto$.

1. The length of tape y and the time of the recording x.
2. The cost of a train ticket y and the length of the journey x.
3. The time the journey takes t and the speed of the train s.
4. The number of pages in a book p and the number of words w.
5. The probability my ticket wins the raffle p and the number of raffle tickets sold n.

Describe the variation shown in each of these tables of values. Use the symbol $\propto$.

6.

x	3	15
y	1	5

7.

x	3	15
y	10	2

8.

x	8	20
y	10	4

9.

x	10	12
y	50	60

10.

x	24	4.8
y	16	3.2

Exercise 18.1b

Describe the variation in each of these, using the symbol $\propto$.

1. The depth of water in a rectangular tank d and the length of time it has been filling t.
2. The number of buses b needed to carry 2000 people and the number of seats on a bus s.
3. The time a journey takes t and the distance covered at a fixed speed s.
4. The number of ice creams you can buy c and the amount of money you have m.
5. The probability I win the raffle p and the number of raffle tickets I buy n.

Describe the variation shown in each of these tables of values. Use the symbol $\propto$.

6.

x	3	15
y	5	1

7.

x	3	15
y	2	10

8.

x	8	20
y	10	25

9.

x	1	0.1
y	50	500

10.

x	16	56
y	6.4	22.4

Variation as a formula

If $y \propto x$ then the same factor is applied to y as was applied to x.

Example 3

Find the formula for x and y.

x	5	15
y	3	9

$y \propto x$ as $5 \times 3 = 15$ for x and $3 \times 3 = 9$ for y.

Now look at the pairs of values of x and y,

(5, 3) and (15, 9). In the first pair, $\dfrac{y}{x} = \dfrac{3}{5}$.

But this is also true for the second pair, as $\dfrac{9}{15} = \dfrac{3}{5}$.

Rewriting the equation gives a formula $y = \frac{3}{5}x$.

Example 4

Find the formula for *Example 2*.

x	4	20
y	10	2

This time $y \propto \dfrac{1}{x}$. Write the values of $\dfrac{1}{x}$ in the table.

$\dfrac{1}{x}$	0.25	0.05
y	10	2

So now $y \div \dfrac{1}{x} = 10 \div 0.25$.

Hence $y \div \dfrac{1}{x} = 40$.

This gives the formula $y = \dfrac{40}{x}$. Check that it works in the table.

There is another way to do this, which you may have spotted already.

In the first table, find the value of $x \times y$. This is 40, so the formula is $xy = 40$, which is equivalent to $y = \dfrac{40}{x}$.

Exercise 18.2a

Find formulae for the variations in Exercise 18.1a, questions 6, 7, 8, 9 and 10.

Exercise 18.2b

Find formulae for the variations in Exercise 18.1b, questions 6, 7, 8, 9 and 10.

Other variation

Sometimes two variables can be related in more complicated ways. We will look at:

$$y \propto x^2, \ y \propto x^3 \text{ and } y \propto \frac{1}{x^2}$$

Example 5

$y \propto x^2$.
If $y = 10$ when $x = 5$, what is y when $x = 15$?

x has been multiplied by $15 \div 5 = 3$,
so y will be multiplied by $3^2 = 9$.
$y = 10 \times 9 = 90$.

Example 6

$y \propto \dfrac{1}{x^2}$ (sometimes called the 'inverse square law' for obvious reasons)
If $y = 10$ when $x = 5$, what is y when $x = 10$?

x has been multiplied by $10 \div 5 = 2$,
so y will be divided by $2^2 = 4$.
$y = 10 \div 4 = 2.5$.

Exercise 18.3a

1. $y \propto x^2$, $y = 3$ when $x = 6$. Find y when $x = 12$.
2. $y \propto x^2$, $y = 9$ when $x = 7.5$. Find y when $x = 5$.
3. $y \propto x^3$, $y = 1$ when $x = 3$. Find y when $x = 6$.
4. $y \propto \dfrac{1}{x^2}$, $y = 4$ when $x = 4$. Find y when $x = 8$.
5. $y \propto x^2$, $y = 5$ when $x = 6$. Find y when $x = 3$.
6. $y \propto \dfrac{1}{x^2}$, $y = 10$ when $x = 3$. Find y when $x = 12$.
7. $y \propto \dfrac{1}{x^2}$, $y = 10$ when $x = 4$. Find y when $x = 6$.
8. $y \propto x^3$, $y = 12$ when $x = 5$. Find y when $x = 10$.
9. $y \propto x^3$, $y = 3$ when $x = 10$. Find y when $x - 5$.
10. $y \propto x^2$, $y = 7$ when $x = 8$. Find y when $x = 6$.

Describe the variation shown in each of these tables of values. Use the symbol $\propto$.

11.

x	5	25
y	5	125

12.

x	5	10
y	5	1.25

13

x	5	15
y	5	135

14.

x	5	2.5
y	5	10

15.

x	4	6
y	18	8

Examiner's tip

When finding the variation or the formula, start by deciding if the proportion is direct or inverse. This reduces the number of possibilities to be tried.

1. $y \propto x^3$, $y = 4$ when $x = 5$. Find y when $x = 10$.
2. $y \propto x^2$, $y = 2$ when $x = 2$. Find y when $x = 8$.
3. $y \propto \dfrac{1}{x^2}$, $y = 7$ when $x = 7$. Find y when $x = 14$.
4. $y \propto \dfrac{1}{x}$, $y = 1$ when $x = 1$. Find y when $x = 0.5$.
5. $y \propto x$, $y = 8$ when $x = 3$. Find y when $x = 10.5$.
6. $y \propto \dfrac{1}{x^2}$, $y = 3$ when $x = 1$. Find y when $x = 0.5$.
7. $y \propto x^3$, $y = 14$ when $x = 12$. Find y when $x = 15$.
8. $y \propto x^2$, $y = 2$ when $x = 6.5$. Find y when $x = 19.5$.
9. $y \propto x^2$, $y = 5$ when $x = 0.6$. Find y when $x = 2.4$.
10. $y \propto \dfrac{1}{x^2}$, $y = 9$ when $x = 3$. Find y when $x = 1$.

Describe the variation shown in each of these tables of values. Use the symbol $\propto$.

11.

x	2	6
y	7	63

12.

x	1	0.25
y	1	4

13

x	54	21.6
y	33	13.2

14.

x	16	8
y	15	1.875

15.

x	24	48
y	4	1

Formulae

Finding formulae for other variations can be done in a similar way to the previous ones. There is another approach, however.

Example 7

Here is the result of Example 5 in a table:

x	5	15
y	10	90

$y \propto x^2$ so try the formula $y = kx^2$, where k is a constant to be found.
Substitute 5 and 10 for x and y.
$$10 = k \times 5^2, \text{ giving } k = 0.4.$$
Substitute 15 and 90 as a check.
$$90 = 0.4 \times 15^2, \text{ which is correct.}$$
So $y = 0.4x^2$

Example 8

Here is the result of of Example 6 in a table:

x	5	10
y	10	2.5

$y \propto \dfrac{1}{x^2}$, so try the formula $y = \dfrac{k}{x^2}$.
Substitute 5 and 10 for x and y.
$$10 = \frac{k}{5^2}, \text{ giving } k = 250.$$
Substitute 10 and 2.5 as a check.
$$2.5 = \frac{250}{100}, \text{ which is correct.}$$
So $y = \dfrac{250}{x^2}$

Exercise 18.4a

Find formulae for each of the questions in Exercise 18.3a.

Exercise 18.4b

Find formulae for each of the questions in Exercise 18.3b.

Key points

- The notation '$\propto$' means 'varies as' or 'is proportional to'.
- Direct proportion includes $y \propto x$, $y \propto x^2$ and $y \propto x^3$ and the formulae for these are $y = kx$, $y = kx^2$, $y = kx^3$, respectively.

- Inverse proportion includes $y \propto \dfrac{1}{x}$ and $y \propto \dfrac{1}{x^2}$ and the formulae for these are $y = \dfrac{k}{x}$ and $y = \dfrac{k}{x^2}$ respectively.

Revision exercise 18a

1. In a desert, a man drinks 7 litres of water in 2 days. How many litres will he drink in 5 days? Find a formula for the number of litres of water, w, drunk in d days.

2. Five men can paint a long wall in 6 days. How long will it take 3 men to paint the same wall? Find a formula for the number of days d it takes n men to paint the wall.

3. The attractive force between two objects is inversely proportional to the square of their distance apart. The force is 0.24 units when the distance is 15 units. What will be the force when the distance is 30 units? Find a formula for the force f in terms of the distance apart d.

4. Complete the table to find the corresponding values of y.

		$y \propto x$	$y \propto x^2$	$y \propto x^3$	$y \propto \dfrac{1}{x}$	$y \propto \dfrac{1}{x^2}$
x	2	10	10	10	10	10
y	5					

5. In each part, find the variation, using $\propto$, and find the formula.

(a)
x	5	10
y	10	5

(b)
x	5	50
y	10	100

(c)
x	2	10
y	0.1	0.02

(d)
x	2	10
y	0.1	2.5

(e)
x	5	10
y	1	0.25

(f)
x	1	10
y	0.4	400

- how to solve linear equations and inequalities
- how to factorise simple expressions and quadratics where the coefficient of $x^2 = 1$
- how to solve simple quadratic equations by factorisation and graphical methods
- how to rearrange simple formulae
- how to expand brackets and manipulate simple algebraic expressions
- how to draw linear, quadratic and cubic graphs.

Factorising quadratic expressions where the coefficient of $x^2 \neq 1$

You have already learnt how to factorise simple quadratic expressions such as

$$x^2 + bx + c$$

You should already know:
- if c is positive find two numbers that multiply to c and add up to b
- if c is negative find two numbers that multiply to c and whose difference is b.

The expression $ax^2 + bx + c$ when factorised will be
$(px + q)(rx + s) = prx^2 + (ps + qr)x + qs$, when expanded.

So $pr = a$, $qs = c$ and $ps + qr = b$. As before the sign of c defines whether you are looking for a sum or a difference.

It is easiest to look at examples.

Example 1

Factorise $3x^2 + 11x + 6$.

As the last sign is +, both signs in the bracket are the same and, as the middle sign is +, they are both +.

The only numbers that can multiply to give 3, for the $3x^2$, are 3 and 1.

So as a start $(3x + \quad)(x + \quad)$.

The numbers that multiply to give 6 are either 3 and 2 or 6 and 1.

So the possible answers are

$(3x + 2)(x + 3)$ or $(3x + 3)(x + 2)$ or $(3x + 6)(x + 1)$ or $(3x + 1)(x + 6)$

By expanding the brackets it can be seen that the first one is correct.

The coefficient of the middle term is $3 \times 3 + 2 \times 1 = 9 + 2 = 11$.

So $3x^2 + 11x + 6 = (3x + 2)(x + 3)$

It is very useful to check completely by multiplying out the two brackets.

Writing out all the possible brackets can be a long process and it is quicker to test the possibilities for the middle term until you find the correct one and then multiply out the brackets to check.

 Example 2

Factorise $4x^2 - 14x + 6$.

The first thing to check is if there is any common factor.

$\quad 4x^2 - 14x + 6 = 2(2x^2 - 7x + 3)$ \qquad Common factor 2.

Now look at the quadratic expression.

Here you can see that both signs in the brackets are − and that everything is added.

The possibilities for first terms in the brackets are 2 and 1 and for the second terms are 3 and 1 or 1 and 3. The middle term is thus $2 \times 1 + 1 \times 3 = 5$ or $2 \times 3 + 1 \times 1 = 7$. The second is correct so the quadratic factorises to $(2x - 1)(x - 3)$ and the full answer is $4x^2 - 14x + 6 = 2(2x - 1)(x - 3)$.

 Example 3

Factorise $5x^2 + 13x + 6$.

No common factor.

Both signs in the brackets are +.

First terms are 5 and 1, second are 1 and 6, 6 and 1, 3 and 2, or 2 and 3.

If you try $5 \times 1 + 1 \times 6 = 11$, $5 \times 6 + 1 \times 1 = 31$, $5 \times 3 + 1 \times 2 = 17$, $5 \times 2 + 1 \times 3 = 13$.

So the answer is $5x^2 + 13x + 6 = (5x + 3)(x + 2)$. Check by multiplying out.

Example 4

Factorise $6x^2 - 17x + 12$.

No common factor.

Both signs in the brackets are $-$.

First terms are 6 and 1 or 3 and 2, second terms are 1 and 12 or 12 and 1 or 2 and 6 or 6 and 2 or 4 and 3 or 3 and 4. This could mean 12 possible products but, if you look at the middle term and see it is 17, you can gather that you will not be multiplying anything by 12 and are unlikely to multiply anything by 6. Try the most likely ones first.

$3 \times 4 + 2 \times 3 = 18$; $3 \times 3 + 2 \times 4 = 17$ which is correct.

So the answer is $6x^2 - 17x + 12 = (3x - 4)(2x - 3)$. Check by multiplying out.

Examiner's tip

First look for any common factor then try the most obvious pairs first and remember if the sign of c is positive, everything is added and both brackets have the same sign as b.

Exercise 19.1a

Factorise the following.

1. $x^2 + 7x + 6$
2. $x^2 - 6x + 8$
3. $2x^2 + 6x + 4$
4. $2x^2 + 9x + 4$
5. $6x^2 - 15x + 6$
6. $3x^2 - 11x + 6$
7. $3x^2 - 11x + 10$
8. $4x^2 + 8x + 3$
9. $5x^2 - 13x + 6$
10. $6x^2 - 19x + 10$

Exercise 19.1b

Factorise the following.

1. $x^2 + 5x + 6$
2. $x^2 - 7x + 10$
3. $3x^2 + 7x + 2$
4. $2x^2 + 7x + 6$
5. $3x^2 - 12x + 12$
6. $3x^2 - 13x + 10$
7. $4x^2 - 16x + 15$
8. $7x^2 + 10x + 3$
9. $5x^2 - 22x + 8$
10. $8x^2 - 18x + 9$

The expressions looked at so far had c positive and so were more straightforward. In expressions where c is negative the brackets have different signs and the middle term is the difference of the products. These are again best shown by examples.

Example 5

Factorise $3x^2 - 7x - 6$.

No common factor.

The signs in the brackets are different.

First terms are 3 and 1, second terms are 1 and 6, 6 and 1, 3 and 2, or 2 and 3.

Middle term products are $3 \times 1 - 1 \times 6 = -3$, $3 \times 6 - 1 \times 1 = 17$, $3 \times 3 - 1 \times 2 = 7$. This is the correct number but the wrong signs. So the 3×3 must be negative, which means that the second term must be -3 in one of the brackets.

So the answer is $3x^2 - 7x - 6 = (3x + 2)(x - 3)$. As there was no common factor the 3s must be in separate brackets. Multiply out to check.

 Example 6

Factorise $6x^2 + 3x - 30$.

Common factor 3 so $3(x^2 + x - 10)$

Look at the quadratic expression. The signs in the brackets are different.

First terms are 2 and 1, second terms are 1 and 10, or 10 and 1 or 5 and 2 or 2 and 5.

Try the easiest products first.

Middle term products are $2 \times 5 - 1 \times 2 = 8$, $2 \times 2 - 1 \times 5 = -1$ which is the correct number but the wrong sign. So it is -2 in one bracket and the answer is $6x^2 + 3x - 30 = 3(2x + 5)(x - 2)$. Check by multiplying out.

 Example 7

Factorise $6x^2 - 5x - 4$.

No common factor.

The signs in the brackets are different.

First terms are 6 and 1 or 3 and 2, second terms are 4 and 1 and 1 and 4 or 2 and 2.

Try the easiest products first.
$3 \times 2 - 2 \times 2 = 2$, $3 \times 4 - 2 \times 1 = 10$, $3 \times 1 - 2 \times 4 = -5$ which is correct.
So the answer is $6x^2 - 5x - 4 = (3x - 4)(2x + 1)$. Check by multiplying out.

Examiner's tip

If the sign of c is negative, find the differences of products, then put numbers in brackets and lastly signs. Always check by multiplying out.

Exercise 19.2a

Factorise the following.

1. $x^2 - x - 6$
2. $x^2 + 3x - 10$
3. $2x^2 + 5x - 3$
4. $3x^2 - 2x - 8$
5. $2x^2 + 9x - 5$

6. $5x^2 - 15x - 50$
7. $4x^2 - 4x - 3$
8. $3x^2 - x - 14$
9. $2x^2 - x - 21$
10. $6x^2 - 17x - 14$

Exercise 19.2b

Factorise the following.

1. $x^2 - 3x - 18$
2. $3x^2 + x - 10$
3. $2x^2 - 18$
4. $3x^2 - 11x - 4$
5. $3x^2 + 4x - 15$

6. $5x^2 + 13x - 6$
7. $7x^2 + 10x - 8$
8. $3x^2 - 11x - 20$
9. $2x^2 - 15x - 8$
10. $6x^2 - 13x - 15$

Quadratic equations

As in an earlier chapter the easiest way to solve a quadratic equation is to factorise and then put each bracket equal to zero.

 Example 8

Solve the equation $2x^2 - 7x + 3 = 0$.

Check the factorisation by multiplying out the brackets.

Factorise: $(2x - 1)(x - 3) = 0$
$2x - 1 = 0$ or $x - 3 = 0$
$2x = 1$ or $x = 3$
$x = \frac{1}{2}$ or 3

One of the brackets is zero.

 Example 9

Solve the equation $6x^2 - 8x = 0$.

Note this has only two terms.

Factorise: $2x(3x - 4) = 0$
$2x = 0$ or $3x - 4 = 0$
$x = 0$ or $\frac{4}{3}$

 Example 10

Solve the equation $2x^2 + x - 10 = 0$.

Factorise: $(2x + 5)(x - 2) = 0$

Check by multiplying out.
$2x + 5 = 0$ or $x - 2 = 0$
$2x = -5$ or $x = 2$
$x = -\frac{5}{2}$ or 2

Example 11 Solve the equation $9x^2 - 16 = 0$.

Factorise $(3x - 4)(3x + 4) = 0$

$3x - 4 = 0$ or $3x + 4 = 0$

$3x = 4$ or $3x = -4$

$x = \frac{4}{3}$ or $-\frac{4}{3}$

You should recognise the expression as the difference of two squares.

Solving quadratic equations by the formula

If the quadratic will not factorise, you will need another method. Trial and improvement is long and tedious but there is a formula!

It is not necessary to prove it at this stage but you should learn how to use it.

For the equation $ax^2 + bx + c = 0$,

the solutions are given by the formula $x = \dfrac{-b \pm \sqrt{b^2 - 4ac}}{2a}$

Use this formula for equations that cannot be factorised, although it can be used in any quadratic equation.

If we use the formula for Example 10, the equation is

$2x^2 + x - 10 = 0$ so $a = 2$, $b = +1$, $c = -10$.

The formula then gives
$$x = \frac{-1 \pm \sqrt{1 - 4 \times 2 \times (-10)}}{4}$$
$$= \frac{-1 \pm \sqrt{1 + 80}}{4}$$
$$= \frac{-1 \pm \sqrt{81}}{4}$$
$$= \frac{-1 \pm 9}{4} = \frac{8}{4} \text{ or } \frac{-10}{4}$$
$$= 2 \text{ or } -2.5$$

which is the same solution as by factorising.

Example 12 Solve the equation $x^2 - 4x + 2 = 0$.
Give your answer to 2 d.p.
$a = 1$, $b = -4$, $c = +2$
$$x = \frac{+4 \pm \sqrt{16 - 4 \times 1 \times 2}}{2}$$
$$= \frac{+4 \pm \sqrt{8}}{2}$$
$$= \frac{4 \pm 2.828}{2} = \frac{6.828}{2} \text{ or } \frac{1.172}{2}$$
$$= 3.414 \text{ or } 0.586$$
$$= 3.41 \text{ or } 0.59 \text{ to 2 d.p.}$$

Examiner's tip

It is sensible to do all the working out on a calculator but it is vital to write down the expression you are going to work out.

Example **E**   Solve the equation $3x^2 + 4x - 2 = 0$ and give the answers to 2 d.p.

$a = 3, b = 4, c = -2$

$$x = \frac{-4 \pm \sqrt{16 - 4 \times 3 \times (-2)}}{6} = \frac{-4 \pm \sqrt{16 + 24}}{6} = \frac{-4 \pm \sqrt{40}}{6}$$

$$= \frac{-4 + 6.324}{6} \text{ or } \frac{-4 + -6.324}{6}$$

$$= \frac{2.324}{6} \text{ or } \frac{-10.324}{6} = 0.3873 \text{ or } -1.7206$$

$x = 0.39$ or -1.72 to 2 d.p.

Examiner's tip

The main errors that occur in using the formula are:
1. errors with the signs, especially with $-4ac$.
2. failure to divide everything by $2a$ and not just the first term.

Exercise 19.3a

Solve the equations in Questions 1 to 8 by factorising.

1. $x^2 - x - 6 = 0$
2. $2x^2 + 9x + 7 = 0$
3. $4x^2 + 2x - 20 = 0$
4. $3x^2 - 2x = 0$
5. $5x^2 + 14x - 3 = 0$
6. $x^2 - 25 = 0$
7. $2x^2 - 3x - 9 = 0$
8. $2x^2 - 11x - 21 = 0$

Use the formula to solve the equations in questions 9 to 15. Give the answers correct to 2 d.p.

9. $x^2 + 8x + 6 = 0$
10. $2x^2 - 2x - 3 = 0$
11. $3x^2 + 5x - 1 = 0$
12. $5x^2 - 12x + 5 = 0$
13. $5x^2 + 9x - 6 = 0$
14. $x^2 - 5x - 1 = 0$
15. $3x^2 + 9x + 5 = 0$

Exercise 19.3b

Solve the equations in Questions 1 to 8 by factorising.

1. $x^2 - x - 12 = 0$
2. $2x^2 - 3x + 1 = 0$
3. $2x^2 + x = 0$
4. $5x^2 - 15x = 0$
5. $4x^2 - 36 = 0$
6. $2x^2 - 5x + 3 = 0$
7. $2x^2 - 13x - 24 = 0$
8. $4x^2 - 16x + 15 = 0$

Use the formula to solve the equations in questions 9 to 15. Give the answers correct to 2 d.p.

9. $x^2 + 7x + 4 = 0$
10. $2x^2 - 3x - 4 = 0$
11. $3x^2 + 2x - 2 = 0$
12. $5x^2 - 13x + 7 = 0$
13. $5x^2 + 9x + 3 = 0$
14. $7x^2 - 5x - 1 = 0$
15. $3x^2 + 2x - 7 = 0$

Algebraic fractions

When an expression involving fractions needs to be simplified
then it should be put over a common denominator.

Example 14 Simplify $\dfrac{x + 3}{2} - \dfrac{x - 3}{3}$.

The common denominator is 6, so $(x + 3)$ is multiplied by $6 \div 2 = 3$ and
$(x - 3)$ is multiplied by $6 \div 3 = 2$

So $\dfrac{x + 3}{2} - \dfrac{x - 3}{3} = \dfrac{3(x + 3) - 2(x - 3)}{6} = \dfrac{3x + 9 - 2x + 6}{6}$

$$= \dfrac{x + 15}{6}$$

Examiner's tip

Do not miss out the first step. Most errors occur because of wrongly
expanding the brackets without writing them down.

If the denominators involve x the procedure is still the same.

Example 15 Simplify $\dfrac{3}{x + 1} - \dfrac{2}{x}$.

The common denominator is $x(x + 1)$, so 3 is multiplied by $x(x + 1) \div (x + 1) = x$
and 2 is multiplied by $x(x + 1) \div x = (x + 1)$

So $\dfrac{3}{x + 1} - \dfrac{2}{x} = \dfrac{3x - 2(x + 1)}{x(x + 1)} = \dfrac{3x - 2x - 2}{x(x + 1)} = \dfrac{x - 2}{x(x + 1)}$

Example 16 Simplify $\dfrac{x}{x + 3} - \dfrac{x - 2}{x} + \dfrac{2}{5}$.

The common denominator is $5x(x + 3)$. Multiply x by $5x$, $(x - 2)$ by $5(x + 3)$ and 2 by $x(x + 3)$

$\dfrac{x}{x + 3} - \dfrac{x - 2}{x} + \dfrac{2}{5} = \dfrac{5x^2 - 5(x + 3)(x - 2) + 2x(x + 3)}{5x(x + 3)} = \dfrac{5x^2 - 5(x^2 + x - 6) + 2x^2 + 6x}{5x(x + 3)}$

$$= \dfrac{5x^2 - 5x^2 - 5x + 30 + 2x^2 + 6x}{5x(x + 3)} = \dfrac{2x^2 + x + 30}{5x(x + 3)}$$

The numerator will not factorise so this is the simplest form. If
it will factorise, look to see if any factors cancel.

Examiner's tip

Do not try to do two steps at once as that is where most mistakes occur.

Cancelling fractions

When cancelling fractions it is factors that cancel, never parts of factors.

Example 17   Simplify $\dfrac{4ab^2}{3c^2} \times \dfrac{9c^2}{2a^2b}$

$$\dfrac{4ab^2}{3c^2} \times \dfrac{9c^2}{2a^2b} = \dfrac{6b}{a}$$

2, 3, a, b and c^2 all cancel

Example 18   Simplify $\dfrac{x^2 + x}{x^2 - 2x - 3}$

As it stands the fraction cannot be cancelled. First both numerator and denominator must be factorised.

$$\dfrac{x^2 + x}{x^2 - 2x - 3} = \dfrac{x(x + 1)}{(x - 3)(x + 1)} = \dfrac{x}{(x - 3)}$$

$(x + 1)$ cancels

Examiner's tip

Errors often occur by cancelling individual terms. Only factors, which can be individual numbers, letters or brackets can be cancelled.

Exercise 19.4a

Simplify.

1. $\dfrac{x}{2} + \dfrac{3x}{5}$

2. $\dfrac{x + 1}{3} - \dfrac{2x - 1}{2}$

3. $\dfrac{x - 3}{5} + \dfrac{2x}{3} - \dfrac{3x - 2}{10}$

4. $\dfrac{1}{x} + \dfrac{2}{x - 1}$

5. $\dfrac{3}{2x} - \dfrac{1}{x + 2}$

6. $\dfrac{2}{x + 1} + \dfrac{3}{x - 1}$

7. $\dfrac{2x}{3x + 1} - \dfrac{5}{x + 3}$

8. $\dfrac{x + 1}{x - 1} + \dfrac{3x - 1}{x + 2}$

9. $\dfrac{x}{x + 1} - \dfrac{3}{5} + \dfrac{x - 2}{x}$

10. $\dfrac{2x}{x - 3} + \dfrac{x - 1}{x + 2} - \dfrac{4}{9}$

11. $\dfrac{2a^3}{b^2} \times \dfrac{3b}{4a}$

12. $\dfrac{4b^3}{a^3} \times \dfrac{2ab}{c}$

13. $\dfrac{2x}{x^2 - 3x}$

14. $\dfrac{3x^2 - 6x}{x^2 + x - 6}$

15. $\dfrac{x^2 - 5x + 4}{x^2 - 2x - 8}$

Simplify.

1. $\dfrac{2x}{3} - \dfrac{3x}{5}$

2. $\dfrac{x-1}{2} - \dfrac{x-6}{5}$

3. $\dfrac{2x-1}{6} + \dfrac{3x}{4} - \dfrac{x-2}{12}$

4. $\dfrac{3}{x} + \dfrac{2}{x+1}$

5. $\dfrac{5}{6x} - \dfrac{1}{2x+1}$

6. $\dfrac{3}{x+2} + \dfrac{5}{x-1}$

7. $\dfrac{2x}{x+1} - \dfrac{x-1}{x+3}$

8. $\dfrac{2x}{x-1} - \dfrac{3x+2}{x+2}$

9. $\dfrac{x}{x+1} + \dfrac{3}{5} - \dfrac{x+3}{x}$

10. $\dfrac{2}{x-1} - \dfrac{3}{x+2} - \dfrac{1}{x+3}$

11. $\dfrac{abc}{2} \times \dfrac{4a}{b^2c}$

12. $\dfrac{9a^2b}{2c^3} \times \dfrac{5ac}{18b}$

13. $\dfrac{5x^2 - 20x}{10x^2}$

14. $\dfrac{x^2 + 2x + 1}{x^2 - 1}$

15. $\dfrac{3x^2 + 5x - 2}{x^2 + 5x + 6}$

Harder equations and inequalities

You need to be able to solve equations involving brackets and fractions. These may be linear or quadratic.

---

 19 Solve $\dfrac{5x}{2} - \dfrac{7x}{3} = \dfrac{4}{5}$

In equations, multiply through by the common denominator.

In this case the common denominator is 30, which means you multiply $5x$ by $30 \div 2 = 15$ etc.

The equation becomes $\quad 75x - 70x = 24$

$$5x = 24$$

$$x = \dfrac{24}{5} = 4.8$$

---

 20 Solve $\dfrac{3}{x+1} - \dfrac{2}{x} = \dfrac{1}{x-2}$

Multiply by $x(x+1)(x-2)$. Make sure you multiply every expression on both sides.

The equation becomes

$$3x(x-2) - 2(x+1)(x-2) = x(x+1)$$

$$3x^2 - 6x - 2(x^2 - x - 2) = x^2 + x$$

$$3x^2 - 6x - 2x^2 + 2x + 4 - x^2 - x = 0 \quad \text{Expanding out and collecting on one side.}$$

$$-5x + 4 = 0 \quad \text{Collect like terms.}$$

$$5x = 4 \quad \text{Rearrange and change signs.}$$

$$x = \tfrac{4}{5}$$

Example 21　Solve $(x - 1)^2 = 7 - x$.

The first thing to do is multiply out the brackets.

The equation becomes　$x^2 - 2x + 1 = 7 - x$　Remember $(x - 1)^2 = (x - 1)(x - 1)$.

$$x^2 - x - 6 = 0$$　Collect all terms on one side.

$$(x - 3)(x + 2) = 0$$

$$x = 3 \text{ or } -2$$

Example 22　Solve $\dfrac{5}{x} = \dfrac{x}{x + 10}$.

Multiply through by $x(x + 10)$

The equation becomes　$5(x + 10) = x^2$

$$5x + 50 = x^2$$　Expand bracket.

$$-x^2 + 5x + 50 = 0$$　Collect all terms on one side.

$$x^2 - 5x - 50 = 0$$　Change all signs.

$$(x - 10)(x + 5) = 0$$

$$x = 10 \text{ or } -5$$

So far inequalities have been treated much as equations, except where changes of signs are involved. e.g. $-x < 3$ leads to $x > 3$, signs changed and inequality changed.

However, inequalities involving quadratics need more care. For equations, if $a \times b = 0$ then $a = 0$ **OR** $b = 0$.

For inequalities, if $a \times b > 0$ then a and b have the same sign, both positive **OR** both negative, either $a > 0$ and $b > 0$ **OR** $a <$ and $b < 0$

If $a \times b < 0$ then a and b have different signs, one positive, one negative, either $a > 0$ and $b < 0$ **OR** $a < 0$ and $b > 0$.

Example 23　Solve $x^2 + 3x - 4 < 0$

This means $(x + 4)(x - 1) < 0$

$(x + 4)$ and $(x - 1)$ have different signs.

Either　$x + 4 < 0$　and $x - 1 > 0$

　　　　　　$x < -4$ and 　　$x > 1$　This is

or　　$x + 4 > 0$　and $x - 1 < 0$　impossible.

　　　　　　$x > -4$ and 　　$x < 1$

This can be written $-4 < x < 1$

Examiner's tip

When checking inequalities, if possible try $x = 0$.

Example **24** Solve $x^2 - 5x + 6 > 0$

Factorise: $(x - 2)(x - 3) > 0$

The signs must be the same.
Either both positive: $x - 2 > 0$ and $x - 3 > 0$
If $x > 3$ it is certainly > 2.

Or both negative: $x - 2 < 0$ and $x - 3 < 0$
If $x < 2$ it is certainly < 3

Solution $x > 3$ **or** $x < 2$.

These two inequalities cannot be combined
as in the previous example.

Examiner's tip

Using a number line can be
helpful.

Example 23:

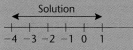

Example 24:

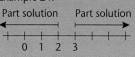

Exercise 19.5a

Solve.

1. $\dfrac{2x}{3} - \dfrac{3x}{5} = \dfrac{1}{3}$

2. $\dfrac{x - 1}{2} - \dfrac{x - 3}{5} = 1$

3. $\dfrac{2x - 1}{6} + \dfrac{3x}{4} = \dfrac{x - 2}{12}$

4. $\dfrac{3}{x} - \dfrac{2}{x + 1} = 0$

5. $\dfrac{5}{6x} - \dfrac{1}{x + 1} = \dfrac{1}{3x}$

6. $x(x + 2) = 2(x + 2)$

7. $2x(x - 2) = x^2 + 5$

8. $4x = \dfrac{3}{x} - 1$

9. $2x^2 - \dfrac{x}{3} = 5$

10. $\dfrac{1}{x - 1} - \dfrac{3}{x + 2} = \dfrac{1}{4}$

11. $3(x - 1) + x < 5x - 6$

12. $(2x - 1)(x + 2) > 2x(x + 1)$

13. $-2 < 3x + 4 < 5$

14. $x^2 + x - 6 < 0$

15. $2x^2 - 3x > 2$

Exercise 19.5b

Solve.

1. $\dfrac{2x}{5} - \dfrac{x}{4} = \dfrac{3}{10}$

2. $\dfrac{2x - 1}{2} - \dfrac{x - 3}{3} = \dfrac{5}{2}$

3. $\dfrac{x - 1}{3} + \dfrac{2x}{5} = \dfrac{3x + 1}{5}$

4. $\dfrac{5}{x} - \dfrac{2}{x - 3} = 0$

5. $\dfrac{4}{x - 2} - \dfrac{1}{x + 1} = \dfrac{3}{x}$

6. $(x + 4)(x + 2) + x + 4 = 0$

7. $(x - 5)(x + 3) = x - 5$

8. $4x + \dfrac{3}{x} = 7$

9. $2x + \dfrac{4}{x} = 9$

10. $\dfrac{2x}{3x + 1} - \dfrac{5}{x + 3} = 0$

11. $4(x + 1) > 5x - 3$

12. $(x - 1)(2x + 1) < 2x^2 - 4$

13. $1 < 3x + 4 < 3$

14. $x^2 - 6x + 8 < 0$

15. $2x^2 + 12 > 11x$

Chapter 19 Harder equations and inequalities

Rearranging formulae

All the formulae that have been covered previously contained the new subject only once, and always as part of the numerator. This is now extended.

Example 25 Rearrange the formula $a = x + \dfrac{cx}{d}$ to make x the subject.

$ad = dx + cx$ Multiply through by d

$dx + cx = ad$ Rearrange to get all terms involving x on the left-hand side

$x(d + c) = ad$ Factorise

$x = \dfrac{ad}{d + c}$ Divide by $(d + c)$

Example 26 Rearrange the formula $a = \dfrac{1}{p} + \dfrac{1}{q}$ to make p the subject.

$apq = q + p$ Multiply through by pq

$apq - p = q$ Collect all terms in p on the left-hand side

$p(aq - 1) = q$ Factorise

$p = \dfrac{q}{aq - 1}$ Divide by $(aq - 1)$

Example 27 Rearrange the formula $a = b + \dfrac{c}{1 + p}$ to make p the subject.

$a(1 + p) = b(1 + p) + c$ Multiply through by $(1 + p)$

$a + ap = b + bp + c$ Expand brackets

$ap - bp = b + c - a$ Collect all terms in p to the left-hand side

$p(a - b) = b + c - a$ Factorise

$p = \dfrac{b + c - a}{a - b}$ Divide by $(a - b)$

Example 28 Rearrange the formula $s = b + \sqrt{\dfrac{t}{p}}$ to make t the subject.

$s - b = \sqrt{\dfrac{t}{p}}$ If a root or power is involved, first rearrange to get that by itself

$(s - b)^2 = \dfrac{t}{p}$ Square both sides

$\dfrac{t}{p} = (s - b)^2$ Get all terms in t to the left-hand side

$t = p(s - b)^2$ Multiply through by p

In this case there is no need to expand $(s - b)^2$.

Exercise 19.6a

For each question rearrange to make the letter in square brackets the subject.

1. $s = at + 2bt$ [t]
2. $P = t - \dfrac{at}{b}$ [t]
3. $s - 2ax = b(x - s)$ [x]
4. $a = \dfrac{t}{b} - st$ [t]
5. $a = \dfrac{1}{b + c}$ [c]

6. $a = b + \dfrac{c}{d + 1}$ [d]
7. $a = b + c^2$ [c]
8. $A = P + \dfrac{PRT}{100}$ [P]
9. $\dfrac{a}{x + 1} = \dfrac{b}{2x - 1}$ [x]
10. $T = 2\pi\sqrt{\dfrac{L}{g}}$ [L]

Exercise 19.6b

For each question rearrange to make the letter in square brackets the subject.

1. $s = ab - bc$ [b]
2. $s = \dfrac{1}{a} + b$ [a]
3. $3(a + y) = by + 7$ [y]
4. $2(a - 1) = b(1 - 2a)$ [a]
5. $\dfrac{a}{b} - 2a = b$ [a]

6. $m = \dfrac{100\,(a - b)}{b}$ [b]
7. $\dfrac{a}{p} = \dfrac{1}{1 + p}$ [p]
8. $a = \dfrac{1}{1 + x^2} - b$ [x]
9. $s = 2r^2 - 1$ [r]
10. $s = \dfrac{uv}{u + v}$ [v]

Using graphs to solve harder equations and inequalities

In an earlier chapter you saw how to solve equations like $x^2 - 5x + 3 = 0$ by drawing the graph of $y = x^2 - 5x + 3$ and reading off where it crossed the x-axis, where $y = 0$.

This now can be extended to include intersections with other lines rather than $y = 0$.

Example The graph of $y = x^2 - 3x + 1$ is drawn. (Do not draw it.)

How can you use the graph to find the solution of

(a) $x^2 - 3x + 1 = 0$,
(b) $x^2 - 3x - 1 = 0$?

(a) This is where the curve crosses the line $y = 0$, i.e. replace y by 0 in the equation.
(b) $x^2 - 3x - 1 = 0$ is the same as $x^2 - 3x + 1 - 2 = 0$ or $x^2 - 3x + 1 = 2$.
     Where the line $y = 2$ meets $y = x^2 - 3x + 1$ will give the solution.

Example 30

(a) Draw the graph of $y = x^2 - 1$, for $x = -3$ to $+3$
(b) Use your graph to solve the equation $x^2 - 2 = 0$
(c) (i) Draw a suitable line so you can find the solution of $x^2 - x - 1 = 0$.
(ii) Solve $x^2 - x - 1$ from your graph.

(a)

x	-3	-2	-1	0	1	2	3
x^2	9	4	1	0	1	4	9
-1	-1	-1	-1	-1	-1	-1	-1
$y = x^2 - 1$	8	3	0	-1	0	3	8

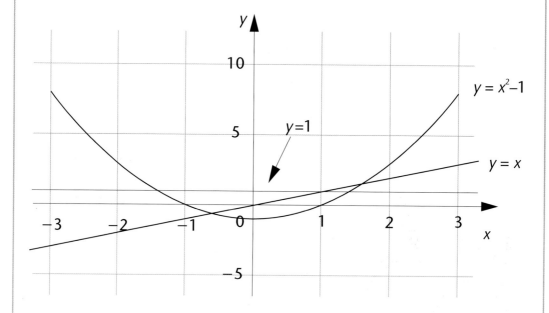

(b) $x^2 - 2 = 0$ is the same as $x^2 - 1 - 1 = 0$ or $x^2 - 1 = 1$. Read where $y = 1$ meets $y = x^2 - 1$.
Solution is $x = -1.4$ or 1.4.
(c) (i) $x^2 - x - 1 = 0$ is the same as $x^2 - 1 = x$. So the required line is $y = x$.
Solution is $x = -0.6$ or 1.6.

Example 31

The graph of $y = x^3 - 5x$ is drawn. (Do not draw the graph.)
What line needs to be drawn to find the solution of $x^3 - 6x - 5 = 0$?

$x^3 - 6x - 5 = 0$ is the same as $x^3 - 5x - x - 5 = 0$ or $x^3 - 5x = x + 5$.
The line that needs to be drawn is $y = x + 5$.

Example 82

(a) Draw the graph of $y = x^2 - 5x + 3$ for $x = -1$ to $+6$.

(b) From your graph solve the inequality $x^2 - 5x + 3 < 0$.

x	-1	0	1	2	3	4	5	6
x^2	1	0	1	4	9	16	25	36
$-5x$	5	0	-5	-10	-15	-20	-25	-30
3	3	3	3	3	3	3	3	3
$y = x^2 - 5x + 3$	9	3	-1	-3	-3	-1	3	9

(a)

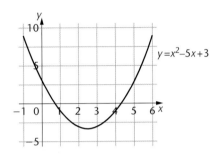

$y = x^2 - 5x + 3$

(b) The solution is where the curve goes below the x-axis since $y < 0$, giving $0.7 < x < 4.3$.

Exercise 19.7a

Do not draw the graphs in questions 1 to 5.

1. The graph of $y = x^2 - 6x + 4$ is drawn. How can you use the graph to find the solution of
   (a) $x^2 - 6x + 4 = 0$ (b) $x^2 - 6x + 2 = 0$?

2. The graph of $y = 2x^2 - 3x$ is drawn. How can you find the solution of $2x^2 - 3x - 5 = 0$?

3. The graphs of $y = x^2$ and $y = 4x - 3$ are drawn on the same grid. What is the equation whose solution is found at the intersection of the two graphs?

4. The graph of $y = x^3 - 4x$ is drawn. What other graph needs to be drawn to find the solution of $x^3 - x^2 - 4x + 3 = 0$ where they cross?

5. The intersection of two graphs is the solution to the equation $x^2 - 4x - 2 = 0$.
   One of the graphs is $y = x^2 - 5x + 1$. What is the other graph?

6. (a) Draw the graph of $y = x^2 - 5$ for $x = -3$ to $+3$.
   (b) From your graph solve the equations
   (i) $x^2 - 5 = 0$ (ii) $x^2 - 3 = 0$

7. (a) Draw the graph of $y = 2x^2 - 3x$ for $x = -2$ to $+4$.
   (b) Use your graph to solve the equation
   $2x^2 - 3x - 5 = 0$.

8. (a) Draw the graphs of $y = x^2 + 5$ and $y = 3x + 7$ for $x = -2$ to $+4$.
   (b) What is the equation of the points where they intersect?
   (c) Solve this equation from your graph.

9. (a) Draw the graph of $y = x^3 - 3x$ for $x = -3$ to $+3$.
   (b) (i) Draw another graph so that the equation of their points of intersection is $x^3 - 6x + 5 = 0$.
   (ii) Use the graph to solve the equation.

10. (a) Draw the graph of $x^2 - 2x - 4$ for $x = -2$ to $+4$.
    (b) Find the solutions of the following from the graph.
    (i) $x^2 - 2x - 7 = 0$ (ii) $x^2 - 4x = 0$
    (iii) $x^2 - 2x - 4 > 0$

Exercise 19.7b

Do not draw the graphs in questions 1 to 5.

1. The graph of $y = x^2 - 8x + 2$ is drawn. How can you use the graph to find the solution of
   (a) $x^2 - 8x + 2 = 0$ (b) $x^2 - 8x + 6 = 0$?

2. The graph of $y = 2x^2 - x - 2$ is drawn. How can you find the solution of
   $2x^2 - x - 5 = 0$?

3. The graphs of $y = x^2 + 3x$ and $y = 4x - 3$ are drawn on the same grid. What is the equation whose solution is found at the intersection of the two graphs?

4. The graph of $y = x^3 - 2x^2$ is drawn. What other graph needs to be drawn to find the solution of $x^3 - x^2 - 4x + 3 = 0$ where they cross?

5. The intersection of two graphs is the solution to the equation $x^2 - 5x + 5 = 0$.
   One of the graphs is $y = x^2 - x + 1$. What is the other graph?

6. (a) Draw the graph of $y = 2x^2 - 10$ for $x = -3$ to $+3$.
   (b) From your graph solve the equations
   (i) $2x^2 - 10 = 0$ (ii) $2x^2 - 3 = 0$

7. (a) Draw the graphs of $y = x^2 + 2$ and $y = 2x + 7$ for $x = -2$ to $+4$.
   (b) What is the equation of the points where they intersect?
   (c) Solve this equation from your graph.

8. (a) Draw the graph of $y = x^2 - 5x$ for $x = -2$ to $+4$.
   (b) (i) Draw another line so that the intersection is $x^2 - 3x - 3 = 0$.
   (ii) Solve this equation from the graph.

9. (a) Draw the graph of $y = x^3 - 5x$ for $x = -3$ to $+3$.
   (b) (i) Draw another graph so that the equation of their points of intersection is $x^3 - x^2 - 5x + 5 = 0$.
   (ii) Use the graph to solve the equation.

10. (a) Draw the graph of $y = x^2 + 5x + 4$ for $x = -6$ to $+1$.
    (b) Find the solutions of the following from the graph.
    (i) $x^2 + 5x + 4 = 0$ (ii) $x^2 + 3x - 3 = 0$
    (iii) $x^2 + 5x + 2 < 0$

1. Factorise.
- (a) $x^2 - 16x + 63$
- (b) $2x^2 - 8x - 42$
- (c) $3x^2 - 8x + 4$
- (d) $2x^2 + x - 15$
- (e) $3x^2 - 48$
- (f) $2x^2 - 11x - 21$
- (g) $6x^2 - 27x - 15$
- (h) $5x^2 - 21x + 18$
- (i) $8x^2 - 6x - 5$
- (j) $6x^2 - 11x - 10$

2. Solve by factorisation.
- (a) $x^2 - 2x - 8 = 0$
- (b) $2x^2 + 9x - 5 = 0$
- (c) $3x^2 - 8x + 5 = 0$
- (d) $2x^2 + 5x - 7 = 0$
- (e) $3x^2 - 8x + 4 = 0$
- (f) $2x^2 - 5x = 0$
- (g) $6x^2 - 7x + 1 = 0$
- (h) $2x^2 - 5x - 12 = 0$
- (i) $7x^2 - 16x + 4 = 0$
- (j) $4x^2 - 9 = 0$

3. Use the formula to solve the following. Give your answers to 2 d.p.
- (a) $x^2 - 5x + 1 = 0$
- (b) $3x^2 + 3x - 2 = 0$
- (c) $5x^2 - 12x + 5 = 0$

4. Simplify.
- (a) $\dfrac{x}{2} + \dfrac{x + 1}{3}$
- (b) $\dfrac{3x - 1}{4} - \dfrac{2x + 3}{5}$
- (c) $\dfrac{1}{x + 1} + \dfrac{2}{3x - 2}$
- (d) $\dfrac{2x}{x - 1} - \dfrac{x - 1}{x + 4}$
- (e) $\dfrac{2x^2 + 2x}{x^2 + 4x + 3}$
- (f) $\dfrac{x^2 - 7x + 10}{2x^2 - 11x + 5}$

5. Solve the equations.
- (a) $x(3x - 2) - 2x(x - 2)$ $= x^2 + 6$
- (b) $\dfrac{2x}{4} - \dfrac{x - 2}{3} = 1$
- (c) $(x + 1)^2 = 9$
- (d) $\dfrac{x^2}{3} - 2x - 9 = 0$
- (e) $\dfrac{1}{x} + \dfrac{4}{3x} + 2$
- (f) $(x + 2) = \dfrac{3}{x}$
- (g) $\dfrac{5}{x + 2} - \dfrac{2}{x - 1} = \dfrac{3}{x}$
- (h) $x - 2 = \dfrac{x - 6}{x - 5}$

6. Solve the inequalities.
- (a) $2x(x + 2) < x(x - 1) + x^2 + 2$
- (b) $x^2 - 2x < 0$
- (c) $x(x - 1) > 30$

7. Rearrange the formula to make p the subject.
- (a) $p + q = 2(q - 3p)$
- (b) $t = \dfrac{2(p - 1)}{p}$
- (c) $\dfrac{1}{p} = \dfrac{1}{q} + \dfrac{1}{s}$
- (d) $T = p + \dfrac{2p}{q}$
- (e) $\dfrac{1}{2p - 1} = \dfrac{2a}{p + 1}$
- (f) $p^2 + 4a = 2b$

8.
- (a) Draw the graph of $y = x^2 + 3x - 7$ for $x = -6$ to $+3$.
- (b) Use the graph to solve
  - (i) $x^2 + 3x - 7 = 0$
  - (ii) $x^2 + 3x - 10 = 0$
- (c) (i) Find the line that must be drawn to solve $x^2 + x - 4 = 0$.
  - (ii) Draw the line and use it to solve $x^2 + x - 4 = 0$.

Key points

- When factorising, look first for common factors and then factorise into two brackets. The middle term of the original expression is the sum or difference of the products of the first and last terms in the different brackets.
- Always check by multiplying out the brackets.
- To solve quadratic equations, factorise if possible, if not use the formula.
- To solve $ax^2 + bx + c = 0$ the formula is $x = \dfrac{-b \pm \sqrt{b^2 - 4ac}}{2a}$
- In the formula, take care with the signs, especially $-4ac$.
- When adding or subtracting fractions, put them over a common denominator.
- When cancelling algebraic fractions, factorise if necessary and then cancel factors.
- When equations involve fractions, multiply through by the common denominator.
- To solve quadratic inequalities, factorise and consider the signs of the product.
- When rearranging formula, first multiply through by the common denominator. Then collect all terms involving the new subject on the left-hand side, factorise and divide by the factor.
- Finally, when using graphs to solve equations, rearrange the equation to make it like the graph drawn and thus find the other line required.

20 Transformations and congruence

Rotation

To be able to rotate a shape requires three separate items of information:

- the angle of rotation
- the direction of rotation
- the centre of rotation

By convention, an anti-clockwise rotation is positive; a clockwise rotation is negative.

You will already have covered rotation of shapes through 90° and 180°. The following example and questions are included as a reminder.

Example ❶ Rotating a shape through 180°.

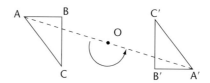

Use tracing paper; trace through the object, triangle ABC. Draw a line through the centre of rotation, O, and point A and extend this line. Rotate the tracing paper using a pin through the centre of rotation until A′ lies on the straight line; prick through the tracing paper to mark the other vertices of the triangle (B′ and C′).

1. In each of the following draw the image of the object after a 180°
   rotation about O.

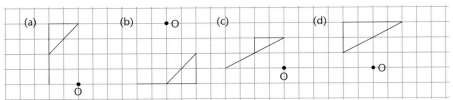

2. In each of the following draw the image of the object after a
   rotation of 90° anticlockwise about O.

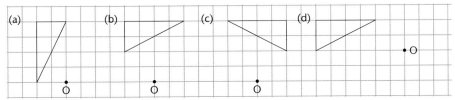

3. Draw a triangle ABC at A(1, 2), B(3, 5), C(6, 2).
   (a) Find the image of triangle ABC under a 90° rotation
       anticlockwise about the origin.
   (b) Find the image of triangle ABC under a 90° rotation clockwise
       about the point (2, −2).

Rotation through any size of angle can be completed using the
same method.

Example 2 Rotate triangle ABC through 40° anti-clockwise about the point O. Label the
image A′B′C′.

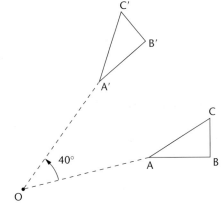

Draw line OA. Measure the angle 40° at O and the distance OA; draw a line
OA′ so that OA = OA′. Use tracing paper and a pin as before.

Chapter 20 Rotation

275

You will need graph paper for this exercise. In each question show the image following the given rotation.
1. Draw a triangle with vertices A(3, 1), B(6, 1), C(6, 3). Rotate this triangle through 30° about the origin.
2. Draw a triangle with vertices A(1, 2), B(1, 6), C(3, 5). Rotate this triangle through 70° about the point (1, 2).
3. Draw a square with vertices A(2, 2), B(5, 2), C(5, 5), D(2, 5). Rotate this square through 45° about the origin.

Exercise 20.2b

You will need graph paper for this exercise. In each question show the image following the given rotation.
1. Draw a triangle at A(2, 6), B(2, 8), C(6, 6). Rotate this triangle through 70° about the point (2, 4).
2. Join the following points to make a T-shape: A(2, 5), B(4, 5), C(6, 5) and D(4, 2). Rotate this shape through −30° about the origin.
3. Join the following points to make a pentagon: A(1, 1), B(3, 1), C(3, 3), D(2, 4), E(1, 3). Rotate this pentagon through 50° about the origin.

To find the centre of rotation is fairly straightforward if you know the position of the object and its image:

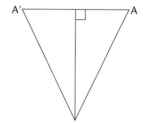

Join A to A′ and construct the perpendicular bisector of the line AA′. The centre of rotation will lie on this line. Thus for an object and its image, such as triangle ABC and its image triangle A′B′C′ as shown below, join A to A′ and B to B′; draw the perpendicular bisectors to lines AA′ and BB′, the point where these bisectors intersect is the centre of rotation.

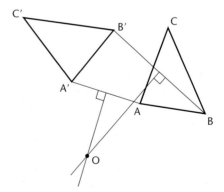

This method can be used to find a single equivalent rotation following two different rotations.

Example 3

Rotate triangle ABC
through 30° about the
origin. Label
its image A′B′C′.
Rotate triangle A′B′C′
through 45° about the
point P(1, 2). Label
this image A″B″C″.

What single rotation
will map triangle ABC
onto triangle A″B″C″?

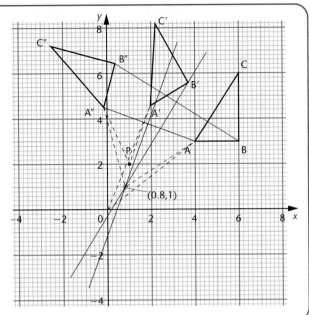

The construction shows a
rotation of 75° about the
point (0.8, 1).

Exercise 20.3a

You will need graph paper for this exercise. In each question show the image following the given rotation.

1. The diagram shows an inverted L-shape.

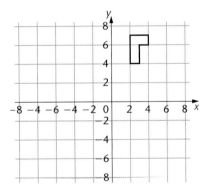

Rotate the L-shape through 90° about the origin.
Rotate this image of the L-shape through 180° about the point (−3, −2).
What single rotation is necessary to return the second image to the original position?

2. Draw a triangle with vertices A(5, 5), B(7, 5), C(5, 8). Rotate this triangle through 90° about the point (2, 1) to give the image A′B′C′. Rotate A′B′C′ through 90° about the origin to give a second image A″B″C″. What rotation will map A″B″C″ onto the original triangle ABC?

3. Draw a triangle A(4, 4), B(1, 4), C(1, 2). Rotate ABC through 40° about the origin giving triangle A′B′C′. Now rotate A′B′C′ through −70° about the point (−1, −1).
What single rotation is equivalent to the combination of these two rotations?

You will need graph paper for this exercise. In each question show the image following the given rotation.

1. Draw and label the following triangles:

   Triangle ABC   A(6, 3), B(6, 1), C(3, 1)
   Triangle DEF   D(−1, 3), E(−1, 6), F(−3, 6)
   Triangle GHI   G(−2, −1), H(−2, 1), I(1, 1)
   Triangle JKL   J(3, −1), K(3, −4), L(5, −4)
   Triangle MNP   M(4, 4), N(1, 4), P(1, 2)

What rotation will map:

(a) ABC onto DEF?   (d) ABC onto MNP?
(b) ABC onto GHI?   (e) MNP onto JKL?
(c) ABC onto JKL?   (f) GHI onto DEF?

Enlargement

Enlargement of shapes was covered in an earlier chapter. Remember that enlargement requires two pieces of information:

- the scale factor
- the centre of enlargement.

 Example 4   Rectangle ABCD is enlarged by a scale factor of 2, the centre of enlargement is the origin.

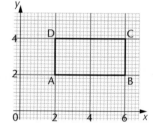

This means that   OA′ = 2 × OA measured along OA extended,
OB′ = 2 × OB measured along OB extended,
OC′ = 2 × OC measured along OC extended,
OD′ = 2 × OD measured along OD extended.

The sides of image A′B′C′D′ are twice the length of the sides of object ABCD.

If the scale factor is negative the image is on the opposite side of the centre of enlargement, i.e. OA′ = −2 × OA measured along the line AO extended. The result is that the image A″B″C″D″ would be inverted.

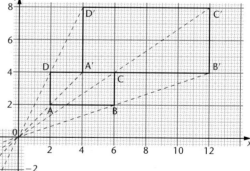

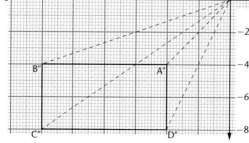

Chapter 20   Transformations and congruence

Example ⑤ Triangle A(2, 3), B(4, 3), C(2, 6) is enlarged by a scale factor −2. The centre of enlargement is the point (−1, 2). This is shown in the diagram below.

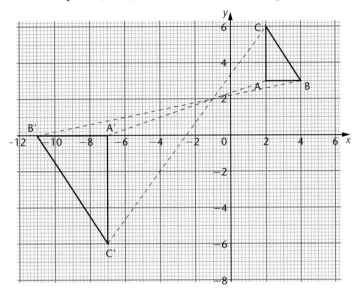

What do you notice about the coordinates of corresponding points?

Exercise 20.4a

1. Draw a set of axes, the *x*-axis from −16 to +6, the *y*-axis from −6 to +4.
   Draw a quadrilateral with coordinates A(2, 2), B(5, 0), C(5, −1), D(2, −1).
   Draw the enlargement by a scale factor of −3 of this quadrilateral; the centre of enlargement is the origin.

2. Using the same axes as in question 1, draw a triangle P(4, 2), Q(6, −1), R(2, −2). Enlarge this triangle by a scale factor of −2 about the origin. Show the enlargement on your graph.

3. For this question you will need a set of axes, the *x*-axis from −4 to +8, the *y*-axis from −10 to +6.
   Plot an inverted L-shape with coordinates A(−2, 2), B(−3, 2), C(−3, 4), D(−4, 4), E(−4, 5), F(−2, 5). (Join F to A.)
   Enlarge this L-shape by a scale factor of −2 about the origin. Write down the coordinates of the image.

Chapter 20 Enlargement

Exercise 20.4b

1. Enlarge the quadrilateral A(2, 1), B(5, 1), C(4, 4), D(2, 3) by a scale factor of -2 about the origin. Write down the coordinates of the enlarged quadrilateral.
2. Enlarge the triangle A(2, -2), B(5, 1), C(2, 2) by a scale factor of -2 about the point $(-1, -1)$. Write down the coordinates of the enlarged triangle.
3. Enlarge the triangle A(1, 6), B(1, 7), C(3, 7) by a scale factor of -3. The centre of enlargement is the point (3, 6). Write down the coordinates of the enlarged triangle.

Congruent triangles

For any two triangles to be congruent they must be the *same shape* and the *same size*. This means that they will fit exactly onto each other when one of them is rotated, reflected or translated.

Thus it can be seen that if two triangles are congruent then:

- the three angles in one triangle equal the corresponding three angles of the other triangle;
- the three sides in one triangle equal the corresponding three sides of the other triangle.

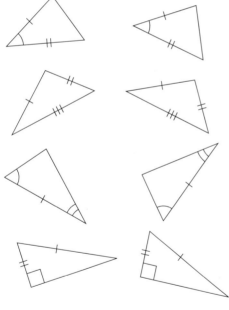

Two triangles are congruent if any of these conditions are satisfied:

- two sides and the included angle of one triangle are equal to the two sides and the included angle of the other triangle (side, angle, side or SAS)
- the three sides of one triangle are equal to the corresponding three sides of the other triangle (side, side, side or SSS)
- two angles and the side 'linking' them in one triangle are equal to the corresponding two angles and side in the other triangle (angle, side, angle or ASA)
- each triangle is right-angled and the hypotenuse and one side of one triangle is equal to the hypotenuse and a side of the other triangle (right angle, hypotenuse, side or RHS)

Note that the test involving two sides and an angle is valid only if the angle is the included angle. If the given angle is not the included angle then there are two possible solutions – the ambiguous case which you may meet when studying the sine rule.

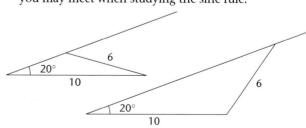

1. Are these triangles congruent?
   Give a reason or explanation for your answer.

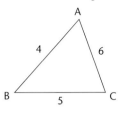 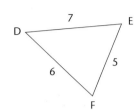

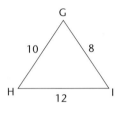 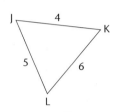

2. Which of these pairs of triangles are congruent?
   Explain your answer in each case.

(a)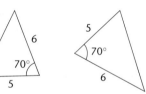

(b)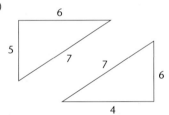

(c)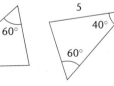

(d)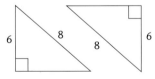

(e)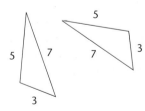

(f)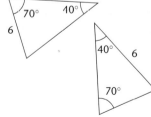

3. (A sketch will prove useful for this question.)
   Prove that the diagonals of a rectangle are equal in length.

4. Draw (sketch), an equilateral triangle. Join the midpoints of each side to make a second triangle. Prove that this triangle is equilateral.

1. Which of the triangles (i), (ii), (iii), (iv), (v), (vi) are congruent to any of triangles A, B or C?
   Explain your answer in each case.

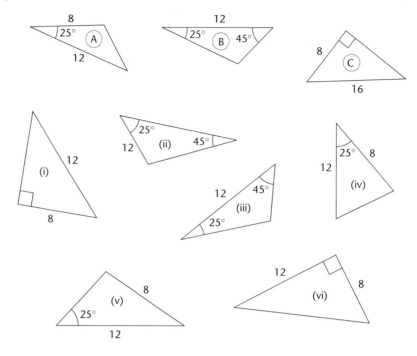

2. Use the property of congruent triangles to prove that the diagonals of a rhombus bisect each other at right angles.

3. Draw (sketch), an isosceles triangle, ABC, with the equal angles at B and C.
   Draw a straight line from the midpoint of side BC to the vertex A.
   Prove that this line bisects angle BAC and is perpendicular to side BC.

Key points

- You should be able to rotate any shape through any angle about any point.
- Anti-clockwise rotation is positive, clockwise rotation is negative.
- Enlargement by a negative scale factor produces an image on the opposite side of the centre of enlargement to the object.

- The basic checks for congruency are:
  (i)   the corresponding sides of each triangle are equal (SSS)
  (ii) 2 sides and the included angle in each triangle are equal (SAS)
  (iii) 2 angles and the 'included' side in each triangle are equal (ASA)
  (iv) for a right-angled triangle the check is 'right angle, hypotenuse and side' in each triangle are equal (RHS).

1. You will need graph paper for this question. Draw quadrilateral A(2, 2), B(6, 2), C(4, 5), D(2, 4). Rotate this quadrilateral through 80° about the origin to give the first image A′B′C′D′. Rotate this image through −120° about the point (−2, −2) to give the second image A″B″C″D″. What single rotation is necessary to map A″B″C″D″ back onto ABCD?

2. Enlarge the triangle A(1, 1), B(3, 1), C(3, 2) by a scale factor of −2, with centre of enlargement the point (4, 3).

3. Enlarge the triangle A(9, 2), B(14, 2), C(14, 6) by a scale factor of $-\frac{1}{2}$, the centre of enlargement is the point (7, 4).

4. Join the midpoints of the sides of a square to form a quadrilateral. Prove that this quadrilateral is a square.

21 Surveys and sampling

Surveys

As described in the Introduction, for part of your GCSE assessment you will have to undertake an extended piece of statistical work. The criteria that will be used to assess this are also given, in a simplified form, in the Introduction. However, important aspects of the criteria are referred to throughout this chapter.

As an overview it might be helpful to consider the four aspects of the handling data cycle:

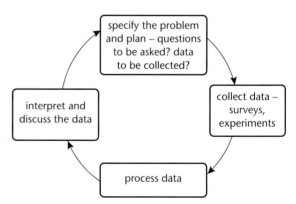

It is important to make sure that at the end of your work the conclusions you make are related back to the initial aims: in other words 'have you answered the question?' You must also try to present a well-structured and coherent report.

In Chapter 7 the design of questionnaires was discussed. Look back at this chapter if you need to; a reminder of some points is given below.

A survey can be thought of as an investigation to establish something, for example:

- people's preferences, likes/dislikes or beliefs
- the number of plants or animals in a particular location
- the presence of oil or gas (a commercial example).

Remember that you should explain how you are going to collect data, consider any practical problems in carrying out the survey and explain how you will plan for these.

One common method of finding information from people is to use a questionnaire. Questionnaires need to be designed to provide answers that are easily analysed. Those with 'yes' or 'no' answers are clearly easy to analyse but remember that you must try to avoid writing questions which have an 'or' statement in them. For example, if you were doing a survey about the number of people who were vegetarian, asking a question like 'do you eat meat or vegetables' will not provide any useful answers!

This is why you should use, and explain why you are using, a pilot survey to pre-test your questionnaire.

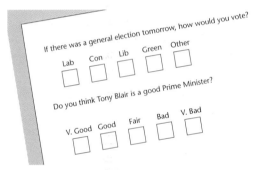

Exercise 21.1

1. Julie is designing a questionnaire for a survey about her local supermarket.
   She has decided on two hypotheses to test:
   (i) local people visit the supermarket more often than people from further away
   (ii) local people spend less money per visit.
   Write two questions which could help her test each hypothesis.
   Each question should include at least three options for a response. The people interviewed are asked to choose one of these options.
2. A Sports and Leisure Club offers a range of facilities for many different sporting activities. As part of their reviewing system the committee issue questionnaires to a sample of members.
   One question said:
   'If you are a regular tennis player and think better facilities are needed how many extra courts should be provided and what other improvements would you like to see?'
   (a) Write down at least two faults in this question.
   (b) How would you improve the question? Write down your improved question.
   (c) How should the committee select a representative sample?

Sampling

This section provides an introduction to sampling and the methods used to obtain a sample.

In data handling the word 'population' is used for a collection, set or group of objects being studied.

A 'sample' is a smaller group (a subset), selected from the population. If the population is large, it is not usually possible or practical to collect data on every member of that population, so one or more samples will be surveyed and conclusions drawn from these which will be applied to the whole population.

In your work you should show that you are using a sample of an adequate size.

If the structure or composition of the population is known then it is important to ensure that the sample (or samples) represent that population and thus any variations in that population should be reflected in that sample. This is called a **representative sample**.

You must explain

- why you have chosen a particular sampling method
- why the sample is the size it is
- what effects the nature of the sample may have on your findings.

There are various methods of choosing a representative sample.

1. **Systematic sampling**
   An example of this method would be the selection of a 10% sample by going through the population picking every tenth item or individual. The drawback is that this would only provide a representative sample if the population was arranged in a random way and not in a way that might introduce bias. (Bias is described later.)

2. **Attribute sampling**
   In this method the selection of the sample is made by choosing some attribute which is totally unrelated to the variable being investigated. For example choosing a sample to investigate any relationship between head size and height from a list of people on the basis of their birthday being on the first of the month.

3. **Stratified or quota sampling**

   The population is divided into strata or sub-groups and the sample chosen to reflect the properties of these sub-groups. For example, if the population contained three times as many people under 25 as over 25 then the sample should also contain three times as many people under 25. The sample should also be large enough for the results to be significant.

4. **Random sampling**

   If there is no information about the characteristics of the population – for example, no knowledge about the ages and sex of the people in the population or about the colours and sizes of the objects in a population – then a sample must be selected on the basis that all members are equally likely to be chosen. This is called random sampling. To ensure a sample is random and as accurate as possible, ideally, the sampling should always be repeated a number of times and the results averaged.

You will find examples of 'sampling' taking place throughout the year:

• in politics with opinion polls reporting on the popularity of the political parties, especially in the weeks before local and general elections;

• in market research – 'eight out of ten owners said their cats preferred Whiskas', or whether the building of the Millennium Dome was a good use of money or . . .

You may well have seen market researchers stopping people in the street.

Exercise 21.2

1. A soap powder company wants to know what percentage of the population use its washing powder.

   Would it be likely to obtain a representative sample by asking:
   - (a) people leaving a public house at 10 p.m. on a Friday night?
   - (b) people leaving a supermarket at 7.30 p.m.?
   - (c) people leaving a supermarket between 9 a.m. and noon each day for a week?
   - (d) people getting off a commuter train on their way home from work?

   Give reasons for each of your answers.

   Can you suggest a way of obtaining a representative sample?

2. You might be able to try the following experiment:
   - (i)   Put 100 counters in a bag. The counters should be the same size but of differing colours e.g. some red, some blue etc.
   - (ii) Choose a colour, e.g. red.
   - (iii) Select 10 counters without looking and make a note of the number of counters selected which are of your chosen colour, e.g. red ones. Return the counters to the bag.
   - (iv) Multiply by 10 to predict the number of red counters in the bag [$10 \times 3 = 30$] (write this number down so you don't forget it).
   - (v) Repeat steps (iii) and (iv) another 9 times giving a total of 10 experiments [e.g. 20, 30, 40, 50, 20, 30, 40, 40, 40]
   - (vi) Find the mean of the 10 experiments, e.g. $\dfrac{340}{10} = 34$.

   This figure ought to be close to the actual number of red counters in the bag.

   How does the answer you obtain compare with the actual number of your chosen colour?

Exercise 21.3

1. Comment on the following ideas for obtaining a random sample. Give a better method if you can.
   - (a) A random sample of all the adults in a town is required.

      Method: stand outside a supermarket and stop every tenth person who leaves between the hours of 9 a.m. and 3 p.m.
   - (b) A random sample of the students at your school is required.

      Method: ask all the students to 'sign up' if they want to take part in a study and promise to pay £1 to all who are chosen. Choose at random until the required number of students is obtained.

2. Which of the following would you study by sampling?
   - (a) the average life of a torch battery
   - (b) the top ten singles for last week

Bias

If each 'item' in the population does not have an equal chance of being selected for the sample then the sample is said to be **biased**.

Examples of biased samples could be:
1. Studying illness in the elderly by finding information from a few residential homes. [Likely to be biased because (i) it may not be representative of the population – those who live in such homes may not be able to look after themselves and (ii) infectious illnesses are more likely to be spread when people live close together.]
2. Investigating the pattern of absence from a school by studying the registers in December. [Might be biased because children are more likely to be ill in the winter months compared with, say, the summer months; and older students might be absent for interviews and the pattern of any truancy might vary.]
3. Finding out opinions about school dinners by asking the first 50 students in the dinner queue one day. [Might be biased because only those eating school dinners might be asked. Students might be queuing by year groups and so not be representative.]

Your work should show what measures you took to avoid any bias in the sample you have chosen.

Stratified random sampling

As mentioned earlier, sampling which is representative of the whole population is called stratified sampling. The method used is as follows:

- Separate the population into appropriate categories or strata e.g. by age.
- Find out what proportion of the population is in each stratum.
- Select a sample from each stratum in proportion to the stratum size.

This can be done by random sampling and so the technique is known as stratified random sampling.

Example ❶

The 240 students in year 9 of a school are split into 4 groups for games. 90 play cricket, 70 play tennis, 30 choose athletics and the remaining 50 opt for volleyball.

Use a stratified random sample of 40 students to estimate the mean weight of all 240 students.

The sample size from each of the 4 groups must be in proportion to the stratum size so the 40 students are selected as follows:

cricket $\quad \dfrac{90}{240} \times 40 = 15$

tennis $\quad \dfrac{70}{240} \times 40 = 11.67$, i.e. 12

athletics $\quad \dfrac{30}{240} \times 40 = 5$

volleyball $\quad \dfrac{50}{240} \times 40 = 8.33$, i.e. 8

Within each sample the actual students will be selected randomly (random sampling is discussed later).
The mean weights for each sample are found to be:

cricket $\quad$ 54.6 kg $\qquad$ tennis $\qquad$ 49.7 kg
athletics $\quad$ 53.1 kg $\qquad$ volleyball $\quad$ 47.9 kg

so the mean weight for all 240 students

$$= \frac{(54.6 \times 15) + (49.7 \times 12) + (53.1 \times 5) + (47.9 \times 8)}{40}$$

$$= 51.6 \text{ kg}$$

This will be an estimate for the mean weight of the population of 240 students.

A different form of sampling is illustrated by this example:

The natterjack toad is an increasingly threatened species. Scientists want to find out how many of the toads live in and around a pond.

To do this they catch 20 natterjack toads and mark them in a harmless way. The toads are then released.

Next day another 20 are caught: 5 of these toads have already been marked, in other words a sample of 25% (5 out of a sample of 20) are marked. But 20 toads were marked initially.

This suggests that 25% of the population is about 20

$$\frac{25}{100} \times P = 20 \qquad \therefore \quad P = 80$$

Therefore the total population is 80.

1. Amy wants to investigate the spending habits of students at her school. The number of students in each year group is as follows:

Year group	7	8	9	10	11
Number of students	208	193	197	190	184

Explain how Amy obtains a stratified sample of 100 students for her survey.

2. The table shows the numbers of boys and girls in year 10 and year 11 of a school.

	Year 10	Year 11
Boys	120	134
Girls	110	100

The headteacher wants to find out their views about changes to the school uniform and takes a stratified random sample of 50 pupils from year 10 and year 11.
Calculate the number of pupils to be sampled from year 11.

3. Scientists need to estimate the number of fish in Lake Hodder. They catch and tag 450 fish and then release them back into the lake.

Day	Sample size	Number tagged
1	36	6
2	38	6
3	40	8
4	32	6

Over the next few days and at various locations they catch samples and count the number of fish that are tagged.
Use these values to estimate the total number of fish in the lake.

4. Repeat Exercise 21.2, question 2, knowing the number of e.g. red counters. Take four samples and use the number of red counters in each sample to estimate the total number of counters. How close is this estimate to the known answer of 100?

Random numbers

Various methods are available in order to select the items for a random sample. These include:

- The random number facility included on scientific and graphical calculators. See your own calculator manual to find out how to use generate random numbers.
- Using random number tables.

Here is part of a random number table.

```
665879945456763513827065475490271764464642329570243503213247...
820347842605870571123900072816943432026466056684303822449549...
159244948684009473282734091187781126547844673719098058246314...
615055443033600350379578187659067986852415477075909015878169...
956274563114960268464210038767899586896714137596982556060606...
711312876894397476172242368922366440241526703346361426215192...
644024152186841200658930516043978253683042801319927682484444...
991282613637566094257066100802082250621853852075036294949888...
```

The following example illustrates a method for writing the table.
You might like to try this if you have time, either on your own or with friends. However, do work through the example so that you understand the method, even if you haven't time to do all the calculations.

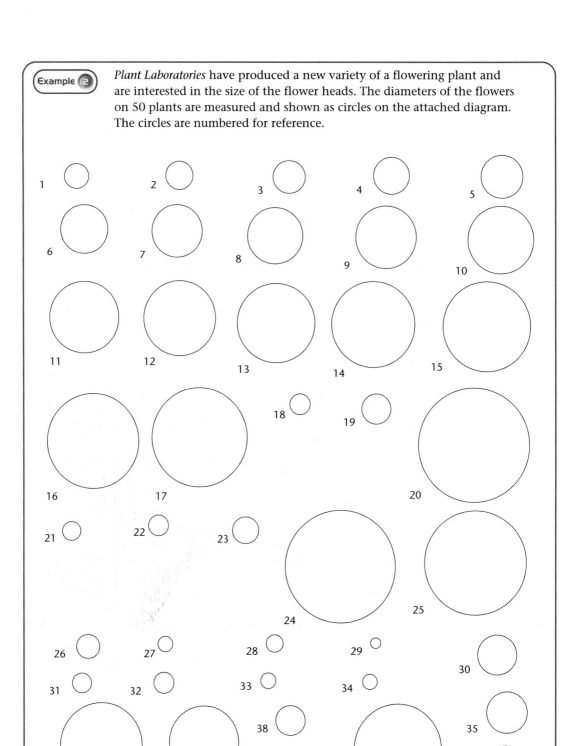

Example 2

Plant Laboratories have produced a new variety of a flowering plant and are interested in the size of the flower heads. The diameters of the flowers on 50 plants are measured and shown as circles on the attached diagram. The circles are numbered for reference.

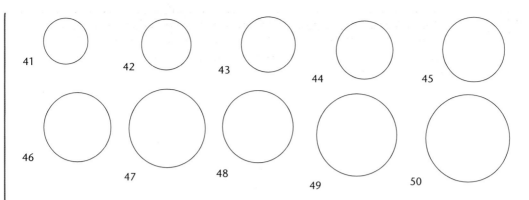

41 42 43 44 45

46 47 48 49 50

1. Select a sample of 5 circles that you think are representative. Measure their diameters and calculate the mean.
2. Repeat for another two samples and find the overall mean.
   [Collect the results from any others in your class who are also doing this activity.]
3. Using a random number table such as the one above:
   (i) Choose a starting number in this table. Once you have fixed this you must move along the row, or down the column and not 'jump about'. Divide the numbers into pairs, starting with your chosen number, to represent the two-digit reference numbers of the flowers, so 03 would represent picture 3. Discard or ignore any two-digit numbers that are greater than 50.
   (ii) Write down the first five two-digit numbers that you get and measure the diameters of those circles and calculate the mean diameter.
   Alternatively use the random number generator on your calculator and follow steps (i) and (ii).

The actual mean diameter for the 50 flowers is 1.43 cm.
   (i) How close were the means calculated by both methods?
   (ii) How did you judge 'representative'? In other words what criteria did you use?
   Discuss this with any others in your class who have completed the experiment.

1. The table shows the times taken for 100 pupils to solve a mathematics problem. The times are all in seconds.

14	20	73	35	28	39	25	17	16	23
20	7	13	30	39	36	17	35	57	26
150	39	25	27	25	40	39	62	47	25
22	16	32	46	29	21	57	10	122	81
90	34	12	68	28	81	32	47	35	37
39	40	23	46	25	43	74	53	24	51
12	30	93	26	17	21	32	37	33	42
93	40	18	55	11	56	34	67	13	15
104	21	25	49	35	18	15	47	26	57
38	92	59	12	32	46	36	25	71	35

   Using a sample, estimate the mean and median time to solve the problem.
   (a) What sample size would you use and why?
   (b) Use your sample to obtain the estimates of the mean and median times.

2. Here is a list of projects that could be attempted or at least planned. In each case you will need to decide:
   - who or what to sample, i.e. how the sample is to be found,
   - what questions need asking or what parameters need measuring.

   Remember to analyse the results explaining why you chose to calculate the median, mean or mode; why you chose to present the results in any particular way, etc.
   (a) What is an average student?
   (b) Old people are more superstitious than young people.
   (c) More babies are born in winter than in summer.
   (d) Do tall people weigh more than short people?
   (e) Estimate the number of blades of grass on the school playing field or a football pitch or your lawn at home.
   (f) Any ideas suggested by any of the questions in this chapter.

Key points

You should be able to:
- design and write questionnaires
- decide an appropriate sample size and how to select this sample.

You should understand:
- random sampling and the use of random number tables or random number generators
- stratified or quota sampling.

Revision exercise 21a

1. Safia surveyed pupils in her school to find out
   their views about background music in shops.
   The size of each year group in the school is
   shown in the table.

Year group	Boys	Girls
7	84	66
8	71	85
9	82	86
10	93	107
11	81	90
Total	411	434

   Safia took a sample of 80 pupils.
   (a) Should she sample different numbers of
       boys and girls in year 7? Give a reason for
       your answer.
   (b) Calculate the number of pupils she should
       sample in year 7.

2. A mobile phone company calls 200 people,
   chosen at random, who subscribe to their
   company to find out how satisfied they are with
   the service they receive.
   Is this a satisfactory method of sampling?
   Give a reason for your answer.

3. Identify which type of sampling has been used
   in the following cases.
   (a) In order to determine whether the
       library facilities in a town are satisfactory,
       all the library cards are numbered and
       questionnaires are sent out to the owners of
       100 cards, selected using random numbers.
   (b) A factory employs 1500 people on
       machines, 400 on packing and distribution
       and 300 in the offices. A sample is taken
       containing 15 machine operators, 4 people
       from packing and distribution and 3 office
       workers.

4. Sweet-tasting apples are used to make apple
   juice. An apple grower needs to find out how
   'sweet' a crop of apples from an orchard is. He is
   advised to select a sample of 50 apples. The
   orchard consists of 1500 trees, each tree
   produces about 50 apples. The grower decides to
   pick 50 apples from one tree that he selects at
   random. Is this a satisfactory method? Give
   reasons for your answer.

22 Indices

Fractional indices

You have already looked at numbers with positive and negative indices and you should know that

$$n^4 = n \times n \times n \times n, \quad n^{-2} = \frac{1}{n^2}, \quad \left(\frac{a}{b}\right)^{-1} = \frac{b}{a} \quad \text{and} \quad n^0 = 1.$$

Suppose $\qquad a^b = \sqrt[3]{a}$

Then $\qquad a^b \times a^b \times a^b = (\sqrt[3]{a})^3 = a = a^1 \qquad$ Cube both sides

$$a^{b+b+b} = a^1$$

$$a^{3b} = a^1$$

$$3b = 1 \qquad\qquad \text{Equate powers}$$

$$b = \frac{1}{3}$$

Therefore $\qquad a^{\frac{1}{3}} = \sqrt[3]{a}$

A similar proof can be given to show that $a^{\frac{1}{2}} = \sqrt{a}$ etc., and also $a^{\frac{1}{n}} = \sqrt[n]{a}$

Similarly, $\qquad a^{\frac{3}{2}} = (a^{\frac{1}{2}})^3 = (\sqrt{a})^3$

or $\qquad (a^3)^{\frac{1}{2}} = \sqrt{a^3}$

Example Write the following in index form, as simply as possible.

(a) the cube of n ⠀⠀ (b) $\dfrac{1}{n^3}$ ⠀⠀ (c) $\sqrt[5]{n}$

(a) n^3 ⠀⠀⠀⠀⠀⠀⠀ (b) n^{-3} ⠀⠀ (c) $n^{\frac{1}{5}}$

You will be asked to work out powers of numbers both with and without a calculator.

Write as whole number or fractions. Do not use a calculator.

(a) 3^2 (b) $16^{\frac{1}{4}}$ (c) $343^{\frac{1}{3}}$ (d) 4^{-2} (e) $\left[\dfrac{1}{3}\right]^{-2}$ (f) 6^0 (g) $125^{\frac{2}{3}}$

(a) $3 \times 3 = 9$ (b) 2 $[2 \times 2 \times 2 \times 2 = 16]$ (c) 7 $[7 \times 7 \times 7 = 343]$

(d) $\dfrac{1}{4^2} = \dfrac{1}{16}$ (e) $3^2 = 9$ (f) 1 (g) 25 $[(\sqrt[3]{125})^2 = 5^2 = 25]$

Examiner's tip

If you have to work out the square root of the cube of a number, it is normally easier to find the root first.

Working with a calculator

On your calculator you will have a key labelled x^y or y^x, which will enable you to work out numbers like 3.1^5 etc. If you are not sure how to use it, practise with something simple like 2^4 which you can work out as 16. Try $\boxed{2}\;\boxed{x^y}\;\boxed{4}\;\boxed{=}$

Similarly you will have a key labelled $x^{1/y}$ or similar (which may be $\boxed{\text{SHIFT}}\;\boxed{x^y}$). This will enable you to work out numbers like $2.5^{\frac{1}{4}}$. Again practise with ones you can calculate in your head to check. You could do Example 2 again using your calculator to check how it works.

Use a calculator to work out the following. Give your answers exactly or to 5 s.f.

(a) 3.5^4 (b) 2.4^6 (c) 1.03^{-3} (d) $2.15^{\frac{1}{4}}$ (e) $3125^{\frac{4}{5}}$

(a) $150.0625 = 150.06$ (b) $191.1029 = 191.10$

(c) $(0.970\,873\,7)^3 = 0.915\,141\,6 = 0.915\,14$

     Note when the index is negative, it may be best to first find the reciprocal and then raise to a positive index.

(d) $1.210\,903 = 1.2109$ (e) 625

Examiner's tip

When finding a root by calculator it is easy to make a mistake. It is very helpful to check by working backwards.

e.g. (d) above $2.15^{\frac{1}{4}} = 1.210\,903$.

Check $1.210\,903^4 = 2.149\,99 \simeq 2.15$ so it checks.

1. Write in index form.

   (a) cube root of n (b) the reciprocal of n^3 (c) $\sqrt[5]{n^2}$

Give the answers as whole numbers or fractions.

2. (a) 4^{-1} (b) $4^{\frac{1}{2}}$ (c) 4^0 (d) 4^{-2} (e) $4^{\frac{3}{2}}$

3. (a) $8^{\frac{1}{3}}$ (b) 8^{-1} (c) $8^{\frac{4}{3}}$ (d) $\left(\frac{1}{8}\right)^{-2}$ (e) 8^1

4. (a) $64^{\frac{1}{2}}$ (b) $64^{-\frac{1}{3}}$ (c) 64^0 (d) $64^{\frac{2}{3}}$ (e) $64^{\frac{5}{6}}$

5. (a) $2^2 \times 9^{\frac{1}{2}}$ (b) $2^5 \times 8^{\frac{1}{3}}$ (c) $81^{\frac{1}{4}} \times 3^{-2}$ (d) $9^{\frac{1}{2}} \times 6^2 \times 4^{-1}$

6. (a) $2^2 + 3^0 + 16^{\frac{1}{2}}$ (b) $\left(\frac{3}{4}\right)^{-2} \times 27^{\frac{2}{3}}$ (c) $4^2 \div 9^{\frac{1}{2}}$ (d) $4^2 - 8^{\frac{1}{3}} + 9^0$

Give the answers exactly or correct to 5 s.f.

7. (a) 1.14^5 (b) 2.79^3 (c) 1.005^9 (d) 4.1^{-4}

8. (a) $923\,521^{\frac{1}{4}}$ (b) $1.051^{\frac{1}{5}}$ (c) $21^{\frac{1}{7}}$ (d) $6.45^{\frac{2}{5}}$

9. (a) 100×1.02^3 (b) $1.6^5 \times 2.1^{\frac{1}{3}}$ (c) $(10^5 \times 4.1)^{\frac{1}{4}}$

10. (a) $1.9^4 - 2.1^3$ (b) $1.9^{\frac{1}{4}} + 0.97^{\frac{1}{5}}$ (c) $14^3 - 196^{\frac{3}{2}}$

1. Write in index form.   (a) $\sqrt[4]{n}$ (b) the reciprocal of $\frac{1}{n}$ cubed   (c) $\sqrt[3]{n^5}$

Give the answers as whole numbers or fractions.

2. (a) 9^{-1} (b) $9^{\frac{1}{2}}$ (c) 9^0 (d) 9^{-2} (e) $9^{\frac{3}{2}}$

3. (a) $27^{\frac{1}{3}}$ (b) $27^{\frac{4}{3}}$ (c) 27^{-1} (d) $\left(\frac{1}{27}\right)^{-\frac{1}{3}}$ (e) 27^0

4. (a) $16^{\frac{1}{2}}$ (b) $16^{-\frac{1}{4}}$ (c) 16^0 (d) $16^{\frac{3}{2}}$ (e) $16^{\frac{7}{4}}$

5. (a) $25^{\frac{3}{2}}$ (b) $36^{\frac{1}{2}}$ (c) $125^{\frac{2}{3}} \times 8^{\frac{2}{3}}$ (d) $49^{\frac{1}{2}} \times 81^{-\frac{1}{4}}$

6. (a) $5^{-2} \times 10^5 \times 16^{-\frac{1}{2}}$ (b) $\left(\frac{4}{5}\right)^2 \times 128^{-\frac{3}{7}}$ (c) $5^3 - 25^{\frac{1}{2}} - \left(\frac{2}{5}\right)^{-2}$ (d) $125^{\frac{1}{3}} - 121^{\frac{1}{2}} + 216^{\frac{1}{3}}$

Give the answers exactly or correct to 5 s.f.

7. (a) 3.25^4 (b) 0.46^5 (c) 1.01^7 (d) 2.91^{-3}

8. (a) $14\,641^{\frac{1}{4}}$ (b) $14\,120^{\frac{1}{5}}$ (c) $9^{\frac{1}{9}}$ (d) $1024^{\frac{2}{5}}$

9. (a) $4^3 + 3^4$ (b) $1.6^4 \times 1.7^{\frac{1}{4}}$ (c) $1^5 \times 4.1^{\frac{1}{4}}$

10. (a) $5.27^5 - 3.49^5$ (b) $4^{\frac{3}{4}} + 5^{\frac{2}{5}}$ (c) $216^{\frac{4}{3}} \times 9^{-\frac{3}{2}}$

Using rules of indices with numbers and letters

Examiner's tip

The most common mistakes are trying to add or subtract a^x and a^y which cannot be done.

You have already learnt the rules for indices:

$$a^n \times a^m = a^{n+m}, \quad a^n \div a^m = a^{n-m}, \quad (a^n)^m = a^{n \times m}$$

These can be used with either numbers or letters.

Example 4

Write as a single power of 2 where possible.

(a) $2 \times \sqrt{2}$ (b) $(\sqrt[3]{2})^2$ (c) $2^3 \div 2^{\frac{1}{2}}$ (d) $2^3 + 2^4$

(e) $8^{\frac{3}{4}}$ (f) $2^3 \times 4^{\frac{3}{2}}$ (g) $2^n \times 4^3$

(a) $2^1 \times 2^{\frac{1}{2}} = 2^{\frac{3}{2}}$ (b) $(2^{\frac{1}{3}})^2 = 2^{\frac{2}{3}}$ (c) $2^{3-\frac{1}{2}} = 2^{2\frac{1}{2}} = 2^{\frac{5}{2}}$

(d) $2^3 + 2^4$ These powers cannot be added   (e) $(2^3)^{\frac{3}{4}} = 2^{3 \times \frac{3}{4}} = 2^{\frac{9}{4}}$

(f) $2^3 \times (2^2)^{\frac{3}{2}} = 2^3 \times 2^3 = 2^6$ (g) $2^n \times (2^2)^3 = 2^n \times 2^6 = 2^{n+6}$

Example 5

Write 132 as a product of its prime factors. Use indices where possible.

$132 = 2 \times 66 = 2 \times 2 \times 33 = 2 \times 2 \times 3 \times 11 = 2^2 \times 3 \times 11$

Example 6

Simplify where possible.

(a) $3a^2b^3 \times 2ab^2$ (b) $15ab^3 \times 3a^2b \div 5a^3b^2$ (c) $(8a^6)^{\frac{1}{3}}$

(d) $4a^2 + 3a^3$ (e) $a^4 \times a^{-2}$ (f) $(2a)^{\frac{1}{2}} \div (8a^3)^{-\frac{1}{2}}$

(a) $[3 \times 2 \times a^{2+1} \times b^{3+2}] = 6a^3b^5$

(b) $[15 \times 3 \div 5 \times a^{1+2-3} \times b^{3+1-2}] = 9b^2$

(c) $[8^{\frac{1}{3}} \times a^{6 \times \frac{1}{2}}] = 2a^2$

(d) $4a^2 + 3a^3$ cannot be simplified

(e) $[a^{4-2}] = a^2$

(f) $2^{\frac{1}{2}} \div 8^{-\frac{1}{2}} \times a^{\frac{1}{2}} \div (a^3)^{-\frac{1}{2}} = 2^{\frac{1}{2}} \times 2^{\frac{3}{2}} \times a^{\frac{1}{2}} \times a^{\frac{3}{2}} = 2^2 \times a^2 = 4a^2$

The steps in square brackets can be missed out with practice.

Example 7

Solve the equations.   (a) $x^{\frac{1}{3}} = 3$ (b) $x^{-2} = 9$ (c) $2^{2x} = 8$

(a) $(x^{\frac{1}{3}})^3 = 3^3$ Cube both sides.

$[x^{\frac{1}{3} \times 3} = 27]$

$x = 27$

(b) $\dfrac{1}{x^2} = 9$

$x^2 = \frac{1}{9}$ Multiply by x^2.

$x = \pm\frac{1}{3}$ Divide by 9.
           Square root.

(c) $2^{2x} = 2^3$ Change both to powers of 2.

$2x = 3$

$x = 1.5$

Example 8

Simplify as far as possible.

(a) $x^2(x^3 - 3x^2) + 4x^3(5x - 2x^2)$ (b) $(x^{\frac{1}{2}} - 1)(x^{\frac{1}{2}} + 1)$

(a) $x^5 - 3x^4 + 20x^4 - 8x^5 = 17x^4 - 7x^5$

(b) $x + x^{\frac{1}{2}} - x^{\frac{1}{2}} - 1 = x - 1$ Notice that this is the difference of two squares.

Chapter 22 Using rules of indices with numbers and letters

Example 9

Put the following in order smallest first.

$x^2, x^{\frac{1}{3}}, x^{-3}, \dfrac{1}{x}$ when $x > 1$.

x^2 is bigger than x, if $x > 1$.

$x^{\frac{1}{3}}$ is smaller than x but bigger than 1.

$\dfrac{1}{x}$ is less than 1 since $x > 1$.

$x^{-3} = \dfrac{1}{x^3}$; $\dfrac{1}{x^3} < \dfrac{1}{x}$ since $x^3 > x$.

Order is $x^{-3}, \dfrac{1}{x}, x^{\frac{1}{3}}, x^2$.

Exercise 22.2a

1. Write as powers of 3 as simply as possible.
   (a) 27   (b) $\frac{1}{3}$ (c) $3 \times \sqrt{3}$ (d) $81^{\frac{3}{2}}$ (e) $3^4 \times 9^{-1}$ (f) $9^n \times 27^{3n}$

2. Write as powers of 5 as simply as possible.
   (a) 625   (b) $25^{-\frac{1}{2}} \times 5^3$ (c) 0.2   (d) $125^{\frac{3}{2}} \times 5^{-3} \div 25^2$ (e) $5^4 - 5^3$ (f) $25^{3n} \times 125^{\frac{n}{3}}$

3. Write as powers of 2 and 3 as simply as possible.
   (a) 24   (b) $6^2 \times 4^2$ (c) $18^{\frac{1}{3}}$ (d) $\frac{4}{9}$ (e) $13\frac{1}{2}$ (f) 12^{2n}

4. Write as a product of the prime factors. Use indices where possible.
   (a) 75   (b) 144   (c) 300   (d) 324

5. Simplify where possible.
   (a) $4a^2b \times 3a^3b^2$ (b) $3a^2b - 2ab^2$ (c) $16a^2b \div 8ab$ (d) $9a^4 \times 2a^{-3}$

6. Simplify where possible.
   (a) $(3a^2)^3$ (b) $(2b)^{-3}$ (c) $(16a^4)^{\frac{1}{2}}$ (d) $\sqrt{4a^2b^6}$ (e) $(2a^4)^{\frac{1}{2}} \times (8a^2)^{-\frac{1}{2}}$

7. Simplify where possible.
   (a) $\dfrac{a^3bc \times 3abc}{a^2b^3c}$ (b) $\dfrac{4a^2b^2c^3 + 2ab^3c}{6ab^2c}$ (c) $2a(3ab - 2b^2) + 3b(2ab - a^2)$

8. Solve the following equations.
   (a) $2^x = 16$ (c) $2^{3x} = 8^2$ (e) $5^{3x} = 25^{3/4}$ (g) $x^{\frac{1}{3}} = 4$
   (b) $3^x = 27^{-1}$ (d) $3^{x+2} = 81$ (f) $8^{x+2} = 32$ (h) $x^{-2} = 25$

9. Simplify as far as possible.
   (a) $(3a^{\frac{1}{2}} - 2)(3a^{\frac{1}{2}} + 2)$ (b) $(a^2 + 2ab + b^2)^{\frac{1}{2}}$ (c) $(a^2 - 3)(a^{-2} + 1)$

10. Put in order of size, smallest first. $x, x^4, x^{-2}, x^{\frac{1}{2}}$ when $0 < x < 1$.

Examiner's tip

Take care when there is an index outside a bracket.
$(3a^2)^3$ is $3^3 \times a^{2 \times 3}$ and not $3 \times 3 \times a^5$!

1. Write as powers of 2 as simply as possible.
   (a) 32   (b) $8^{\frac{2}{3}}$ (c) $2 \times \sqrt[3]{64}$ (d) 0.25   (e) $2^{2n} \times 4^{\frac{n}{2}}$ (f) $2^{3n} \times 16^{-2}$

2. Write each as a power of a prime number as simply as possible.
   (a) 343   (b) $25^{\frac{1}{6}}$ (c) $16^{\frac{1}{2}} \times 64^{-\frac{2}{3}}$ (d) $27^2 \div 81^{\frac{3}{2}}$ (e) $2^5 + 2^2$ (f) $9^{2n} \times 3^{-2n}$

3. Write as a product of the prime factors. Use indices where possible.
   (a) 36   (b) 96   (c) 60   (d) 392

4. Write as products of prime numbers.
   (a) 15^3 (b) $12^{\frac{1}{2}} \times 9^{-\frac{1}{4}}$ (c) 40^n (d) $20^{2n} \times 100^n$

5. Simplify where possible.
   (a) $2p^2q \times 3pq$ (b) $3p^2 \times p^{-3}$ (c) $12p^2q \div 8pq^2$ (d) $9p^3q \times 2pq^{-2}$

6. Simplify where possible.
   (a) $(2q^2)^3$ (b) $\left(\frac{p}{8}\right)^{-2}$ (c) $\left(\frac{q}{p}\right)^{-2}$ (d) $(16q^6)^{\frac{1}{2}}$ (e) $(25p^2)^{\frac{1}{2}} \times (16p^2)^{-\frac{1}{2}}$

7. Simplify.
   (a) $3a^2bc^2 \times 4a^2b^2c \div 6a^5b^2c^3$ (b) $\dfrac{4pqr \times 2p^2qr^2}{5p^3r}$ (c) $a^2 \times a^{-1} \times a^{\frac{3}{2}} \times a^{-\frac{7}{2}}$

8. Solve the following equations.
   (a) $2^x = 32$ (c) $2^{2x} = 16^{\frac{1}{2}}$ (e) $5^{x+1} = (125)^{-1}$ (g) $x^{\frac{1}{2}} = 6$
   (b) $3^x = \frac{1}{9}$ (d) $7^{\frac{x}{3}} = 49$ (f) $4^{-x} = 32^{\frac{1}{2}}$ (h) $x^{-3} = 125$

9. Simplify as far as possible.
   (a) $(5a^{\frac{1}{2}} - 1)(5a^{\frac{1}{2}} + 1)$ (b) $\dfrac{p^2q + pq^2}{pq}$ (c) $(p^2 + 3q)(p^{-2} + q^{-1})$

10. Put in order of size, smallest first. $x, x^4, x^{-2}, \sqrt{x}$ when $x > 1$.

Exponential growth

£200 is invested at 5% per year compound interest.

After 1 year the investment will be worth
   $200 \times 1.05 = £210$
After 2 years the investment will be worth
   $210 \times 1.05 = £220.50$
After 3 years the investment will be worth
   $£220.50 \times 1.05 = £231.53$

and so on.

This calculation, where there is a constant multiplier involved, is an example of exponential growth. If the multiplier is a larger number the figures get very large, very quickly.

To do the calculation for a high number of years in the same way, using a constant multiplier, is time consuming. It would be easier if it was possible to find a formula for the calculation.

Look again at the calculations for two and three years.

Another way of looking at the calculation for 2 years is
$$200 \times 1.05 \times 1.05 = 200 \times 1.05^2$$

Similarly the calculation for 3 years is
$$200 \times 1.05 \times 1.05 \times 1.05 = 200 \times 1.05^3$$

So, after 20 years, for example, the investment will be worth 200×1.05^{20}.

On the calculator this calculation is done using the power button.
This is usually labelled $\boxed{y^x}$, $\boxed{x^y}$ or, on most modern calculators, $\boxed{\wedge}$
The calculation is then simply $200 \times 1.05 \boxed{\wedge} 20 = £530.66$

The formula for this calculation is $A = 200 \times 1.05^n$,

where A is the amount the investment is worth and n is the number of years.

 Example 10

The number of bacteria present doubles every hour. If there were 500 present at 12 noon, find the number present

(a) at 2 p.m.
(b) 3 p.m.
(c) at midnight
(d) after n hours

(a) $500 \times 2 \times 2 = 2000$
(b) $2000 \times 2 = 4000$
(c) $500 \times 2^{12} = 2\ 048\ 000$
(d) Number present $= 500 \times 2^n$

Exponential decay

A car depreciates in value by 15% per year. It cost £12 000 when it was new.

After 1 year it will be worth $12\ 000 \times 0.85 = £10\ 200$
After 2 years it will be worth $10\ 200 \times 0.85 = £8670$
After 3 years it will be worth $8670 \times 0.85 = £7369.50$

and so on.

This calculation where the constant multiplier is less than 1 is an example of exponential decay.

The calculations involved work exactly like the ones with exponential growth except for the fact that the multiplier is less than one and so the numbers get smaller instead of bigger.

After 10 years the car will be worth £12 000 $\times 0.85^{10}$ = £2362.49.

The formula for this calculation is $A = 12\,000 \times 0.85^{n}$,

where A is the amount the car is worth and n is the number of years.

Example 11

The population of a certain species of bird is dropping by 20% every 10 years. If there were 50 000 birds in 1970, how many will there be
(a) in 2010,   (b) 2020   (c) 2100   (d) n years after 1970?

(a) $\dfrac{2010 - 1970}{10} = 4$ $50\,000 \times 0.8^{4} = 20\,480$

(b) $\dfrac{2020 - 1970}{10} = 5$ $50\,000 \times 0.8^{5} = 16\,384$

(c) $\dfrac{2100 - 1970}{10} = 13$ $50\,000 \times 0.8^{13} = 2749$

(d) Since the population is multiplied by 0.8 every 10 years, the number will be $50\,000 \times 0.8^{\frac{n}{10}}$.

The calculations in Examples 10 and 11 show the dramatic changes that can take place with exponential growth and decay.

Exponential decay can be expressed using a negative power. For example if a population starts at 1 million and is halved every year:

After 5 years the population is $1\,000\,000 \times 0.5^{5} = 31\,250$
After n years the population is $1\,000\,000 \times 0.5^{n}$

Since $0.5 = \frac{1}{2} = 2^{-1}$

the calculation can be written:
after 5 years the population is $1\,000\,000 \times 2^{-5} = 31\,250$
after n years the population is $1\,000\,000 \times 2^{-n}$

Graphs of exponential growth and decay functions

Look again at Example 10.
The table of values for the number of bacteria is:

Number of hours	0	1	2	3	4
Number of bacteria	500	1000	2000	4000	8000

The graph is:

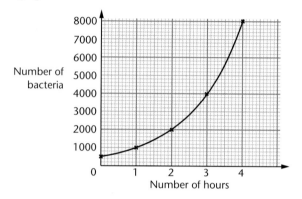

The shape of this graph is typical of an exponential growth function.

Look again at Example 11.

The table of values is:

Year	1970	1980	1990	2000	2010	2020
Number of birds	50 000	40 000	32 000	25 600	20 480	16 384

The graph is

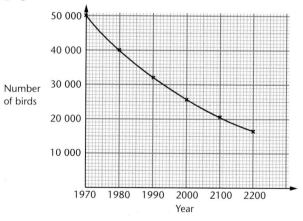

The shape of this graph is typical of an exponential decay function.

Example 12

Plot a graph of $y = 3^x$ for values of x from -2 to 3.
Use your graph to estimate
(a) the value of y when $x = 2.4$ (b) the solution to the equation $3^x = 20$.

The table of values is

x	-2	-1	0	1	2	3
y	0.111	0.333	1	3	9	27

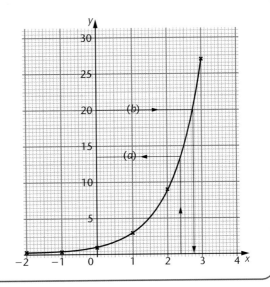

(a) 13.5   (b) 2.75

Example 13

Plot a graph of $y = 2^{-x}$ for values of x from -4 to 2.
Use your graph to estimate
(a) the value of y when $x = 0.5$
(b) the solution to the equation $2^{-x} = 10$.

x	-4	-3	-2	-1	0	1	2
y	16	8	4	2	1	0.5	0.25

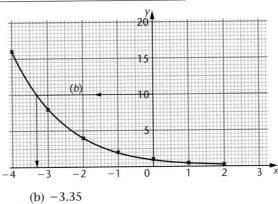

(a) 0.7   (b) -3.35

Note that, although the scales make it difficult to show here,
neither graph ever reaches the x-axis.

1. £2000 is invested at 6% compound interest.
   (a) Calculate the value of the investment after
      (i) 3 years   (ii) 15 years.
   (b) Find a formula for the amount the investment is worth after n years.

2. A car costs £9000 when new. It depreciates in value by 12% per year.
   (a) Calculate the value of the car after
      (i) 4 years   (ii) 10 years.
   (b) Find a formula for the value of the car after n years.

3. The population of a country is rising by 5% every 10 years. If the population was 15 million in 1990, estimate what will it be in
   (a) 2020   (b) 2100.

4. A radioactive element has a mass of 50 g and its decay reduces its mass by 10% every year.
   (a) Calculate its mass after 3 years.
   (b) Find a formula for its mass after n years.
   (c) Use trial and improvement to estimate the time when its mass will have halved.

5. Two people start a rumour that goes round a school. The following table shows the number of people, n, who have heard the rumour after t hours.

Time (t) in hours	0	1	2	3	4	5
Number of people (n)	2	6	18	54	162	486

Find a formula for n in terms of t.

6. A report estimated that the number of people actively playing sport in this country was reducing by 3% per year. There were 11 million actively playing sport in 1995.
   (a) Estimate how many were playing in 2000.
   (b) Estimate how many will be playing in 2010.
   (c) Write down a formula for the number playing n years after 1995.

7. Plot a graph of $y = 2^x$ for values of x from -2 to 5. Use a scale of 2 cm to 1 unit on the x-axis and 2 cm to 5 units on the y-axis.
   Use your graph to estimate.
   (a) the value of y when $x = 3.2$
   (b) the solution to the equation $2^x = 20$.

8. Copy and complete the table of values for $y = 3^{-x}$.

x	0	0.5	1	1.5	2	2.5	3	3.5	4
y	1								

Plot the graph of $y = 3^{-x}$ for these values. Use a scale of 2 cm to 1 unit on the x-axis and 1 cm to 0.1 units on the y-axis.
Use your graph to estimate
   (a) the value of y when $x = 1.2$
   (b) the solution to the equation $3^{-x} = 0.1$.

1. £5000 is invested at 3% compound interest.
   (a) Calculate the value of the investment after
      (i) 4 years (ii) 20 years.
   (b) Find a formula for the amount the investment is worth after n years.

2. A car costs £16 000 when new. It depreciates in value by 16% per year.
   (a) Calculate the value of the car after
      (i) 3 years (ii) 8 years.
   (b) Find a formula for the value of the car after n years.

3. An antique increases in value by 15% per year. It was worth £300 in 1998.
   (a) What will it be worth in (i) 2004 (ii) 2010?
   (b) Find a formula for its value n years after 1998.

4. A colony of bacteria is found to increase in number by 50% every hour.
   (a) If there are 2 million bacteria at noon, find the number at (i) 2 p.m. (ii) 4.30 p.m.
   (b) Find a formula for the number after n hours.

5. The mass, m, of a chemical present after t minutes during a chemical reaction is given in the table below.

Time (t) in minutes	0	1	2	3	4	5
Mass in grams (m)	100	50	25	12.5	6.25	3.125

Find a formula for n in terms of t.

6. A ball is dropped onto a hard surface. After each bounce it rebounds to $\frac{3}{4}$ of the height from which it fell. It was originally dropped from 4 m.
   (a) Find the height it reaches on
      (i) the third bounce (ii) eighth bounce.
   (b) Find a formula for the height of the nth bounce.

7. Plot a graph of $y = 1.5^x$ for values of x from -3 to 5. Use a scale of 2 cm to 1 unit on both axes. Use your graph to estimate
   (a) the value of y when $x = 2.4$
   (b) the solution to the equation $1.5^x = 6$.

8. Copy and complete the table of values for $y = 4^{-x}$

x	-2.5	-2	-1.5	-1	-0.5	0	0.5	1
y		16						

Plot the graph of $y = 4^{-x}$ for these values. Use a scale of 2 cm to 1 unit on the x-axis and 2 cm to 5 units on the y-axis.
Use your graph to estimate
(a) the value of y when $x = -1.8$
(b) the solution to the equation $4^{-x} = 25$.

Key points

- The rules of indices are $a^n \times a^m = a^{n+m}$, $a^n \div a^m = a^{n-m}$,
  $(a^n)^m = a^{n \times m}$, $a^0 = 1$, $a^n = a \times a \times a \dots n$ times, $a^{-n} = \dfrac{1}{a^n}$, $a^{1/n} = \sqrt[n]{a}$

- The use of the keys such as x^y and $x^{\frac{1}{y}}$ on the calculator.

- When solving equations of the type $2^x = 32$, change everything to powers of 2 and then equate the indices.

- When a value is multiplied by a constant multiplier (greater than one), this is an example of exponential growth.

- When a value is multiplied by a constant multiplier (less than one), this is an example of exponential decay.

1. Write in index form as simply as possible.
   (a) the reciprocal of n (b) the cube root of m (c) the square root of $\dfrac{1}{n}$

2. Write as whole numbers or fractions. Do not use a calculator.
   (a) 4^{-1} (b) 5^0 (c) $25^{\frac{1}{2}}$ (d) 2^4 (e) $8^{\frac{2}{3}}$

   (f) $125^{-\frac{2}{3}}$ (g) $\left(\dfrac{1}{8}\right)^{-\frac{1}{3}}$ (h) $64^{\frac{5}{6}}$ (i) $\left(\dfrac{4}{9}\right)^{-\frac{1}{2}}$ (j) $\left(\dfrac{1}{12}\right)^{-2}$

3. Write as whole numbers or fractions. Do not use a calculator.
   (a) $8^0 \times 25^2$ (c) $2^7 \times 4^{-2}$ (e) $5^2 - 4^3 + 3^4$ (g) $14^2 \times 49^{-1}$

   (b) $4^2 \times 25^{\frac{1}{2}}$ (d) $6^3 \div 9^{\frac{3}{2}}$ (f) $25^{\frac{3}{2}} \times 64^{\frac{1}{3}}$ (h) $\left(\dfrac{4}{5}\right)^{-2} \times \left(\dfrac{16}{9}\right)^{\frac{1}{2}}$

4. Use a calculator for these questions. Give the answers exactly or to 5 s.f.
   (a) 1.43^3 (b) 0.87^5 (c) 2^{12} (d) 7.9^{-4}

5. Use a calculator for these questions. Give the answers exactly or to 5 s.f.
   (a) $59\,049^{\frac{1}{5}}$ (b) $7.9^{\frac{1}{4}}$ (c) $4000^{\frac{1}{6}}$ (d) $32\,768^{\frac{3}{5}}$

6. Write as a power of a prime number as simply as possible.
   (a) 128 (b) 27^2 (c) $343^{\frac{1}{5}}$ (d) $9^2 \div 81^{-\frac{1}{2}}$ (e) $2^n \times 32^{n+1}$

7. Write as a product of the prime factors. Use indices where possible.
   (a) 40 (b) 90 (c) 136 (d) 588

8. Write as powers of primes as simply as possible.
   (a) 15^2 (b) $40^{\frac{1}{3}}$ (c) $14^3 \times 56^{\frac{1}{3}}$ (d) $72^{\frac{3}{2}} \times 24^{-\frac{1}{2}}$

9. Simplify where possible.
   (a) $(2ab^2)^3$ (b) $(9a^4)^{\frac{1}{2}}$ (c) $2b^2 \times b^{-3}$ (d) $ab^2c \times 2a^2b^{-1}c^{-2}$

   (e) $(64a^6b^{-3})^{-\frac{1}{3}}$ (f) $14ab^2 \div 2a^2b$ (g) $\sqrt[3]{125a^3b^6}$ (h) $\dfrac{a^2b - 2ab^2}{3a^2 - 6ab}$

10. (a) Solve the following.
    (i) $2^x = 4^2$ (iii) $2^{2x} = 4^{\frac{1}{2}}$ (v) $5^{2x+1} = (125)^{\frac{1}{2}}$ (vii) $x^{\frac{1}{2}} = 11$

    (ii) $3^x = 9^{-1}$ (iv) $49^x = 7^3$ (vi) $8^{-x} = 32^{\frac{1}{3}}$ (viii) $x^{-2} = 169$

    (b) Given that $x > 1$, put the following in order, smallest first.
    $$x^{\frac{1}{2}},\ x^{-1},\ x^4,\ \sqrt[3]{x}$$

11. During an epidemic the number of people infected is rising by 5% per day. 300 000 were infected on January 31st.
    (a) How many were infected by (i) February 5th (ii) February 10th?
    (b) Find a formula for the number infected n days after January 31st.
    (c) Use trial and improvement to find the number of days for the number infected to be doubled.

12. Copy and complete the table of values for $y = 2^{-x}$.

x	0	0.5	1	1.5	2	2.5	3	3.5	4
y	1								

Plot the graph of $y = 2^{-x}$ for these values. Use a scale of 2 cm to 1 unit on the x-axis and 1 cm to 0.1 units on the y-axis.

Use your graph to estimate
(a) the value of y when $x = 1.8$
(b) the solution to the equation $2^{-x} = 0.6$.

You will need to know:

- how to find the circumference and area of circles
- how to find the volume of a prism
- how to rearrange formulae
- how to use Pythagoras' theorem and trigonometry.

Arcs and sectors

A sector is a fraction of a circle.

It is $\frac{\theta}{360}$ ths of the circle,

where $\theta°$ is the sector angle at
the centre of the circle.

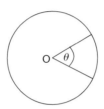

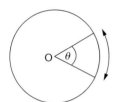

$$\text{Arc length} = \frac{\theta}{360} \times \text{circumference}$$

$$= \frac{\theta}{360} \times 2\pi r$$

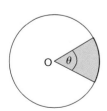

$$\text{Sector area} = \frac{\theta}{360} \times \text{area of circle}$$

$$= \frac{\theta}{360} \times \pi r^2$$

Example ①

Calculate the arc length and area of this sector to 3 s.f.

Arc length $= \dfrac{\theta}{360} \times 2\pi r$

$= \dfrac{37}{360} \times 2\pi \times 5.6$

$= $ **3.62 cm** to 3 s.f.

Sector area $= \dfrac{\theta}{360} \times \pi r^2$

$= \dfrac{37}{360} \times \pi \times 5.6^2$

$= $ **10.1 cm^2** to 3 s.f.

Example ②

Calculate the sector angle of a sector with arc length 6.2 cm in a circle with radius 7.5 cm to 1 d.p.

Arc length $= \dfrac{\theta}{360} \times 2\pi r$

$6.2 = \dfrac{\theta}{360} \times 2\pi \times 7.5$

$\theta = \dfrac{6.2 \times 360}{2\pi \times 7.5}$

$ = $ **47.4°** to 1 d.p.

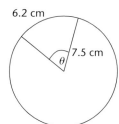

Examiner's tip

You can rearrange the formula before you substitute, if you prefer.

Example ③

A sector makes an angle of 54° at the centre of a circle. The area of the sector is 15 cm^2. Calculate the radius of the circle to 3 s.f.

Sector area $= \dfrac{\theta}{360} \times \pi r^2$

$15 = \dfrac{54}{360} \times \pi r^2$

$r^2 = \dfrac{15 \times 360}{54 \times \pi}$

$ = 31.83 \ldots$

$r = \sqrt{31.83 \ldots}$

$ = $ **5.64 cm** to 3 s.f.

1. Calculate the arc length of these sectors. Give your answers to 3 s.f.

(a)
40° 5.1 cm

(b)
3.7 cm
210°

(c)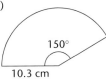
150°
10.3 cm

(d)
9.6 cm
74°

(e)
4.3 cm   112°

2. Calculate the areas of the sectors in question 1. Give your answers to 3 s.f.

3. Calculate the perimeters of these sectors. Give your answers to 3 s.f.

(a)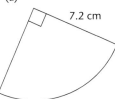
7.2 cm

(b)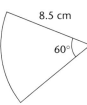
8.5 cm
60°

(c)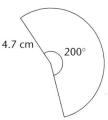
4.7 cm   200°

4. Calculate the sector angle in each of these sectors. Give your answers to the nearest degree.

(a)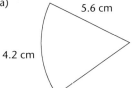
5.6 cm
4.2 cm

(b)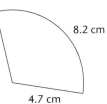
8.2 cm
4.7 cm

(c)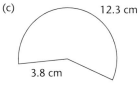
12.3 cm
3.8 cm

(d)
Area =
10.3 cm²
4.5 cm

(e)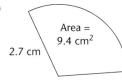
Area =
9.4 cm²
2.7 cm

Exercise 23.la continued

5. Calculate the radius of each of these sectors.

(a)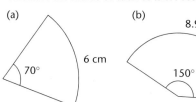

6 cm

70°

(b)

8.9 cm

150°

(c) 19 cm

225°

(d)

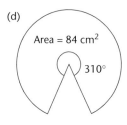

Area = 84 cm²

310°

(e)

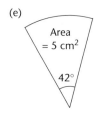

Area = 5 cm²

42°

(f)

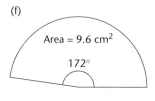

Area = 9.6 cm²

172°

Exercise 23.lb

1. Calculate the arc length of these sectors. Give your answers to 3 s.f.

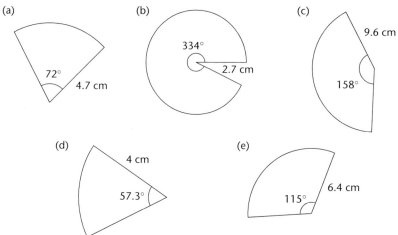

(a)

72°

4.7 cm

(b)

334°

2.7 cm

(c)

9.6 cm

158°

(d)

4 cm

57.3°

(e)

6.4 cm

115°

2. Calculate the areas of the sectors in question 1. Give your answers to 3 s.f.

3. Calculate the perimeters of these sectors. Give your answers to 3 s.f.

(a)

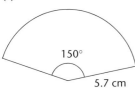

150°

5.7 cm

(b)

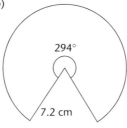

294°

7.2 cm

(c)

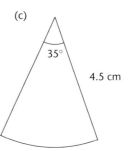

35°

4.5 cm

4. Calculate the sector angle in each of these sectors. Give your answers to the nearest degree.

(a)

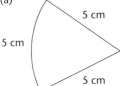

5 cm

5 cm

5 cm

(b)

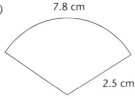

7.8 cm

2.5 cm

(c)

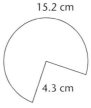

15.2 cm

4.3 cm

(d)

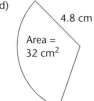

4.8 cm

Area = 32 cm²

(e)

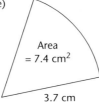

Area = 7.4 cm²

3.7 cm

(f)

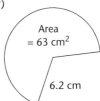

Area = 63 cm²

6.2 cm

5. Calculate the radius of each of these sectors.

(a)

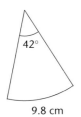

42°

9.8 cm

(b)

12.3 cm

127°

(c)

17.9 cm

222°

(d) sector area = 19.7 cm², sector angle = 52°

(e) sector area = 12.7 cm², sector angle = 136°

(f) sector area = 6.2 m², sector angle = 218°.

Volumes

In an earlier chapter you learned how to find the volume of a prism: a shape where the cross-section stays the same throughout its length.

Volume of a prism = area of cross-section × length.

For a shape whose cross-section, though similar, decreases to a point, its volume is given by

Volume = $\frac{1}{3}$ area of cross-section at base × height.

The particular shapes of this type that you need to know are the pyramid, with a square or rectangular cross-section, and the cone. So for a cone with base radius r and height h,

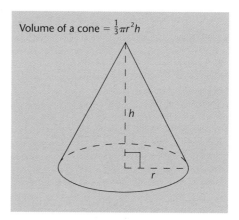

Volume of a cone = $\frac{1}{3}\pi r^2 h$

You also need to know about a different type of 3D shape: the sphere.

Volume of sphere of radius $r = \frac{4}{3}\pi r^3$

Surface areas

Think of the label around a cylindrical can.
It can be opened out flat to form a rectangle.

The length of the rectangle is the circumference of the can. Its width is the height of the can. The area of the rectangle is the curved surface area of the cylinder.

This gives:

Curved surface area of cylinder $= 2\pi r h$

The curved surface area of a cone can be opened out to form the sector of a circle of radius, l, where l is the slant height of the cone. The arc length of the sector is the circumference of the base of the cone.

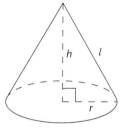

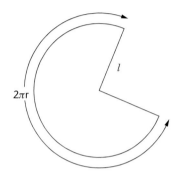

You might like to use the work on sectors that you did earlier in this chapter to prove for yourself the formula:

Curved surface area of cone $= \pi r l$

Last in this section comes the surface area of a sphere of radius r. This is given by:

Surface area of sphere $= 4\pi r^2$

Example 4

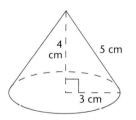

This cone has a solid base. Find
(a) the volume of the cone
(b) the total surface area of the cone.

(a) Volume $= \frac{1}{3}\pi \times 3^2 \times 4 = 12\pi = 37.7$ cm^3
(b) Curved surface area $= \pi \times 3 \times 5 = 15\pi$
Area of base $= \pi \times 3^2 = 9\pi$
Total surface area $= 24\pi = \mathbf{75.4}$ cm^2.

1. Calculate the volumes of these pyramids. Their bases are squares or rectangles:

(a)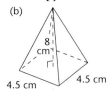

6 cm

3 cm   3 cm

(b)

8 cm

4.5 cm   4.5 cm

(c)

6 m

5 m   7 m

2. Calculate the volumes of these cones.

(a)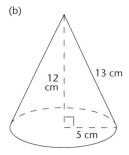

7.0 cm

5.6 cm

4.2 cm

(b)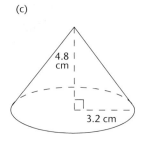

13 cm

12 cm

5 cm

(c)

4.8 cm

3.2 cm

3. Find the volume of a sphere of radius
   (a) 5 cm   (b) 6.2 cm   (c) 2 mm

4. Calculate the curved surface area of these cylinders:
   (a) radius = 4.7 cm, height = 8.2 cm
   (b) radius = 1.2 m, height = 2.5 m
   (c) radius = 3.5 cm, height = 4.6 cm.

5. Calculate the curved surface area of the cones in question 2 (a) and (b).

6. Calculate the surface area of the spheres in question 3.

7.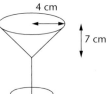

4 cm

7 cm

Calculate the capacity of this glass.
Give your answer in millilitres.

> **Examiner's tip**
>
> Capacity is the amount (volume) that a container can hold.

8. How many ball bearings of radius 0.3 cm can be made from 10 cm^3 of metal when it is melted?

9. What is the total surface area of this wooden cylindrical brick?

3 cm

5 cm

10. A sphere has the same volume as this cone. Calculate the radius of the sphere.

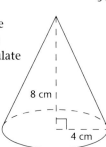

8 cm

4 cm

1. Calculate the volumes of these pyramids. Their bases are squares or rectangles.

(a)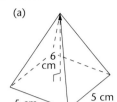
5 cm   5 cm   6 cm

(b)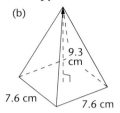
9.3 cm   7.6 cm   7.6 cm

(c)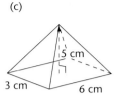
5 cm   3 cm   6 cm

2. Calculate the volumes of these cones.

(a)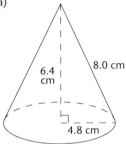
6.4 cm   8.0 cm   4.8 cm

(b)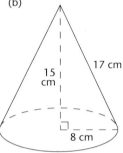
15 cm   17 cm   8 cm

(c)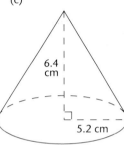
6.4 cm   5.2 cm

3. Find the volume of a sphere of radius
   (a) 3 cm   (b) 4.7 cm   (c) 5 mm
4. Calculate the curved surface area of these cylinders.
   (a) radius = 2.7 cm, height = 3.4 cm
   (b) radius = 1.9 m, height = 1.6 m
   (c) radius = 7.2 cm, height 15.7 cm.
5. Calculate the curved surface area of the cones in question 2 (a) and (b).
6. Calculate the surface area of the spheres in question 3.
7.   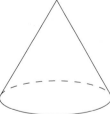   This glass paperweight in the shape of a cone has a volume of 75 cm^3. Its base radius is 3 cm. Calculate its height.

8. How many glass marbles of radius 7 mm can be made from 100 cm^3 of glass?

9. A plastic pipe is a cylinder 2 m long. The internal and external radii of the pipe are 5 mm and 6 mm. Calculate the volume of plastic in the pipe.

10. A solid cone and a solid cylinder both have base radius 6 cm. The height of the cylinder is 4 cm. The cone and the cylinder each have the same volume.
    (a) Find the height of the cone.
    (b) Calculate the curved surface area of the cylinder.

More complex problems

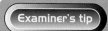

When you have to work out how to solve a problem, follow these steps.
Read the question carefully and plan:

- What do I know?
- What do I have to find?
- What methods can I apply?

Look back when you have finished and ask 'Have I answered the question?'
There may be one last step you have forgotten to do.

These may involve combining shapes you have met earlier. Or they may use topics you have met in other chapters, such as Pythagoras' theorem and trigonometry. Be prepared for anything, and enjoy the problem-solving!

One shape you may not have met before is the **frustum** of a cone. This is the shape remaining when a solid cone has a smaller cone removed from it as shown in this diagram.

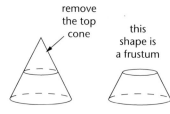

remove the top cone

this shape is a frustum

Calculate the area of this segment.

Area of segment = area of sector − area of triangle.

$$\text{Area of sector} = \frac{100}{360} \times \pi \times 5^2$$

$$= 21.816... \text{ cm}^2$$

$$\text{Area of triangle} = \tfrac{1}{2}ab\sin C$$

$$= \tfrac{1}{2} \times 5^2 \times \sin 100°$$

$$= 12.31... \text{ cm}^2$$

$$\text{Area of segment} = 21.816... - 12.31...$$

$$= \mathbf{9.51 \ cm^2} \text{ to 3 s.f.}$$

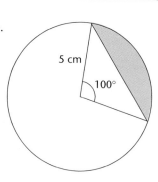

5 cm

100°

Write down more figures than you need in the working, and round the final answer. Using the calculator memory means you do not have to rekey figures.

Calculate the curved surface area of this cone.

First, the slant height *l* must be found.

$$l^2 = 5^2 + 6^2 = 51$$

$$l = \sqrt{51}$$

$$\text{Curved surface area} = \pi r l$$

$$= \pi \times 5 \times \sqrt{51}$$

$$= \mathbf{112 \ cm^2} \text{ to 3 s.f.}$$

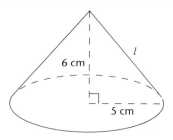

6 cm

5 cm

l

1. A solid cylinder has a base radius of 3 cm. Its volume is 95 cm³. Calculate its curved surface area.

2.

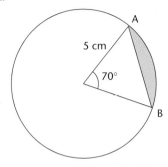

Calculate (a) the length of the chord AB
           (b) the perimeter of the shaded segment.

3.

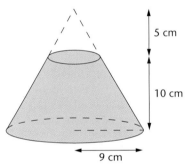

A cone of height 15 cm and base 9 cm has a cone of height 5 cm removed from its top as shown.
(a) What is the radius of the base of the top cone?
(b) Calculate the volume of the remaining frustum of the cone.

4.

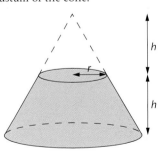

Show that the volume of this frustum is $\frac{7}{3}\pi r^2 h$.

5.

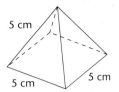

All the edges of this square-based pyramid are 5 cm. Calculate
(a) its perpendicular height   (b) its volume.

6.

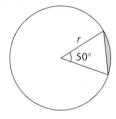

(a) Show that the area of this shaded segment can be expressed as
$$r^2\left(\frac{50\pi}{360} - \frac{\sin 50°}{2}\right)$$
(b) Calculate the radius of the circle if the area of the segment is 2 cm².

7. A cone has height 6 cm and volume 70 cm³.
(a) Calculate its base radius.
(b) Calculate its curved surface area.

8. A paintball sphere has capacity 1 litre. Calculate the surface area of the sphere.

9.

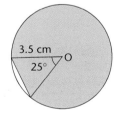

Calculate the area of the shaded major segment in this diagram.

10.

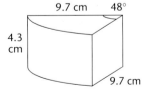

A piece of cheese is a prism whose cross-section is the sector of a circle with measurements as shown. Calculate the volume of the piece of cheese.

1.

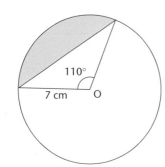

Calculate the area of this shaded segment.

2.

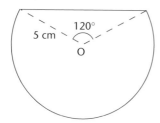

Calculate the perimeter of this segment of a circle of radius 5 cm.

3.

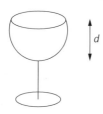

The bowl of this glass is part of a sphere. The radius of the sphere is 5 cm. The radius of the top of the glass is 3.7 cm. Calculate the depth d of the glass.

4.

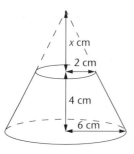

(a) Explain why $x + 4 = 3x$.
(b) Calculate the volume of the frustum.

5. A cone has base radius 5 cm and perpendicular height 12 cm. Calculate its curved surface area.

6. A cone's perpendicular height is equal to its base radius. The volume of the cone is 24 cm³. Calculate its perpendicular height.

7.

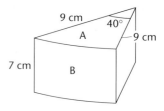

The faces labelled A and B of this slice of cake are covered in chocolate. The complete cake is a cylinder of radius 9 cm and depth 7 cm. What area of the slice is covered in chocolate?

8. A spherical ball has a curved surface area of 120 cm³. Calculate its volume.

9.

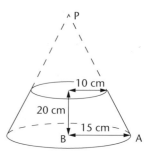

A lampshade is made from the frustum of a hollow cone.
(a) Show that the slant height, AP, of the complete cone is $15\sqrt{17}$ cm.
(b) Calculate the curved surface area of the lampshade.

10.

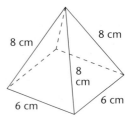

All the sloping edges of this square-based pyramid are 8 cm long. Calculate the volume of the pyramid.

Volumes and surface areas of similar figures

This cube has a volume of 8 cm³.

This cube has a volume of 512 cm³.
The lengths of the small cube have been enlarged
with scale factor 4.
The volume has been enlarged with scale factor 64.

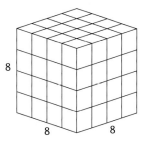

Since there are three dimensions for volume, and each
dimension has been enlarged with scale factor 4, the
volume scale factor = 4^3.

Similarly, considering the area of a face of each cube:

For the small cube, the area is 4 cm².
For the large cube, the area is 64 cm².
The area has been enlarged with scale factor 16.

There are two dimensions for area, so the area scale factor is 4^2.

> For mathematically similar shapes:
> area scale factor = (length scale factor)²
> volume scale factor = (length scale factor)³

Example 7

A model aircraft is made to a scale of 1:50. The area of the wing on the
model is 18 cm². What is the area of the wing on the real aircraft?

Length scale factor = 50
Area scale factor   = 50^2
Area of real wing   = 18×50^2
　　　　　　　　　 = 45 000 cm²
　　　　　　　　　 = **4.5 m²**

Examiner's tip

Remember that　1 m = 100 cm
　　　　　　　　1 m² = 10 000 cm²
　　　　　　　　1 m³ = 1 000 000 cm³

Alternative solution to this problem:
With this scale, 2 cm represents 1 m
So 4 cm² represents 1 m².

So 18 cm² represents $\dfrac{18}{4}$ = **4.5 m²**

Example 8

A jug holding 50 cl is 12 cm high. A similar jug holds 2 litres.
What is its height?

50 cl = 0.5 litres

Volume scale factor = $\dfrac{2}{0.5}$ = 4

Length scale factor = $\sqrt[3]{4}$
Height of larger jug = 12 cm $\times \sqrt[3]{4}$
　　　　　　　　　　 = **19.0 cm** to 1 d.p.

1. State the area scale factor for these length scale factors:
   (a) 2   (b) 3   (c) 5

2. State the volume scale factor for these length scale factors:
   (a) 10   (b) 4   (c) 5

3. State the length scale factor for the following:
   (a) area scale factor of 16
   (b) volume scale factor of 216.

4. A model of a theatre set is made to a scale of 1:20. What area on the model will represent 1 m^2 on the real set?

5. A medicine bottle holds 125 ml. How much does a similar bottle twice as high hold?

6. A tray has an area of 160 cm^2. What is the area of a similar tray whose lengths are one and a half times as large?

7. To what scale is a model if an area of 5 m^2 in real life is represented by 20 cm^2 on the model?

8. Two mugs are similar. One contains twice as much as the other. The smaller one is 10 cm high. What is the height of the larger one?

9. Three similar wooden boxes have heights in the ratio 3:4:5. What is the ratio of their volumes?

10. A model of a room is made to a scale of 1:25.
    (a) What is the real height of a cupboard which is 8 cm high on the model?
    (b) What is the real area of a rug which has an area of 48 cm^2 on the model?
    (c) What is the volume of a waste paper basket which has a volume of 1.2 cm^3 on the model?

1. State the area scale factor for these length scale factors:
   (a) 3   (b) 6   (c) 10

2. State the volume scale factor for these length scale factors:
   (a) 2   (b) 3   (c) 8

3. State the length scale factor for the following:
   (a) area scale factor of 64
   (b) volume scale factor of 1000.

4. A model of a building is to scale of 1 to 50. A room in the model is a cuboid with dimensions 7.4 cm by 9.8 cm by 6.5 cm high. Calculate the floor area of the room in
   (a) the model (b) the actual building.

5. A glass holds 15 cl. The heights of this and a larger similar glass are in the ratio 1:1.2. Calculate the capacity of the larger glass.

6. The area of a table is 1.3 m^2. Calculate the area of a similar table with lengths and width twice as large.

7. The volumes of two similar jugs are in the ratio 1:4. What is the ratio of their heights?

8. The amount of fabric required to cover a small sofa is 9 m^2. What area of fabric is required to cover a similar sofa 1.5 times as long?

9. Two vases are similar. The capacity of the smaller one is 250 ml. The capacity of the larger one is 750 ml. The height of the larger one is 18 cm. Calculate the height of the smaller one.

10. The area of a rug is 2.4 times as large as the area of a similar rug. The length of the smaller rug is 1.6 m. Find the length of the larger rug.

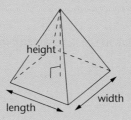

Arc length $= \dfrac{\theta}{360} \times 2\pi r$

Sector area $= \dfrac{\theta}{360} \times \pi r^2$

Volume of pyramid $= \frac{1}{3}$ length $\times$ width $\times$ height

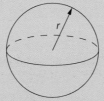

Volume of sphere $= \frac{4}{3}\pi r^3$

Surface area of sphere $= 4\pi r^2$

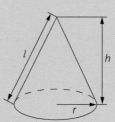

Volume of cone $= \frac{1}{3}\pi r^2 h$

Curved surface area of cone $= \pi r l$

For mathematically similar shapes:
Area scale factor $\quad$ = (length scale factor)^2
Volume scale factor = (length scale factor)^3

1. Calculate (a) the arc length and (b) the sector area of a sector with angle 75° in a circle of radius 6.5 cm.

2. Calculate the sector angle of these sectors.

(a)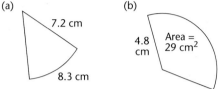
7.2 cm

8.3 cm

(b)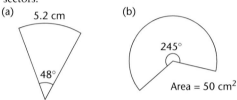
4.8 cm

Area = 29 cm²

3. Calculate the radii of the circles with these sectors.

(a)
5.2 cm

48°

(b)
245°

Area = 50 cm²

4. Joni blows up a spherical balloon until it has a radius of 12 cm. Find the volume of air she has blown into the balloon.

5.
3.6 m

10 m

A concrete water tower has its internal volume in the shape of an inverted cone.
The radius of the top is 3.6 m.
The depth of the cone is 10 m.
Calculate the volume of water which can be stored in the tower.

6. Two bottles are similar. Their heights are in the ratio 1:1.5. The larger one holds 2700 ml. What does the smaller one hold?

7. The areas of two similar pieces of paper are in the ratio 1:8. The larger piece of paper is 21.0 cm wide. What is the width of the smaller piece?

8.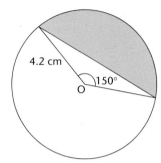

4.2 cm

150°

O

O is the centre of the circle. Calculate the area of the shaded segment.

9. A sphere has volume 50 cm³. Calculate its surface area.

10.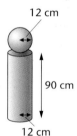
12 cm

90 cm

12 cm

A traffic bollard consists of a sphere on top of a cylinder. The radii of the sphere and cylinder are each 12 cm. The height of the cylinder is 90 cm. One litre of black paint covers 4 m². How many of these bollards can be painted with 10 litres of paint?

- that when a measurement is given as, for example, 18.6 seconds to 1 decimal place, its value lies between 18.55 and 18.65 seconds.

Reminder: If $t = 18.6$ s to 1 decimal place, then

$$18.55 \leqslant t < 18.65$$

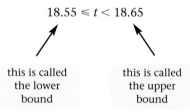

this is called the lower bound

this is called the upper bound

Examiner's tip

Many people are confused about the upper bound. The convention is that the lower bound is contained in the interval – the upper bound would be in the next higher interval. The measured value 18.6 could be 18.55, 18.59, 18.63, or even 18.649 999, but it must be less than 18.65, the upper bond.

Sums and differences of measurements

Consider two kitchen units, of width 300 mm and 500 mm correct to the nearest millimetre.

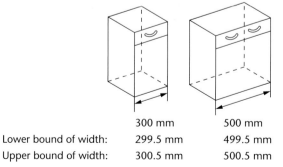

	300 mm	500 mm
Lower bound of width:	299.5 mm	499.5 mm
Upper bound of width:	300.5 mm	500.5 mm

> To find the lower bound of a sum, add the corresponding lower bounds. Similarly to find the upper bound of a sum, add the upper bounds.

If the units are put next to each other then
the lower bound of w, their joint
width = 299.5 + 499.5 = 799.0 mm
the upper bound of w, their joint
width = 300.5 + 500.5 = 801.0 mm

So $799.0 \leqslant w < 801.0$

> To find the upper bound of a difference, subtract the lower bound of the smaller from the upper bound of the larger.

However, if we want to consider the difference between the widths of the kitchen units, subtracting a smaller number makes the difference bigger.

Upper bound of the difference in their
widths = 500.5 − 299.5 = 201.0 mm
Lower bound of the difference in their
widths = 499.5 − 300.5 = 199.0 mm

Example

A piece of red ribbon is 35.2 cm to the nearest millimetre. A piece of blue ribbon is 12.6 cm to the nearest millimetre.
(a) What is the minimum length of the two pieces of ribbon laid end to end?
(b) What is the lower bound of the difference in the lengths of the two pieces?

For red piece: LB = 35.15 cm   UB = 35.25 cm
For blue piece: LB = 12.55 cm   UB = 12.65 cm
(a) Minimum total length = sum of lower bounds
    = 35.15 + 12.55 = **37.7 cm**
(b) Lower bound of difference in lengths = LB of greater − UB of smaller piece
    = 35.15 − 12.65 = **22.5 cm**

Exercise 24.1a

1. Calculate the upper bounds of the sums of these measurements.
   (a) 29.7 s and 31.4 s (both to 3 s.f.)
   (b) 11.04 s and 13.46 s (both to nearest hundredth of a second)
   (c) 6.42 m and 5.97 m (both to nearest centimetre)
   (d) 1.248 kg and 0.498 kg (both to nearest gram)

2. Find the lower bounds of the sums of the measurements in question 1.

3. Find the upper bounds of the differences of these measurements.
   (a) 947 g and 1650 g (to nearest gram)
   (b) 16.4 cm and 9.8 cm (to nearest millimetre)
   (c) 1650 g and 870 g (to nearest 10 g)
   (d) 24.1 s and 19.8 s (to nearest 0.1 s)

4. Calculate the lower bounds of the differences between the measurements in question 3.

5. A piece of paper 21.0 cm long is taped side by side to another piece 29.7 cm long, both measurements given to the nearest millimetre. What is the upper bound of the total length?

1. Calculate the upper bounds of the sums of these measurements.
   (a) 86 mm and 98 mm, to nearest millimetre.
   (b) 11.042 kg and 1.695 kg, to nearest gram
   (c) 78.5 cm and 69.7 cm, to 3 s.f.
   (d) 46.03 s and 59.82 s, to nearest $\frac{1}{100}$ s
2. Find the lower bounds of the sums of the measurements in question 1.
3. Find the upper bounds of the differences of these measurements.
   (a) 14.86 s and 15.01 s to the nearest $\frac{1}{100}$ s
   (b) 493 m and 568 m to nearest metre
   (c) 12 700 m and 3800 m to nearest 100 m
   (d) 1.824 g and 1.687 g to nearest milligram
4. Calculate the lower bounds of the differences between the measurements in question 3.

5.

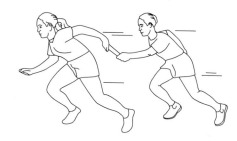

Two stages of a relay race are run in times of 14.07 s and 15.12 s to the nearest 0.01 s.
(a) Calculate the upper bound of the total time for these two stages.
(b) Calculate the upper bound of the difference between the times for these two stages.

Multiplying and dividing measurements

Consider a piece of A4 paper whose measurements are given as 21.0 cm and 29.7 cm to the nearest millimetre.

What are the upper and lower bounds of the area of the piece of paper?

Upper bound

29.75 cm
21.05 cm

Upper bound of area
= 29.75 × 21.05
= 626.2375 cm²

Lower bound

29.65 cm
20.95 cm

Lower bound of area
= 29.65 × 20.95
= 621.1675 cm²

When multiplying:
multiply the upper bounds to find the upper bound,
multiply the lower bounds to find the lower bound.

When dividing, however, the situation is different.
Dividing by a larger number makes the answer smaller.

When dividing:
to find the upper bound, divide the upper bound by the lower bound,
to find the lower bound, divide the lower bound by the upper bound.

Pete cycles 14.2 km (to 3 s.f.) in a time of 46 minutes to the nearest minute. What is the upper bound of his average speed, in km/h? Give your answer to 3 s.f.

Upper bound of speed = $\dfrac{\text{upper bound of distance}}{\text{lower bound of time}}$

$= \dfrac{14.25}{45.5}$ km/minute

$= \dfrac{14.25}{45.5} \times 60$ km/h

$= \mathbf{18.8\ km/h}$ to 3 s.f.

Examiner's tip

To find the upper bound of any combined measurement, work out which of the upper and lower bounds of the given measurements you need to use to give you the greatest result. If you aren't sure, experiment!

Exercise 24.2a

1. Find the upper bound of the floor areas of rectangular rooms with these measurements.
   (a) 3.8 m by 4.2 m to 2 s.f.
   (b) 5.26 m by 3.89 m to nearest centimetre
   (c) 8.42 m by 6.75 m to 3 s.f.
   (d) 7.6 m by 5.2 m to nearest 10 cm

2. Find the lower bounds of the floor areas of the rooms in question 1.

3. Find the lower bound of the average speeds for these measured times and distances. Give your answers to 3 significant figures.
   (a) 6.4 cm in 1.2 s
   (b) 12.4 cm in 9.8 s
   (c) 106 m in 10.0 s

4. Calculate the upper bounds of the speeds for the measurements in question 3, giving your answers to 3 s.f.

5. The mass of an object is given as 1.657 kg, to the nearest gram. Its volume is 72.5 cm^3 to 3 s.f. Find the upper bound of its density. Give your answer to 4 s.f.

1. Calculate the upper bounds of the distance travelled for these given speeds and times.
    (a) 92.4 cm/s for 12.3 s
    (b) 1.54 m/s for 8.2 s
    (c) 57 km/h for 2.5 hours
    (d) 5.61 m/s for 2.08 s

2. Calculate the lower bounds of the distances for the data in question 1.

3. Calculate, to 3 s.f., the minimum width of a rectangle given the following data:
    (a) area = 210 cm^2 to 3 s.f.,
        length = 17.8 cm to nearest millimetre
    (b) area = 210 cm^2 to 2 s.f.,
        length = 19.2 cm to nearest millimetre
    (c) area = 615 cm^2 to 3 s.f.,
        length = 30.0 cm to nearest millimetre

4. Calculate, to 3 s.f., the upper bound of the heights of the following cuboids:
    (a) volume = 72 cm^3, length = 6.2 cm, width = 4.7 cm (all to 2 s.f.)
    (b) volume = 985 cm^3, length = 17.0 cm, width = 11.3 cm (all to 3 s.f.)
    (c) volume = 84 m^3, length = 6.2 m, width = 3.8 m (all to 2 s.f.)

5. The population of a town is 108 000 to the nearest 1000. Its area is given as 129 square miles. Calculate the upper and lower bounds of its population density, giving your answers to 3 s.f.

Key points

- To find the upper bound of any combined measurement, work out which of the upper and lower bounds of the given measurements you need to use to give you the greatest result. To find the lower bound, you need the smallest result.

Here is a summary of how this works in practice:

- To find the lower bound of a sum, add the corresponding lower bounds. Similarly to find the upper bound of a sum, add the upper bounds.
- To find the upper bound of a difference, subtract the lower bound of the smaller from the upper bound of the larger.

- To find the lower bound of a difference, subtract the upper bound of the smaller from the lower bound of the larger.

- When multiplying:
  multiply the upper bounds to find the upper bound,
  multiply the lower bounds to find the lower bound.

- When dividing,
  to find the upper bound, divide the upper bound by the lower bound,
  to find the lower bound, divide the lower bound by the upper bound.

1. Paul measures out 250 g flour, 150 g butter, 120 g sugar, all to the nearest 10 g. Calculate the upper and lower bounds of the total mass of flour, butter and sugar.

2. Two pieces of string measure 19.7 cm and 11.4 cm respectively, to the nearest millimetre. Calculate:
   (a) the upper bound of the total length of the two pieces placed end to end
   (b) the lower bound of the difference in the lengths of the two pieces.

3. The times for two stages of a mountain bike course were 9 min 46.32 s and 5 min 37.85 s. Calculate the lower bound of the total time for these two stages.

4.

   The space for some base kitchen units is measured as 1000 mm to the nearest millimetre. Two base units are 500 mm each, to the nearest millimetre.
   (a) Explain why the two units will not necessarily fit into the space.
   (b) Calculate the upper bound of the gap remaining if two units do fit in.

5. A cylinder's diameter and height are measured as 8.2 cm and 7.6 cm respectively, to the nearest millimetre.
   (a) Calculate the lower bound of the radius.
   (b) Calculate the lower bound of the volume of the cylinder, giving your answer to 3 s.f.

6. The length of a side of a cube is given as 4.6 cm to the nearest millimetre. Calculate the upper and lower bounds of the volume of the cube, giving your answers to 3 s.f.

7. A cylinder has a capacity of 500 ml, to 3 s.f. Its height is measured as 9.6 cm to the nearest millimetre. Calculate, to 3 s.f., the lower bound of its radius.

8. A 100 m race was won in a time of 13.62 s, correct to the nearest hundredth of a second. Calculate, to 3 s.f., the upper bound of the average speed
   (a) if the distance is 100 m to 3 s.f.
   (b) if the distance is 100.0 m to 4 s.f.

9. Jane walks on an exercise machine for 7.2 minutes at a speed of 130 m per minute, both measurements to 2 s.f. Calculate the upper bound of the distance she walked.

10. A town has a population of 94 300 to the nearest 100. Its area is 156 km², to the nearest square kilometre. Calculate the lower bound of its population density, giving your answer to 3 s.f.

Problems in 3D and non-right-angled triangles

You will need to know:

- how to apply Pythagoras' theorem
- how to use trigonometry in right-angled triangles
- the convention for labelling sides and angles in a triangle.

Section A: 3D problems

Example 1

The rectangular box measures 4 cm by 3 cm by 6 cm.

Calculate
(a) AC
(b) AR
(c) angle RBC
(d) angle ARC.

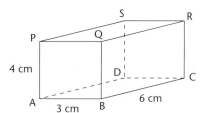

(a)

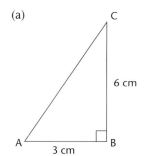

$AC^2 = AB^2 + BC^2$
$AC^2 = 3^2 + 6^2$
$AC^2 = 45$
$AC = 6.71$ cm

Examiner's tip

Identify the triangle required and draw it out separately. Label the corners and mark on any lengths and angles known.

(b)

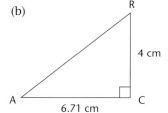

$AR^2 = AC^2 + RC^2$
$AR^2 = 45 + 4^2$
$AR^2 = 61$
$AR = 7.81$ cm

Examiner's tip

Don't use 6.71^2; this has been rounded. You need AC^2 and this is 45.

(c)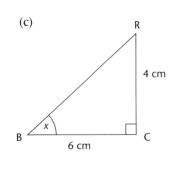

$$\tan x = \frac{4}{6}$$

$$x = \tan^{-1}\left(\frac{4}{6}\right)$$

$$x = 33.7°$$

Examiner's tip

When there is a choice of trig. formulae to use, use the one which contains as many given values as possible. You may have calculated a value incorrectly.

(d)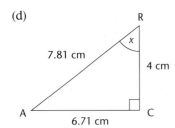

$$\cos x = \frac{4}{7.81\ldots}$$

$$x = \cos^{-1}\frac{4}{7.81\ldots}$$

$$x = 59.2°$$

Examiner's tip

You can't avoid a calculated value here. Using 7.81 will give a correct 3 s.f. answer but it may be worth using a more accurate value: $\sqrt{61}$ for instance. Round at the end.

Example 2

A tree, TC, is 20 m north of point A. The angle of elevation of the top of the tree, T, from A is 35°. A point B is 30 m east of point A. A, B and C are on horizontal ground. Calculate:

(a) the height of the tree, TC
(b) the length BC
(c) the angle of elevation of T from B.

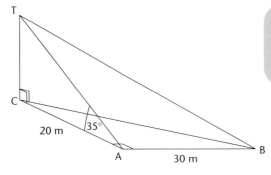

Examiner's tip

First, a diagram of the situation is needed.

(a)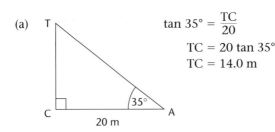

$$\tan 35° = \frac{TC}{20}$$

$$TC = 20 \tan 35°$$

$$TC = 14.0 \text{ m}$$

(b)

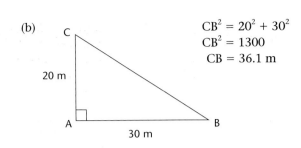

$$CB^2 = 20^2 + 30^2$$
$$CB^2 = 1300$$
$$CB = 36.1 \text{ m}$$

(c)

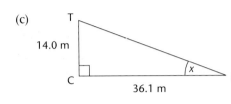

$$\tan x = \frac{14.0...}{36.1...}$$
$$x = \tan^{-1}\left(\frac{14.0...}{36.1...}\right)$$
$$x = 21.2°$$

Example 3

A mast MG is 50 m high. It is supported by two ropes, AM and BM as shown in the diagram. ABG is horizontal. Other measurements are shown in the diagram. Is the mast vertical?

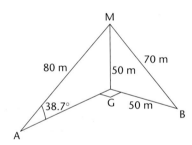

Does $\sin 38.7° = \dfrac{50}{80}$? $\sin^{-1}\left(\dfrac{50}{80}\right) = 38.68...$

Yes angle MGA is a right-angle.

Is angle MGB a right-angle?
$$50^2 + 50^2 = 5000$$
$$\sqrt{5000} = 70.7...$$
No, MB is shorter than this.
The mast leans towards B (angle MGB < 90°).

1.

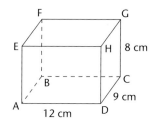

ABCDEFGH is a rectangular box with dimensions as shown. Calculate:
(a) angle GDC
(b) EG
(c) EC
(d) angle GEC.

2.

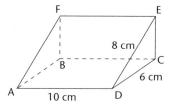

A wedge has a rectangular base ABCD on horizontal ground. The rectangular face BCEF is vertical. Calculate:
(a) EC
(b) angle DEC
(c) FD
(d) angle FDB.

3. Three points A, B and C are on horizontal ground with B due west of C and A due south of C. A chimney, CT, at C is 50 m high. The angle of elevation of the top, T, of the chimney is 26° from A and 38° from B. Calculate:
(a) how far A and B are from C
(b) the distance between A and B
(c) the bearing of B from A

4.

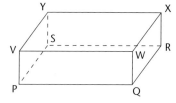

In the cuboid, PQ = 7.5 cm, QR = 4 cm and PX = 12 cm. Calculate:
(a) XR
(b) angle PXR.

5.

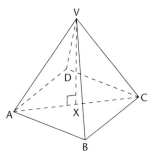

The figure shows a square-based pyramid with V vertically above the centre, X, of the square ABCD. Given that AB = 8 cm and AV = 14 cm, calculate:
(a) angle CAB
(b) angle VCB (Hint: triangle VCB is isosceles.)
(c) AC
(d) AX
(e) VX
(f) angle VAX.

6.

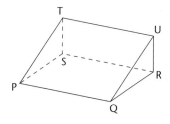

PQRSTU is a triangular prism.
PQ = SR = TU = 5.7 cm,
PT = QU = 4.3 cm, PR = 6.9 cm
Calculate: (a) PU   (b) QR
UR = 2.1 cm
(c) Is angle URQ a right-angle?
   Show how you decide.

1.

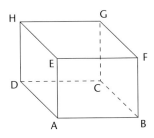

ABCDPQ is a triangular prism with ABPQ horizontal and ADP vertical. Calculate:

(a) DP

(b) AC

(c) angle CAQ

(d) the volume of the prism.

2. A pyramid has a rectangular base ABCD with AB = 15 cm and BC = 8 cm. The vertex, V, of the pyramid is directly above the centre, X, of ABCD with VX = 10 cm.

(a) Calculate:

   (i)   AC

   (ii)   AV

   (iii) angle AVB.

(b) Given that M is the mid-point of AB, calculate:

   (i)   VM

   (ii)   angle VMX.

3.

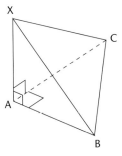

ABCDEFGH is a cuboid. AB = 7 cm, AC = 8.6 cm and angle GBC = 41°. Calculate:

(a) BC

(b) angle GAC.

4.

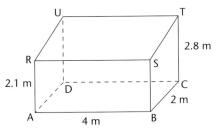

Triangle ABC is horizontal. X is vertically above A. AC = AX = 15 cm. Angle ACB = 27° and angle BAC = 90°. Calculate:

(a) XC

(b) BC

(c) BX.

5.

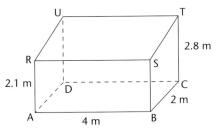

The figure shows a garden shed with the floor horizontal and the walls vertical. Calculate:

(a) AT

(b) ST

(c) the angle that the roof of the shed makes with the horizontal

(d) RT.

6. A field is a quadrilateral with opposite sides equal.

   AD = BC = 80 m

   DC = AB = 35 m

   A vertical post CE is at one corner of the field.

   The angles of elevation of the top of the post, E, are 7.8° from A and 8.5° from B.

   Is the field a rectangle? Show how you decide.

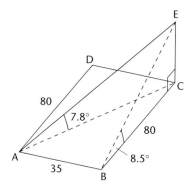

The angle between a line and a plane

In the previous exercises of this chapter, you have already been finding the angle between a line and a plane though it has been specified by the required letters. This next sub-section deals with finding the angle when only the line and the plane are given.

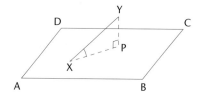

The end X of the line XY is on the plane ABCD. The angle between the line and the plane is the angle YXP, where P is the point on the plane vertically below Y.

Example 4   For this triangular prism, sketch the triangle and label the angle between the line and the plane given.

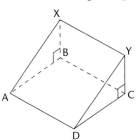

(a) DY and ABCD
(b) AY and ABCD
(c) AY and BCYX
(d) BY and ABX.

(a) Angle YDC

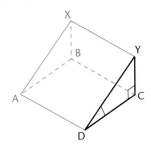

(b) Angle YAC

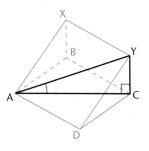

(c) Angle AYB

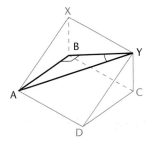

(d) Angle YBX

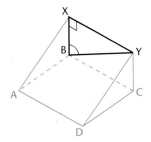

Example **5**

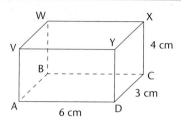

ABCDVWXY is a cuboid.
Calculate the angle between the
following lines and planes.
(a) DW and ABCD.
(b) DW and ABWV.

(a)

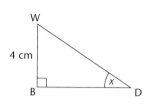

Angle BDW is the required angle.
First find length BD.
$BD^2 = 6^2 + 3^2$
$BD^2 = 45$
$BD = 6.71... \text{ cm}$

$\tan x = \dfrac{4}{6.71...}$

$x = \tan^{-1}\dfrac{4}{6.71...}$

$x = 30.8°$

(b)

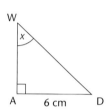

Angle DWA is the required angle.
First find length WA.
$WA^2 = 3^2 + 4^2$
$WA^2 = 25$
$WA = 5 \text{ cm}$

$\tan x = \dfrac{6}{5}$

$x = \tan^{-1}\dfrac{6}{5}$

$x = 50.2°$

Exercise 25.2a

1.

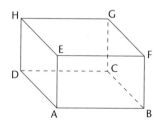

For this cuboid sketch the triangle and label
the angle between the following lines and planes.
(a) EB and ABCD
(b) EB and ADHE
(c) AG and ABCD
(d) AG and CDHG.

2. Given that, for the cuboid in Question 1, AB = 8 cm, BC = 6 cm and GC = 5 cm, calculate the angles between the lines and the planes listed above.

3.

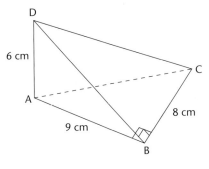

ABC is a right-angled triangle on a horizontal plane. D is vertically above A and angle DBC = 90°. Calculate:
(a) the angle between BD and ABC
(b) the angle between DC and ABD.

Exercise 25.2b

1.

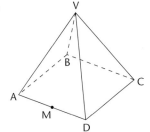

In the pyramid, ABCD is a rectangle and V is vertically above the centre of the rectangle. M is the midpoint of AD. Sketch the triangle and label the angle between the following lines and planes:
(a) VC and ABCD
(b) VM and ABCD.

2. Given that, for the pyramid in Question 1, AD = 8 cm, DC = 6 cm and that VA = VB = VC = VD = 12 cm, calculate the angles between the lines and the planes listed above.

3.

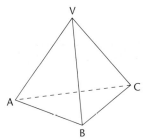

The diagram is of a tetrahedron.
AB = AC = BC = 4 m and VA = VB = VC = 6 m. Calculate the angle that line VA makes with plane ABC.

Hint: V lies directly above a point X, which is $\frac{2}{3}$ of the way from A, along the bisector of angle CAB.)

Section B: non-right-angled triangles

All trigonometry so far in this book has been based on finding lengths and angles in right-angled triangles. Triangles are often not right-angled. Some method needs to be established to find lengths and angles in these triangles.

Notation

It is common practice in this work to use a single letter to represent each side and each angle of the triangle. We use a capital letter to signify an angle and a lower case letter for a side. It is usual for the side opposite an angle to take the same, lower case letter, as shown in the diagram below.

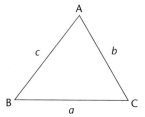

The rules

The two major rules for dealing with non-right-angled triangles are called the **sine rule** and the **cosine rule**. It will be obvious why they have these names when you see the formulae.
You do not have to memorise the formulae, as they are on the formulae sheet in the examination, but you do have to know when and how to use them.

The sine rule

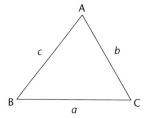

$$\frac{a}{\sin A} = \frac{b}{\sin B} = \frac{c}{\sin C}$$

or $$\frac{\sin A}{a} = \frac{\sin B}{b} = \frac{\sin C}{c}$$

This formula is made up of *three* equal fractions. When using it you take two of the fractions. The two parts are chosen so that there is one unknown and three known values. When finding a length the top formula is used, when finding an angle use the bottom one. This will mean that the unknown is on top and makes the solution easier.

It is quite easy to prove the sine rule, should you wish to do so. You will not be required to do this in an examination.

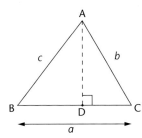

In triangle ADC, AD = $b \sin C$
In triangle ADB, AD = $c \sin B$
$b \sin C = c \sin B$

or $\dfrac{b}{\sin B} = \dfrac{c}{\sin C}$

Using another perpendicular will involve a and A.

When to use the sine rule

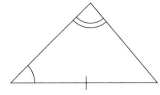

When any two angles and one side are known.

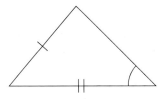

When two sides and the non-included angle are known.

Example 6

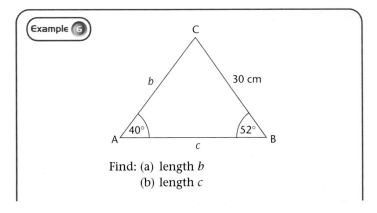

Find: (a) length b
     (b) length c

Examiner's tip

Since you are finding a length, choose the formula with lengths on top. Choose pairs of angles and opposite sides where three of the four values are known and substitute into the formula.

(a) $\dfrac{b}{\sin 52°} = \dfrac{30}{\sin 40°}$

$b = \dfrac{30}{\sin 40°} \times \sin 52°$

$b = 36.8$ cm

(b) Before c can be found, angle C is needed

$C = 180° - (40 + 52)°$

$C = 88°$

$\dfrac{c}{\sin 88°} = \dfrac{30}{\sin 40°}$

$c = \dfrac{30}{\sin 40°} \times \sin 88°$

$c = 46.6$ cm

Examiner's tip

Though you could use the pair b and B you should always prefer to use values that are given rather than values that have been calculated.

Example 7

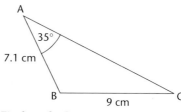

Find angle C.

$\dfrac{\sin C}{7.1} = \dfrac{\sin 35°}{9}$

$\sin C = \dfrac{\sin 35°}{9} \times 7.1$

$\sin C = 0.4524...$

$C = \sin^{-1}(0.4524...)$

$C = 26.9°$

The third angle can now be found. Notice that it is obtuse (118.1°). You can find the third side using the sine rule again:

$\dfrac{b}{\sin 118.1} = \dfrac{9}{\sin 35°}$

You calculator will find sin 118.1°, so the problem may be solved. Further consideration of sine and cosines of angles greater than 90° will be given in Chapter 31.

1.
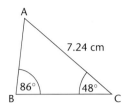

Find c, A and a.

2.
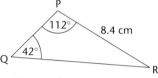

Find p, R and r.

3.
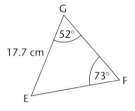

Find g, E and e.

4.
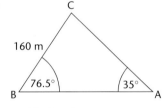

Find b, C and c.

5.
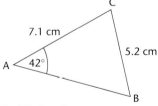

Find B, C and c.

6.
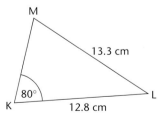

Find M, L and l.

7.
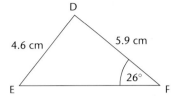

Find E, D and d.

8. Calculate the largest angle of the triangle ABC given that A = 35°, a = 8.9 cm and c = 12 cm.

9.
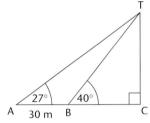

From two points, A and B, on horizontal ground, the angle of elevation of the top, T, of a vertical tower, TC, are 27° and 40° respectively. Given that AB = 30 m, find:

(a) AT

(b) BT

(c) the height of the tower, TC.

10.
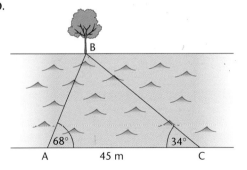

A river has two parallel banks. Points A and C are on one side of the river, 45 m apart. The angles from these points to a tree, B on the opposite bank are 68° and 34°, as shown in the diagram. Find:

(a) AB

(b) BC

(c) the width of the river.

1.

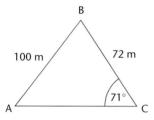

Find A, B and *b*.

2.

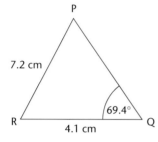

Find P, R and *r*.

3.

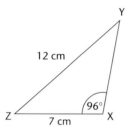

Find Y, Z and *z*.

4.

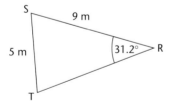

Find T, S and *s*.

5.

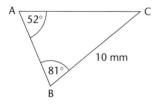

Find *b*, C and *c*.

6.

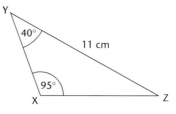

Find *y*, Z and *z*.

7.

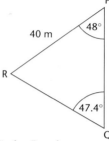

Find *p*, R and *r*.

8.

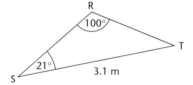

Find *s*, T and *t*.

9.

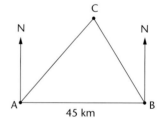

Town B is 45 km due east of town A. Town C is on a bearing 057° from town A and a bearing of 341° from town B. Find how far town C is from towns A and B.

10.

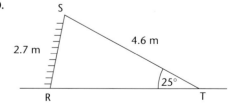

A child's slide, RST, is shown in the picture. Find the distance RT.

The cosine rule

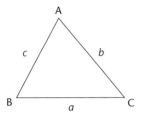

$$a^2 = b^2 + c^2 - 2bc \cos A$$
$$b^2 = c^2 + a^2 - 2ca \cos B$$
$$c^2 = a^2 + b^2 - 2ab \cos C$$

or $\cos A = \dfrac{b^2 + c^2 - a^2}{2bc}$

$\cos B = \dfrac{c^2 + a^2 - b^2}{2ca}$

$\cos C = \dfrac{a^2 + b^2 - c^2}{2ab}$

There are three versions of each of the formulae, but notice that they have exactly the same structure and pattern. Once again, there is one form to use when finding lengths and one for finding angles.

Again, although you do not need to be able to do this, here is a simple proof, using Pythagoras.

In triangle ADC: $b^2 = AD^2 + DC^2$
$$DC = a - BD$$
$$\therefore DC^2 = a^2 - 2aBD + BD^2$$

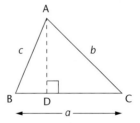

In triangle ADB: $AD^2 = c^2 - BD^2$
and $BD = c \cos B$
$$DC^2 = a^2 - 2ac \cos B + BD^2$$
$$b^2 = c^2 - BD^2 + a^2 - 2ac \cos B + BD^2$$
$$= c^2 + a^2 - 2ac \cos B.$$

When to use the cosine rule

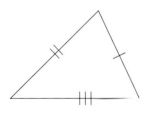

When all three sides are known

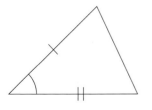

When two sides and the included angle are known.

Example 8

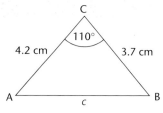

Find c.
$c^2 = 4.2^2 + 3.7^2 - (2 \times 4.2 \times 3.7 \times \cos 110°)$
$c^2 = 17.64 + 13.69 - (-10.63)$
$c^2 = 41.96$
$c\ = 6.48$ cm

Examiner's tip

Notice that the cosine of an obtuse angle is negative. Your calculator will give $\cos 110° = -0.342...$
More detail in Chapter 31.

Example 9

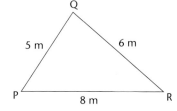

Find R.
$$\cos R = \frac{6^2 + 8^2 - 5^2}{2 \times 6 \times 8}$$

$\cos R = 0.781\ 25$
$\quad R = \cos^{-1}(0.781\ 25)$
$\quad R = 38.6°$

Exercise 25.4a

1.

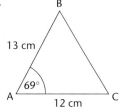

Find a.

2.

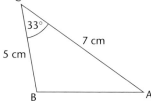

Find c.

3.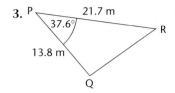

Find *p*.

4.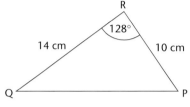

Find *r*.

5.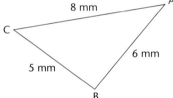

Find C.

6.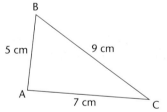

Find B.

7.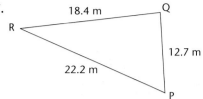

Find R.

8.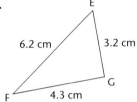

Find G.

9. A cross-country runner runs 4 km due north and then 6.7 km in a south-east direction. How far is she from her starting point?

10.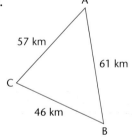

Three towns, A, B and C are positioned as shown in the diagram. Find the three angles inside the triangle formed.

1.

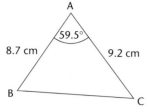

Find length BC.

2.

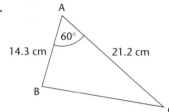

Find *a*.

3.

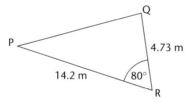

Find length PQ.

4.

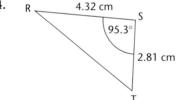

Find *s*.

5.

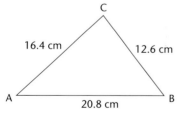

Find angle ABC.

6.

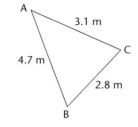

Find angle B.

7.

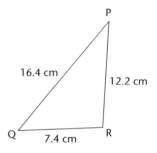

Find P.

8.

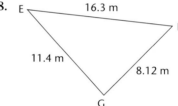

Find G.

9.

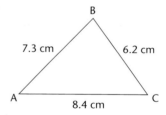

Find the smallest angle in the triangle.

10. A parallelogram has sides of length 5.1 cm and 2.5 cm. Adjacent sides are separated by an angle of 70°. Find the length of each of the diagonals of the parallelogram.

General formula for the area of any triangle

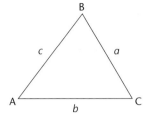

$$\text{Area of triangle} = \tfrac{1}{2}\, ab \sin C$$
$$= \tfrac{1}{2}\, bc \sin A$$
$$= \tfrac{1}{2}\, ac \sin B$$

Once again, there are three versions of the formula and again the letters have a 'circular' structure. Each formula requires two adjacent sides and the included angle.

This formula is also easily derived.

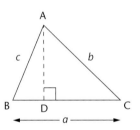

$$\text{Area of triangle} = \tfrac{1}{2} \times BC \times AD$$
$$= \tfrac{1}{2} \times a \times c \sin B$$
$$= \tfrac{1}{2}\, ac \sin B$$

Example 10

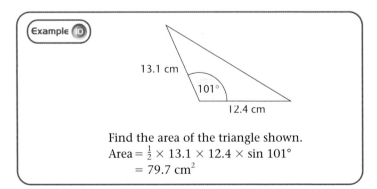

Find the area of the triangle shown.
$$\text{Area} = \tfrac{1}{2} \times 13.1 \times 12.4 \times \sin 101°$$
$$= 79.7 \text{ cm}^2$$

Find the area of each of the following triangles.

1.

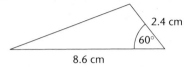

2.

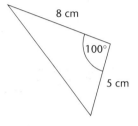

3.

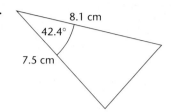

4. In triangle ABC, a = 10 cm, c = 6 cm and B = 150°. Find the area of the triangle.

5. Calculate the area of parallelogram ABCD in which AB = 6 cm, BC = 9 cm and angle ABC = 41.4°.

Find the area of each of the following triangles.

1.

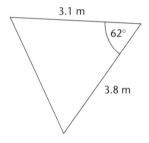

2.

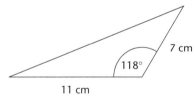

3.

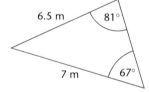

4. The area of triangle PQR is 273 cm². Given that PQ = 12.8 cm and angle PQR = 107°, find QR.

5. In triangle ABC, a = 4 cm, c = 7 cm and its area is 13.4 cm². Find the size of angle B.

Key points

Calculating lengths and angles in 3D objects:
- identify a triangle containing an unknown side/angle and sketch it.
- if the triangle has a right-angle, use Pythagoras and trigonometry.

- if the triangle has no right-angle, use the **sine rule** when what is known is:
  (i) two angles and one side
  (ii) two sides and the non-included angle.

  the **cosine rule** when what is known is:
  (i) all the sides
  (ii) two sides and the included angle.

Revision exercise 25a (Section A)

1.

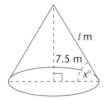

A street light suspended 7.5 m above the ground illuminates a circle with circumference 30.8 m. Calculate:
(a) the angle marked $x°$
(b) the length l.

2.

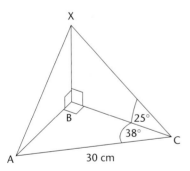

In the diagram, triangle ABC is horizontal with angle ABC = 90°. XB is vertical.
Find the length of XB.

3.

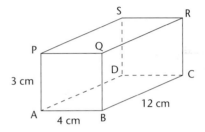

ABCDPQRS is a cuboid.
(a) Calculate the area of the rectangle PQCD.
(b) Which line, BS or AS, is more steeply inclined to the base ABCD?
(c) Calculate the volume of the pyramid ABCDR.
(Hint: Volume of pyramid = $\frac{1}{3}$ area of base × height)

4.

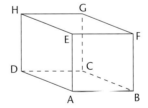

ABCDEFGH is a cube. Specify the angle between:
(a) the line BH and the plane DCGH
(b) the line AG and the plane BCGF.

5.

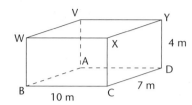

A classroom measures 10 m by 7 m by 4 m.
Calculate:
(a) the angle between AC and ADVY
(b) the angle between BY and ABWV.

6.

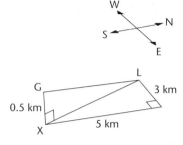

A glider, G, is 3 km east and 5 km south of its landing strip, L. It is at an altitude of $\frac{1}{2}$ km above a point X on the ground. Calculate:
(a) the bearing of the point X from L
(b) the distance it has to fly to reach the landing strip
(c) the gliders inclination as measured from L.

Revision exercise 25a (Section B)

1.

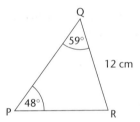

In triangle PQR, find:
(a) PR
(b) angle PRQ
(c) PQ.

3.

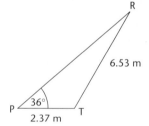

In triangle PRT, find:
(a) angle PRT
(b) angle PTR
(c) PR.

2.

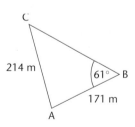

In triangle ABC, find:
(a) angle ACB
(b) the area of triangle ABC.

4.

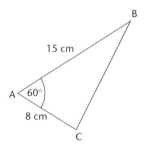

In triangle ABC, find:
(a) BC
(b) angle ABC
(c) the area of triangle ABC.

5.

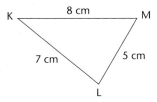

In triangle KLM, find:
(a) angle LKM
(b) angle KML.

6.

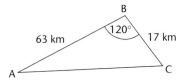

In triangle ABC, find:
(a) AC
(b) angle BAC.

7.

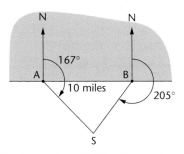

Two towns A and B, 10 miles apart are on a straight coastline with B due east of A.
A ship, S, is observed out to sea on a bearing of 167° from A and a bearing of 205° from B.
Calculate:
(a) the distance of S from A
(b) the distance of S from B.

8.

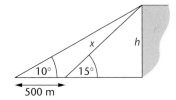

A boat sails directly towards a cliff. As the boat sails 500 m, the angle of elevation of the top of the cliff increases from 10° to 15°. Calculate:
(a) the distance x
(b) the height, h, of the cliff.

9.

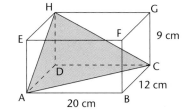

ABCDEFGH is a cuboid. AHC is a triangle within the cuboid. Calculate:
(a) the angle HAC
(b) the area of triangle AHC.

10.

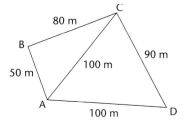

ABCD is a field with dimensions as shown in the diagram. Calculate the area of the field.

26 Conditional probability

Conditional probability

In Chapter 13 you learned this rule for independent events A and B

$$P(A \text{ and } B) = P(A) \times P(B).$$

For instance if you toss a coin and a die, the probability of a head is $\frac{1}{2}$ and the probability of a six is $\frac{1}{6}$.

The events are independent since what happens to the coin cannot possibly affect what happens to the die.

So the probability of getting a head and a six $= \frac{1}{2} \times \frac{1}{6} = \frac{1}{12}$.

There are many events, however, where the outcome of the second event is affected by the outcome of the first event. In this situation the probability of the second event depends on what has happened in the first event.

These events are not independent and are thus called **dependent events**.

In this situation the probability of the second event is called a **conditional probability** since it is conditional on whether the first event has happened or not.

There will be situations when you can work out the conditional probability yourself and others where you will be told what it is. These situations are illustrated in the following examples.

Example 1

There are four red balls and six black balls in a bag. If the first one selected is black and not replaced what is the probability that the second one is also black?

There are now four red and five black balls left in the bag so the probability is $\frac{5}{9}$.

There are seven blue balls and three red balls in the bag. A ball is selected at random and not replaced. A second ball is then selected.

Find the probability that (a) two blue balls are chosen (b) two balls of the same colour are chosen.

A tree diagram is still one of the best ways to organise the work and the first step is the same as in the replacement situation.

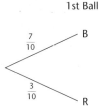

For the second ball, however the situation is different. If the first ball was blue there are now six blue balls and three red balls left in the bag. The probabilities are therefore $\frac{6}{9}$ and $\frac{3}{9}$.

If the first ball was red there are now seven blue and two red balls left in the bag. The probabilities are therefore $\frac{7}{9}$ and $\frac{2}{9}$.

The tree diagram now looks like this.

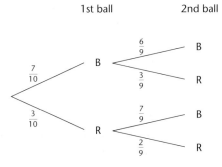

(a) The probability that the two balls are both blue $= \frac{7}{10} \times \frac{6}{9} = \frac{42}{90} = \frac{7}{15}$.
(b) The probability that both balls are the same colour (i.e. both blue **or** both red).

$$= \frac{7}{10} \times \frac{6}{9} + \frac{3}{10} \times \frac{2}{9} = \frac{42}{90} + \frac{6}{90} = \frac{48}{90} = \frac{8}{15}.$$

Notice that the multiplication part of the rule still applies. It is the probabilities that are different from the independent case.

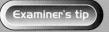

Although final answers should always be 'cancelled down' to their simplest form, it is usually unwise to cancel down the probabilities of the second (and third) event. This is because you often need to add the probabilities at the end and so you need them with a common denominator.

Chapter 26 Conditional probability

Example 3

I have sandwiches for lunch on 70% of school days, otherwise I have a school meal. If I have sandwiches, the probability that I buy a drink from the canteen is 0.2. If I have a school meal the probability that I buy a drink is 0.9.

Find the probability that I buy a drink.

Here the probabilities are given to us. The tree diagram for this situation is this.

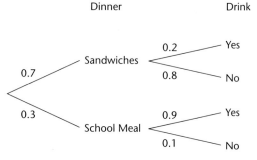

The probability of buying a drink
= 0.7 × 0.2 + 0.3 × 0.9 = 0.14 + 0.27 = 0.41

Note that, once the probabilities have been put onto the tree diagram, the methods are the same.

Examiner's tip

Some questions may instruct you to draw a tree diagram, others may not. Whilst it is not essential to draw a tree diagram for all questions it is a very powerful method for tackling probability problems. Even if you are not told to do so, it is a good idea to draw one.

In problems involving selections from bags etc., always assume that the probabilities are **dependent** unless you are specifically told that there is replacement or that the events are independent.

1. There are five blue balls in a bag and four white ones. If a white one is selected first what is the probability that the second ball is blue?

2. There are 500 tickets sold in a raffle. I buy two tickets. I did not win the first prize. What is the probability that I win the second prize?

3. There are eight green balls in a bag and two white ones. Two balls are selected at random without replacement.
   (a) Draw a tree diagram to show the probabilities of the possible outcomes.
   (b) Find the probability of selecting two white balls.
   (c) Find the probability of selecting two balls of different colour.

4. There are 1000 tickets sold in a raffle. I buy two tickets. What is the probability that I win both the first two prizes?

5. There are seven yellow balls and four red balls in a bag. Two balls are selected at random without replacement. Find the probability of selecting at least one red ball.

6. There are five red balls, three yellow balls and two green balls in a bag. Two balls are selected at random without replacement.
   (a) Find the probability of selecting two red balls.
   (b) Find the probability of selecting two balls of the same colour.

7. On average, Gary takes sandwiches to school dinners on two days a week, otherwise he has a school meal. If he takes sandwiches the probability that he has time to play football is 0.8. If he has a school meal the probability that he has time to play football is 0.3.
   (a) Draw a tree diagram to show the probabilities of the possible outcomes.
   (b) Find the probability that on any given day Gary has time to play football.

8. The probability that the school win the first hockey match of the season is 0.6. If they win the first match of the season the probability that they win the second is 0.7 otherwise it is 0.4.
   (a) Copy and complete the tree diagram.

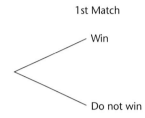

1st Match

Win

Do not win

   (b) Find the probability that they win only one of the first two matches.
   (c) Find the probability that they win at least one of the first two matches.

9. Salima walks to school or cycles or goes by bus. The probability that she walks is 0.5. The probability that she cycles is 0.2. If she walks the probability that she is late is 0.2. If she cycles it is 0.1 and if she goes by bus it is 0.4.
   (a) Draw a tree diagram to show the probabilities of the possible outcomes.
   (b) Find the probability that, on any given day, she is on time for school.

10. If Ryan is fit to play the probability that United win their next match is 0.9. If he is not fit to play the probability is 0.8. The physiotherapist says there is a 60% chance he will be fit.
    What is the probability that United will win their next match?

1. Soraya and Robert are selecting cards in turn from an ordinary pack of 52 playing cards. Soraya selects a heart and does not replace it. What is the probability that Robert also selects a heart?

2. There are 80 tulip bulbs and 120 daffodil bulbs in a tub. Alan chose two bulbs and there was one of each. Charlie then chose a bulb. What is the probability that Charlie's bulb was a tulip?

3. There are three red pens and five blue ones in a pencil case. Jenny chose two pens at random.
   (a) Draw a tree diagram to show the probabilities of Jenny's possible choices.
   (b) Find the probability that Jenny chose at least one blue pen.

4. There are five grey socks, three black socks and four navy-blue socks in Lisa's drawer. She selects two socks at random.
   What is the probability that she selects a pair of the same colour socks?

5. Sanjay selects three cards without replacement from a normal pack of 52 playing cards. What is the probability he selects three aces?

6. There are five men and four women on a committee. Two are selected at random to represent the committee on a working party. What is the probability that the two selected are:
   (a) both women
   (b) both men
   (c) one woman and one man?

7. In a game I toss a coin and spin one of these fair spinners

   If I toss a head I spin the five-sided spinner.
   If I toss a tail I spin the six-sided spinner.
   I need a five to win the game.
   What is the probability that I win the game? (Hint. If you use a tree diagram take the events for the spinner as 'five' and 'not a five'.)

8. If it is fine when he gets up there is a probability of 0.7 that Richard will cycle to school. If it is raining when he gets up there is a probability of 0.05 that he will cycle. The weatherman estimates that there is a 20% chance that it will rain tomorrow morning. Using the weatherman's estimate, find the probability that Richard will cycle to school tomorrow.

9. Paul chooses two cards without replacement from an ordinary pack of 52 playing cards. Find the probability that he chooses:
   (a) two hearts
   (b) two kings
   (c) a king and a queen

10. There are seven blue balls and three red ones in a bag. Rosemary selects three balls at random without replacement.
    (a) Draw a tree diagram to show the probabilities of the possible outcomes.
    (b) Find the probability that Rosemary chooses at least one blue ball.
    (c) Find the probability that she chooses two red balls and one blue ball.

Key points

- If the outcome of the second event is affected by the outcome of the first event, the probability of the second event will vary according to what happens in the first event.
- These events are called **dependent events**.
- In this situation the probability of the second event is called a **conditional probability** since it is conditional on whether the first event has happened or not.
- Once the conditional probabilities have been established they can be placed on a tree diagram and the multiplication and addition rules still apply.

1. There were 2000 tickets sold for a raffle. Winston bought three tickets. He did not win first prize. What is the probability that he won second prize?

2. There are seven red balls, five green balls and four yellow balls in a bag. Gary chose four balls at random without replacement. The first three he chose were all different colours. What is the probability that the fourth ball was yellow?

3. Jill is choosing cards from an ordinary set of 52 playing cards. The first three she chooses are all picture cards. What is the probability that the fourth one is also a picture card?

None of the following questions ask for tree diagrams but you may wish to draw one to help you solve the problem.

4. There are 40 crocus bulbs and 60 hyacinth bulbs in a basket. Anna chooses two bulbs at random. What is the probability that she chooses at least one crocus bulb?

5. A company uses two machines, A and B, to manufacture car components. 70% are made by machine A. There is a probability of 0.05 that a component made by machine A is faulty. The probability of a faulty component from machine B is 0.01. A component is selected at random from the company's output. What is the probability that it is faulty.

6. Dipak and Simon have seven cards labelled A to G. Dipak chooses one of the cards at random and does not replace it. Simon then chooses one. What is the probability that:
   (a) they both choose a vowel
   (b) one chooses a vowel and the other a consonant?

7. There are 15 fiction and five non-fiction books on Cynthia's bookshelf. She chooses three books at random without replacement. What is the probability that she chooses:
   (a) three fiction books
   (b) two fiction and one non-fiction books?

8. In bag A there are four red balls and three white ones. In bag B there are three red balls and two white ones. A ball is chosen at random from bag A and placed in bag B without its colour being noted. A ball is then chosen at random from bag B.
   What is the probability that the ball chosen from bag B is white?

9. To simplify a model of the weather, days are classified as dry or wet. The probability that a dry day follows a dry day is 0.7. The probability that a dry day follows a wet day is 0.4. Tomorrow is Monday. The weather man says that the probability that it is dry tomorrow is 0.8. Find the probability that it will be:
   (a) dry on Tuesday
   (b) dry on Wednesday.

10. In the game of tennis, a player has two serves. If the first serve is successful the game continues. If the first serve is not successful the player serves again. If this second serve is successful the game continues. If both serves are unsuccessful the player has served a 'double fault' and loses the point.
    Martina plays tennis. She is successful with 55% of her first serves and 95% of her second serves.
    (a) What is the probability that she serves a double fault?
    If Martina is successful with her first serve she has a probability of 0.9 of winning the point.
    If she is successful with her second serve she has a probability of 0.6 of winning the point.
    (b) Calculate the probability that Martina wins the point.

27 Algebraic laws

General laws in symbolic form

In previous chapters you have seen how to recognise sequences and how to write the nth term in terms of n. In this chapter the idea will be extended and other algebraic formulae will be expressed.

The most important thing, before starting to write down an algebraic formula, is to define carefully the letters you are using to stand for quantities and, if units are involved, what they are.

Example 1   Write down a formula for the cost of a pens and b notebooks.

> Let p be the cost of a pen in pence.
> Let n be the cost of a notebook in pence.
> Let T be the total cost in pence.
>
> The formula is then $T = ap + bn$

The next important step is to make sure that, if you have spotted a rule, you write it down accurately using correct algebra.

Example 2   Write down a formula for the mean of three numbers.

> Let the three numbers be a, b and c.
> Let the mean $= m$
>
> The formula is $m = \dfrac{a + b + c}{3}$.

Note that it is usual to use fraction lines rather than the ÷ sign in algebraic formulae. Even if you do use the ÷ sign it is important to use brackets to make sure the order of operations is right.

$m = a + b + c ÷ 3$ is **not** correct as it would mean that c was divided by 3 first and then added to $a + b$.

$m = (a + b + c) ÷ 3$, whilst mathematically correct, is not the usually way to write a formula.

$m = \frac{1}{3}(a + b + c)$ is an acceptable algebraic formula.

Some formulae use both the capital version of a letter and the small version as well. For this reason it is important to keep the version of the letter as defined.

For example, the formula for the area of the shaded section in this diagram is

$A = \pi R^2 - \pi r^2$

where A = the area in cm^2,
            R = the radius of the large circle in cm,
            r = the radius of the small circle in cm.

Sequences

 Example 3

Find a formula for the nth term of this sequence.

2, 6, 18, 54, 162…

When you are doing a question like this it is usually best to form a table.

Let U_n = the nth term.

n	1	2	3	4	5
U_n	2	6	18	54	162

It is fairly easy to spot a 'term to term' rule as each term is three times the previous one.

This is written as $U_{n+1} = 3 \times U_n$ and, together with $U_1 = 1$, defines the sequence. To get, for example the 20th term, however it is necessary to get the previous 19 terms first. So an algebraic rule would be better.

The 2nd term = 2×3
The 3rd term = $2 \times 3 \times 3 = 2 \times 3^2$
The 4th term = $2 \times 3 \times 3 \times 3 = 2 \times 3^3$
The 5th term = $2 \times 3 \times 3 \times 3 \times 3 = 2 \times 3^4$
        $\vdots$

The nth term = $2 \times 3^{n-1}$

So $U_n = 2 \times 3^{n-1}$

$U_{20} = 2 \times 3^{19} = 2\ 324\ 522\ 934$

> This sequence, where each term is multiplied by a fixed number to get the next, is called a geometric sequence.

Example 4️⃣ Find a formula for the *n*th triangle number. Use the formula to find the 40th triangle number.

$$1 \qquad 3 \qquad 6 \qquad 10 \qquad 15$$

Let T_n be the *n*th triangle number.

The term-to-term rule is fairly easy. For the 4th, you add 4 to the third, for the fifth you add 5 to the 4th and so on, but the algebraic rule is somewhat harder.

n	1	2	3	4	5
T_n	1	3	6	10	15

Even when the numbers are put into a table the formula is difficult to spot. Add another row to the table for $n + 1$.

n	1	2	3	4	5
$n + 1$	2	3	4	5	6
T_n	1	3	6	10	15

Even now it is not easy, but notice that

$$3 = \frac{2 \times 3}{2} \qquad 6 = \frac{3 \times 4}{2} \qquad 10 = \frac{4 \times 5}{2}$$

So $T_n = \dfrac{n(n + 1)}{2}$

$$T_{40} = \frac{40 \times 41}{2} = 20 \times 41 = 820$$

> This formula is worth remembering as triangle numbers arise quite often in investigation work.

Exercise 27.1a

In questions where you choose your own letters make sure you define them carefully.

1. A factory makes chairs and tables. A chair takes 5 hours to make and a table 4 hours. Find a formula for the total time spent making chairs and tables in a week.

2. Minibuses carry 10 passengers and taxis carry 4 passengers. Find a formula for the total number of people carried by taxis and minibuses.

3. To find the geometric mean of two numbers, you multiply the numbers together and find the square root of the answer. Write this relationship as a formula.

4. A two-digit number has the first digit a and the second digit b. Write down a formula for the number.

5. A ferry carries cars and lorries. On average a car takes up 20 m² of space and a lorry takes up 50 m² space. The decks have a total space of 5500 m². Write down an inequality satisfied by the number of cars and lorries.

6. Here is a sequence:
   4, 20, 100, 500, 2500,...
   Find (a) the *n*th term (b) the 10th term.

7. Here is a sequence:
   128, 64, 32, 16, 8,...
   Find (a) the *n*th term (b) the 10th term.

8. When a stone is dropped down a well, the distance it falls is proportional to the square of the time for which it has been falling. Write this relationship algebraically:
   (a) using the symbol $\propto$
   (b) as a formula using the constant k.

9. Peter invests £P at 5% per annum compound interest.
   Write down a formula for the amount the investment is worth after
   (a) 1 year   (b) 3 years   (c) n years.

10. The coordinates of P are (a, b). The coordinates of Q are (c, d). Find a formula for the distance PQ.

Exercise 27.lb

In questions where you choose your own letters make sure you define them carefully.

1. An electricity bill is made up of a fixed charge plus a charge for each unit of electricity used. Write a formula for the total bill.

2. Jane buys some books for £3 each. She sells some of them for £5 each. To get rid of the remainder she sells them at £2 each.
   Find, and simplify, a formula for her profit.

3. Asif buys some cans of cola at 50p each and some packets of crisps at 30p each. He has £5. Write down an inequality satisfied by the number of cans of cola and the number of packets of crisps he buys.

4. A three-digit number has the first digit a, the second digit b and the third digit c. Write down a formula for the number.

5. To find the volume of a pyramid multiply the area of the base by the height and divide by 3. Write a formula for the volume of a pyramid with a base that is:
   (a) square   (b) a rectangle.

6. Here is a sequence:
   0.5,   2,   8,   32,   128,...
   Find   (a)   the nth term
            (b)   the 10th term.

7. Here is a sequence:
   2,   5,   10,   17,   26,...
   Find   (a)   the 7th term
            (b)   the nth term
            (c)   the 20th term.

8. Newton's law of gravitation states that the force of attraction between two bodies is inversely proportional to the square of the distance between them.
   Write this relationship algebraically:
   (a) using the symbol $\propto$
   (b) as a formula using the constant k.

9. The value of a car depreciates by 15% per year. If the car was worth £C when new, write a formula for the value after
   (a) 1 year   (b) 3 years   (c) n years.

10. Write down a formula for the gradient of the line PQ in terms of the coordinates of P and Q.

11. The total stopping distance for a car consists of two parts. A thinking distance which is proportional to the speed plus a braking distance that is proportional to the square of the speed.
    Using two constants write down a formula for the total stopping distance in terms of the speed.

Approximation to linear graphs

Often in scientific experiments you will have plotted graphs of your results.

For example if you hang weights on a light spring you can measure the extension in the spring and plot the tension against the extension. The table might look like this.

Tension in newtons (T)	1	2	3	4	5
Extension in mm (e)	9.2	17.3	26.1	37.1	43.8

These results lead to the graph below.

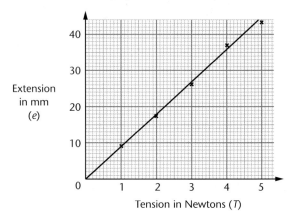

The points are not exactly in a straight line but, since the figures came from an experiment, it seems likely that the true relationship is linear and the variations are caused by experimental error.

If the points lie in a sufficiently good straight line to make you believe the relationship is linear then you can draw the best straight line you can through the points. This has been done on the above diagram.

This is similar to the lines of best fit you drew for correlation graphs. In the same way the line should reflect the slope of the points and have approximately the same number of points on either side. If one point lies a long way from the straight line then the experiment should be repeated for that reading.

When you drew correlation graphs it was quite common for the line of best fit not to go through the origin. In experimental situations the real situation should be examined to see if it is expected that the graph should go through the origin. In the above case it seems logical that if there is no tension there will be no extension and so the line will go through the origin.

Once the line of best fit is drawn you can find its equation. This will give you the relationship between the two quantities you have graphed. The two quantities that you need to read off from the graph are gradient and y-intercept. These can then be substituted into $y = mx + c$ to find the relationship.

In the above case $c = 0$ and $m = \dfrac{45}{5} = 9$.

So the relationship is $e = 9T$

In writing the relationship, it is particularly important that the variables are well defined together with their units.

Here T is the tension in newtons and e is the extension in millimetres.

Non-linear graphs

When the relationship is non-linear it is a little more difficult to find.

The table below shows the results of an experiment where two quantities x and y were being measured.

x	1	2	3	4	5
y	1.5	6.7	14	24	41

The graph for this relationship is shown below.

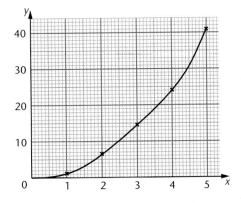

The graph look rather like a parabola ($y = kx^2$) but to confirm this draw the graph of y against x^2.

The table for this is shown below.

x	1	2	3	4	5
x^2	1	4	9	16	25
y	1.5	6.7	14	24	41

The graph for y against x^2 is shown below.

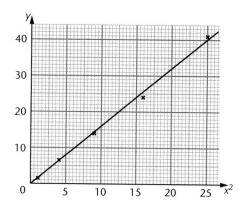

This graph is approximately a straight line and so the line of best fit can be drawn.

This line has a gradient of $\dfrac{40}{25} = 1.6$ and goes through the origin.

Since the graph is for y against x^2 the equation of a straight line is $y = mx^2 + c$ and in this case $m = 1.6$ and $c = 0$.

The equation that fits the relationship is $y = 1.6x^2$.

 Example 5

In an experiment the quantities x and y are measured. The table of values is given below.

x	1	2	5	10	15	20
y	6.2	4.3	3	2.9	2.6	2.5

(a) draw a graph of y against x.
(b) It is thought that the relationship between y and x is of the form
$y = \dfrac{a}{x} + b$.

Confirm this by plotting a graph of y against $\dfrac{1}{x}$.
(c) Draw a line of best fit and use it to estimate the values of a and b.

(a)

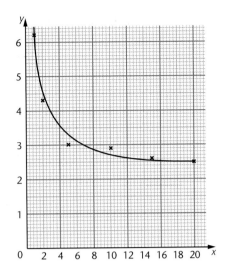

Since the graph is similar to the $y = \dfrac{1}{x}$ graph translated in the y-direction the given relationship seems likely.

(b) The table for the second graph is

x	1	2	5	10	15	20
$\dfrac{1}{x}$	1	0.5	0.2	0.1	0.067	0.05
y	6.2	4.3	3	2.9	2.6	2.5

The graph is drawn below

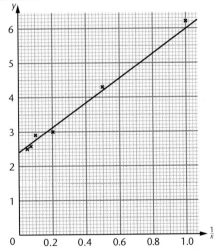

Since the graph is reasonably linear this confirms the relationship.

(c) The gradient of the line of best fit = $(6 - 2.4) \div 1 = 3.6$. So $a = 3.6$.
The y-intercept is 2.4 so $b = 2.4$.

The relationship is therefore $y = \dfrac{3.6}{x} + 2.4$.

It must be emphasised that this result is only conjecture since the data is experimental, and that the values of a and b are only estimates.

In general if a relationship is thought to be of the form $y = a\text{f}(x) + b$ this can be tested by plotting y against $\text{f}(x)$.

a and b can be estimated using the line of best fit.
a = the gradient and b = the y-intercept.

Exercise 27.2a

1. In an experiment the quantities x and y are measured. The table of values is given below.

x	1	2	3	4	5
y	2.4	10.1	22	41	62

   (a) Draw a graph of y against x.
   (b) It is thought that the relationship between x and y is of the form $y = ax^2$.
       Confirm this by plotting a graph of y against x^2.
   (c) Draw a line of best fit and use it to estimate the value of a.

2. In an experiment the quantities x and y are measured. The table of values is given below.

x	1	2	3	4	5
y	14.9	27	62	124	237

   (a) Draw a graph of y against x.
   (b) It is thought that the relationship between x and y is of the form $y = ax^3 + b$. Confirm this by plotting a graph of x^3 against y.
   (c) Draw a line of best fit and use it to estimate the values of a and b.

3. In an experiment the quantities x and y are measured. The table of values is given below.

x	5	10	15	20	25
y	13	6.4	4.3	3.1	2.5

   (a) Draw a graph of y against x.
   (b) It is thought that the relationship between x and y is of the form $y = \dfrac{a}{x}$.
       Confirm this by plotting a graph of y against $\dfrac{1}{x}$.
   (c) Draw a line of best fit and use it to estimate the value of a.

4. In an experiment the quantities x and y are measured. The table of values is given below.

x	10	20	30	40	50
y	117	292	515	782	1080

   (a) Draw a graph of y against x.
   (b) It is thought that the relationship between x and y is of the form $y = ax^{1.5} + b$.
       Confirm this by plotting an appropriate graph.
   (c) Draw a line of best fit and use it to estimate the values of a and b.

1. In an experiment the quantities x and y are measured. The table of values is given below.

x	1	2	3	4	5
y	48.5	44	37.1	28.1	14.5

(a) Draw a graph of y against x.

(b) It is thought that the relationship between x and y is of the form $y = ax^2 + b$.
Confirm this by plotting an appropriate graph.

(c) Draw a line of best fit and use it to estimate the values of a and b.

2. In an experiment the quantities x and y are measured. The table of values is given below.

x	10	20	30	40	50
y	19.5	28.2	34.5	39.4	44.5

(a) Draw a graph of y against x.

(b) It is thought that y is proportional to the square root of x.
Confirm this by plotting a graph of y against $\sqrt{x}$.

(c) Draw a line of best fit and use it to find the equation connecting x and y.

3. In an experiment the quantities x and y are measured. The table of values is given below.

x	5	10	15	20	25
y	10.4	18.8	42.9	89.5	166

(a) Draw a graph of y against x.

(b) It is thought that the relationship between x and y is of the form $y = ax^3 + b$.
Confirm this by plotting an appropriate graph.

(c) Draw a line of best fit and use it to estimate the values of a and b.

4. In an experiment the quantities x and y are measured. The table of values is given below.

x	5	10	15	20	25
y	78	17.2	6	2.2	0.3

(a) Draw a graph of y against x.

(b) It is thought that the relationship between x and y is of the form $y = \dfrac{a}{x^2} + b$.
Confirm this by plotting an appropriate graph.

(c) Draw a line of best fit and use it to estimate the values of a and b.

Key points

- When writing general rules in algebraic form, you must
  - (i) define all the variables precisely including the units
  - (ii) make sure that the correct rules of algebra are followed in writing the formula that fits the rule.

- If a relationship is thought to be of the form $y = af(x) + b$, this can be tested by plotting y against $f(x)$.
  a and b can be estimated using the line of best fit.
  a = the gradient and b = the y-intercept.

In questions where you choose your own letters make sure you define them carefully.

1. A tailor makes jackets and trousers. Jackets take him 5 hours to make and trousers 2 hours. He works for a maximum of 40 hours a week. Write down an inequality in terms of the number of trousers and jackets he makes each week.

2. To find the diagonal of a cuboid you square the length, square the width and square the height. You then add the answers together and find the square root of the result. Write this rule as a formula.

3. Rowena is trying to find the number of circles she can cut from a rectangle of card. She says:

    let l = length of rectangle

    let w = width of rectangle

    let r = radius of circle

    let N = number of circles

    (a) What is wrong with her statements?

    She suggests the formula $N = \dfrac{lw}{\pi r^2}$.

    (b) Why will her formula not work?

4. A two-digit number has the first digit a and the second digit b.

    (a) What is the number?

    (b) If the digits are reversed, what is the new number?

    (c) If the two numbers are added together what is the result?

    (d) What number will always go into the result of adding two numbers with the digits reversed?

5. The time of swing for a pendulum is proportional to the square root of its length. Write this relationship algebraically:

    (a) using the symbol $\propto$

    (b) as a formula using the constant k.

6. Here is a sequence:

    $$4, \quad 6, \quad 9, \quad 13.5, \quad 20.25, \ldots$$

    Find:

    (a) the sixth term,

    (b) the nth term,

    (c) the 15th term correct to 3 d.p.

7. (a) Find a formula for the nth term of the sequence:

    $$\frac{1}{5}, \quad \frac{3}{10}, \quad \frac{5}{20}, \quad \frac{7}{40}, \quad \frac{9}{80}, \quad \cdots$$

    (b) Use the formula to find the 20th term.

8. In the diagram there are 4 points on the circle and 6 lines joining them.

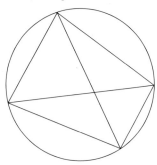

    (a) Find a formula for the number of lines joining n points on a circle.

    (b) Use the formula to find the number of lines joining 30 points on a circle.

9. Rushna has £P to invest in a bank which gives compound interest annually.

    Find a formula for the amount the investment will be worth at the end of n years, if the interest rate is:

    (a) 4%   (b) 6%   (c) r%.

10. In an experiment the quantities x and y are measured. The table of values is given below.

x	5	10	15	20	25
y	0.7	5.5	16.3	43.5	87.2

    It is thought that y is proportional to x^3.

    (a) Draw a graph to confirm this.

    (b) Draw a line of best fit and use it to find an equation connecting y and x.

You will need to know:

- the exterior angle of a triangle equals the sum of the interior opposite angles
- the sum of the angles in a triangle is 180°
- the sum of the angles on a straight line is 180°
- the opposite angles of a cyclic quadrilateral add to 180°
- the properties of congruent triangles
- the angle in a semi-circle is 90°.

Examiner's tip

In a proof you should write out each step of your thinking and reasoning together with the reason or justification for each statement you write down.

Angles at the centre of a circle

AB is a diameter of the circle whose centre is O. C is a point on the circumference.

Chord AC subtends angle AOC at the centre of the circle and angle ABC at the circumference.

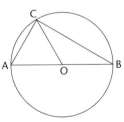

'Subtends' means 'forms'

Here is a simple proof that angle AOC = twice angle OBC.

If we draw CA and CB then:
For triangle OCB
angle AOC = angle OCB + angle OBC.   exterior angle of triangle

But   OC = OB   radii
Therefore triangle OCB is isosceles.
Therefore angle   OCB = angle OBC
Therefore angle   AOC = 2 × angle OBC

the angle at the centre = 2 × the angle at the circumference.

Challenge 1

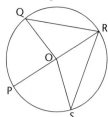

Try to prove that angle QOS = 2 × angle QRS.

(The solution is given below – try to write out your own proof and then use this to **check** your work.)

Solution

Angle POQ = angle OQR + angle ORQ   exterior angle of triangle OCR

      But OQ = OR   radii

∴   Angle OQR = angle ORQ   opposite angles of isosceles triangle

∴   angle POQ = 2 × angle ORQ

Similarly angle POS = 2 × angle ORS

∴ Angle POQ + angle POS = 2 × angle ORQ + 2 × angle ORS

i.e.   angle QOS = 2 × angle QRS

What has just been proved can be expressed in words as:

The angle at the centre of a circle = twice the angle at the circumference subtended by the same arc (or the same chord).
[In this proof the arc is arc QPS]

 In this diagram O is the centre of the circle. Calculate the value of angle *a*.

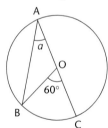

Angle *a* = 30°

angle at the centre
= 2 × angle at the circumference

Exercise 28.1a

In each of the following diagrams O is the centre of the circle. Find the size of each of the lettered angles. Try to write down each step with the reasons for your deductions.

1.

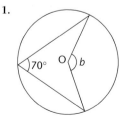

2.

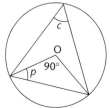

3.

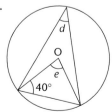

4.

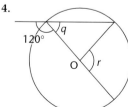

Exercise 28.1b

In each of the following diagrams O is the centre of the circle. Find the size of each of the lettered angles. Try to write down each step with the reasons for your deductions.

1.

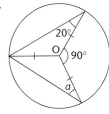

2.

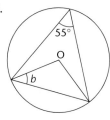

3.

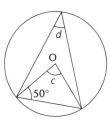

4.

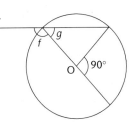

Challenge 2

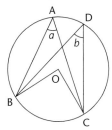

Prove that angle a = angle b

(The solution is given below – try to write out your own proof and then use this to **check** your work.)

Proof

Angle a $= \frac{1}{2} \times$ angle BOC (angle at centre $= \frac{1}{2}$ angle at circumference)

Angle b $= \frac{1}{2} \times$ angle BOC (angle at centre $= \frac{1}{2}$ angle at circumference)

$\therefore$ angle a = angle b

Exercise 28.2a

In the following questions O is the centre of the circle. Calculate the angles marked with letters.

1.

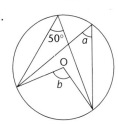

2.

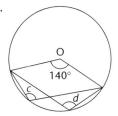

3.

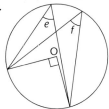

4.

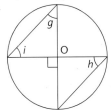

Exercise 28.2b

In the following questions O is the centre of the circle. Calculate the angles marked with letters.

1.

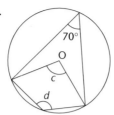

2.

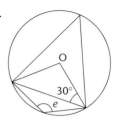

3.

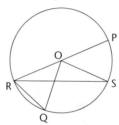

Sometimes the angle at the circumference is in the same semicircle as the arc.

Challenge 3

Prove angle QRS = $\frac{1}{2}$ × angle QOS

(The solution is given below – try to write out your own proof and then use this to **check** your work.)

Proof

Let angle ORQ = x and angle ORS = y.

Triangle ORQ is isosceles.   OR and OQ are radii

∴ angle ROQ = 180° − 2x angle sum of triangle

Triangle ORS is isosceles   OR and OS are radii

∴ angle y = angle OSR

∴ angle ROS = 180° − 2y angle sum of triangle

angle QOS = angle ROS − angle ROQ

= (180° − 2y) − (180° − 2x)

= 2x − 2y

= 2(x − y)

but angle QRS = angle ORQ − angle ORS

= x − y

∴ angle QRS = $\frac{1}{2}$ × angle QOS

Exercise 28.3a

Calculate the sizes of the angles marked with letters. O is the centre of each circle. Give the reasons for each step of your working.

1.

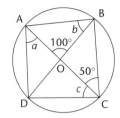

2.

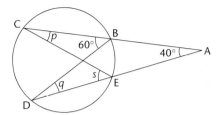

3.

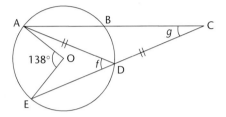

4.

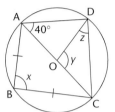

Exercise 28.3b

Calculate the sizes of the angles marked with letters. O is the centre of each circle. Give the reasons for each step of your working.

1.

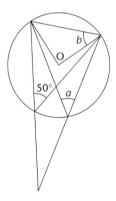

2.

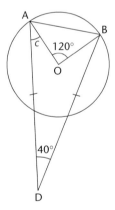

3.

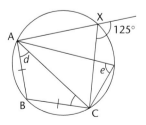

4.

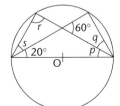

Tangents

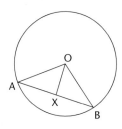

AB is a chord to the circle centre O.
X is the midpoint of AB.

In triangles OXA and OXB

OA = OB   radii

AX = XB   X is the midpoint

OX is common

∴ Triangles OXA and OXB are congruent   SSS

∴ angle OXA = angle OXB = 90°

What has just been proved is:

The straight line which joins the centre of a circle to the midpoint of a chord is at right angles to the chord and bisects the chord.

If the line OX is extended to become a radius, as in the diagram below, the chord AB will become the tangent at X.

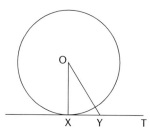

This fact is proved below. Work through the proof and make sure you can follow it.

TX is the tangent to the circle centre O. OX is the radius at the point of contact. If angle OXT is **not** 90° it must be possible to draw a line at right angles to TX – the line OY and so angle OYX = 90°. If angle OYX = 90° then OX is the hypotenuse of triangle OYX and OX > OY. What follows from this statement is that Y must be inside the circle because OX is a radius.

∴ line TYX must cut the circle, ie line YX would be part of a chord.

This is impossible because TX is defined as a tangent.

∴ It is impossible for angle OXT not to be 90°.

∴ angle OXT is 90°.

This is an example of a proof by contradiction.

In the following questions calculate the angles marked with letters. O is the centre of each circle.
X and Y are the points of contact of the tangents to each circle.

1.

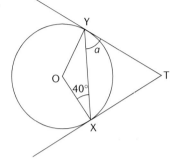

2.

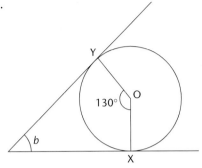

3.

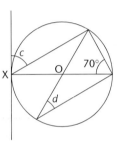

4.

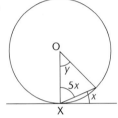

In the following questions calculate the angles marked with letters. O is the centre of each circle.
X and Y are the points of contact of the tangents to each circle.

1.

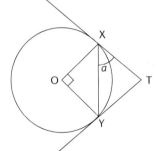

2.

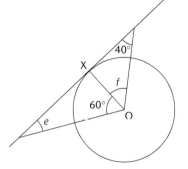

3.

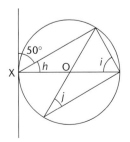

4.

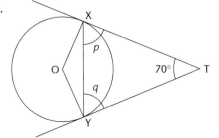

Challenge 4

T is a point outside a circle, centre O.

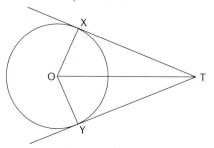

TX and TY are the tangents from T to the circle.
Prove triangles OTX and OTY are congruent.
(The solution is given below – try to write out your own proof
and then use this to **check** your work.)

Proof

OX = OY   radii

Angles OXT and OYT are 90°.   angle between radius and tangent

TO is common.

Therefore triangle OTX is congruent to triangle OTY.   RHS

If the triangles OTX and OTY are congruent then XT = YT;
angle XTO = angle YTO; angle TOX = angle TOY
In words:
**Tangents drawn from a point to a circle are equal in length.
They subtend equal angles at the centre of the circle and
they make equal angles with the straight line joining the
centre of the circle to the point.**

Challenge 5

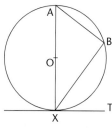

BX is a chord of the circle centre O.
TX is a tangent meeting the circle at X;
AX is a diameter.

Prove angle BXT = angle BAX

(The solution is given below – try to write out your
own proof and then use this to **check** your work.)

Proof

angle ABX = 90°   angle in a semi-circle

angle OXT = 90°   angle between a diameter and a tangent

∴ angle AXB = 90° − angle BXT   angle sum of triangle

but angle AXB + angle BAX + angle ABX = 180°

ie   angle AXB + angle BAX = 90°

∴ 90° − angle BXT + angle BAX = 90°

∴ angle BXT = angle BAX

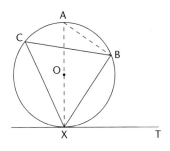

This is a general result since angle XCB = angle XAB (subtended by arc XB).

So the result may be stated as:

The angle between a tangent and a chord drawn from the point of contact is equal to the angle subtended by the chord in the alternate segment, that is on the other side of the chord.

Exercise 28.5a

In the questions 1–4, TX is a tangent to the circle, find the angles marked with letters. Give reasons for your answers.

1.

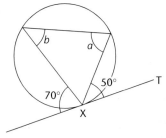

2.

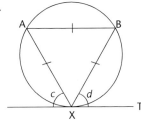

3.

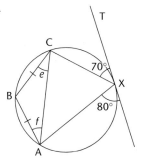

4.

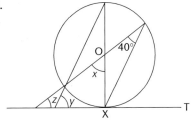

5

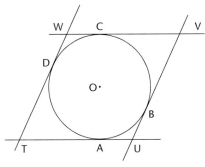

The sides of the quadrilateral TUVW are all tangents to the circle centre O.

Prove TU + WV = UV + WT.

In the following questions find the angles marked with letters. Give reasons for your answers.

1.

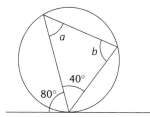

2.

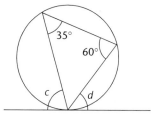

3.

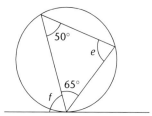

4.

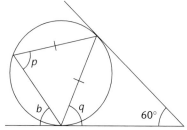

Key points

- The angle at the centre of a circle = twice the angle at the circumference subtended by the same arc (or same chord).
- The straight line which joins the centre of a circle to the midpoint of a chord is at right angles to the chord.
- Tangents drawn from the same point to the same circle are equal in length. They subtend equal angles at the centre of the circle and they make equal angles with the straight line joining the centre of the circle to the point.
- The angle between a tangent to a circle and a chord drawn from the point of contact is equal to the angle subtended by the chord in the alternate segment.

Revision exercise 28a

In the following questions O is the centre of each circle. In each question calculate the size of the angles marked with letters.

1.

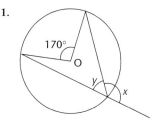

2.

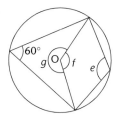

3.

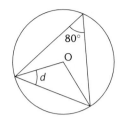

4.

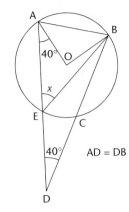

AD = DB

5.

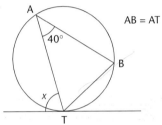

AB = AT

6.

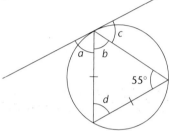

7.

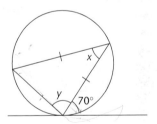

29 Equations and manipulation 4

You will need to know:

- how to solve linear equations and inequalities
- how to factorise expressions and quadratics
- how to solve linear simultaneous equations
- how to solve quadratic equations by factorisation, graphical methods and the formula
- how to rearrange formulae
- how to expand brackets and manipulate algebraic expressions
- how to draw linear, quadratic and cubic graphs
- the equation of a straight line with gradient m and intercept on the y-axis c is $y = mx + c$.

Revision of earlier algebra

Before going on to the new topics in this chapter it is useful to revise the earlier algebraic work as this is needed. If you have difficulty with any of the questions in Exercise 29.1a or 29.1b, look back at the examples in the earlier chapters.

Exercise 29.1a

1. Solve by factorisation.
   (a) $x^2 - 7x - 18 = 0$ (b) $2x^2 + 5x - 3 = 0$
   (c) $3x^2 - 10x + 3 = 0$ (d) $2x^2 - 7x = 0$
   (e) $6x^2 - 5x + 1 = 0$

2. Use the formula to solve the following. Give the answers to 2 d.p.
   (a) $x^2 - 6x + 2 = 0$ (b) $3x^2 + 4x - 2 = 0$
   (c) $2x^2 - 8x + 5 = 0$

3. Simplify.
   (a) $\dfrac{x}{2} + \dfrac{x+2}{3}$ (b) $\dfrac{2x-1}{4} - \dfrac{2x+3}{5}$
   (c) $\dfrac{1}{x+1} + \dfrac{2}{x-2}$ (d) $\dfrac{2x}{x-1} - \dfrac{x-1}{x+2}$
   (e) $\dfrac{3x^2 + 9x}{x^2 + 4x + 3}$

4. Solve the equations.
   (a) $x(x-2) - 2x(x-2) = 12 - x^2$
   (b) $\dfrac{2x}{3} + \dfrac{x-2}{2} = 1$ (c) $(x+1)^2 = 16$
   (d) $\dfrac{x^2}{3} - \dfrac{x}{3} - 4 = 0$ (e) $\dfrac{1}{x+1} = \dfrac{4}{3x+2}$
   (f) $(x+2) = \dfrac{15}{x}$ (g) $\dfrac{5}{x+1} - \dfrac{2}{x-1} = \dfrac{1}{3}$

5. Rearrange the formula to make x the subject.
   (a) $2x - 3y = 7$ (b) $5x - 9y = 8z$
   (c) $3x + 2y - 4 = 0$ (d) $5x + 5z = 4y$
   (e) $5(2x - 3y) = 4x - 7$

6. Solve the simultaneous equations.
   (a) $2x - 3y = 7$ (b) $3x - 2y = 5$
       $3x + y = 16$ $2x + 3y = 12$
   (c) $5x + 2y = 6$ (d) $4x - 3y = 11$
       $3x - 4y = 1$ $3x + 2y = 4$
   (e) $5x + 3y = 7$
       $3x + 7y = 12$

1. Solve these equations by factorisation.
   (a) $x^2 + 5x - 14 = 0$ (b) $2x^2 + 3x - 9 = 0$
   (c) $3x^2 - 14x + 8 = 0$ (d) $16x^2 - 9 = 0$
   (e) $7x^2 - 19x + 10 = 0$

2. Use the formula to solve the following. Give the answers to 2 d.p.
   (a) $x^2 - 3x + 1 = 0$ (b) $3x^2 + 2x - 3 = 0$
   (c) $3x^2 - 9x + 2 = 0$

3. Simplify.
   (a) $\dfrac{x+1}{2} + \dfrac{x-2}{3}$ (b) $\dfrac{4x-1}{3} - \dfrac{2x+3}{5}$
   (c) $\dfrac{4}{x+3} + \dfrac{2}{x-2}$ (d) $\dfrac{2x+1}{x-1} - \dfrac{x}{x+2}$
   (e) $\dfrac{4x^2 + 12x}{x^2 + 2x - 3}$

4. Solve
   (a) $\dfrac{2x}{5} - \dfrac{x}{2} = \dfrac{7}{10}$ (b) $\dfrac{3x}{x-2} = 5$

   (c) $\dfrac{4}{x-2} - \dfrac{1}{x+1} = 0$ (d) $3\left(\dfrac{x-3}{4}\right) - \dfrac{2}{5}x + \dfrac{1}{2} = 0$
   (e) $(4 - 3x)^2 - 6x = 0$

5. Rearrange the formula to make a the subject.
   (a) $2a - b = 7$ (b) $5a - 2c = 8$
   (c) $3a - 2b = 2c$ (d) $5a - 5c = 4b$
   (e) $3(2a - 3b) = 4b - 3a$

6. Solve the simultaneous equations.
   (a) $x - 3y = 1$ (b) $2x - 3y = 0$
       $2x + y = 9$ $3x + 4y = 17$
   (c) $7x + 2y = 11$ (d) $5x + 3y = 9$
       $3x - 5y = -7$ $3x - 2y = 13$
   (e) $4x + 3y = 5$
       $6x + 7y = 10$

 Examiner's tip

Always check the simultaneous equation answers. If there are any errors, check the adding or subtracting as this is where most errors occur.

Further simultaneous equations

The method that was covered in Chapter 21 was the method of elimination. This is the method you most likely used in question 6 of Exercises 29.1a and 29.1b.

Example 1

Solve the simultaneous equations $2x + 3y = 13$, $6x + 2y = 11$.

$$2x + 3y = 13 \quad ①$$
$$6x + 2y = 11 \quad ②$$

(a) To solve by elimination the easiest way is to multiply equation **1** by 3 and then subtract.

$$6x + 9y = 39 \quad ③ \quad ① \times 3$$
$$6x + 2y = 11 \quad ②$$
$$7y = 28 \qquad ③ - ②$$
$$y = 4$$
$$2x + 12 = 13 \qquad \boxed{\text{Substitute in } ①}$$
$$2x = 1$$
$$x = \tfrac{1}{2}$$

The solution is $x = \tfrac{1}{2}$, $y = 4$.

Check in equation②: $6x + 2y = 3 + 8 = 11$ which is correct.

These equations can also be solved by substitution.

(b) $\qquad 2x + 3y = 13 \qquad$ ①

$\qquad\qquad 6x + 2y = 11 \qquad$ ②

First rearrange ① to make x the subject.

$$2x = 13 - 3y$$

$$x = \left(\frac{13 - 3y}{2}\right)$$

Substitute this in ②.

$$6\left(\frac{13 - 3y}{2}\right) + 2y = 11$$

$$39 - 9y + 2y = 11 \qquad \text{Cancelling 6 and 2 and expanding the bracket}$$

$$39 - 7y = 11$$

$$7y = 28$$

$$y = 4$$

The rest is the same as in (a) giving the solution $x = \frac{1}{2}$, $y = 4$.

Either x or y can be used to substitute from either equation into the other.

Before looking at the harder simultaneous equations it is best to see another of the type you have already solved by substitution.

Solve by substitution the simultaneous equations

$$3x + 2y = 12 \qquad ①$$

and $\qquad 5x - 3y = 1 \qquad$ ②

Either x or y can be substituted.

Here the easiest is to substitute for y from ① into ②.

① gives $2y = 12 - 3x$

$$y = \frac{12 - 3x}{2}$$

Substitute in ②.

$$5x - 3\left(\frac{12 - 3x}{2}\right) = 1 \qquad \text{Multiply through by 2.}$$

$$10x - 3(12 - 3x) = 2$$

$$10x - 36 + 9x = 2$$

$$19x = 38$$

$$x = 2$$

Substitute in ①.

$$6 + 2y = 12$$

$$2y = 6$$

$$y = 3$$

The solution is $x = 2$, $y = 3$.

Check in ②. $5x - 3y = 10 - 9 = 1$ which is correct.

A harder type of simultaneous equations to be solved include one linear equation and one quadratic, e.g. $y = 3x + 2$ and $y = x^2 - 2x + 8$. These have previously been solved by a graphical method. To solve them algebraically use the method of substitution.

Example 3

Solve the simultaneous equations

$$y = x^2 + 3x - 7 \qquad \text{①}$$
$$\text{and} \quad y = x - 4 \qquad \text{②}$$

(a) graphically using values of x from -5 to $+2$,

(b) algebraically.

(a) $y = x^2 + 3x - 7$

x	-5	-4	-3	-2	-1	0	1	2
x^2	25	16	9	4	1	0	1	4
$+3x$	-15	-12	-9	-6	-3	0	3	6
-7	-7	-7	-7	-7	-7	-7	-7	-7
$y = x^2 + 3x - 7$	3	-3	-7	-9	-9	-7	-3	3

$y = x - 4$

x	-5	0	2
y	-9	-4	-2

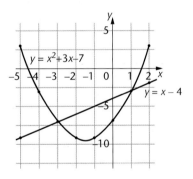

The curve and the line cross at $x = 1$, $y = -3$ and $x = -3$, $y = -7$.

(b) Substitute y from ② into ①.

Substituting gives $x - 4 = x^2 + 3x - 7$

$$x^2 + 2x - 3 = 0$$
$$(x - 1)(x + 3) = 0 \qquad \text{rearranging}$$
$$x = 1 \text{ or } -3$$

Substitute in ① for $x = 1$:

$$y = 1 + 3 - 7 = -3$$

for $x = -3$:

$$y = 9 - 9 - 7 = -7$$

Check in ② for $x = 1$:

$$y = 1 - 4 = -3, \text{ checks}$$

for $x = -3$:

$$y = -3 - 4 = -7, \text{ checks}$$

The solutions are $x = 1$, $y = -3$ or $x = -3$, $y = -7$.

Chapter 29 Further simultaneous equations

Example 4 Solve algebraically the simultaneous equations

$$3x + 2y = 7 \qquad \text{①}$$
$$\text{and} \qquad y = x^2 - 2x + 3 \qquad \text{②}$$

Either x or y can be substituted but the easier method is to substitute for y from ② into ①.

$$3x + 2(x^2 - 2x + 3) = 7$$
$$3x + 2x^2 - 4x + 6 = 7$$
$$2x^2 - x - 1 = 0$$
$$(2x + 1)(x - 1) = 0$$
$$x = -\tfrac{1}{2} \text{ or } 1$$

Substitute in ① for $x = -\tfrac{1}{2}$:

$$-\tfrac{3}{2} + 2y = 7, \ 2y = 8\tfrac{1}{2}, \ y = 4\tfrac{1}{4}$$
$$\text{for } x = 1:$$
$$3 + 2y = 7, \ 2y = 4, \ y = 2$$

Check in ② for $x = -\tfrac{1}{2}$:

$$y = (-\tfrac{1}{2})^2 - 2(-\tfrac{1}{2}) + 3 = \tfrac{1}{4} + 1 + 3 = 4\tfrac{1}{4}$$
$$\text{for } x = 1: y = 1 - 2 + 3 = 2, \text{ both check.}$$

The solutions are $x = -\tfrac{1}{2}$, $y = 4\tfrac{1}{4}$ or $x = 1$, $y = 2$.

Examiner's tip

Always substitute for the letter that needs least manipulation, often the letter y.

Exercise 29.2a

Solve the following simultaneous equations by the method of substitution.

1. $y = 2x - 1$
    $x + 2y = 8$
2. $3y = 11 - x$
    $3x - y = 3$
3. $3x + 2y = 7$
    $2x - 3y = -4$
4. $3x - 2y = 3$
    $2x - y = 4$
5. $y = 10 - 2x$
    $y = x^2 - 5x + 6$
6. $y - 4x - 7 = 0$
    $y = x^2 - 3x - 1$
7. $3x + 2y = 7$
    $y = x^2 - x + 3$
8. $x + 2y = 8$
    $y = x^2 + x + 3$

9. (a) (i) Draw the graph of $y = x^2 - 5x + 5$
          for $x = -2$ to $+5$.
       (ii) On the same grid draw the graph of
          $2x + y = 9$.
       (iii) Write down the coordinates of the
          points where the curve and line cross.
    (b) Solve algebraically the equations
          $y = x^2 - 5x + 5$ and $2x + y = 9$.
10. (a) (i) Draw the graph of $y = x^2 - 3x - 1$
          for $x = -4$ to $+3$.
       (ii) On the same grid draw the graph of
          $4x + y = 5$.
       (iii) Write down the coordinates of the
          points where the curve and line cross.
    (b) Solve algebraically the equations
          $y = x^2 - 3x - 1$ and $4x + y = 5$.

Solve the following simultaneous equations by the method of substitution.

1. $y = 2x - 3$
    $7x - 4y = 10$

2. $4x - 2y = 3$
    $x - y = 0$

3. $3x - y = 7$
    $5x + 2y = 8$

4. $2x + 3y = 7$
    $5y = 11 - 3x$

5. $y = 4 - 3x$
    $y = x^2 - 6x - 6$

6. $y = 2x - 3$
    $y = x^2 - 4x + 5$

7. $y = x^2 + x + 3$
    $2x + y = 1$

8. $y = x^2 + x - 2$
    $x + 5y + 2 = 0$

9. (a) (i) On one grid draw the graphs of
    $y = x^2 + 3$ and $y = 3x + 7$
    for $x = -2$ to $+5$.
    (ii) Find the simultaneous solutions of the two equations from your graph.
    (b) Solve algebraically the equations
    $y = x^2 + 3$ and $y = 3x + 7$.

10. (a) (i) Draw the graph of $y = x^2 - 5x + 3$
    for $x = -2$ to $+4$.
    (ii) On the same grid draw the graph of
    $7x + 2y = 11$.
    (iii) Write down the coordinates of the points where the curve and line cross.
    (b) Solve algebraically the equations
    $y = x^2 - 5x + 3$ and $7x + 2y = 11$.

The equation of a circle

Draw the graph of $x^2 + y^2 = 25$

Examiner's tip

Working out the values in the usual way may cause problems! Remember Pythagoras' theorem. It looks like this equation. Can you spot a pair of values for x and y which fit. What about (3, 4)? (4, 3)? (5, 0). These all satisfy the equation.

These points satisfy the equation $(-5, 0)$, $(-4, 3)$, $(-3, 4)$, $(0, 5)$, $(3, 4)$, $(4, 3)$ $(5, 0)$, $(4, -3)$, $(3, -4)$, $(0, -5)$, $(-3, -4)$, $(-4, -3)$.

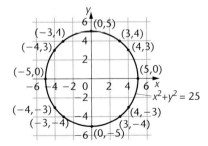

Can you see why the graph is a circle?
The general equation of a circle centre (0, 0) and radius r is $x^2 + y^2 = r^2$, as shown by Pythagoras' theorem.

Draw the graph of $x^2 + y^2 = 9$.

This is the graph of the circle centre (0, 0) and radius 3. The only integer values it passes through are (−3, 0) (0, 3), (3, 0), (0, −3).

When $x = 2$ or -2, $\qquad 4 + y^2 = 9$
$$y^2 = 5$$
$$y = \sqrt{5} = +2.24 \text{ or } -2.24$$

All these 8 points can be plotted and the circle will pass through them.

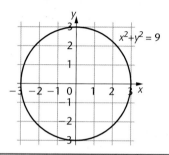

Examiner's tip

It is easier to find the radius and use compasses rather than calculate points.

(a) On the same grid draw the graphs of $x^2 + y^2 = 16$ and $y = x + 2$.

(b) Use the graph to solve the two equations simultaneously, giving the answers correct to 1 d.p.

(a)

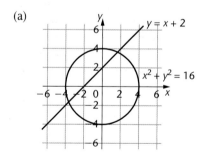

(b) The solution is where the two graphs cross (−3.6, −1.6) or (1.6, 3.6).

The simultaneous equations of this form can also be solved by substitution but you will only be asked to solve those where the solutions are exact.

Example 7

Use algebra to solve simultaneously the equations
$$x^2 + y^2 = 25 \qquad ①$$
$$y = x + 1 \qquad ②$$

Substitute ② in ① $\quad x^2 + (x + 1)^2 = 25$

$$x^2 + x^2 + 2x + 1 = 25 \qquad \text{Expand the bracket}$$
$$2x^2 + 2x - 24 = 0 \qquad \text{Collect the terms.}$$
$$x^2 + x - 12 = 0 \qquad \text{Divide by 2.}$$
$$(x + 4)(x - 3) = 0$$
$$x = -4 \text{ or } +3$$

Substitute in ② for $x = -4$:
$$y = -4 + 1 = -3$$
for $x = 3$:
$$y = 3 + 1 = 4$$

Check in ① for $x = -4, y = -3$:
$$x^2 + y^2 = 16 + 9 = 25$$
for $x = 3, y = 4$:
$$x^2 + y^2 = 9 + 16 = 25, \text{ checks.}$$

The solution is $x = -4, y = -3$ or $x = 3, y = 4$.

Exercise 29.3a

1. Draw the graph of $x^2 + y^2 = 64$. Use a scale of 1 cm to 2 units for both x and y.

2. (a) Draw the graphs of $x^2 + y^2 = 100$ and $y = x + 2$ on the same grid. Use a scale of 1 cm to 2 units for both x and y.

   (b) Find the coordinates of the points where the two graphs cross.

3. (a) Draw the graphs of $x^2 + y^2 = 64$ and $y = 2x + 8$ on the same grid. Use a scale of 1 cm to 2 units for both x and y.

   (b) Use the graph to solve simultaneously the equations $x^2 + y^2 = 64$ and $y = 2x + 8$. Give the answers either as whole numbers or correct to 1 d.p.

4. Use algebra to solve simultaneously the equations $x^2 + y^2 = 49$ and $y = 7 - x$.

5. Use algebra to solve simultaneously the equations $x^2 + y^2 = 169$ and $y = x + 7$.

6. Use algebra to solve simultaneously the equations $x^2 + y^2 = 25$ and $x + y = 5$.

7. Use algebra to solve simultaneously the equations $x^2 + y^2 = 100$ and $y = x + 2$.

8. Use algebra to solve simultaneously the equations $x^2 + y^2 = 64$ and $y = 2x + 8$.

Chapter 29 The equation of a circle

1. Draw the graph of $x^2 + y^2 = 625$. Use a scale of 1 cm to 5 units for both x and y.

2. (a) Draw the graphs of $x^2 + y^2 = 25$ and $y + x = 7$ on the same grid. Use a scale of 1 cm to 1 unit for both x and y.
   (b) Find the coordinates of the points where the two graphs meet.

3. (a) Draw the graphs of $x^2 + y^2 = 49$ and $y = x + 5$ on the same grid. Use a scale of 1 cm to 2 units for both x and y.
   (b) Use the graph to solve simultaneously the equations $x^2 + y^2 = 49$ and $y = x + 5$.
   Give the answers either as whole numbers or correct to 1 d.p.

4. Use algebra to solve simultaneously the equations $x^2 + y^2 = 4$ and $y = 2 - x$.

5. Use algebra to solve simultaneously the equations $x^2 + y^2 = 225$ and $y = x + 3$.

6. Use algebra to solve simultaneously the equations $x^2 + y^2 = 9$ and $x + y = 3$.

7. Use algebra to solve simultaneously the equations $x^2 + y^2 = 100$ and $y = 14 - x$.

8. Use algebra to solve simultaneously the equations $x^2 + y^2 = 34$ and $y = x - 2$.

Gradients of parallel and perpendicular lines

You have already worked out the gradient of a line by dividing the increase in y by the increase in x as shown in this diagram.

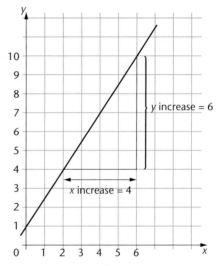

As you can see the gradient is $\frac{6}{4} = 1.5$.

In a similar way the line joining two points (a, b) and (c, d) will have the gradient $\frac{b - d}{a - c}$.

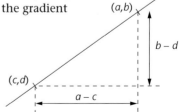

Example 8 — Find the gradient of the line joining the points
(a) (1, 3) and (3, 9)   (b) (2, 5) and (3, 1).

(a) Gradient $= \dfrac{9-3}{3-1} = \dfrac{6}{2} = 3$.

(b) Gradient $= \dfrac{1-5}{3-2} = \dfrac{-4}{1} = -4$.

Examiner's tip

The main mistake that occurs with finding the gradient is the sign, positive or negative. This can be checked by a sketch of the line. Lines sloping upwards from left to right have a positive gradient and those sloping the opposite way have a negative gradient.

To find the equation of a line, use $y = mx + c$. First find the gradient m and then substitute one of the points in the equation to find the value of c.

Example 9 — Find the equation of the line joining the points
(a) (1, 3) and (3, 9)   (b) (2, 5) and (3, 1)

(a) In Example 8 the gradient was found as 3.
The equation is $y = 3x + c$.
Substitute $x = 1$, $y = 3$ in the equation
$3 = 3 + c$
$c = 0$
The equation is $y = 3x$.

(b) In Example 8 the gradient was found as -4.
The equation is $y = -4x + c$.
Substitute $x = 2$, $y = 5$ in the equation.
$5 = -8 + c$, so $c = 13$
The equation is $y = -4x + 13$ or $y + 4x = 13$.

The gradient of a line defines its direction, so lines that are parallel have equal gradients.

Example 10 — Find the equation of the line that is parallel to the line $y = 3x + 5$ and passes through the point (1, 4).

The equation of this line is $y = 3x + c$, as it has the same gradient as $y = 3x + 5$.
It passes through (1, 4) so substitute $x = 1$ and $y = 4$ in $y = 3x + c$.
$4 = 3 \times 1 + c$
$c = 1$
The equation is $y = 3x + 1$.

Example ⓫

Find the equation of the line that is parallel to the line $2y + 3x = 7$ and passes through the point $(-4, 5)$.

Rearrange the equation $2y + 3x = 7$ to $y = -\frac{3}{2}x + \frac{7}{2}$

The gradient is therefore $-\frac{3}{2}$.

The equation is $y = -\frac{3}{2}x + c$

Substitute $x = -4$, $y = 5$ in the equation.

$$5 = -\frac{3}{2} \times -4 + c$$
$$5 = +6 + c$$
$$c = 5 - 6 = -1$$

The equation is $y = -\frac{3}{2}x - 1$ or $2y + 3x + 2 = 0$.

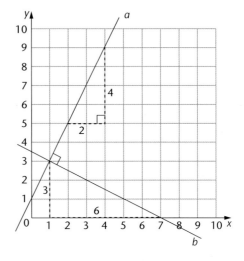

The two lines drawn on the diagram are at right angles and the gradients are for line a, $\frac{4}{2} = 2$, and for line b, $-\frac{3}{6} = -\frac{1}{2}$.

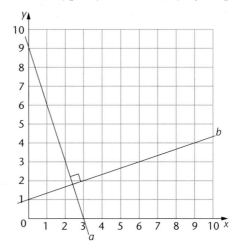

Here the two gradients are -3 and $\frac{1}{3}$.

This suggests that when two lines are perpendicular and have gradients m and n the product of their gradients is -1.
i.e. $m \times n = -1$.

This can be proved using similar triangles.

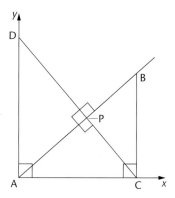

The two line AB and CD cross at right angles at P.

The gradient of AB is $m = \dfrac{BC}{AC}$ and the gradient CD is $n = -\dfrac{AD}{AC}$.

In triangles ADC and ABC.

      angle DAC = angle ACB   Both 90°

      angle ADC = angle BAC   Both 90° – angle PAD

So triangles ADC and ABC are similar.   (equiangular)

and $\dfrac{BC}{AC} = \dfrac{AC}{AD}$ ratio of corresponding sides.

So $m = -\dfrac{1}{n}$ or $m \times n = -1$.

Examiner's tip

The easiest way to find the gradient of a perpendicular line is to find the reciprocal of the gradient and change the sign.

Example 2 Find the equation of the line that is perpendicular to the line $y = 2x + 5$ and passes through the point $(2, 4)$.

The gradient of the given line is 2. So the gradient of any line that is perpendicular is $-\frac{1}{2}$.

The equation is $y = -\frac{1}{2}x + c$.
Substitute $x = 2, y = 4$.
                  $4 = -1 + c$ so $c = 5$.

The equation is $y = -\frac{1}{2}x + 5$, or $2y + x = 10$.

1. Find the gradient of the lines joining the points
    (a) (2, 4) and (3, 8)   (b) (3, −1) and (5, 7)
    (c) (−2, 1) and (2, −11).

2. What are the equations of the lines drawn in the diagrams?
    (a)

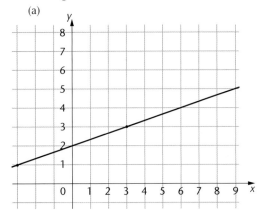

    (b)

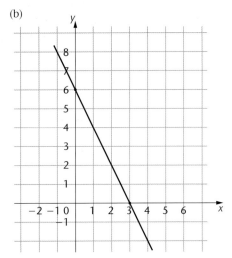

3. Find the equation of the lines through the points
    (a) (1, 6) and (4, 12)
    (b) (3, −1) and (5, −7)
    (c) (−2, −3) and (2, 5).

4. Find the equation of the line that is parallel to the line $y = x − 5$ and passes through the point (1, 4).

5. Find the equation of the line that is parallel to the line $y + 3x = 7$ and passes through the point (0, 3).

6. Find the equation of the line that is perpendicular to the line $y = 2x + 1$ and passes through the point (2, 3).

7. Find the equation of the line that is perpendicular to the line $2y + x = 9$ and passes through the point (1, 4).

8. Which of these lines are parallel or perpendicular:
    $$y = 4x + 3, \ 2y − 3x = 5, \ 6y + 4x = 1?$$

9. Two lines cross at right angles at the point (5, 3). One passes through the point (6, 0). What is the equation of the other line?

10.

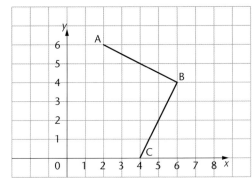

    In the diagram the lines drawn are two sides of a rectangle ABCD.
    Work out (a) the equation of the line AD
            (b) the equation of the line DC
            (c) the coordinates of D.

1. Find the gradients of the lines joining the points
   - (a) (1, 4) and (3, 5)
   - (b) (0, −1) and (2, 7)
   - (c) (−4, 3) and (−2, 11).
2. What are the equations of the lines drawn in the diagrams?
   - (a)

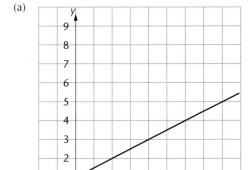

   - (b)

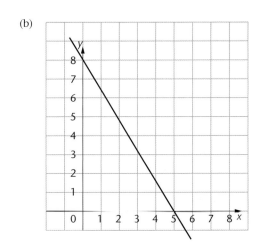

3. Find the equations of the lines through the points
   - (a) (1, 1) and (3, 9)
   - (b) (−3, 1) and (−5, −7)
   - (c) (2, −3) and (2, 5).
4. Find the equation of the line that is parallel to the line $y = 4x − 5$ and passes through the point (3, 4).
5. Find the equation of the line that is parallel to the line $2y + 5x = 9$ and passes through the point (3, −1).
6. Find the equation of the line that is perpendicular to the line $2y = x − 2$ and passes through the point (2, 3).
7. Find the equation of the line that is perpendicular to the line $3y + x = 9$ and passes through the point (0, 0).
8. Which of these lines are parallel or perpendicular:
   $$y + 4x + 3 = 0, 2y − 8x = 5, 4y − x = 1?$$
9. Mark axes from 0 to 8 for both x and y.
   - (a) (i) Draw the line passing through (0, 8) and (6, 0).
     - (ii) What is the equation of this line? Draw the parallel line that passes through (0, 6).
   - (b) Where does it cross the x-axis?
10. Three corners of a parallelogram are A (1, 6), B (3, 4) and C (5, 8).
    - (a) Find the equation of the line AD.
    - (b) Without drawing the graph, work out the coordinates of the point D.

Key points

- When solving two linear simultaneous equations the method of elimination or substitution can be used.
- When solving simultaneous equations involving a quadratic equation substitute for one letter from one equation to the other.

- The equation of a circle centre $(0, 0)$ radius r is $x^2 + y^2 = r^2$.
- When two lines are parallel they have the same gradient.
- When two lines are perpendicular the product of their gradients is -1.

Revision exercise 29a

1. Solve these equations by factorisation.
   (a) $x^2 + 4x - 12 = 0$
   (b) $3x^2 + 4x - 4 = 0$
   (c) $x^2 - 14x + 45 = 0$
   (d) $4x^2 - 9x = 0$
   (e) $2x^2 - 9x + 10 = 0$

2. Use the formula to solve the following. Give the answers to 2 d.p.
   (a) $x^2 - 4x + 1 = 0$
   (b) $2x^2 + 5x - 1 = 0$
   (c) $3x^2 + 9x + 2 = 0$

3. Simplify.
   (a) $\dfrac{x+1}{3} + \dfrac{x-2}{6}$
   (b) $\dfrac{4}{x+3} + \dfrac{2}{x-1}$
   (c) $\dfrac{x}{3x-1} - \dfrac{4}{3x+1}$

4. Solve
   (a) $\dfrac{4x}{5} - \dfrac{x}{2} = \dfrac{7}{10}$
   (b) $\dfrac{3}{x-2} = 5$
   (c) $\dfrac{4}{x-2} - \dfrac{1}{x-3} = 0$

5. Rearrange the formula to make a the subject.
   (a) $a - 2b = c$
   (b) $2a - 3c = 3b$
   (c) $3a - 2b = 2a$
   (d) $3a - 5c = 2b - 5a$
   (e) $3(a + 2b) = 2b + 5a$

6. Solve the simultaneous equations.
   (a) $x - 3y = 3$
       $x + y = 7$
   (b) $2x - y = 8$
       $3x + 2y = 19$
   (c) $3x + 2y = 13$
       $2x - 3y = 0$
   (d) $5x + 3y = 9$
       $3x - 5y = 2$
   (e) $4x + 3y = 5$
       $6x + 7y = 5$

7. (a) Draw the graphs of $y = x^2 - 2x + 3$ and $y = 4x + 1$, on the same grid. Use values of x from 0 to 6.
   (b) Use the graphs to solve simultaneously the equations $y = x^2 - 2x + 3$ and $y = 4x + 1$. Give the answers correct to 1 d.p.

8. (a) Draw the graphs of $x^2 + y^2 = 9$ and $y = x + 2$ on the same grid. Use a scale of 1 cm to 1 unit for both x and y.
   (b) Use the graph to solve simultaneously the equations $x^2 + y^2 = 9$ and $y = x + 2$. Give the answers correct to 1 d.p.

9. Solve these equations simultaneously.
   (a) $y = x^2 - 2x + 3$ and $y = 2x$
   (b) $y = 2x^2 - 3x + 3$ and $y = 3x - 1$
   (c) $y = x^2 - 4x + 5$ and $y + 4x = 6$
   (d) $x^2 + y^2 = 36$ and $y = x + 6$

10. Find the equations of the lines through the points
    (a) $(1, 0)$ and $(2, -3)$
    (b) $(-2, 1)$ and $(-3, -7)$,
    (c) $(4, 3)$ and $(5, 5)$.

11. Find the equation of the line that is parallel to the line $2y + x = 4$ and passes through the point $(0, 1)$.

12. Find the equation of the line that is perpendicular to the line $2y + x = 4$ and passes through the point $(1, 5)$.

Histograms and standard deviation 30

You will need to know:

- how to calculate the mean of a set of data
- how to calculate the mean for grouped data
- the meaning of the symbols $\leqslant$ and $<$.

Histograms

Histograms and bar charts are closely related.

- In a histogram the frequency of the data is shown by the area of each bar. (In a bar chart the frequency is shown by the height of each bar.)
- The data is continuous. (Bar charts can be for discrete data.)
- Histograms have bars, or columns, whose width is in proportion to the size of the group of data each bar represents – the class width – so the bars may have different widths. (In a bar chart the widths of each bar are usually the same.)
- The vertical scale is 'frequency density'.
  Frequency density = frequency ÷ class width. (In a bar chart the vertical scale is the actual frequency.)

 Example 1

An airline investigated the ages of passengers flying between London and Johannesburg.

The table shows the findings.

Age (A years)	Frequency
$0 \leqslant A < 20$	28
$20 \leqslant A < 30$	36
$30 \leqslant A < 40$	48
$40 \leqslant A < 50$	20
$50 \leqslant A < 70$	30
$70 \leqslant A < 100$	15

To draw a histogram you must first calculate the frequency density:

Age (A years)	Class width	Frequency (f)	Frequency density
$0 \leqslant A < 20$	20	28	$28 \div 20 = 1.4$
$20 \leqslant A < 30$	10	36	$36 \div 10 = 3.6$
$30 \leqslant A < 40$	10	48	$48 \div 10 = 4.8$
$40 \leqslant A < 50$	10	20	$20 \div 10 = 2$
$50 \leqslant A < 70$	20	30	$30 \div 20 = 1.5$
$70 \leqslant A < 100$	30	15	$15 \div 30 = 0.5$

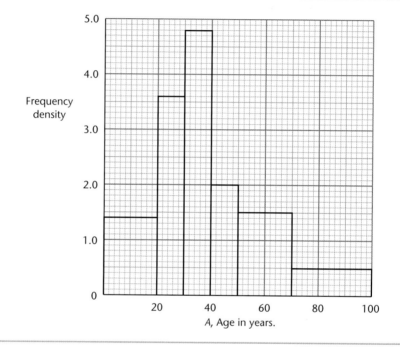

A, Age in years.

Exercise 30.1a

1. Two hundred commuters were surveyed to find the distances they travelled to work. The table shows the results. Draw a histogram to show this information.

Distance (d km)	Frequency (f)
$0 \leqslant d < 5$	3
$5 \leqslant d < 10$	9
$10 \leqslant d < 15$	34
$15 \leqslant d < 20$	49
$20 \leqslant d < 30$	17
$30 \leqslant d < 40$	41
$40 \leqslant d < 60$	27
$60 \leqslant d < 100$	20

2. The table shows the sizes of 48 marrows grown on an allotment.

Length (L cm)	Frequency (f)
$0 \leqslant L < 20$	4
$20 \leqslant L < 40$	6
$40 \leqslant L < 50$	13
$50 \leqslant L < 60$	11
$60 \leqslant L < 90$	14

Show this information on a histogram.

3. The table shows the results of a survey to find the areas, to the nearest hectare, of 160 farms.

Area (A hectares)	Frequency (f)
$1 \leqslant A < 4$	29
$4 \leqslant A < 8$	18
$8 \leqslant A < 12$	34
$12 \leqslant A < 16$	26
$16 \leqslant A < 24$	28
$24 \leqslant A < 30$	11
$30 \leqslant A < 34$	8
$34 \leqslant A < 40$	6

4. The manager of a shop recorded the number of customers in the shop between 9 a.m. and 9:30 a.m. on 50 Saturday mornings during one year.

4	6	11	4	12	5	18	3	10	4
9	3	13	8	15	0	6	7	1	7
28	5	23	1	39	14	33	2	7	2
16	30	13	1	17	7	41	3	22	1
18	24	38	8	3	26	41	0	43	9

After the shop had been redecorated and refitted he repeated the survey. (During this survey the shop was only open for 49 Saturdays.)

10	31	17	22	7	31	9	36	5	13
26	28	36	0	24	30	11	20	28	8
18	38	3	36	12	23	15	7	21	12
8	37	22	11	19	40	18	39	6	13
30	27	3	28	4	29	41	40	14	

(a) Choosing sensible class widths construct frequency tables for both sets of data and show them using histograms.

(b) Compare the two sets of data. What comments can you make?

1. The age of each person on a holiday coach tour is recorded. The table shows the results.

   Draw a histogram to show this information.

Age (A years)	Frequency (f)
$0 \leqslant A < 10$	0
$10 \leqslant A < 20$	2
$20 \leqslant A < 30$	3
$30 \leqslant A < 45$	8
$45 \leqslant A < 50$	5
$50 \leqslant A < 70$	18
$70 \leqslant A < 100$	12

2. A clothing manufacturer needs to know how long to make the sleeves of sweatshirts. 100 teenagers had their arm lengths measured. The results are shown in the table:

   Draw a histogram to show this information.

Arm length (L cm)	Frequency (f)
$40 \leqslant L < 45$	4
$45 \leqslant L < 50$	22
$50 \leqslant L < 55$	48
$55 \leqslant L < 60$	14
$60 \leqslant L < 70$	10
$70 \leqslant L < 80$	2

3. An insurance company records the ages of people who were insured for holiday accidents etc. during a two-week period in August.

   Draw a histogram to show this information.

Age (A years)	Frequency (f)
$0 \leqslant A < 5$	20
$5 \leqslant A < 10$	54
$10 \leqslant A < 20$	106
$20 \leqslant A < 30$	223
$30 \leqslant A < 40$	180
$40 \leqslant A < 60$	252
$60 \leqslant A < 90$	54

4. A forestry worker measures the diameters of a type of tree in two woods. His results are given in the table:

   (a) Draw histograms to show this data
   (b) What conclusions can you make about the trees?

Diameter (D cm)	Groves Wood frequency (f)	River Wood frequency (f)
$0 \leqslant D < 10$	11	18
$10 \leqslant D < 20$	13	12
$20 \leqslant D < 30$	34	28
$30 \leqslant D < 50$	48	28

If the information is already given in a histogram it is possible
to find out the frequencies and also estimate the mean.

This example shows how.

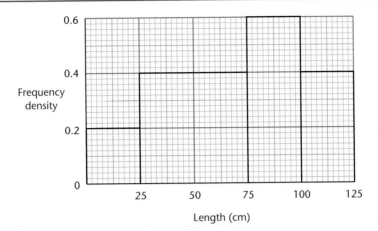

The frequency density = frequency ÷ column width.
The frequencies therefore are: $0.2 \times 25 = 5$
$$0.4 \times 50 = 20$$
$$0.6 \times 25 = 15$$
$$0.4 \times 25 = 10$$

The total frequency = 50.

The mean can be estimated using the midpoint of each class width.
$\Sigma fx = (5 \times 12.5) + (20 \times 50) + (15 \times 87.5) + (10 \times 112.5) = 3500$
Therefore $\bar{x} = \dfrac{3500}{50} = 70$

Exercise 30.2a

1. This histogram shows the
   ages of people who live in
   a small village.
   (a) How many people live
       in the village?
   (b) Estimate their mean age.

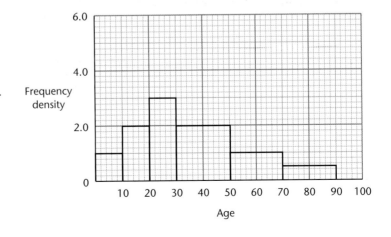

Exercise 30.2a continued

2. This histogram shows the distribution of the weights of all the people living in a street.
   (a) How many people live in the street?
   (b) What is their mean weight?

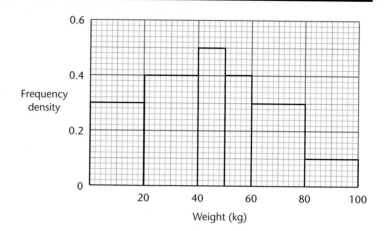

Exercise 30.2b

1. This histogram shows the results of a survey into the distance travelled by people going to work each day.
   (a) Find the number of people who were surveyed.
   (b) Calculate an estimate of the mean distance travelled to work.

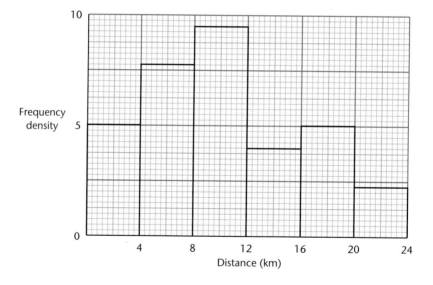

2. A survey of pupils in a school was made in order to find the times it took them to travel from home to school each morning. The survey was made on one particular day. The results are shown in the histogram.
   (a) Find the number of pupils surveyed.
   (b) Calculate an estimate of the mean travelling time.

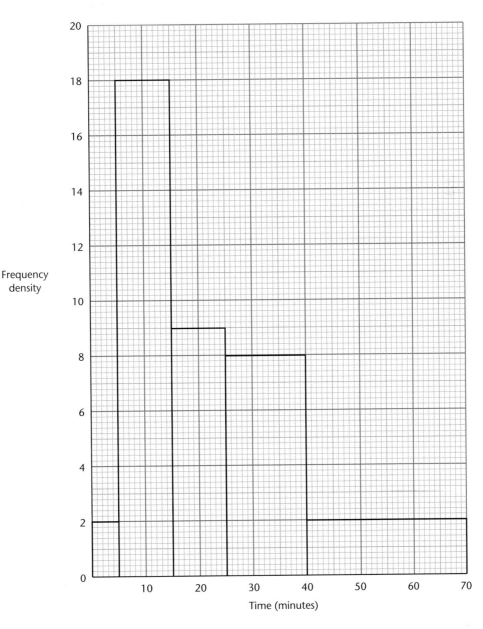

Frequency density

Time (minutes)

Standard deviation

As has been mentioned in earlier chapters you need to be able to interpret graphs and calculations using a range of appropriate techniques.

One technique of statistical analysis, which might prove useful, is the standard deviation. Remember, in Chapter 7, box-and-whisker plots were introduced as a diagrammatical method of illustrating, for example, interquartile range and the spread of a set of data. The standard deviation is a different and more sophisticated way of measuring the spread.

As the use of the standard deviation will not be tested in GCSE examinations, it is only briefly mentioned here with a description and examples. You may find the technique useful when comparing sets of data. If further information is required then you should refer to appropriate A-level textbooks.

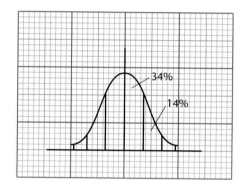

Approximately 68% of a normal population should lie within one standard deviation of the mean: that is 34% on either side. Within two standard deviations approximately 96% of the population should occur. The usual formula for calculating standard deviation is:

$$s = \sqrt{\frac{\Sigma(x - \bar{x})^2}{n}} \quad \text{an alternative form is: } s = \sqrt{\frac{\Sigma x^2}{n} - \left\{\frac{\Sigma x}{n}\right\}^2}$$

However if the standard deviation is calculated for a frequency distribution the formula is:

$$s = \sqrt{\frac{\Sigma f(x - \bar{x})^2}{n}}$$

The formula is best dealt with in a series of steps:
(i) subtract the mean, $\bar{x}$, from each value, x, in the data and square the result.
(ii) if necessary multiply by the frequency, f, that each value has.
(iii) add all the results, Σ, and divide by the number of entries in the data set, n.
(iv) find the square root.

Find the mean and standard deviation of the following set of numbers: 2, 3, 7, 9, 10, 12, 13.

The mean, $\bar{x} = \dfrac{\Sigma x}{n} = \dfrac{2 + 3 + 7 + 9 + 10 + 12 + 13}{7} = 8$

x	$(x - \bar{x})$	$(x - \bar{x})^2$
2	−6	36
3	−5	25
7	−1	1
9	1	1
10	2	4
12	4	16
13	5	25
		$\Sigma = 108$

Standard deviation, $s = \sqrt{\dfrac{\Sigma(x - \bar{x})^2}{n}} = \sqrt{\dfrac{108}{7}} = 3.93$ to 2 d.p.

To explain the significance of the standard deviation: if the numbers, 2, 3, 7, 9, 10, 12, 13 in the question represented people in a shop each day between 11:00 and 11:30 then the standard deviation of 3.93 i.e. 4 suggests that the number of people in the shop between these times would normally be within 4 of the mean. The mean is 8, so between 4 and 12 people will be in the shop.

This table shows the examination marks for the students in year 11. Calculate the standard deviation.

Mark (x)	Frequency (f)	(xf)*
$0 \leqslant x < 10$	2	10
$10 \leqslant x < 20$	4	60
$20 \leqslant x < 30$	7	175
$30 \leqslant x < 40$	13	455
$40 \leqslant x < 50$	26	1170
$50 \leqslant x < 60$	47	2585
$60 \leqslant x < 70$	52	3380
$70 \leqslant x < 80$	30	2250
$80 \leqslant x < 90$	19	1615
$90 \leqslant x < 100$	6	570
Totals	206	12 270

*Remember to use the mid-value; so for the mark band $0 \leqslant x < 10$ the mid-value is 5 and $xf = 5 \times 2 = 10$

$$\bar{x} = \dfrac{12\ 270}{206} = 59.56 \text{ to 2 d.p.}$$

Mark (x)	Frequency (f)	($x - \bar{x}$)	($x - \bar{x}$)^2	$f(x - \bar{x})^2$
$0 \leqslant x < 10$	2	-54.56	2976.8	5953.6
$10 \leqslant x < 20$	4	-44.56	1985.6	7942.4
$20 \leqslant x < 30$	7	-34.56	1194.4	8360.8
$30 \leqslant x < 40$	13	-24.56	603.2	7841.6
$40 \leqslant x < 50$	26	-14.56	212.0	5512.0
$50 \leqslant x < 60$	47	-4.56	20.8	977.6
$60 \leqslant x < 70$	52	5.44	29.7	1544.4
$70 \leqslant x < 80$	30	15.44	238.4	7152.0
$80 \leqslant x < 90$	19	25.44	647.2	12 296.8
$90 \leqslant x < 100$	6	35.44	1256.0	7536.0
			Total	65 117.2

$$s = \sqrt{\frac{\Sigma f(x - \bar{x})^2}{n}} = \sqrt{\frac{65\ 117.2}{206}} = 17.78 \text{ to 2 d.p.}$$

It is clearly more efficient to use the statistics function of your calculator. Check to see that your calculator will calculate the standard deviation and make sure you are familiar with its operation.

Key points

- Histograms represent frequency by the area of the columns

Revision exercise 30a

1. Draw a histogram to show the following distribution of the weights, to the nearest kilogram, of 50 year 9 pupils.

Weight (W kg)	Frequency (f)
$32 \leqslant W < 34$	1
$34 \leqslant W < 39$	5
$39 \leqslant W < 43$	7
$43 \leqslant W < 47$	8
$47 \leqslant W < 51$	14
$51 \leqslant W < 59$	9
$59 \leqslant W < 70$	6

2. This histogram shows the masses, in grams, of plums picked in an orchard.

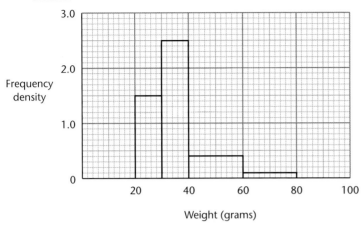

Weight (grams)

How many plums were picked?

3. The heights of students in two classes are measured. The results are given in the table below:

Class 11A

Height (H cm)	Frequency (f)
$130 \leqslant H < 140$	1
$140 \leqslant H < 150$	4
$150 \leqslant H < 160$	9
$160 \leqslant H < 170$	8
$170 \leqslant H < 180$	2
$180 \leqslant H < 190$	2

Class 11B

Height (H cm)	Frequency (f)
$120 \leqslant H < 130$	4
$130 \leqslant H < 140$	5
$140 \leqslant H < 150$	8
$150 \leqslant H < 160$	3
$160 \leqslant H < 170$	3
$170 \leqslant H < 180$	1

Show the data on two histograms.

31 Trigonometrical functions

Trigonometrical functions of any angle

You have already learned how to use the sine, cosine and tangent functions with angles up to 90°. With the sine and cosine rules, you have used sin and cos for angles up to 180°. However, if you enter any angle on your calculator, you will find it will give you a value for the sin, cos or tan of that angle.

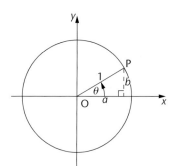

In this diagram, for an acute angle you can see that

$$\cos \theta = \frac{a}{1} \text{ so } a = \cos \theta$$

$$\sin \theta = \frac{b}{1} \text{ so } b = \sin \theta$$

$$\tan \theta = \frac{b}{a} = \frac{\sin \theta}{\cos \theta}$$

So P has coordinates $(\cos \theta, \sin \theta)$.

For other angles, the trig. functions are defined in a similar way, where the angle is measured anticlockwise from the x-axis.

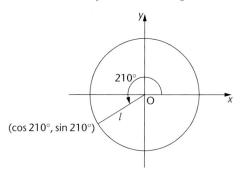

(cos 210°, sin 210°)

In this diagram you can see that $\cos 210°$ and $\sin 210°$ are both negative.

You can use symmetry to see that

$$\cos 210° = -\cos 30°$$

$$\sin 210° = -\sin 30°$$

$$\tan 210° = \frac{\sin 210°}{\cos 210°}$$

$$= \frac{-\sin 30°}{-\cos 30°} = \tan 30°,$$

so $\tan 210°$ is positive.

Continuing in a similar way we obtain these graphs.

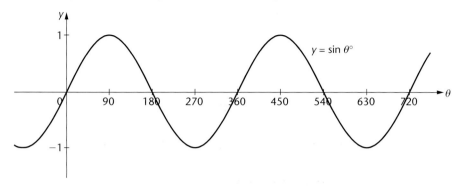

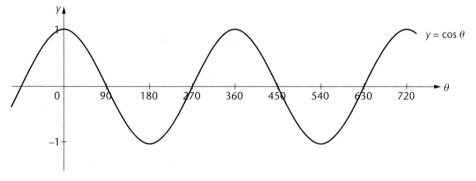

These graphs are both wave-shaped and repeat every 360°.
The 'length' of a repeating pattern is called the **period**. Here
the period is 360°.
For a wave, the amount it varies from its mean is called the
amplitude. For these graphs the amplitude is 1.

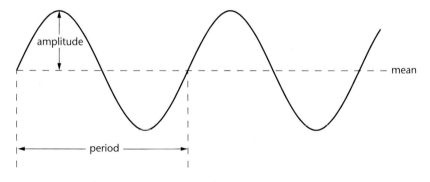

The graph of $y = \tan \theta$ has a different shape.

Since $\tan \theta = \dfrac{\sin \theta}{\cos \theta}$, there is a problem when $\cos \theta = 0$.

For instance, if you try using your calculator to find tan 90°,
you will get an error message. Try entering different angles
from 80°, getting closer to 90°, and you will see why.

The graph of $y = \cos\theta$ shows that $\cos\theta = 0$ when $\theta = 90°$, 270°, 450° etc, and the graph of $y = \tan\theta$ is discontinuous at these values.

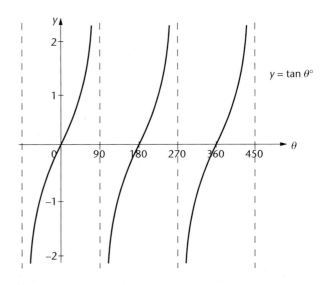

The graph of $y = \tan\theta$ is not a wave but does repeat. Its period is 180°. The graph approaches, but never meets, the lines $\theta = 90°$, $\theta = 270°$ etc. These lines are called **asymptotes** and are shown on the graph by dotted lines.

You may need to draw accurate graphs of these functions or to sketch their shapes, showing important values on the axes. The shape of the graphs can also help you to find the values of x that satisfy equations such as $\sin x° = 0.5$.

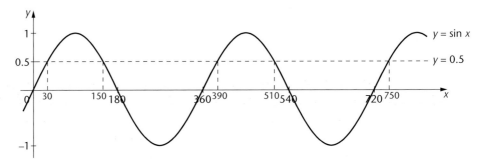

On the calculator, finding the inverse sine of 0.5 will give you the answer of 30°. However, the graph shows that there is an infinite number of solutions. Use the symmetry of the graph to see that −210°, 150°, 390°, 510° etc. are other solutions. You can use your calculator as a check to see that the sine of all these angles is 0.5.

Example ❶

Sketch the graph of $y = \cos x$ for values of x from 0 to 360°. Use the graph and your calculator to find two values of x between 0 and 360° for which $\cos x = -0.8$. Give your answers to 1 d.p.

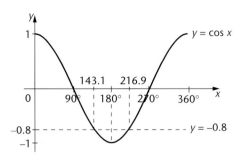

From the calculator, $\cos^{-1}(-0.8) = 143.1°$
$180 - 143.1 = 36.9$.
From the symmetry of the graph, the other solution is $x = 180 + 36.9 = 216.9°$.

Exercise 31.1a

1. Draw accurately the graph of $y = \sin x$ for values of x from 0 to 360°, plotting values every 10°. Use a scale of 1 cm to 20° for x and 2 cm to 1 unit for y.

2. Sketch the graph of $y = \cos x$ for values of x from $-180°$ to 360°. Use the graph and your calculator to find, to 1 d.p., the three solutions of $\cos x = 0.3$ between $-180°$ and 360°.

3. With the help of a sketch graph, or otherwise, find two solutions of $\tan x = -2$ between 0 and 360°. Give your answers to the nearest degree.

4. On the same diagram, sketch the graphs of $y = \sin x$ and $y = \cos x$ for values of x between 0 and 360°. State the values of x between 0 and 360° for which $\sin x = \cos x$.

5. One solution of $\cos x = 0.5$ is $x = 60°$. Without using a calculator, use the symmetry of the graph of $y = \cos x$ to find the four solutions of $\cos x = -0.5$ between 0 and 720°.

Exercise 31.1b

1. Draw accurately the graph of $y = \tan x$ for values of x from 0 to 360°, plotting values every 10°. Use a scale of 1 cm to 20° for x and 2 cm to 1 unit for y, scaling y from -4 to 4.

2. Sketch the graph of $y = \sin x$ for values of x from 0 to 540°. Use your graph and calculator to find four solutions of $\sin x = 0.8$. Give your answers to 1 d.p.

3. With the help of a sketch graph, or otherwise, find two solutions of $\sin x = -0.2$ between 0 and 360°. Give your answers to the nearest degree.

4. One value of x for which $\cos x = -0.3$ is 107°, to the nearest degree. Without using your calculator, find two other solutions of this equation between 0 and 540°.

5. One solution of $\tan x = 1$ is $x = 45°$. Without using a calculator, use the symmetry of the graph $y = \tan x$ to find the two solutions of $\tan x = -1$ between 0 and 360°.

Other trigonometrical graphs

If instead of plotting $y = \sin x$ you plot $y = 3 \sin x$, what difference does it make? Here are both these graphs plotted together.

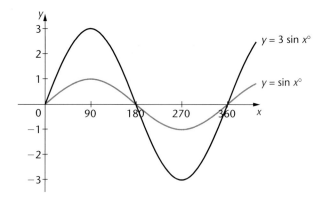

The period has stayed the same, 360°, but the amplitude has increased from 1 to 3.

Similarly the graph of $y = 5 \cos x$ has a period of 360° but an amplitude of 5.

The graph of $y = \cos 3x$ is different. $\cos 3x$ means $\cos (3x)$. Here are the graphs of $y = \cos x$ and $y = \cos 3x$ plotted together for comparison:

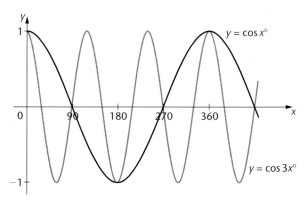

$y = \cos 3x$ has an amplitude of 1 but a period of $\dfrac{360}{3} = 120°$.

> The graphs of $y = a \sin bx$ and $y = a \cos bx$ each have amplitude a and period $\dfrac{360}{b}$.

Example 2 Sketch the graph of $y = 3 \sin 2x$ for $x = 0$ to $360°$. Find the solutions of $3 \sin 2x = 2$ between 0 and $90°$, giving your answer to 1 d.p.

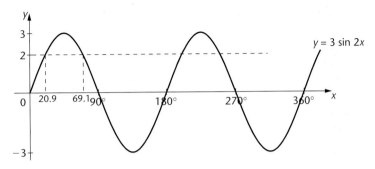

$3 \sin 2x = 2$

$\sin 2x = \dfrac{2}{3}$

From inverse sine function on calculator, $2x = 41.810°...$

$x = 20.9°$ to 1 d.p.

From the symmetry of the graph, the other solution is $90 - 20.9 = 69.1°$

Exercise 31.2a

1. Draw accurately the graph of $y = 2 \sin x$ for values of x from 0 to 180°, plotting values every 10°.

2. Draw accurately the graph of $y = \cos 2x$ for values of x from 0 to 180°, plotting values every 10°.

3. State the amplitude of
   (a) $y = 3 \sin x$ (b) $y = 4 \cos 2x$
   (c) $y = 2 \cos 0.5x$.

4. State the period of each of the graphs in question 3.

5.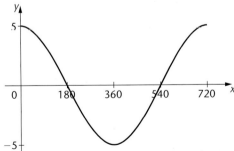

   This is part of the graph of $y = a \cos bx°$. State the values of a and b.

6.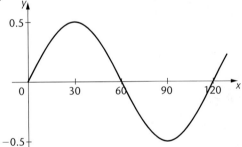

   This is part of the graph of $y = a \sin bx°$. State the values of a and b.

7. Sketch the graph of $y = \sin \frac{1}{2}x$ for values of x from 0 to 360°.

8. Find the four solutions of $\sin 2x = 0.5$ between 0 and 360°.

9. Find the solutions of $\cos 2x = 0$ for $0 < x \leqslant 360°$.

10. On the same diagram, sketch the curves $y = \cos 2x$ and $y = \sin x$ for $0 \leqslant x \leqslant 90°$. How many solutions of the equation $\cos 2x = \sin x$ are there for $0 \leqslant x \leqslant 90°$?

1. Draw accurately the graph of $y = 3 \cos x$ for values of x from 0 to 180°, plotting values every 10°.

2. Draw accurately the graph of $y = \sin 4x$ for values of x from 0 to 180°, plotting values every 10°.

3. State the amplitude of
   (a) $y = 5 \cos x$ (b) $y = 2 \sin 3x$
   (c) $y = 4 \sin \frac{1}{3}x$.

4. State the period of each of the graphs in question 3.

5.

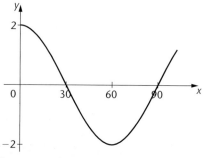

This is part of the graph of $y = a \cos bx°$. State the values of a and b.

6.

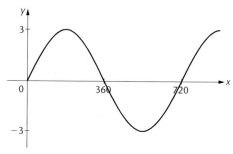

This is part of the graph of $y = a \sin bx°$. State the values of a and b.

7. Sketch the graph of $y = \cos \frac{1}{3}x$ for values of x from 0 to 540°.

8. Find all the solutions of $\cos 3x = -1$ between 0 and 360°.

9. Find the solutions of $2 \sin x = 1$ for $0 < x \leqslant 360°$.

10. On the same diagram, sketch the curves $y = \sin 3x$ and $y = \cos x$ for $0 \leqslant x \leqslant 90°$. How many solutions of the equation $\sin 3x = \cos x$ are there for $0 \leqslant x \leqslant 90°$?

Key points

- The shapes and main features of trigonometrical graphs:

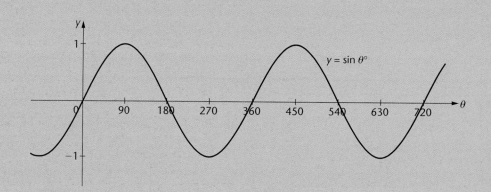

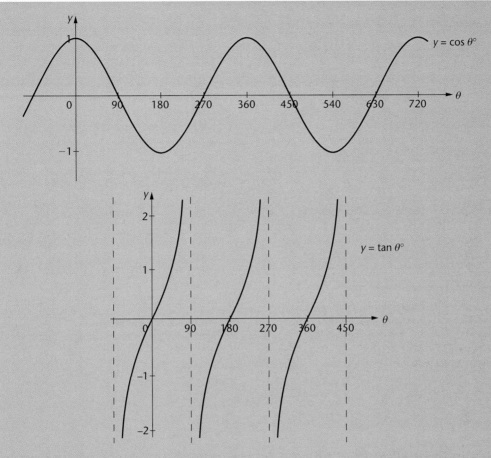

- Your calculator and the symmetry of these graphs help you to find solutions to trigonometrical equations.
- The 'length' of a repeating pattern is called the **period**. For a wave, the amount it varies from its mean is called the **amplitude**.

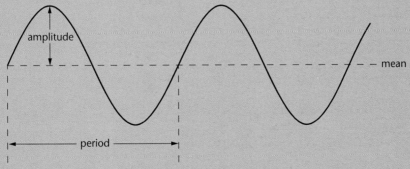

- The graphs of $y = a \sin bx$ and $y = a \cos bx$ each have amplitude a and period $\dfrac{360}{b}$.

1. Sketch the graph of $y = \tan x$ for values of x from $-90°$ to $450°$.

2. For what angles between 0 and 360° does $\tan x = 1$?

3. Sketch the graph of $y = \cos x$ for $0 \leqslant x \leqslant 360°$. Given that one solution of $\cos x = -0.8$ is $143°$ to the nearest degree, find the other solution between 0 and 360°.

4.

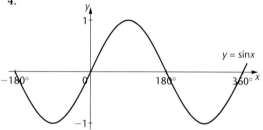

Given that one solution of $\sin x = -\frac{1}{2}$ is $x = -30°$, use the symmetry of this graph to find the solutions between 0 and 360°.

5. Using a calculator and sketch graph, or otherwise, solve the equation $\cos x = 0.2$ for $0 \leqslant x \leqslant 360°$.

6. Given that one solution of $\sin x = -0.4$ is 204° to the nearest degree, find the other angle between 0 and 360° which is a solution to this equation. Give your answer to the nearest degree.

7. On the same set of axes, sketch the graphs of $y = \cos x$ and $y = \cos 2x$ for $0 \leqslant x \leqslant 360°$.

8. For $0 \leqslant x \leqslant 360°$, for what values of x does $\sin 2x = 1$?

9.

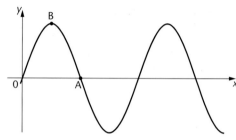

This is the graph of $y = 2 \sin 3x$. State the coordinates of A and B.

10. Sketch the graph of $y = 3 \cos 2x$ for $0 \leqslant x \leqslant 360°$.

Rational and irrational numbers 32

Rational numbers

To solve equations such as $\qquad x + 3 = 8$

the only set of numbers necessary is the set of **natural numbers**
1, 2, 3, 4, 5, ...

To solve equations such as $\qquad x + 8 = 3$

it is necessary to introduce negative numbers.

This gives the set of **integers** ... $-4, -3, -2, -1, 0, 1, 2, 3, 4, ...$

To solve equations such as $\qquad 4x = 3$ or $3x = 8$ or $-7x = 5$,

Numbers like $\frac{3}{4}, \frac{8}{3}, -\frac{5}{7}, ...$ need to be introduced.

These numbers are called **rational numbers**. A rational number is one that can be written as a fraction with integers as numerator and denominator.

As well as the obvious fractions, rational numbers include

Natural numbers $\qquad$ as, e.g. 5 can be written $\frac{5}{1}$

Integers $\qquad$ as, e.g. -6 can be written $-\frac{6}{1}$

Terminating decimals as, e.g. 3.24 can be written as $\frac{324}{100}$

Recurring decimals as, e.g. $0.\dot{6} = 0.66666...$ can be written as $\frac{2}{3}$.

Irrational numbers

What numbers are left?

To solve equations like $x^2 = 2$
numbers such as $\sqrt{2}$ need to be introduced.

$$\sqrt{2} = 1.414\ 213\ 562\ldots$$

This is a decimal that neither terminates nor recurs, so it cannot be written as a fraction.

A number such as this is called an **irrational number** as it cannot be written as a fraction with two integers. Its decimal will go on for ever without recurring.

Irrational numbers include:
(a) all non-exact square roots, e.g. $\sqrt{7}$ but **not** $\sqrt{16}$ or $\sqrt{\frac{1}{25}}$.
(b) special numbers that occur in mathematics. The only one that you have met so far is π, which is $3.141\ 592\ 654\ldots$ Another that is on your calculator but which you will not use unless you study mathematics beyond GCSE is 'e' which is $2.718\ 281\ 828\ldots$

It can be proved that $\sqrt{2}$ is irrational but that is not necessary at this stage.

The rational numbers include the natural numbers and integers and the irrational numbers are all those numbers that are not rational. These two sets comprise all the real numbers that you will need to use at GCSE.

Example 1

State which of these numbers are irrational.

(a) $\frac{3}{4}$ (b) $\frac{2}{3}$ (c) $\sqrt{11}$ (d) 2π (e) 3.142 (f) $-1\frac{1}{4}$

Clearly (a) and (b) are rational.
3.142, although an approximation to π is a terminating decimal and can be written as $\dfrac{3142}{1000}$

$-1\frac{1}{4}$ can be written as $-\frac{5}{4}$

The only two of these numbers that cannot be written as fractions are $\sqrt{11}$ and 2π, so these are irrational.

Recurring decimals and fractions

Fractions can easily be converted to decimals using the ÷ button on the calculator.

e.g. $\frac{5}{9} = 5 \div 9 = 0.555\,555... = 0.\dot{5}$

$\frac{256}{111} = 256 \div 111 = 2.306\,306\,306... = 2.\dot{3}0\dot{6}$

Converting recurring decimals to fractions is less straight forward. It may be worth remembering that, as above $0.\dot{5} = \frac{5}{9}$ and similarly $0.\dot{7} = \frac{7}{9}$ etc, but if more figures recur a more formal method is needed.

This method is illustrated in the following example.

Examiner's tip

The dots over the digits show how many recur. If it is more than two, only the first and last have a dot.

Example 2

Express $0.\dot{4}\dot{2}$ as a fraction in its lowest terms.

Let $r = 0.\dot{4}\dot{2} = 0.424\,242\,42...$

$100r = 42.424\,242\,42...$ Multiply by 100

$r = 0.424\,242\,42...$

$99r = 42$ Subtract

$r = \frac{42}{99} = \frac{14}{33}$

So $0.\dot{4}\dot{2} = \frac{14}{33}$

The method always works provided you multiply by the correct power of 10.
If one figure recurs multiply by 10.
If two figures recur multiply by 100.
If three figures recur multiply by 1000 and so on.

Example 3

Write $0.4\dot{2}0\dot{7}$ as a fraction in its lowest terms.

Let $r = 0.4\dot{2}0\dot{7} = 0.420\,720\,720\,7..$ NB three figures recur

$1000r = 420.720\,720\,720\,7...$ Multiply by 1000

$r = 0.420\,720\,720\,7...$

$999r = 420.3$ Subtract

$r = \frac{420.3}{999} = \frac{4203}{9990} = \frac{1401}{3330} = \frac{467}{1110}$

So $0.4\dot{2}0\dot{7} = \frac{467}{1110}$

For numbers such as $3.4\dot{2}0\dot{7}$ the three can be added at the end.

So $3.4\dot{2}0\dot{7} = 3\frac{467}{1110}$

Exercise 32.1a

1. State whether each of these numbers is rational or irrational, showing how you decide.
   (a) $\frac{17}{20}$ (b) 0.46
   (c) $\sqrt{5}$ (d) $\sqrt{169}$
   (e) 5π (f) 3.141 59
   (g) $-0.2\dot{3}\dot{4}$ (h) $5 + \sqrt{3}$
   (i) $-6\sqrt{2}$ (j) $\sqrt{\frac{4}{25}}$

2. Convert these fractions to recurring decimals using the dot notation.
   (a) $\frac{7}{11}$ (b) $\frac{3}{7}$ (c) $\frac{3}{70}$ (d) $\frac{23}{90}$ (e) $\frac{2079}{4995}$

3. Convert these recurring decimals to fractions or missed numbers in their lowest terms.
   (a) $0.\dot{2}$ (b) $0.4\dot{8}$
   (c) $0.2\dot{3}$ (d) $0.\dot{1}3\dot{2}$
   (e) $2.\dot{1}\dot{8}$

Exercise 32.1b

1. State whether each of these numbers is rational or irrational, showing how you decide.
   (a) 0.49 (b) $0.\dot{5}\dot{3}$
   (c) $\sqrt{324}$ (d) $\sqrt{27}$
   (e) $5\pi + 2$ (f) -2.718
   (g) $\frac{4\pi}{3\pi}$ (h) $2\sqrt{3} + \sqrt{5}$
   (i) $\sqrt{2} - 7$ (j) $\sqrt{1\frac{7}{9}}$

2. Convert these fractions to recurring decimals using the dot notation.
   (a) $\frac{7}{33}$ (b) $\frac{5}{13}$ (c) $\frac{5}{1300}$ (d) $\frac{17}{36}$ (e) $\frac{481}{1100}$

3. Convert these recurring decimals to fractions or missed numbers in their lowest terms.
   (a) $0.\dot{7}$ (b) $0.4\dot{3}$
   (c) $0.40\dot{2}$ (d) $0.23\dot{6}$
   (e) $0.\dot{1}23\dot{4}$

Simplifying surds

An irrational number like $\sqrt{3}$ or $6 + 2\sqrt{5}$ is called a surd.

Surds can often be simplified by using the result
$$\sqrt{(a \times b)} = \sqrt{a} \times \sqrt{b}$$

This result can be demonstrated using $\sqrt{36}$.
$$\sqrt{36} = 6 = 2 \times 3 = \sqrt{4} \times \sqrt{9} \quad \text{so} \quad \sqrt{36} = \sqrt{(4 \times 9)} = \sqrt{4} \times \sqrt{9}$$

 Example **4** Simplify $\sqrt{50}$.
$$\sqrt{50} = \sqrt{(25 \times 2)} = \sqrt{25} \times \sqrt{2} = 5\sqrt{2}$$

 Example **5** Simplify $\sqrt{72}$.

9 is a factor of 72 so $\sqrt{72} = \sqrt{9} \times \sqrt{8} = 3\sqrt{8}$,

but 4 is a factor of 8 so $3 \times \sqrt{8} = 3 \times \sqrt{4} \times \sqrt{2} = 3 \times 2 \times \sqrt{2} = 6\sqrt{2}$

Or if you spot straight away that 36 is a factor of 72:
$$\sqrt{72} = \sqrt{(36 \times 2)} = \sqrt{36} \times \sqrt{2} = 6\sqrt{2}$$

Look for as large a factor of the number as possible which has an exact square root. In examples 4 and 5 they are 25 and 36 respectively.

Example 6

Simplify $\sqrt{12} \times \sqrt{27}$

Method 1 $\sqrt{12} = \sqrt{(4 \times 3)} = \sqrt{4} \times \sqrt{3} = 2 \times \sqrt{3}$

$\sqrt{27} = \sqrt{(9 \times 3)} = \sqrt{9} \times \sqrt{3} = 3 \times \sqrt{3}$

So $\sqrt{12} \times \sqrt{27} = 2 \times \sqrt{3} \times 3 \times \sqrt{3} = 2 \times 3 \times \sqrt{3} \times \sqrt{3} = 6 \times 3 = 18$

Method 2 $\sqrt{12} \times \sqrt{27} = \sqrt{(12 \times 27)} = \sqrt{324} = 18$

Although method 2 is probably easier if you have a calculator, method 1 is probably easier if the question comes on the non-calculator paper.

Note that, by definition of what we mean by a square root, $\sqrt{a} \times \sqrt{a} = a$.

This example also illustrates the fact that the product of two irrational numbers can be rational.

Manipulation of numbers like $a + b\sqrt{c}$

A number like $2 + \sqrt{3}$ which is the sum of a rational number and an irrational number is irrational.

This is because $2 + 1.732\,050\,808... = 3.732\,050\,808...$ which is itself a decimal which goes on for ever without recurring and so is irrational.

These numbers can be manipulated using the ordinary rules of algebra and arithmetic.

Example 7

If $x = 5 + \sqrt{3}$ and $y = 3 - 2\sqrt{3}$, simplify
(a) $x + y$ (b) $x - y$ (c) xy

(a) $x + y = 5 + \sqrt{3} + 3 - 2\sqrt{3} = 5 + 3 + \sqrt{3} - 2\sqrt{3} = 8 - \sqrt{3}$

(b) $x - y = 5 + \sqrt{3} - (3 - 2\sqrt{3}) = 5 + \sqrt{3} - 3 + 2\sqrt{3} = 5 - 3 + \sqrt{3} + 2\sqrt{3} = 2 + 3\sqrt{3}$

These two results illustrate the fact that, when adding and subtracting these numbers, you can deal with the rational and irrational parts separately.

(c) $xy = (5 + \sqrt{3})(3 - 2\sqrt{3}) = 15 - 10\sqrt{3} + 3\sqrt{3} - 2 \times \sqrt{3} \times \sqrt{3}$

$= 15 - 2 \times 3 - 10\sqrt{3} + 3\sqrt{3}$

$= 9 - 7\sqrt{3}$

Chapter 32 Manipulation of numbers like $a + b\sqrt{c}$

If $x = 5 + \sqrt{2}$ and $y = 3 - \sqrt{2}$, simplify

(a) $x + y$ (b) y^2

(a) $x + y = 5 + \sqrt{2} + 3 - \sqrt{2} = 5 + 3 + \sqrt{2} - \sqrt{2} = 8$

Note that this result indicates that it is possible for the sum of two irrational numbers to be rational.

(b) $y^2 = (3 - \sqrt{2})^2 = (3 - \sqrt{2})(3 - \sqrt{2})$
$$= 9 - 3\sqrt{2} - 3\sqrt{2} + \sqrt{2} \times \sqrt{2}$$
$$= 9 + 2 - 6\sqrt{2}$$
$$= 11 - 6\sqrt{2}$$

Note that this result is also an application of the algebraic result

$$(a - b)^2 = a^2 - 2ab + b^2$$

Rationalising denominators

When dealing with fractions it is often preferable to have the numerator as an irrational number rather than the denominator. This is particularly so when no calculator is available as it is far easier to divide a long decimal by a whole number rather than dividing a whole number by a long decimal.

It is possible, using the rules of fractions, to convert numbers with irrational denominators to ones with irrational numerators. The method is illustrated in the following two examples.

Rationalise the denominator in these irrational fractions

(a) $\dfrac{5}{\sqrt{2}}$ (b) $\dfrac{7}{\sqrt{12}}$

(a) Multiply the numerator and the denominator by $\sqrt{2}$. By the rules of fractions, since we have multiplied both the numerator and denominator by the same quantity, we have not changed the value of the fraction.

This gives $\dfrac{5 \times \sqrt{2}}{\sqrt{2} \times \sqrt{2}} = \dfrac{5\sqrt{2}}{2}$ and the denominator is now a rational number.

(b) First simplify the denominator and then repeat the process in part (a), this time multiplying by $\sqrt{3}$.

$$\frac{7}{\sqrt{12}} = \frac{7}{2\sqrt{3}} = \frac{7 \times \sqrt{3}}{2\sqrt{3} \times \sqrt{3}} = \frac{7\sqrt{3}}{2 \times 3} = \frac{7\sqrt{3}}{6}$$

Exercise 32.2a

1. Simplify the following, stating whether the result is rational or irrational.
   (a) $\sqrt{12}$
   (b) $\sqrt{1000}$
   (c) $\sqrt{45}$
   (d) $\sqrt{300}$
   (e) $\sqrt{75}$
   (f) $\sqrt{8} \times \sqrt{2}$
   (g) $\sqrt{20} \times \sqrt{18}$
   (h) $\sqrt{20} \div \sqrt{5}$
   (i) $\sqrt{80} \times \sqrt{50}$
   (j) $\sqrt{75} \times \sqrt{15}$

2. If $x = 4 + \sqrt{3}$ and $y = 4 - \sqrt{3}$, simplify
   (a) $x + y$
   (b) $x - y$
   (c) xy

3. If $x = 3 + \sqrt{5}$ and $y = 4 - 3\sqrt{5}$, simplify
   (a) $x + y$
   (b) $x - y$
   (c) x^2

4. If $x = 5 + 2\sqrt{3}$ and $y = 4 - 3\sqrt{2}$ simplify
   (a) $x\sqrt{3}$
   (b) x^2
   (c) y^2

5. Rationalise the denominator in these irrational fractions
   (a) $\dfrac{1}{\sqrt{2}}$
   (b) $\dfrac{2}{\sqrt{5}}$
   (c) $\dfrac{5}{\sqrt{7}}$
   (d) $\dfrac{11}{\sqrt{18}}$
   (e) $\dfrac{9}{\sqrt{20}}$

6. Simplify the following including rationalising the denominator
   (a) $\dfrac{6}{\sqrt{8}}$
   (b) $\dfrac{6}{\sqrt{300}}$
   (c) $\dfrac{12}{\sqrt{75}}$
   (d) $\dfrac{\sqrt{48}}{\sqrt{18}}$

Exercise 32.2b

1. Simplify the following, stating whether the result is rational or irrational.
   (a) $\sqrt{40}$
   (b) $\sqrt{54}$
   (c) $\sqrt{98}$
   (d) $\sqrt{800}$
   (e) $\sqrt{363}$
   (f) $\sqrt{27} \times \sqrt{3}$
   (g) $\sqrt{250} \times \sqrt{40}$
   (h) $\sqrt{108} \div \sqrt{12}$
   (i) $\sqrt{90} \times \sqrt{20}$
   (j) $\dfrac{\sqrt{60} \times \sqrt{20}}{\sqrt{12}}$

2. If $x = 5 + \sqrt{7}$ and $y = 3 - \sqrt{7}$, simplify
   (a) $x + y$
   (b) $x - y$
   (c) xy

3. If $x = 4 + \sqrt{11}$ and $y = 9 - 2\sqrt{11}$, simplify
   (a) $x + y$
   (b) $x - y$
   (c) x^2

4. If $x = 6 - 2\sqrt{5}$ and $y = 3 - 5\sqrt{3}$ simplify
   (a) $x\sqrt{5}$
   (b) $y\sqrt{3}$
   (c) x^2
   (d) y^2

5. Simplify $\sqrt{2}(5 + 3\sqrt{2})^2$.

6. Rationalise the denominator in these irrational fractions
   (a) $\dfrac{1}{\sqrt{7}}$
   (b) $\dfrac{3}{\sqrt{2}}$
   (c) $\dfrac{5}{\sqrt{11}}$
   (d) $\dfrac{7}{\sqrt{50}}$
   (e) $\dfrac{9}{\sqrt{32}}$

7. Simplify the following and write your answers with rational denominators.
   (a) $\dfrac{10}{\sqrt{5}}$
   (b) $\dfrac{15}{\sqrt{50}}$
   (c) $\dfrac{20}{\sqrt{32}}$
   (d) $\dfrac{\sqrt{12}}{\sqrt{20}}$

Key points

- A rational number is a number which can be written as a ratio or fraction with both numerator and denominator as integers.

- An irrational number is a number which cannot be written as a ratio or fraction with both numerator and denominator as integers. It is a number which, as a decimal, does not terminate or recur.

- Any recurring decimal can be written as a fraction.

- Surds can be simplified using $\sqrt{(a \times b)} = \sqrt{a} \times \sqrt{b}$.

- Numbers which are the sum of a rational part and irrational part $(a + b\sqrt{c})$ can be dealt with using the normal rules of algebra.

- To rationalise a fraction with an irrational denominator, multiply the numerator and the denominator by the surd that is in the denominator.
  e.g. $\dfrac{5}{2\sqrt{3}} = \dfrac{5}{2\sqrt{3}} \times \dfrac{\sqrt{3}}{\sqrt{3}} = \dfrac{5\sqrt{3}}{6}$

1. State which of these numbers are rational and which are irrational.
   (a) -1.6
   (b) $0.7\dot{3}$
   (c) $\dfrac{5\pi}{3}$
   (d) $7 + 2\sqrt{3}$
   (e) 1.414

2. Convert these fractions to recuring decimals using the dot notation.
   (a) $\dfrac{5}{11}$
   (b) $\dfrac{212}{999}$
   (c) $\dfrac{37}{495}$

3. Convert these recurring decimals to fractions or mixed numbers in their lowest terms.
   (a) $0.5\dot{4}$
   (b) $3.1\dot{4}\dot{7}$
   (c) $0.\dot{2}03\dot{4}$

Questions 4–8 should be done without a calculator.

4. Simplify.
   (a) $\sqrt{32}$
   (b) $\sqrt{150}$
   (c) $\sqrt{128}$
   (d) $\sqrt{12} \times \sqrt{75}$
   (e) $\sqrt{10} \times \sqrt{18}$
   (f) $\sqrt{72} \div 3$
   (g) $\sqrt{288} \times \sqrt{48}$

5. If $x = 3 + \sqrt{7}$ and $y = 5 - 4\sqrt{7}$, simplify:
   (a) $x + y$
   (b) $x - y$
   (c) xy

6. If $x = 5 + 2\sqrt{3}$ and $y = 5 - 2\sqrt{3}$ simplify:
   (a) x^2
   (b) y^2
   (c) xy

7. Simplify $\sqrt{10}(5 + 2\sqrt{10})^2$.

8. Rationalise the denominator in the following, simplifying where possible.
   (a) $\dfrac{11}{\sqrt{2}}$
   (b) $\dfrac{15}{\sqrt{12}}$
   (c) $\dfrac{6}{\sqrt{27}}$

- the basic transformations of reflections and translations
- how to find the equation of a straight line
- how to use function notation
- the shapes of basic graphs such as $y = x^2$, $y = x^3$, $y = \sin x$

Function notation

$y = f(x)$ means that y is a function of x.

If $y = 4x - 3$ then $f(x) = 4x - 3$.

$f(2)$ means the value of the function when $x = 2$. In this case, $f(2) = 4 \times 2 - 3 = 5$.

Function notation is a useful shorthand when several different functions are being described. As well as $f(x)$, $g(x)$ and $h(x)$ are commonly used to describe functions.

Example 1 If $f(x) = 3x^2 - 5$, find (a) $f(2)$ (b) $f(-1)$

(a) $f(2) = 3 \times 2^2 - 5 = 7$
(b) $f(-1) = 3 \times (-1)^2 - 5 = -2$

Example 2 If $g(x) = 5x + 6$, (a) solve $g(x) = 8$
(b) write an expression for (i) $g(3x)$, (ii) $3g(x)$.

(a) $g(x) = 8$
       $5x + 6 = 8$
       $5x = 2$
       $x = 0.4$
(b) (i) $g(3x) = 5(3x) + 6 = 15x + 6$
    (ii) $3g(x) = 3(5x + 6) = 15x + 18$

Exercise 33.1a

1. If $f(x) = 2x - 7$, find the values of
   (a) $f(4)$ (b) $f(-5)$

2. If $f(x) = x^2 - 5x + 6$
   (a) find the values of (i) $f(0)$ (ii) $f(8)$
   (b) solve by factorisation the equation $f(x) = 0$

3. $f(x) = 4x + 5$ and $h(x) = 8x - 2$.
   (a) Find the values of $f(10)$ and $h(10)$,
   (b) solve $f(x) = h(x)$.

4. $f(x) = 9x - 1$. Write expressions for
   (a) $f(2x)$ (b) $3f(x)$ (c) $f(x) + 5$

5. If $g(x) = \cos x + 2$, write in the form
   $a \cos bx + c$, expressions for:
   (a) $g(x) + 1$ (b) $3g(x)$ (c) $g(2x)$ (d) $5g(3x)$

Exercise 33.1b

1. If $f(x) = 5x + 3$, find the values of
   (a) $f(4)$ (b) $f(-2)$

2. If $f(x) = 2x^2 + 9x - 5$
   (a) find the values of (i) $f(0)$ (ii) $f(5)$
   (b) solve by factorisation the equation $f(x) = 0$

3. $f(x) = 6x + 1$ and $h(x) = 4x - 2$.
   (a) Find the values of $f(5)$ and $h(5)$,
   (b) solve $f(x) = h(x)$.

4. $f(x) = 5x + 2$. Write expressions for
   (a) $f(2x)$ (b) $4f(x)$ (c) $f(x) - 3$

5. If $g(x) = \sin 2x$, write in the form $a\cos bx + c$,
   expressions for:
   (a) $3g(x)$ (b) $g(3x)$
   (c) $g(x) + 4$ (d) $5g(x) - 3$

Translations

You already know that the graph of $y = 4x$ is a straight line through the origin with gradient 4. The graph of $y = 4x + 3$ is a straight line with gradient 4 through the point (0, 3). You can think of this as a transformation by saying that the first graph has been translated by $\begin{pmatrix} 0 \\ 3 \end{pmatrix}$ to get the second.

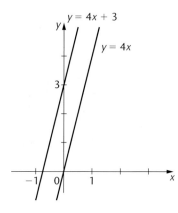

Similarly, the graph of $y = x^2 - 5$ is the same shape as the graph of $y = x^2$, translated by $\begin{pmatrix} 0 \\ -5 \end{pmatrix}$.

The same thing is true for all families of graphs:

> The graph of $y = f(x) + a$ is the graph of $y = f(x)$ translated by $\begin{pmatrix} 0 \\ a \end{pmatrix}$.

Translating parallel to the x-axis, a different pattern emerges.

The equation $(x - 2)^2 = 0$ has root $x = 2$.
Looking at the graphs of $y = x^2$ and $y = (x - 2)^2$,

it is clear that $y = x^2$ has been translated by $\begin{pmatrix} 2 \\ 0 \end{pmatrix}$.

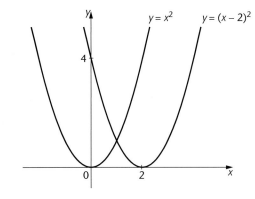

In general:

> The graph of $y = f(x - a)$ is the graph of
> $y = f(x)$ translated by $\begin{pmatrix} a \\ 0 \end{pmatrix}$.

> **Examiner's tip**
>
> It is not necessary to learn all these and the later results. You must understand them so that you can work them out when needed.

Example 3

State the equation of the sine curve drawn here.

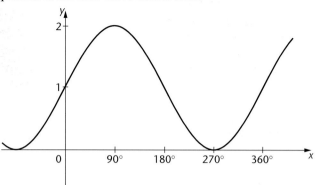

The curve of $y = \sin x$ has been translated by $\begin{pmatrix} 0 \\ 1 \end{pmatrix}$.
So its equation is $y = \sin x + 1$.

Example 4

The graph shows $y = f(x)$.
Sketch on the same diagram
the graphs of
(a) $y = f(x) + 3$.
(b) $y = f(x + 3)$

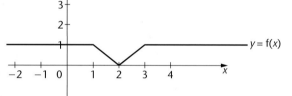

(a) is a translation of
the graph of $y = f(x)$
by $\begin{pmatrix} 0 \\ 3 \end{pmatrix}$.

(b) is a translation of
the graph of $y = f(x)$
by $\begin{pmatrix} -3 \\ 0 \end{pmatrix}$.

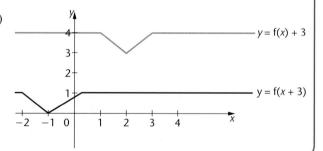

Exercise 33.2a

1. Sketch on the same diagram the graphs of
   (a) $y = x^2$ and (b) $y = x^2 + 3$. State the transformation which maps (a) onto (b).

2. Sketch on the same diagram the graphs of
   (a) $y = x^3$
   (b) $y = (x + 2)^3$.
   What transformation maps (a) onto (b)?

3. Sketch on the same diagram the graphs of
   (a) $y = x^2$
   (b) $y = (x - 2)^2$
   (c) $y = (x - 2)^2 + 3$.
   What transformation maps (a) onto (c)?

4. Sketch the result of translating the graph of $y = \sin x$ by $\begin{pmatrix} 0 \\ -1 \end{pmatrix}$. State the equation of the transformed graph.

5. State the equation of the graph of $y = f(x)$ after it has been translated by
   (a) $\begin{pmatrix} 0 \\ -5 \end{pmatrix}$ (b) $\begin{pmatrix} -2 \\ 0 \end{pmatrix}$

6.

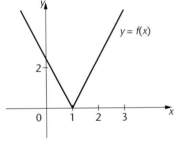

   This is the graph of $y = f(x)$. Sketch the graphs of
   (a) $y = f(x) - 2$ (b) $y = f(x - 2)$.

7.

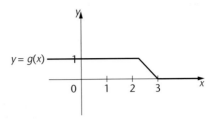

   This is the graph of $y = g(x)$. Sketch the graphs of
   (a) $y = g(x + 1)$ (b) $y = g(x) + 1$.

8. State the equation of the graph of $y = x^2$ after it has been translated by $\begin{pmatrix} 1 \\ 2 \end{pmatrix}$.

9. This graph is a transformed cosine curve.

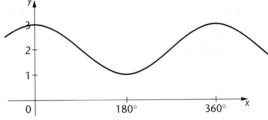

   State its equation.

10. The graph of $y = x^2$ is translated by $\begin{pmatrix} -2 \\ 3 \end{pmatrix}$.
    (a) State the equation of the transformed graph.
    (b) Show that this equation can be written as $y = x^2 + 4x + 7$.

Exercise 32.2b

1. Sketch on the same diagram the graphs of
   (a) $y = -x^2$ and   (b) $y = 2 - x^2$.
   State the transformation which maps (a) onto (b).

2. Sketch on the same diagram the graphs of
   (a) $y = x^3$ (b) $y = (x + 3)^3$.
   What transformation maps (a) onto (b)?

3. Sketch on the same diagram the graphs of
   (a) $y = x^2$ (b) $y = (x + 2)^2$
   (c) $y = (x + 2)^2 - 3$.
   What transformation maps (a) onto (c)?

4. Sketch the result of translating the graph of $y = \cos x$ by $\begin{pmatrix} 0 \\ 1 \end{pmatrix}$. State the equation of the transformed graph.

5. State the equation of the graph of $y = f(x)$ after it has been translated by
   (a) $\begin{pmatrix} 3 \\ 0 \end{pmatrix}$
   (b) $\begin{pmatrix} 0 \\ 4 \end{pmatrix}$

6.

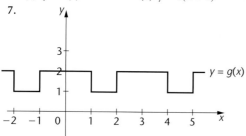

This is the graph of $y = f(x)$. Sketch the graphs of

(a) $y = f(x) - 2$ (b) $y = f(x + 2)$

7.

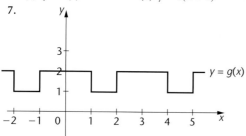

This is the graph of $y = g(x)$. Sketch the graphs of

(a) $y = g(x) - 3$ (b) $y = g(x + 0.5)$

8. State the equation of the graph of $y = x^3$ after it has been translated by $\begin{pmatrix} 3 \\ -4 \end{pmatrix}$.

9. This graph is a transformed sine curve.

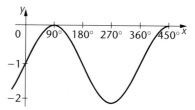

State its equation.

10. Show that the equation $y = x^2 - 6x + 1$ can be written as $y = (x - 3)^2 - 8$. Hence state the coordinates of the minimum point on the graph of $y = x^2 + 6x + 1$.

One-way stretches and reflections

In Chapter 31 you learned about the shapes of sine and cosine graphs.

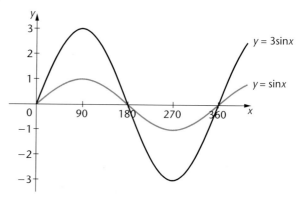

This diagram shows the graphs of $y = \sin x$ and $y = 3\sin x$.

To get from $y = \sin x$ to $y = 3 \sin x$, the graph has been stretched parallel to the y-axis with scale factor 3. This is an example of the general principle:

> The graph of $y = kf(x)$ is a one-way stretch of the graph of $y = f(x)$ parallel to the y-axis with scale factor k.

The next diagram shows the graphs of $y = \cos x$ and $y = \cos 2x$.

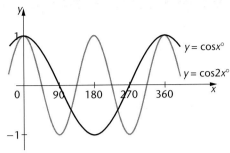

For the graph of $y = \cos 2x$ compared with the graph of $y = \cos x$, twice as much curve has been squashed into each part of the x-axis. This is described formally as a one-way stretch parallel to the x-axis with scale factor $\frac{1}{2}$. This is an example of the general principle:

> The graph of $y = f(kx)$ is a one-way stretch of the graph of $y = f(x)$ parallel to the x-axis with scale factor $\frac{1}{k}$.

When $k = -1$ in these one-way stretches, there is a much simpler way of describing the transformations: as reflections. For example, the graph of $y = -x^2$ is a reflection of $y = x^2$ in the x-axis.

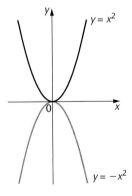

> The graph of $y = -f(x)$ is a reflection in the x-axis of the graph of $y = f(x)$.

Comparing the graphs of $y = x^3 + 1$ and $y = -x^3 + 1$ (or $y = (-x)^3 + 1$), you can see that one is a reflection of the other in the y-axis.

> The graph of $y = f(-x)$ is a reflection in the y-axis of the graph of $y = f(x)$.

Examiner's tip

Take care not to confuse $f(-x)$ with $-f(x)$.

Example 5

If $f(x) = x^2 + 2$, state in the form $y = ax^2 + bx + c$ the equation of
(a) $y = f(4x) + 2$ (b) $y = 3f(x)$

(a) $y = (4x)^2 + 2$
    $y = 16x^2 + 2$
(b) $y = 3(x^2 + 2)$
    $y = 3x^2 + 6$

Example 6

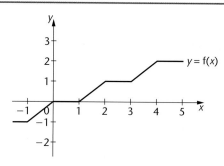

Assuming the graph of $y = f(x)$ continues in the same pattern, draw the graphs of
(a) $y = -f(x)$ (b) $y = 3f(x)$ (c) $y = f(2x)$

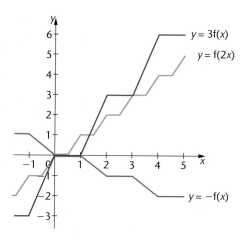

Exercise 33.3a

1. Sketch on the same diagram the graphs of
   $y = \cos x$ and $y = 2 \cos x$ for $0 \le x \le 360°$.
   Describe the transformation that maps
   $y = \cos x$ onto $y = 2 \cos x$.

2. Sketch on the same diagram the graphs of
   $y = \sin x$ and $y = \sin \frac{1}{2}x$ for $0 \le x \le 360°$.
   Describe the transformation that maps $y = \sin x$
   onto $y = \sin \frac{1}{2}x$.

3. Describe the transformation that maps $y = \sin x$
   onto $y = \sin 3x$.

4. Describe the transformation that would map:
   (a) $y = \sin x + 1$ onto $y = \sin (-x) + 1$
   (b) $y = x^2 + 2$ onto $y = -x^2 - 2$
   (c) $y = x^2$ onto $y = 3x^2$

5. The graph of $y = \cos x$ is transformed by a
   one-way stretch parallel to the x-axis with s.f. $\frac{1}{3}$.
   State the equation of the resulting graph.

6. State the equation of the graph of $y = x^2 + 5$
   after reflection:
   (a) in the y-axis
   (b) in the x-axis.

7. State the equation of the graph of $y = \frac{1}{x}$ after
   (a) a one-way stretch parallel to the y-axis
       with s.f. 3
   (b) a one-way stretch parallel to the x-axis
       with s.f. $\frac{1}{2}$.

8. Describe transformations to map $y = g(x)$ onto:
   (a) $y = g(x) + 1$ (b) $y = 3g(x)$
   (c) $y = g(2x)$ (d) $y = 5g(\frac{x}{3})$.

9. State the equation of the graph of $y = x^3$ after:
   (a) reflection in the x-axis
   (b) reflection in the y-axis
   (c) a one-way stretch parallel to the x-axis
       with scale factor 0.5.

10. The graph of $y = x^2$ is stretched parallel to the
    x-axis with scale factor 2.
    (a) State the equation of the resulting graph.
    (b) What point does (1, 1) map onto under
        this transformation?
    (c) (i) What is the scale factor of the stretch
             parallel to the y-axis which maps
             $y = x^2$ onto the same graph?
        (ii) What point does (1, 1) map onto
             under this transformation?

Exercise 33.3b

1. Sketch on the same diagram the graphs of
   $y = \cos x$ and $y = -\cos x$ for $0 \le x \le 360°$.
   Describe the transformation that maps $y = \cos x$
   onto $y = -\cos x$.

2. Sketch on the same diagram the graphs of
   $y = \sin x$ and $y = \sin 2x$ for $0 \le x \le 360°$.
   Describe the transformation that maps $y = \sin x$
   onto $y = \sin 2x$.

3. Describe the transformation that maps
   $y = \sin x$ onto $y = \sin \frac{1}{3}x$.

4. Describe the transformation that would map:
   (a) $y = \cos x + 1$ onto $y = -\cos x - 1$
   (b) $y = x^3 + 2$ onto $y = -x^3 + 2$
   (c) $y = x^2$ onto $y = 5x^2$.

5. The graph of $y = \sin x$ is transformed by a one
   way stretch parallel to the x-axis with s.f. $\frac{1}{4}$.
   State the equation of the resulting graph.

6. State the equation of the graph of $y = x^2 - 1$
   after reflection:
   (a) in the y-axis
   (b) in the x-axis.

7. State the equation of the graph of $y = \frac{3}{x}$ after
   (a) a one-way stretch parallel to the y-axis
       with s.f. 4
   (b) a one-way stretch parallel to the x-axis
       with s.f. 0.5.

8. Describe transformations to map $y = h(x)$ onto:
   (a) $y = h(x) - 2$ (b) $y = 3h(x)$
   (c) $y = h(0.5x)$ (d) $y = 4h(2x)$.

9. State the equation of the graph of $y = x^3 + 3$
   after:
   (a) reflection in the x-axis
   (b) reflection in the y-axis
   (c) a one-way stretch parallel to the x-axis
       with scale factor 0.5.

10. Use the shape of the graph of $y = \sin x$ to
    sketch on the same axes the graphs for
    $0 \le x \le 180°$ of
    (a) $y = \sin \frac{1}{2}x$
    (b) $y = 3 \sin \frac{1}{2}x$.

Transforming relationships to a linear form

When a graph is linear, it is easy to find its equation using $y = mx + c$, where m is the gradient of the graph and c its intercept on the y-axis. You have already seen this for experimental results in Chapter 27.

When a graph is not linear, it is much more difficult to find its equation, although transformations can help, as you have seen already in this chapter.

Example 7

The table shows the cost, £C, of circular tablecloths of various diameters d m.

d	0.5	0.6	0.9	1.2	1.5
C	2.80	3.24	5.04	7.56	10.80

Since the cost may be related in some way to the area of fabric used, it is suspected that a relationship of the form $C = ad^2 + b$ exists.
Draw a graph of C against d^2 and hence find C in terms of d.

d^2	0.25	0.36	0.81	1.44	2.25
C	2.80	3.24	5.04	7.56	10.80

The graph of C against d^2 is a straight line.

Gradient $= \dfrac{8.00}{2.00} = 4$

Intercept on y-axis $= 1.80$

So $C = 4d^2 + 1.80$

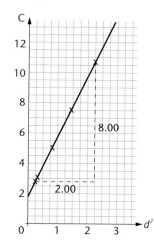

1. State the variables you would need to plot to obtain a straight-line graph of the following equations:
   (a) $y = 3.6x^2 + 5$
   (b) $V = 10d^3$
   (c) $C = 5\sqrt{m} + 3$.

2. Use these graphs to find the equations connecting the variables.

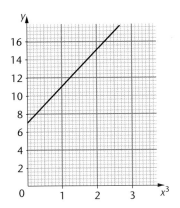

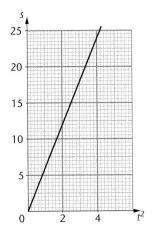

3. Find the equations of these graphs.

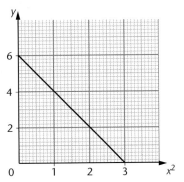

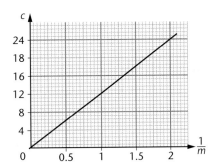

4. (a) Complete the missing row in this table of values.

x	2	5	6	9
x^2				
y	2	65	98	233

   (b) Plot a graph of y against x^2 and hence find the equation connecting y and x.

5.

t	1	2	3	4	5
y	3.0	4.7	7.8	12.1	17.4

   There is an approximate equation connecting y and t of the form $y = at^2 + b$. Plot the graph of y against t^2 and use your graph to estimate the values of a and b.

6. An equation of the form $x = at^3 + b$ connects the values in this table. Draw a suitable straight-line graph and obtain this equation.

t	1	1.5	2	2.5	3
x	6.4	7.35	9.2	12.25	16.8

1. State the variables you would need to plot to obtain a straight line graph of the following equations:
   (a) $s = 4t^3 + 6$
   (b) $A = \pi r^2$
   (c) $P = \dfrac{4}{x} + 3$.

2. Use these graphs to find the equations connecting the variables.
   (a)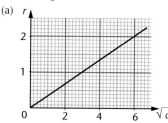

   (b)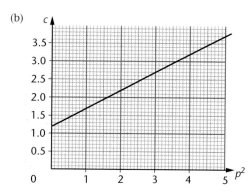

3. Find the equations of these graphs.
   (a)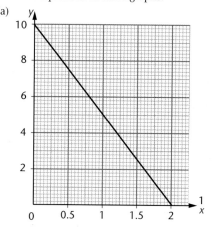

   (b)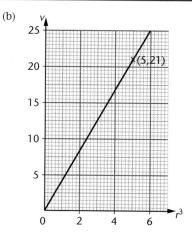

4. (a) Complete the missing row in this table of values.

x	1	2	4	5
$\dfrac{1}{x}$				
y	6	4	3	2.8

   (b) Plot a graph of y against $\dfrac{1}{x}$ and hence find the equation connecting y and x.

5.

x	1	2	3	4	5
C	-3	1.5	9	19.5	33

   There is an equation connecting C and x of the form $C = ax^2 + b$. Plot the graph of C against x^2 and use your graph to find the values of a and b.

6. By drawing a graph, or otherwise, calculate the values of a and b in the equation $y = ax^3 + b$ satisfied by the following values:

x	1	2	5	10
y	-37	-16	335	2960

Using functions to model problems

Exponential functions

These are functions of the form $y = ab^x$.
Since $b^0 = 1$ for any value of b, these graphs always go through $(0, a)$.

For a growth situation, such as a population of bacteria doubling each hour, an appropriate function is

$$y = 50 \times 2^x,$$

where y is the size of population, 50 is the number of bacteria present at the start of counting time, and x is the number of hours after the start.

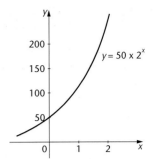

For a decay situation, such as a population of butterflies declining at 20% each year, an appropriate function is

$$y = 250 \times 0.8^x$$

where y is the size of population, 250 is the number of butterflies in the population at the start of counting time, and x is the number of years after the start.

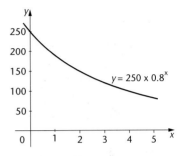

Using other functions

For some problems which involve repeating patterns, trigonometric functions are appropriate. For instance sine or cosine functions may be used to model the height of tides.

Example 3

The depth, h metres, of water in a tidal marina is modelled by the function
$$h = 2.5\cos 30t + 4.6$$
where t is the time in hours.

(a) Sketch one period of the function.
(b) According to this model, what is the time between successive high tides?
(c) What is the state of the tide when $t = 0$?
(d) What is the minimum depth of water in the marina?

(a)

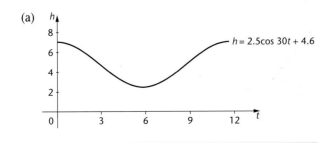

(b) 12 hours
(c) High tide
(d) $4.6 - 2.5 = 2.1$ m

Chapter 33 Using functions to model problems

1. (a) Complete the following table for a sum of money, £y, growing at 12% each year for x years.

x	0	1	2	3	4	5
y	500	560	627.20			

   (b) Using trial and improvement, or otherwise, solve the equation $500 \times 1.12^x = 750$, giving the value of x correct to 1 d.p.

2. (a) Draw the graph of $y = 2^x$ for $x = 0$ to 6.
   (b) Use your graph to find the value of x when $y = 200$.

3. The size y of a population of bacteria is growing according to the rule
   $$y = 25 \times 1.02^t$$
   where t minutes is the measured time.
   (a) How many bacteria are there at time $t = 0$?
   (b) Draw a graph to show the growth in the population during the first hour.
   (c) Use your graph to find how long it took the population to double in size.
   (d) What will the population be 5 hours after starting to measure the time?

4.  In 2000, the value of Bharat's stamp collection was £85. Assume the value increases at 5% each year.
   (a) What will be its value in 2004?
   (b) Write as simply as possible an expression for the value x years after 2000.
   (c) Find by drawing a graph or by calculation how many years it takes for the value of his stamp collection to double.

5.  A population of bats is declining at a rate of 15% each year. At the start of 2000 there were 140 bats.
   (a) Draw a graph to show the size of the population over the next 5 years.
   (b) How many years after the start of 2000 would the population consist of 80 bats? Give your answer to 1 d.p.

6. Use the shape of the graph of $y = \sin x$ to sketch the graphs of
   (a) $y = 2 \sin x$ (b) $y = 2 \sin x - 3$.

7. The height h metres of the water in a harbour is given by $h = 4 + 3\cos (30t)°$ where t hours is the time after high water.
   (a) What is the mean height of water in the harbour?
   (b) What is the minimum height of water in the harbour?
   (c) What is the value of t at the next high water?
   (d) A yacht can enter this harbour if the height of the water is at least 5.5 m. Between which values of t is this possible?

8. A cuboid has a square base of side x cm. The height of the cuboid is $(8 - x)$ cm.
   (a) Find a formula, in terms of x of the volume, V cm^3, of the cuboid.
   (b) Draw a graph of V against x for $x = 0$ to 8.
   (c) Use your graph to find the dimensions, to the nearest millimetre, which give the maximum volume for the cuboid.

9. The function $y = 3\sin (40x)°$ is used to generate a wave pattern for a fabric design, where y cm is measured from the centre of the pattern, and x cm is measured along the pattern.
   (a) What is the length of one repeat of the pattern?
   (b) What width does the pattern take up on the fabric?

10.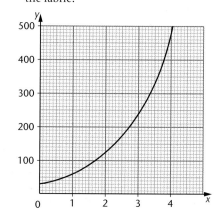

The graph shows a function of the form $y = ab^x$. Find the values of a and b.

1. (a) Complete this table for the function $y = 3^x$.

x	0	1	2	3	4	5
y						

   (b) Find the value of y when $x = 12$.
   (c) Using trial and improvement, or otherwise, find correct to 1 d.p. the value of x when $y = 6000$.

2. The number of bacteria in a colony doubles every 15 minutes. At the start of measuring time, there were 50 bacteria.
   (a) Complete the table to show the number of bacteria during the first 2 hours.

Time (hours)	0.25	0.5	0.75	1.0	1.25	1.5	1.75	2.0
Number of bacteria								

   (b) Draw a graph to show the number of bacteria in the colony during the first two hours.
   (c) Use your graph to find how long it took for the population to reach 4000.
   (d) Calculate the population after 6 hours. Give your answer in standard form, to 2 s.f.

3. The value of an investment is declining at a rate of 10% per year. Initially the investment was worth £2000.
   (a) Calculate how much it is worth after 4 years.
   (b) Calculate, by trial and improvement or otherwise, how long after the start the investment will be worth £1000, giving your answer in years correct to 1 d.p.

4. A population of bacteria is decreasing at a rate of 14% per hour. Initially it is estimated that there are 2000 bacteria.
   (a) Draw a graph to show the size of the population during the first 10 hours.
   (b) Use your graph to find the number of hours after which the population is 750.

5. Sketch the shape of the graphs of
   (a) $y = \cos 2x$ (b) $y = 3\cos 2x - 1$.

6.

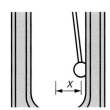

   A grandfather clock has a long pendulum. The distance, x cm, of the bob from the vertical position as it moves is given by
   $$x = 4\cos (180t)°,$$
   where t is the time in seconds.
   (a) Calculate to 1 d.p. the value of x when $t = 1.2$.
   (b) What does it mean when x is negative?
   (c) Sketch the graph of x against t for $t = 0$ to 2.
   (d) What is the greatest distance of the bob from the vertical?
   (e) What is the value of t when the pendulum is first vertical?

7. In an experiment, the values of x and y are connected by the formula $y = 5\sin 4x + 3.2$.
   (a) What is the maximum value of y?
   (b) Find a value of x for which $y = 7$, giving your answer to 1 d.p.

8. (a) Draw an accurate graph of the function $y = 4\cos 20x + 2$ for $0 \leqslant x \leqslant 18$.
   (b) Use your graph to find two value of x for which $y = -1$.

9. The curve of $y = ab^x$ passes through the points (0, 5) and (3, 20.48). Find the values of a and b.

10. Use graphical or other methods to find, correct to 1 d.p., the minimum value of the function $y = x^3 - 8x^2 + 12x$ for values of x between 0 and 6, and the value of x which gives this minimum.

Key points

- The graph of $y = f(x) + a$ is the graph of $y = f(x)$ translated by $\begin{pmatrix} 0 \\ a \end{pmatrix}$.

- The graph of $y = f(x - a)$ is the graph of $y = f(x)$ translated by $\begin{pmatrix} a \\ 0 \end{pmatrix}$.

- The graph of $y = kf(x)$ is a one-way stretch of the graph of $y = f(x)$ parallel to the y-axis with scale factor k.

- The graph of $y = f(kx)$ is a one-way stretch of the graph of $y = f(x)$ parallel to the x-axis with scale factor $\frac{1}{k}$.

- The graph of $y = -f(x)$ is a reflection in the x-axis of the graph of $y = f(x)$.

- The graph of $y = f(-x)$ is a reflection in the y-axis of the graph of $y = f(x)$.

- Transforming variables so that a linear graph can be plotted means the equation of the graph can easily be found.

- Exponential functions are functions of the form $y = ab^x$. Since $b^0 = 1$ for any value of b, these graphs always go through $(0, a)$.

Revision exercise 33a

1. $f(x) = x^2 - 2$. Find the values of
   (a) $f(6)$ (b) $f(-4)$.

2. $g(x) = 2 - 5x$. Write as simply as possible expressions for
   (a) $g(3x)$ (b) $4g(x)$ (c) $g(-x)$.

3. Describe the transformation which would map $y = g(x)$ onto the graph of
   (a) $y = g(3x)$ (b) $y = 4g(x)$ (c) $y = g(-x)$.

4. (a) Draw accurately the graph of $y = \sin(4x)$ for values of x from 0 to 100.
   (b) Find two values of x for which $\sin(4x) = -0.5$.

5. Sketch the graph of $y = \sin(x + 90)$. State the equation of this graph more simply.

6. State the equation of the graph $y = \cos x$ after
   (a) a translation of $\begin{pmatrix} 0 \\ 3 \end{pmatrix}$
   (b) a one-way stretch parallel to the x-axis with scale factor 0.25.

7. (a) A graph of y against x^2 is a straight line with a gradient of 3 and an intercept of -5. State the equation connecting y and x.
   (b) A graph of P against $\sqrt{t}$ is a straight line with a gradient of -3 and an intercept of 2. State the equation connecting P and t.

8. It is thought that x and y are connected by an equation of the form
   $$y = \frac{a}{x} + b.$$
   Given these experimental results, plot a suitable graph to enable you to draw a line of best fit and find the values of a and b.

x	2	4	6	8	10
y	11.4	10.4	10.0	9.8	9.7

9. The size y of a population of flies after t days is given by $y = 100 \times 1.2^t$.
   (a) What was the size of the population at $t = 0$?
   (b) What was the size of the population after 5 days?
   (c) Use numerical or graphical methods to find the number of days it took for the population to reach 1000, assuming this rate of growth continued.

10. The curve $y = ab^x$ passes through $(0, 10)$ and $(2, 6.4)$. Find the values of a and b.

A vector has both length and direction but can be in any position. The vector going from A to B can be labelled $\overrightarrow{AB}$, or it can be given a letter **a** in heavy type. When handwritten put a wavy line under a̰.

All the four lines drawn below are of equal length and go in the same direction and they can all be called **a**.

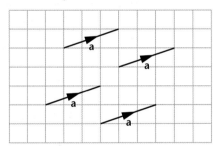

If you look at this diagram

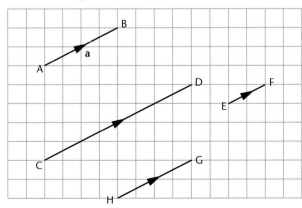

$\overrightarrow{AB} = \mathbf{a}$.

The line CD is parallel to AB and twice as long so $\overrightarrow{CD} = 2\mathbf{a}$.

EF is parallel to AB and half the length so $\overrightarrow{EF} = \frac{1}{2}\mathbf{a}$.

GH is parallel and equal length to BA (opposite direction to AB) so $\overrightarrow{GH} = -\mathbf{a}$.

Example 1

For the diagram below write down the vectors $\overrightarrow{CD}, \overrightarrow{EF}, \overrightarrow{GH}, \overrightarrow{PQ}$ in terms of $\mathbf{a}$.

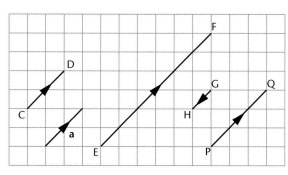

$\overrightarrow{CD} = \mathbf{a}$, $\overrightarrow{EF} = 3\mathbf{a}$, $\overrightarrow{GH} = -\frac{1}{2}\mathbf{a}$, $\overrightarrow{PQ} = \frac{3}{2}\mathbf{a}$.

Example 2

ABCD is a rectangle and E, F, G and H are the midpoints of the sides.
$\overrightarrow{AB} = \mathbf{a}$ and $\overrightarrow{AD} = \mathbf{b}$.
Write the vectors $\overrightarrow{BC}, \overrightarrow{CD}, \overrightarrow{AE}, \overrightarrow{AH}, \overrightarrow{EG}, \overrightarrow{CF}$ and $\overrightarrow{FH}$ in terms of $\mathbf{a}$ or $\mathbf{b}$.

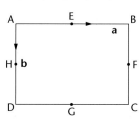

$\overrightarrow{BC} = \mathbf{b}$, $\overrightarrow{CD} = -\mathbf{a}$, $\overrightarrow{AE} = \frac{1}{2}\mathbf{a}$, $\overrightarrow{AH} = \frac{1}{2}\mathbf{b}$, $\overrightarrow{EG} = \mathbf{b}$, $\overrightarrow{CF} = -\frac{1}{2}\mathbf{b}$, $\overrightarrow{FH} = -\mathbf{a}$

Column vectors

If a vector is drawn on a coordinate grid, then it can be described by a column vector, $\begin{pmatrix} x \\ y \end{pmatrix}$, where x is the length across to the right and y is the length upwards.

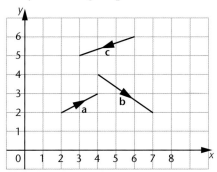

In the diagram $\mathbf{a} = \begin{pmatrix} 2 \\ 1 \end{pmatrix}$, $\mathbf{b} = \begin{pmatrix} 3 \\ -2 \end{pmatrix}$, $\mathbf{c} = \begin{pmatrix} -3 \\ -1 \end{pmatrix}$.

Examiner's tip

Column vectors must be columns. If you write them down as coordinates it will be marked wrong.

Example ③ Write down the column vectors for $\overrightarrow{AB}$, $\overrightarrow{BC}$, $\overrightarrow{CD}$, $\overrightarrow{AD}$, $\overrightarrow{BD}$ and $\overrightarrow{DC}$.

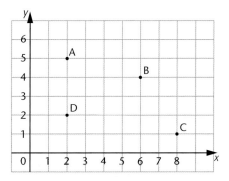

$$\overrightarrow{AB} = \begin{pmatrix} 4 \\ -1 \end{pmatrix}, \ \overrightarrow{BC} = \begin{pmatrix} 2 \\ -3 \end{pmatrix}, \ \overrightarrow{CD} = \begin{pmatrix} -6 \\ 1 \end{pmatrix}, \ \overrightarrow{AD} = \begin{pmatrix} 0 \\ -3 \end{pmatrix}, \ \overrightarrow{BD} = \begin{pmatrix} -4 \\ -2 \end{pmatrix}, \ \overrightarrow{DC} = \begin{pmatrix} 6 \\ -1 \end{pmatrix}.$$

Examiner's tip

In examinations, candidates often make an error of 1 when working out the values for the vector. Take care with the counting.

Translations

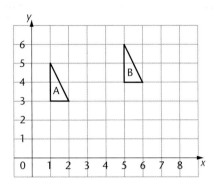

Previously you described the transformation that maps A onto B as 'A translation of 4 to the right and 1 up'. It can now be described as a translation with vector $\begin{pmatrix} 4 \\ 1 \end{pmatrix}$.

Example 4

For the diagram below
(a) describe the transformation that maps A onto B
(b) translate A by $\begin{pmatrix} 4 \\ -1 \end{pmatrix}$. Label the image C.

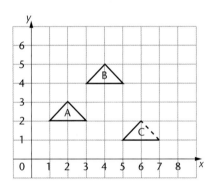

(a) The transformation is a translation by $\begin{pmatrix} 2 \\ 2 \end{pmatrix}$.

(b) C is on the diagram.

1. For the diagram below write down the vectors $\overrightarrow{AB}$, $\overrightarrow{CD}$, $\overrightarrow{EF}$, $\overrightarrow{GH}$, $\overrightarrow{PQ}$ and $\overrightarrow{RS}$ in terms of **a**.

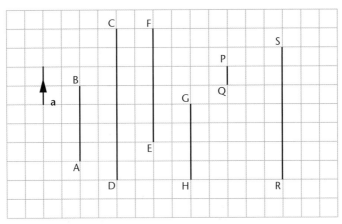

2. For the diagram below write down the vectors $\overrightarrow{AB}$, $\overrightarrow{CD}$, $\overrightarrow{EF}$, $\overrightarrow{GH}$, $\overrightarrow{PQ}$ and $\overrightarrow{RS}$ in terms of **a** or **b**.

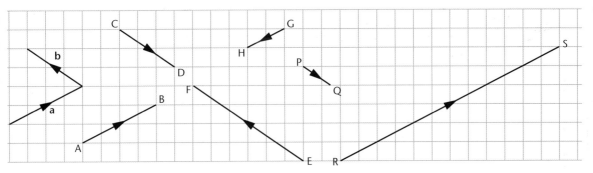

3. ABCD is a parallelogram. E, F, G and H are the midpoints of the sides. $\overrightarrow{AE} = $ **a** and $\overrightarrow{AH} = $ **b**.

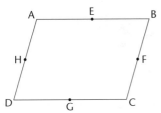

Write down the vectors $\overrightarrow{AB}$, $\overrightarrow{CD}$, $\overrightarrow{EB}$, $\overrightarrow{GD}$, $\overrightarrow{HF}$ and $\overrightarrow{FC}$ in terms of **a** or **b**.

4. Write down the column vectors for $\overrightarrow{AB}$, $\overrightarrow{CD}$, $\overrightarrow{CB}$, $\overrightarrow{AD}$ and $\overrightarrow{CA}$.

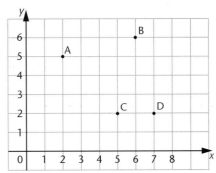

5. Write down the column vectors for $\vec{EF}$, $\vec{GH}$, $\vec{EH}$, $\vec{GF}$ and $\vec{FH}$.

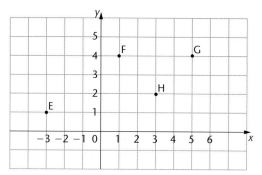

6. Translate the triangle A by

(a) $\begin{pmatrix} 2 \\ 1 \end{pmatrix}$ and label the image B,

(b) $\begin{pmatrix} 3 \\ -2 \end{pmatrix}$ and label the image C.

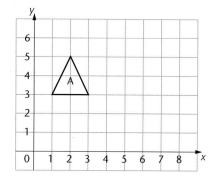

7. For the shapes in the diagram, describe fully the transformation that maps

(a) A onto B

(b) B onto C

(c) A onto C.

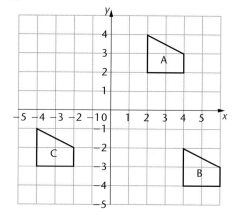

8. Find the column vector that maps

(a) (1, 2) to (1, 4)

(b) (2, 3) to (−2, 3)

(c) (1, 0) to (−1, 3)

(d) (4, 2) to (5, 9)

(e) (−3, 2) to (5, −4)

(f) (6, 1) to (0, 5)

Exercise 34.1b

1. For the diagram below write down the vectors $\vec{AB}$, $\vec{CD}$, $\vec{EF}$, $\vec{GH}$, $\vec{PQ}$ and $\vec{RS}$ in terms of **a**.

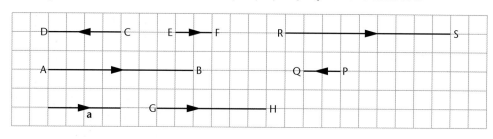

2. For the diagram below write down the vectors $\overrightarrow{AB}$, $\overrightarrow{CD}$, $\overrightarrow{EF}$, $\overrightarrow{GH}$, $\overrightarrow{PQ}$ and $\overrightarrow{RS}$ in terms of **a** or **b**.

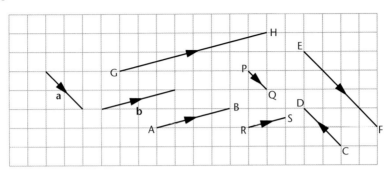

3. ABCD is a square. E, F, G and H are the midpoints of sides AB, BC, CD, DA respectively. $\overrightarrow{AB} = \mathbf{a}$ and $\overrightarrow{AD} = \mathbf{b}$.

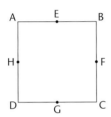

Write down the vectors $\overrightarrow{BC}$, $\overrightarrow{CD}$, $\overrightarrow{EB}$, $\overrightarrow{HD}$, $\overrightarrow{HF}$ and $\overrightarrow{FB}$ in terms of **a** or **b**.

4. Write down the column vectors for $\overrightarrow{AB}$, $\overrightarrow{BC}$, $\overrightarrow{CD}$, $\overrightarrow{AD}$ and $\overrightarrow{CA}$.

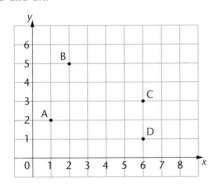

5. Write down the column vectors for $\overrightarrow{AB}$, $\overrightarrow{CD}$, $\overrightarrow{CB}$, $\overrightarrow{AD}$ and $\overrightarrow{CA}$.

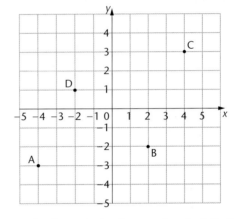

6. For the shapes in the diagram, describe fully the transformation that maps (a) A onto B (b) B onto C (c) C onto D (d) D onto A (e) D onto B.

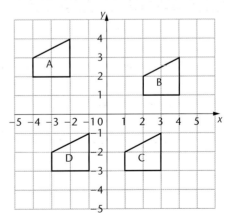

Exercise 34.1b continued

7. Translate the shape A by

(a) $\begin{pmatrix} 3 \\ 2 \end{pmatrix}$ and label the image B

(b) $\begin{pmatrix} -1 \\ 2 \end{pmatrix}$ and label the image C

(c) $\begin{pmatrix} 0 \\ -4 \end{pmatrix}$ and label the image D.

8. Find where the point is mapped by the vector.

(a) (1, 2) by $\begin{pmatrix} 3 \\ 2 \end{pmatrix}$ (b) (2, 3) by $\begin{pmatrix} 4 \\ 1 \end{pmatrix}$

(c) (1, 0) by $\begin{pmatrix} -3 \\ 2 \end{pmatrix}$ (d) (4, 2) by $\begin{pmatrix} 0 \\ -3 \end{pmatrix}$

(e) (−3, 2) by $\begin{pmatrix} -5 \\ -2 \end{pmatrix}$ (f) (6, 1) by $\begin{pmatrix} -6 \\ -1 \end{pmatrix}$

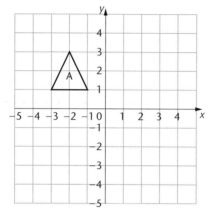

Combining column vectors

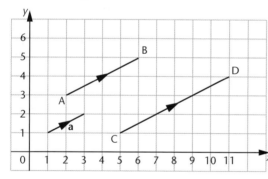

In the diagram you can see that
$\overrightarrow{AB} = 2\mathbf{a}$ and $\overrightarrow{CD} = 3\mathbf{a}$

$\mathbf{a} = \begin{pmatrix} 2 \\ 1 \end{pmatrix}$

$\overrightarrow{AB} = \begin{pmatrix} 4 \\ 2 \end{pmatrix} = 2 \times \begin{pmatrix} 2 \\ 1 \end{pmatrix} = 2\mathbf{a}$

$\overrightarrow{CD} = \begin{pmatrix} 6 \\ 3 \end{pmatrix} = 3 \times \begin{pmatrix} 2 \\ 1 \end{pmatrix} = 3\mathbf{a}$

This shows that $p \times \begin{pmatrix} a \\ b \end{pmatrix} = \begin{pmatrix} p\mathbf{a} \\ p\mathbf{b} \end{pmatrix}$

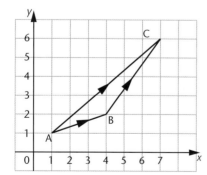

In this diagram you can see that
$\overrightarrow{AB} = \begin{pmatrix} 3 \\ 1 \end{pmatrix}$, $\overrightarrow{BC} = \begin{pmatrix} 3 \\ 4 \end{pmatrix}$, $\overrightarrow{AC} = \begin{pmatrix} 6 \\ 5 \end{pmatrix}$

$\overrightarrow{AC} = \overrightarrow{AB} + \overrightarrow{BC} = \begin{pmatrix} 3 \\ 1 \end{pmatrix} + \begin{pmatrix} 3 \\ 4 \end{pmatrix} = \begin{pmatrix} 6 \\ 5 \end{pmatrix}$

This shows that $\begin{pmatrix} a \\ b \end{pmatrix} + \begin{pmatrix} c \\ d \end{pmatrix} = \begin{pmatrix} a + c \\ b + d \end{pmatrix}$.

Example 5 Given $\mathbf{a} = \begin{pmatrix} 3 \\ 1 \end{pmatrix}$, $\mathbf{b} = \begin{pmatrix} 1 \\ 3 \end{pmatrix}$, $\mathbf{c} = \begin{pmatrix} -2 \\ 1 \end{pmatrix}$, work out the following

(a) $2\mathbf{a}$　　(b) $\mathbf{a} + 2\mathbf{b}$　　(c) $\mathbf{a} - \mathbf{b} + \mathbf{c}$　　(d) $2\mathbf{a} + \mathbf{b} - \mathbf{c}$　　(e) $\frac{1}{2}\mathbf{a}$.

(a) $2\mathbf{a} = 2 \times \begin{pmatrix} 3 \\ 1 \end{pmatrix} = \begin{pmatrix} 6 \\ 2 \end{pmatrix}$

(b) $\mathbf{a} + 2\mathbf{b} = \begin{pmatrix} 3 \\ 1 \end{pmatrix} + 2 \times \begin{pmatrix} 1 \\ 3 \end{pmatrix} = \begin{pmatrix} 5 \\ 7 \end{pmatrix}$

(c) $\mathbf{a} - \mathbf{b} + \mathbf{c} = \begin{pmatrix} 3 \\ 1 \end{pmatrix} - \begin{pmatrix} 1 \\ 3 \end{pmatrix} + \begin{pmatrix} -2 \\ 1 \end{pmatrix} = \begin{pmatrix} 0 \\ -1 \end{pmatrix}$

(d) $2\mathbf{a} + \mathbf{b} - \mathbf{c} = 2 \times \begin{pmatrix} 3 \\ 1 \end{pmatrix} + \begin{pmatrix} 1 \\ 3 \end{pmatrix} - \begin{pmatrix} -2 \\ 1 \end{pmatrix} = \begin{pmatrix} 9 \\ 4 \end{pmatrix}$

(e) $\frac{1}{2}\mathbf{a} = \frac{1}{2} \times \begin{pmatrix} 3 \\ 1 \end{pmatrix} = \begin{pmatrix} 1.5 \\ 0.5 \end{pmatrix}$

Examiner's tip

When combining column vectors be very careful with the signs as most errors are made in that way.

Exercise 34.2a

1. Work out

(a) $2 \times \begin{pmatrix} 2 \\ 3 \end{pmatrix}$　　(b) $\begin{pmatrix} 6 \\ 2 \end{pmatrix} + \begin{pmatrix} 3 \\ 1 \end{pmatrix}$　　(c) $\frac{1}{2}\begin{pmatrix} 4 \\ 6 \end{pmatrix}$　　(d) $\begin{pmatrix} 3 \\ 1 \end{pmatrix} - \begin{pmatrix} 2 \\ 1 \end{pmatrix}$　　(e) $\begin{pmatrix} 3 \\ 4 \end{pmatrix} + 2 \times \begin{pmatrix} 1 \\ 4 \end{pmatrix}$

2. Work out

(a) $2 \times \begin{pmatrix} -3 \\ 0 \end{pmatrix}$　　(b) $\begin{pmatrix} 3 \\ 1 \end{pmatrix} - \begin{pmatrix} 4 \\ 3 \end{pmatrix}$　　(c) $\frac{1}{2}\begin{pmatrix} 1 \\ -3 \end{pmatrix}$　　(d) $\begin{pmatrix} 2 \\ -1 \end{pmatrix} + 2 \times \begin{pmatrix} 2 \\ 1 \end{pmatrix}$　　(e) $\frac{1}{2}\begin{pmatrix} 1 \\ 4 \end{pmatrix} - \frac{1}{4}\begin{pmatrix} 2 \\ 4 \end{pmatrix}$

3. Given that $\mathbf{a} = \begin{pmatrix} 6 \\ 3 \end{pmatrix}$, work out

(a) $2\mathbf{a}$　　(b) $-\mathbf{a}$　　(c) $4\mathbf{a}$　　(d) $\frac{1}{2}\mathbf{a}$　　(e) $-\frac{1}{3}\mathbf{a}$.

4. Given that $\mathbf{a} = \begin{pmatrix} 1 \\ 3 \end{pmatrix}$, $\mathbf{b} = \begin{pmatrix} 3 \\ 4 \end{pmatrix}$, work out

(a) $3\mathbf{a}$　　(b) $\mathbf{a} + \mathbf{b}$　　(c) $\mathbf{b} - \mathbf{a}$　　(d) $2\mathbf{a} + \mathbf{b}$　　(e) $3\mathbf{a} - 2\mathbf{b}$.

5. Given that $\mathbf{a} = \begin{pmatrix} 2 \\ 3 \end{pmatrix}$, $\mathbf{b} = \begin{pmatrix} -3 \\ 4 \end{pmatrix}$, $\mathbf{c} = \begin{pmatrix} -1 \\ -3 \end{pmatrix}$ work out

(a) $3\mathbf{c}$　　(b) $4\mathbf{c} - 2\mathbf{b}$　　(c) $\mathbf{a} - \mathbf{b} + \mathbf{c}$　　(d) $2\mathbf{a} + 3\mathbf{b} + 2\mathbf{c}$　　(e) $\frac{1}{2}\mathbf{a} - \mathbf{b} - \frac{1}{2}\mathbf{c}$

1. Work out

   (a) $3 \times \begin{pmatrix} 1 \\ 4 \end{pmatrix}$
   (b) $\begin{pmatrix} 3 \\ 4 \end{pmatrix} + \begin{pmatrix} 5 \\ 8 \end{pmatrix}$
   (c) $\frac{1}{2}\begin{pmatrix} 8 \\ 10 \end{pmatrix}$
   (d) $2 \times \begin{pmatrix} 5 \\ 4 \end{pmatrix} - \begin{pmatrix} 3 \\ 4 \end{pmatrix}$
   (e) $2 \times \begin{pmatrix} 1 \\ 4 \end{pmatrix} + 5 \times \begin{pmatrix} 1 \\ 2 \end{pmatrix}$

2. Work out

   (a) $2 \times \begin{pmatrix} -1 \\ 0 \end{pmatrix}$
   (b) $\begin{pmatrix} 1 \\ 6 \end{pmatrix} - \begin{pmatrix} 7 \\ 3 \end{pmatrix}$
   (c) $\frac{1}{2}\begin{pmatrix} -2 \\ 4 \end{pmatrix}$
   (d) $\begin{pmatrix} 1 \\ -4 \end{pmatrix} - 2 \times \begin{pmatrix} 2 \\ 3 \end{pmatrix}$
   (e) $\frac{1}{2}\begin{pmatrix} 2 \\ 6 \end{pmatrix} - \frac{1}{2}\begin{pmatrix} 3 \\ -5 \end{pmatrix}$.

3. Given that $\mathbf{p} = \begin{pmatrix} 5 \\ 8 \end{pmatrix}$, work out

   (a) $4\mathbf{p}$
   (b) $-2\mathbf{p}$
   (c) $\frac{1}{2}\mathbf{p}$
   (d) $9\mathbf{p}$
   (e) $\frac{2}{5}\mathbf{p}$.

4. Given that $\mathbf{p} = \begin{pmatrix} 4 \\ 1 \end{pmatrix}$, $\mathbf{q} = \begin{pmatrix} 5 \\ 3 \end{pmatrix}$, work out

   (a) $2\mathbf{p}$
   (b) $\mathbf{p} + \mathbf{q}$
   (c) $\mathbf{q} - \mathbf{p}$
   (d) $2\mathbf{p} + \mathbf{q}$
   (e) $3\mathbf{q} - 2\mathbf{p}$.

5. Given that $\mathbf{a} = \begin{pmatrix} -2 \\ 4 \end{pmatrix}$, $\mathbf{b} = \begin{pmatrix} 3 \\ 5 \end{pmatrix}$, $\mathbf{c} = \begin{pmatrix} -2 \\ -3 \end{pmatrix}$, work out

   (a) $3\mathbf{c}$
   (b) $3\mathbf{c} + 2\mathbf{b}$
   (c) $\mathbf{a} - \mathbf{b} + \mathbf{c}$
   (d) $\mathbf{a} + 4\mathbf{b} - 2\mathbf{c}$
   (e) $\frac{1}{2}\mathbf{a} + \mathbf{b} - \frac{1}{2}\mathbf{c}$

Vector geometry

The resultant of two vectors

In the diagram, $\overrightarrow{OA} = \mathbf{a}$,
$\overrightarrow{OB} = \mathbf{b}$ and OACB is a
parallelogram.

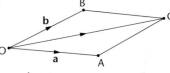

AC is parallel and equal to OB, so $\overrightarrow{AC} = \mathbf{b}$
$\overrightarrow{OC} = \overrightarrow{OA} + \overrightarrow{AC} = \mathbf{a} + \mathbf{b}$
$\overrightarrow{OC}$ is known as the **resultant** of $\mathbf{a}$ and $\mathbf{b}$.

You can also see that $\overrightarrow{OC} = \overrightarrow{OB} + \overrightarrow{BC} = \mathbf{b} + \mathbf{a}$
This shows that $\mathbf{a} + \mathbf{b} = \mathbf{b} + \mathbf{a}$, which shows that the vectors
can be added in either order.

In the diagram below A, B, C, D, E are marked.

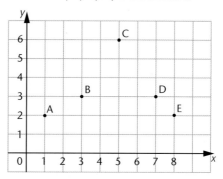

$$\overrightarrow{AB} = \begin{pmatrix} 2 \\ 1 \end{pmatrix},\ \overrightarrow{BC} = \begin{pmatrix} 2 \\ 3 \end{pmatrix},\ \overrightarrow{CD} = \begin{pmatrix} 2 \\ -3 \end{pmatrix},\ \overrightarrow{DE} = \begin{pmatrix} 1 \\ -1 \end{pmatrix},\ \overrightarrow{AE} = \begin{pmatrix} 7 \\ 0 \end{pmatrix}.$$

To get from A to E you can go direct or ABCDE. The direct vector is $\binom{7}{0}$.

ABCDE is $\overrightarrow{AB} + \overrightarrow{BC} + \overrightarrow{CD} + \overrightarrow{DE} = \binom{2}{1} + \binom{2}{3} + \binom{2}{-3} + \binom{1}{-1} = \binom{7}{0}$,

which is the same.

Another way is ABDE and you might like to show this again gives the same vector. In fact resultant vector $\overrightarrow{AE} = \binom{7}{0}$, no matter which way you go from A to E

This is a very important rule which is used to find vectors in geometrical figures.

Example 6

In the triangle ABC, $\overrightarrow{AB} = \mathbf{p}$, and $\overrightarrow{AC} = \mathbf{q}$, and D is the midpoint of BC.

Work out the vectors
(a) $\overrightarrow{BC}$ (b) $\overrightarrow{AD}$ (c) $\overrightarrow{AD}$.

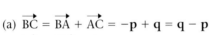

(a) $\overrightarrow{BC} = \overrightarrow{BA} + \overrightarrow{AC} = -\mathbf{p} + \mathbf{q} = \mathbf{q} - \mathbf{p}$
(b) $\overrightarrow{BD} = \frac{1}{2}\overrightarrow{BC} = \frac{1}{2}(\mathbf{q} - \mathbf{p})$
(c) $\overrightarrow{AD} = \overrightarrow{AB} + \overrightarrow{BD} = \mathbf{p} + \frac{1}{2}(\mathbf{q} - \mathbf{p}) = \mathbf{p} + \frac{1}{2}\mathbf{q} - \frac{1}{2}\mathbf{p} = \frac{1}{2}\mathbf{p} + \frac{1}{2}\mathbf{q} = \frac{1}{2}(\mathbf{p} + \mathbf{q})$

Examiner's tip

If you were just asked to find $\overrightarrow{AD}$ directly, it would be an example of a multi-step question and you would need to work out which other vectors to find.

Example 7

In this diagram OC = 2 × OA and OD = 2 × OB.
$\overrightarrow{OA} = \mathbf{a}$ and $\overrightarrow{OB} = \mathbf{b}$.
(a) Work out the vectors
    (i) $\overrightarrow{OC}$ (ii) $\overrightarrow{OD}$ (iii) $\overrightarrow{AB}$ (iv) $\overrightarrow{DC}$.
(b) What does this show about the lines AB and DC?

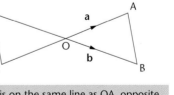

(a) (i) $\overrightarrow{OC} = -2 \times \overrightarrow{OA} = -2\mathbf{a}$ OC is on the same line as OA, opposite direction and twice as long.

    (ii) $\overrightarrow{OD} = -2 \times \overrightarrow{OB} = -2\mathbf{b}$ Same reasoning as above

    (iii) $\overrightarrow{AB} = \overrightarrow{AO} + \overrightarrow{OB} = -\mathbf{a} + \mathbf{b} = \mathbf{b} - \mathbf{a}$

    (iv) $\overrightarrow{DC} = \overrightarrow{DO} + \overrightarrow{OC} = 2\mathbf{b} - 2\mathbf{a} = 2(\mathbf{b} - \mathbf{a})$

(b) AB and DC are parallel and DC is twice as long as AB. This is because the vector for DC is twice the vector for AB.

1. On a square grid with x and y from 0 to 8, plot A (1, 3) and B (3, 5).

   (a) Write down $\overrightarrow{AB}$ as a column vector.

   (b) Mark any two points as C and D and work out

      (i) $\overrightarrow{AC} + \overrightarrow{CB}$ (ii) $\overrightarrow{AD} + \overrightarrow{DB}$

      (iii) $\overrightarrow{AC} + \overrightarrow{CD} + \overrightarrow{DB}$

   (c) What do you notice?

2. The vectors **a** and **b** are drawn on the grid. Draw the resultant of **a** and **b**.

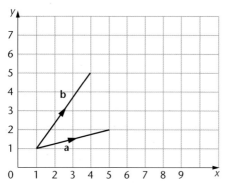

3. A is the point $(-2, 1)$, B is the point $(4, 3)$, C is the point $(7, 4)$.

   (a) Work out the column vectors (i) $\overrightarrow{AB}$ (ii) $\overrightarrow{BC}$.

   (b) What can you say about A, B and C?

4. In the triangle $\overrightarrow{AB} = \mathbf{a}$, $\overrightarrow{AC} = 2\mathbf{b}$. Find the vector $\overrightarrow{BC}$ in terms of **a** and **b**.

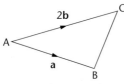

5. In this diagram $\overrightarrow{OA} = 2\mathbf{a}$, $\overrightarrow{OB} = \mathbf{a} - \mathbf{b}$, and $\overrightarrow{OC} = 2\mathbf{b} - 3\mathbf{a}$.

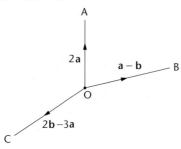

   Work out as simply as possible

   (a) $\overrightarrow{AB}$ (b) $\overrightarrow{BC}$ (c) $\overrightarrow{AC}$.

6. ABCD is a parallelogram, $\overrightarrow{AB} = \mathbf{a}$ and $\overrightarrow{AD} = \mathbf{b}$.

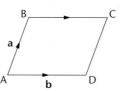

   Work out the vectors $\overrightarrow{BC}$, $\overrightarrow{CD}$, $\overrightarrow{BD}$, and $\overrightarrow{AC}$ in terms of **a** and/or or **b**.

7. In the triangle OAB, C is a point on AB so that AC = 2 × CB. $\overrightarrow{OA} = \mathbf{a}$ and $\overrightarrow{OB} = \mathbf{b}$.

   Work out the vectors $\overrightarrow{AB}$, $\overrightarrow{CB}$, and $\overrightarrow{OC}$ in terms of **a** and/or **b**.

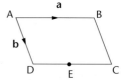

8. ABCD is a parallelogram. E is the midpoint of the line DC, $\overrightarrow{AB} = \mathbf{a}$ and $\overrightarrow{AD} = \mathbf{b}$.

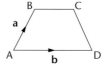

   Write down the vector $\overrightarrow{EB}$ in terms of **a** and/or **b**. (multi-step).

9. In the trapezium ABCD, AD is parallel to BC and AD = 2 × BC, $\overrightarrow{AB} = \mathbf{a}$ and $\overrightarrow{AD} = \mathbf{b}$.

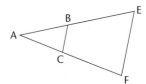

   Write down the vector $\overrightarrow{CD}$ in terms of **a** and **b** (multi-step).

10. Triangle AEF is a 3× enlargement of triangle ABC, $\overrightarrow{AB} = \mathbf{a}$ and $\overrightarrow{AC} = \mathbf{b}$.

   (a) Write down the vectors $\overrightarrow{AE}$, $\overrightarrow{AF}$, $\overrightarrow{BC}$ $\overrightarrow{EF}$ in terms of **a** and/or **b**.

   (b) What do the vectors show about BC and EF?

1. On a square grid with x and y from 0 to 8, plot A (2, 3) and B (3, 1).

   (a) Write down $\overrightarrow{AB}$ as a column vector.

   (b) Mark any two points as C and D and work out

   (i) $\overrightarrow{AC} + \overrightarrow{CB}$ (ii) $\overrightarrow{AD} + \overrightarrow{DB}$
   (iii) $\overrightarrow{AC} + \overrightarrow{CD} + \overrightarrow{DB}$

   (c) What do you notice?

2. The vectors **a** and **b** are drawn on the grid.

   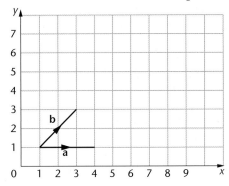

   Draw the resultant of 2**a** and **b**.

3. A is the point (2, 1), B is the point (4, 4), C is the point (7, 4), D is the point (3, −2).

   (a) Work out the column vectors
   (i) $\overrightarrow{AB}$ (ii) $\overrightarrow{CD}$.

   (b) What can you say about AB and CD?

4. In the triangle ABC, $\overrightarrow{AB} = 2\mathbf{a}$ and $\overrightarrow{CB} = 3\mathbf{b}$. Work out the vector $\overrightarrow{AC}$.

   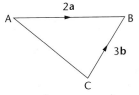

5. In this diagram $\overrightarrow{OA} = 2\mathbf{a}$ and $\overrightarrow{OB} = 2\mathbf{a} + 3\mathbf{b}$, $\overrightarrow{OC} = 3\mathbf{b}$

   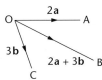

   (a) Write down the vectors $\overrightarrow{AB}$ and $\overrightarrow{BC}$ in terms of **a** and/or **b**.

   (b) What can you say about the shape OABC?

6. Work out the vector $\overrightarrow{AB}$ for this shape.

   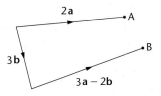

7. ABCD is a parallelogram. E, F, G and H are the midpoints of the sides. $\overrightarrow{AE} = \mathbf{a}$ and $\overrightarrow{AH} = \mathbf{b}$.

   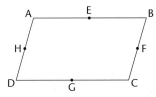

   (a) Write down the vectors $\overrightarrow{EB}$, $\overrightarrow{BF}$, $\overrightarrow{EF}$, $\overrightarrow{HD}$, $\overrightarrow{DG}$ and $\overrightarrow{HG}$ in terms of **a** and/or **b**.

   (b) What does this show about EF and HG?

8. OAB is a triangle with E a point on OA so that OE = 2 × EA. $\overrightarrow{OA} = \mathbf{a}$ and $\overrightarrow{OB} = \mathbf{b}$. Work out the vector $\overrightarrow{EB}$ in terms of **a** and/or **b** (multi-step).

9. ABCD is a kite. E is the point where the diagonals cross, BE = ED and CE = 3 × AE in length. $\overrightarrow{AB} = \mathbf{a}$ and $\overrightarrow{AD} = \mathbf{b}$.

   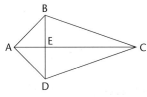

   (a) Work out the vectors $\overrightarrow{BD}$, $\overrightarrow{BE}$, $\overrightarrow{AE}$, $\overrightarrow{EC}$ and $\overrightarrow{BC}$ in terms of **a** and/or **b**.

   (b) Explain why the vectors show that BC is not parallel to AD.

10. In the triangle OCD, AC = 3 × OA and BD = 3 × OB. $\overrightarrow{OA} = \mathbf{a}$ and $\overrightarrow{OB} = \mathbf{b}$.

    (a) Use vectors to show that AB is parallel to CD.

    (b) What is the ratio of the lengths of AB and CD?

Key points

- A vector has magnitude (length) and direction but can start at any point.
- Lines that are parallel have vectors that are multiples of each other.
- If $\vec{BC} = n \times \vec{AB}$, then ABC is a straight line and BC is n times AB in length.
- To add or subtract column vectors, add or subtract the two components separately.

- To multiply a column vector by a number, multiply each component by that number.
- The resultant of two vectors is the third side of the triangle formed by those vectors.
- The vector $\vec{AB}$ is equal to the sum of the vectors $\vec{AC} + \vec{CD} + ... + \vec{PQ} + \vec{QB}$ where C, D, E... P, Q are any points.

Revision exercise 34a

1. (a) (i) Write down the column vectors for $\vec{AB}$, $\vec{BC}$, $\vec{CD}$.

   (ii) Add together the three vectors.

   (b) Write down the column vector for $\vec{AD}$.
   What do you notice?

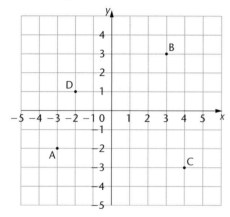

2. Translate shape T by

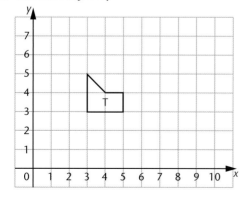

   (a) $\begin{pmatrix} 3 \\ 0 \end{pmatrix}$ and label the image A

   (b) $\begin{pmatrix} 4 \\ -3 \end{pmatrix}$ and label the image B

   (c) $\begin{pmatrix} -1 \\ 2 \end{pmatrix}$ and label the image C.

3. Describe fully the transformation that maps
   (a) A onto B
   (b) A onto C
   (c) B onto C.

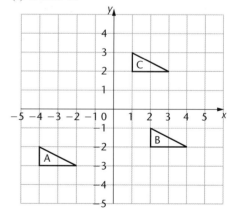

4. Given that $\mathbf{a} = \begin{pmatrix} 1 \\ 2 \end{pmatrix}$, $\mathbf{b} = \begin{pmatrix} -2 \\ 1 \end{pmatrix}$, $\mathbf{c} = \begin{pmatrix} -1 \\ -3 \end{pmatrix}$, work out

   (a) $2\mathbf{a}$ (b) $\mathbf{a} - \mathbf{b}$

   (c) $\mathbf{a} - \mathbf{b} + \mathbf{c}$ (d) $\mathbf{a} + 2\mathbf{b}$

   (e) $3\mathbf{a} + 2\mathbf{c}$ (f) $\frac{1}{2}\mathbf{a}$

   (g) $2\mathbf{a} - 3\mathbf{c}$ (h) $\frac{1}{2}\mathbf{b} - \frac{1}{2}\mathbf{c}$

   (i) $\mathbf{a} - \frac{1}{2}\mathbf{c} - \mathbf{b}$

5. What are the coordinates of the image when

   (a) the point $(-2, 1)$ is translated by $\begin{pmatrix} 1 \\ 0 \end{pmatrix}$?

   (b) the point $(4, 3)$ is translated by $\begin{pmatrix} -4 \\ -3 \end{pmatrix}$?

   (c) the point $(2, -4)$ is translated by $\begin{pmatrix} 3 \\ -1 \end{pmatrix}$?

6. In the triangle ABC, $\overrightarrow{AB} = \mathbf{a}$ and $\overrightarrow{AC} = 2\mathbf{b}$.

   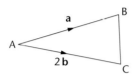

   Write down the vector $\overrightarrow{BC}$ in terms of $\mathbf{a}$ and $\mathbf{b}$.

7. In the diagram $\overrightarrow{OA} = \mathbf{a}$, $\overrightarrow{OB} = 2\mathbf{b} - \mathbf{a}$,
   $\overrightarrow{OC} = 6\mathbf{b} - 5\mathbf{a}$

   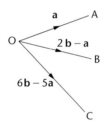

   (a) Work out the vectors $\overrightarrow{AB}$ and $\overrightarrow{BC}$ in terms of $\mathbf{a}$ and/or $\mathbf{b}$.

   (b) What can you say about AB and BC?

8. ABCD is a parallelogram. E, F, G and H are the midpoints of the sides.

   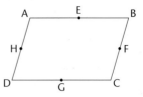

   $\overrightarrow{AB} = \mathbf{p}$ and $\overrightarrow{AD} = \mathbf{q}$.

   (a) Find the vectors $\overrightarrow{EB}$, $\overrightarrow{BF}$, $\overrightarrow{EF}$, $\overrightarrow{HD}$, $\overrightarrow{DG}$ and $\overrightarrow{HG}$ in terms of $\mathbf{p}$ and $\mathbf{q}$.

   (b) What can you say about HG and EF?

9. ABCD is a rectangle E is a point on the diagonal AC so that AE = 2 × EC.
   $\overrightarrow{AB} = \mathbf{p}$ and $\overrightarrow{AD} = \mathbf{q}$.

   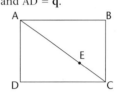

   Work out the vector $\overrightarrow{EB}$ (multi-step).

10. ABCD is a quadrilateral with $\overrightarrow{AB} = 3\mathbf{p}$, $\overrightarrow{AD} = \mathbf{q}$ and $\overrightarrow{BC} = \mathbf{q} + 2\mathbf{p}$. Use vectors to identify the type of quadrilateral.

Answers

Chapter I

1. (a) 5.48; 5.5
    (b) 12.08; 12.1
    (c) 0.21; 0.2
    (d) 0.57; 0.6
    (e) 9.02; 9.0
    (f) 78.04; 78.0
    (g) 7.01; 7.0
    (h) 0.07; 0.1
2. (a) 7.4
    (b) 7.42

3. 9.43
4. (a) 0.333
    (b) 0.286
    (c) 0.273
    (d) 0.308
5. 7.3
6. 9.34

1. (a) 460
    (b) 250
    (c) 120
    (d) 1000
    (e) 5700
    (f) 9900
    (g) 8800
    (h) 200

2. (a) 130; 100
    (b) 450; 500
    (c) 550; 500
    (d) 4560; 4600
    (e) 1410; 1400

1. (a) 67 900
    (b) 54.1
    (c) 1800
    (d) 1 564 400
2. (a) 4200
3. $(2 \times 3.65 \times 2.2) + (2 \times 2.44 \times 2.2)$
    $= 26.796 = 27 \text{ m}^2$
4. (a) £252.72 i.e. £253
    (b) £12 888 i.e. £13 000
5. (a) 77 000
    (b) 680
    (c) 0.81

    (e) 0.0068
    (f) 1.5
    (g) 0.09
    (h) 45.3
    (b) 710

    (d) 3.1
    (e) 0.71

6. (a) 1.19
    (b) 5.48
    (c) 2.53
7. (a) $6 \times 0.2 = 1.2$, 1.0999, 1.1
    (b) $20 \div 4 = 5$, 4.9519, 5.0
    (c) $40 \times 20 = 800$, 585.1269, 590
    (d) $10 \div 0.05 = 200$, 190.7949, 190
    (e) $2 \times 6 \times 1 = 12$, 12.417 44, 12

    (d) 2.20
    (e) 0.47

1. $\frac{3}{6}, \frac{3}{5}, \frac{4}{6}, \frac{3}{4}, \frac{4}{5}, \frac{5}{6}, \frac{6}{5}, \frac{5}{4}, \frac{4}{3}, \frac{6}{4}, \frac{5}{3}, \frac{6}{3}$
2. 0.000280, 0.0014, 0.0042, 0.0098, 0.0126, 0.5

3. 1 560 005, 156 005, 15 605, 15 565, 15 065
4. 0.62, 0.6, 0.0624, 0.006 004

Exercise 1.5a (page 12)

1. (a) $6:24$ (b) $12:30$ (c) $32:40$
   (d) $12:15:18$
2. (a) $1:10$ (b) $4:1$ (c) $4:5$ (d) $1:18$
3. (a) $1:5$ (b) $1:3$ (c) $1:4$ (d) $1:300$
4. 2.28 km
5. 2.8 cm
6. (a) 40   (b) $14\,800-15\,000$
7. (a) $1:50$ (b) $1:5$ (c) $1:60$
8. (a) $1:3$ (b) £120, £360
9. (a) 13, 21, 34, 55, 89,
   (b) Tends to 1.618...

Exercise 1.6a (page 14)

1. (a) 54   (d) 400   (g) -3
   (b) -72 (e) 420   (h) -22
   (c) -42 (f) 108   (i) -16
2.

$\times$	8	-6	4	-3
10	80	-60	40	-30
-7	-56	42	-28	21
3	24	-18	12	-9
-5	-40	30	-20	-15

3. (a) $(-3 \div -6) \times 2 = 1$
   (b) $(-6 \div -3) - 2 = 0$
   (c) $(2 - -3) \times -6 = -30$
4. (a) -9 (d) 27   (g) 39
   (b) -1.33 (e) -27 (h) 144
   (c) $-\frac{3}{4}$ (f) -9

Exercise 1.7a (page 16)

1. (a) 3^5
   (b) 7^3
   (c) 8^5
   (d) $3^2 \times 5^3$
   (e) $2^3 \times 3^2 \times 4^5$
2. (a) 5^5
   (b) 6^9
   (c) 10^7
   (d) 3^{11}
   (e) 8^5
   (f) 5^{-6}
3. (a) 3^{-3}
   (b) 2^7
   (c) 5^{-4}

Exercise 1.8a (page 17)

1. (a) 5×10^3
   (b) 5×10^1
   (c) 7×10^4
   (d) 4.6×10^1
   (e) 2×10^{-2}
   (f) 5.46×10^5
   (g) 4.5×10^{-4}
   (h) 1.6×10^7
2. (a) 500
   (b) 400 000
   (c) 0.006
   (d) 4500
   (e) 0.0084
   (f) 0.0000287
   (g) 9700
   (h) 0.000 055

Exercise 1.9a (page 18)

(a) $5000 + 70\,000 \Rightarrow 75\,000 \Rightarrow 7.5 \times 10^4$
(b) $7\,000\,000 - 3000 \Rightarrow 6\,997\,000 \Rightarrow 6.997 \times 10^6$
(c) $3000 + 300 \Rightarrow 3300 \Rightarrow 3.3 \times 10^3$
(d) $6000 - 500 \Rightarrow 5500 \Rightarrow 5.5 \times 10^3$

Exercise 1.10a (page 18)

1. (a) 49
   (b) 144
   (c) 625
   (d) 1600
   (e) 121
2. (a) 7
   (b) 11
   (c) 13
   (d) 17
   (e) 5
3. (a) 64
   (b) 125
   (c) 216
   (d) 1000
   (e) 512
4. (a) 7
   (b) 9
   (c) 11
   (d) 100
5. (a) 7.48
   (b) 5.20
   (c) 7.75
   (d) 16.73
   (e) 26.04

Exercise 1.11a (page 19)

1. (a) $\frac{1}{3}$
   (b) $\frac{1}{6}$
   (c) $\frac{1}{49}$
   (d) $\frac{1}{100}$
   (e) $\frac{1}{640}$
2. (a) 16
   (b) 9
   (c) 52
   (d) 67
   (e) 1000

Revision exercise 1a (page 20)

1. (a) 7.90   (c) 0.24
   (b) 13.12   (d) 0.68
2. 12.69 (2 d.p.)
3. (a) 0.429   (c) 0.154
   (b) 0.182   (d) 0.538
4. £29.36
5. (a) 130   (e) 7900
   (b) 540   (f) 9800
   (c) 1000   (g) 8900
   (d) 1240   (h) 100

6. (a) 6790   (e) 0.0059
   (b) 57.1   (f) 1.8
   (c) 1900   (g) 0.08
   (d) 1 576 400   (h) 40.3

7. 0.000 98, 0.0098, 0.0926,
   0.9, 0.9042, 0.914

8. (a) $1:4$ (c) $1:3$
   (b) $1:2$ (d) $1:30$

9. 2.15 km or 215000 cm

10. (a) $1:200$
   (b) $1:500\,000$
   (c) $1:10$

11. (a) 72   (f) 96
   (b) -150 (g) -9
   (c) -18 (h) -3
   (d) 36   (i) -8
   (e) 30

12. (a) -20 (e) -125
   (b) -2 (f) -17
   (c) -2.5 (g) 119
   (d) 75   (h) 400

13. (a) 7^5 (e) 8^6
   (b) 6^9 (f) 6^{-2}
   (c) 10^{12} (g) 4^{-1}
   (d) 3^{12} (h) 9^4

14. (a) 7.6×10^3
   (b) 8.99×10
   (c) 6×10^4
   (d) 4.66×10^2
   (e) 5.6×10^{-2}
   (f) 5.646×10^5
   (g) 5.5×10^{-3}
   (h) 2.4×10^7

15. (a) 6000
   (b) 500
   (c) 0.007
   (d) 450
   (e) 0.084
   (f) 0.002 87
   (g) 4700
   (h) 0.0555

16. (a) 1.4×10^4
   (b) 6.8×10^4

Chapter 2

Activity 2 (page 22)

Exterior angle of a triangle

Proof: Either $b = p$ (because they are corresponding angles)
             $a = s$ (because they are alternate angles)
   ∴ $a + b = p + s$
        $a + b = r$
   ∴ $r = p + s$
   Or $p + s + q = 180°$ (because angles in a triangle add up to 180°)
        $a + b + q = 180°$ (because angles on a straight line add up to 180°)
   ∴ $a + b = p + s$
   ∴ $r = p + s$

Exercise 2.la (page 22)

1. (a) $x = 116°$ (c) $a = 120°$
   (b) $b = 83°$ (d) $c = 12°$

2. $x = 48°$ (angles in a triangle), $d = 132°$, $e = 120°$
   (angles on a straight line) or $d = 132°$
   (exterior angle of a triangle), $x = 48°$
   ∴ $e = 360° - (48° + 132° + 60°)$
   (angles round a point) $= 120°$
   or $y = 42°$ (angle sum of triangle)
   ∴ $e = 78° + 42° = 120°$
   (exterior angle of triangle)
   or $e = 180° - 60° = 120°$
   (angles on a straight line)

3. (a) $x = 94°$
   (b) $a = 70°$
   (c) $a = 120°$
   (d) $y = 80°$

4. (a) $x = 129°$
   (b) $x = 30°$
   (c) $x = 135°$
   (d) $a = 28.75°$
   (e) $5x = 180°$ ∴ $x = 36°$ ∴ $y = 3 \times 36° = 108°$

Activity 3 (page 24)

1. The lines OA, OP and OB are equal because they are radii.
2. The angles marked a are equal to each other because they are opposite angles in an isosceles triangle.
3. The angles marked b are equal to each other because they are opposite angles in an isosceles triangle.
4. In triangle APB angles $a + a + b + b = 180°$ because the sum of the angles of the triangle $= 180°$.
   So $2(a + b) = 180°$ and angle APB $= a + b = 90°$.

Finding the centre of the circle:

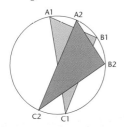

Exercise 2.2a (page 25)

1. (a), (b) a and b are equal, (isosceles triangle)
   c and d are equal (isosceles triangle)
   $\therefore c = d = 50°$
   $b = 90° - 50° = 40°$ (angle in a semi-circle)
   $\therefore a = 40°$
   (c) $a = b = 40°$ as angle at O $= 80°$
   (exterior angle of triangle)
2. $a = 44°$ (angle sum of triangle)
3. (a) $x = y = 90°$ (angles in semi-circle);
   $a = 360° - (90° + 90° + 99°) = 81°$
   (b) Because the angles at A and B would both have to be 90° which they are not.
4. The interior angle of a hexagon $= 120°$. The base angles of the isosceles triangle are 30° and 30° therefore angle APB $= 120° - 30° = 90°$. Therefore AB is a diameter.

Activity 4 (page 26)

	Odd number of sides			Even number of sides		
Number of sides	3	5	7	4	6	8
right angles	1	3	5	4	5	6

For an odd number of sides the relation is 'number of sides − 2' or $n − 2$.

For an even number of sides it is 'half the number of sides + 2' or $^n/_2 + 2$.

Some 'What if … ?' questions could be:
- if sides are not vertical or horizontal, or
- if the polygons are concave …

Exercise 2.3a (page 26)

1. (a) 12
   (b) 8
   (c) 9
   (d) 3
   (e) 15
2. Yes
   (a) $360° ÷ 6 = 60°$
   (b) Exterior angle $= 120°$ therefore it has three sides and is therefore an equilateral triangle and it is possible.
3. (a) $176.4°$
   (b) $179.64°$

Exercise 2.4a (page 28)

1. $a = 80°$, $b = 50°$, $c = 30°$, $d = 80°$, $e = 30°$, $f = 80°$, $g = 70°$
2. $p = 90°$, $q = 40°$, $r = 115°$, $s = 115°$, $t = 65°$, $x = 140°$, $y = 135°$

Revision exercise 2a (page 29)

1. (a) $x = 58°$, $z = 58° + 71° = 129°$ (b) $x = 140°$
   (c) The fourth angle of the quadrilateral
   $= 360° - (50° + 70° + 130°) = 110°$, $x = 70°$, $y = 60°$
2. (a) $x = 47°$ (b) $x = 40°$ (c) $x = 135°$
3. The exterior angle $= 360° ÷ 20 = 18°$ so the interior angle $= 162°$.
4. The interior angle $= 168°$ so the exterior angle $= 12°$.
   The number of sides $= 360 ÷ 12 = 30$.
5. $a = 90°$, $b = 100°$, $c = 30°$, $d = 70°$, $e = 140°$, $f = 80°$, $g = 35°$, $h = 145°$, $i = 80°$

Answers

Chapter 3

Exercise 3.1a (page 32)

1. (a) Frequencies: 2, 3, 4, 1
   (b) 12
   (c) 11.4
2. (a) 40
   (b) 1078
   (c) 26.95

3. (a) 27
   (b) 5
4. 10.15
5. (a) 26
   (b) 2
   (c) 2.3

Exercise 3.2a (page 36)

1. (a) 17.5 cm ≤ length < 18.5 cm
   (b) 34.5 m ≤ length < 35.5 m
   (c) 4.5 g ≤ mass< 9.5 g, 9.5 g ≤ mass < 14.5 g
   (d) 1.5 s ≤ time < 3.5 s, 3.5 s ≤ time < 5.5 s
2. (a) 15 cm
   (b) 2.25 m
   (c) 82.5 kg
   (d) 83 kg, 88 kg
   (e) 35.5 s, 45.5 s
3. (a) 5.2 s to 1 d.p.
   (b)

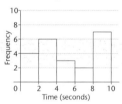

4. (a) 72.8 cm
   (b)

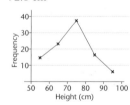

5. 1.5 m
6.

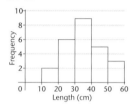

7. (a) 30 ≤ y < 40
   (b) 35.4 cm
8.

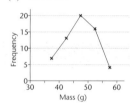

9. (a) 20 g
   (b) 47.25 g to 2 d.p.

10. (a)

Mass (g)	40−50	50−60	60−70	70−80	80−90
Frequency	5	13	21	8	3

(b) 63.2 g

Revision exercise 3a (page 40)

1. 4.4 to 1 d.p.
2. (a) 30   (c) 4
   (b) 93   (d) 3
3. (a) 5
   (b) 6
   (c)

Number of videos	0	1	2	3	4	5	6
Frequency	5	7	2	1	6	8	3

(d) 2.9 to 1 d.p.

4. (a) 3
   (b) 25
   (c) 4
   (d) 4.44
   (e) Very few people ate more than 5 chocolates but they have affected the mean.

5. (a)

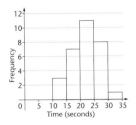

(b) 20 cm

6. 22.0 cm

7. (a)

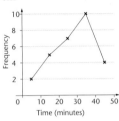

(b) 28.2 minutes to 1 d.p.

8. (a) $8 < x \leqslant 12$
   (b) 16 m
   (c) 10.6 m
9. (a) 28
   (b) (i) 3.5
       (ii) 7.5
   (c) 3.3 hours to 1 d.p.
10. (a) 5.45 hours
    (b) by the manufacturer advertising how long they last.

Chapter 4

Exercise 4.1a (page 46)

1., 2.

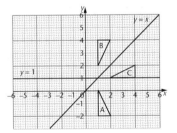

3., 4.

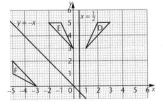

5., 6.

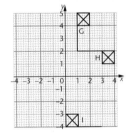

7., 8.

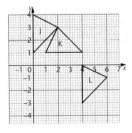

9. (a) Rotation through 90° clockwise about (2, 4).
   (b) Reflection in the line $x = -1$.
   (c) Reflection in the line $y = -x$

   (d) Rotation through 180° about (4, 2).
   (e) Rotation through 90° clockwise about (3, −1).
   (f) Reflection in the line $y = -2\frac{1}{2}$.

Exercise 4.2a (page 52)

1., 2.

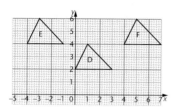

3., 4.

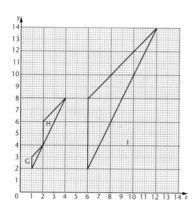

5., 6.

7., 8.

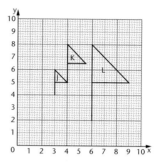

9. (a) Translation through $\begin{pmatrix} 3 \\ -5 \end{pmatrix}$.

(b) Enlargement, scale factor 2, centre (0, 4).

(c) Translation through $\begin{pmatrix} -8 \\ -3 \end{pmatrix}$.

(d) Enlargement, scale factor $2\frac{1}{2}$, centre (0, 0).

(e) Translation through $\begin{pmatrix} -6 \\ 4 \end{pmatrix}$.

(f) Enlargement, scale factor $\frac{1}{3}$, centre (5, 3).

Exercise 4.3a (page 57)

1. Translation through $\begin{pmatrix} 7 \\ -2 \end{pmatrix}$.

2. Translation through $\begin{pmatrix} 4 \\ 2 \end{pmatrix}$.

3. Translation through $\begin{pmatrix} a+b \\ c+d \end{pmatrix}$.

4. Enlargement, scale factor 6. centre (0, 2).
5. Enlargement, scale factor 3, centre ($1\frac{1}{2}$, 5).
6. Enlargement, scale factor pq.

7. Rotation through 90° anticlockwise about (1, 1).
8. Rotation through 90° anticlockwise about ($\frac{1}{2}$, $-\frac{1}{2}$).
9. Rotation about the point where the mirror lines cross. (The angle is twice the angle between the mirror lines, but students are unlikely to spot this.)
10. Rotation through 90° anticlockwise about (5, 0).
11. Translation through $\begin{pmatrix} 4 \\ -4 \end{pmatrix}$.

1., 2.

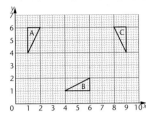

3. Reflection in the line $x = 5$.

4., 5.

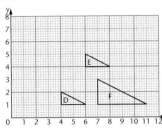

6. Enlargement, scale factor 2, centre (1, 1).

7. (a) Translation through
$$\begin{pmatrix} -6 \\ 0 \end{pmatrix}.$$

(b) Reflection in the line $x = -4\frac{1}{2}$.

(c) Rotation through 90° clockwise about (0, 2).

(d) Rotation through 90° anticlockwise about $(-3, -1)$.

(e) Enlargement, scale factor $\frac{1}{2}$, centre (0, 2).

(f) Reflection in the line $y = -x$.

Chapter 5

Exercise 5.1a (page 63)

1. (a) $\frac{1}{7} = \frac{2}{14} = \frac{5}{35}$
(b) $\frac{4}{9} = \frac{16}{36} = \frac{32}{72}$

2. (a) $\frac{3}{4}$
(b) $\frac{4}{5}$
(c) $\frac{1}{2}$
(d) $\frac{2}{9}$

3. (a) 1
(b) $\frac{5}{6}$
(c) $\frac{17}{20}$
(d) $\frac{5}{6}$
(e) $\frac{31}{40}$
(f) $\frac{11}{12}$

4. (a) $\frac{1}{7}$
(b) $\frac{1}{2}$
(c) $\frac{5}{12}$
(d) $\frac{1}{4}$
(e) $\frac{7}{24}$
(f) $\frac{13}{36}$

5. (a) $\frac{9}{10}$
(b) $\frac{23}{30}$
(c) $\frac{11}{12}$
(d) $\frac{11}{40}$
(e) 0
(f) $\frac{2}{7}$

Exercise 5.2a (page 65)

1. (a) $1\frac{3}{4}$
(b) $2\frac{2}{5}$
(c) $5\frac{2}{3}$
(d) $3\frac{3}{4}$
(e) $12\frac{1}{2}$

2. (a) $\frac{3}{2}$
(b) $\frac{13}{5}$
(c) $\frac{43}{8}$
(d) $\frac{18}{7}$
(e) $\frac{37}{4}$

3. (a) $4\frac{7}{12}$
(b) $3\frac{9}{10}$
(c) $6\frac{3}{20}$
(d) $10\frac{5}{18}$
(e) $1\frac{1}{7}$
(f) $4\frac{5}{8}$

4. (a) $1\frac{1}{5}$
(b) $3\frac{1}{8}$
(c) $3\frac{1}{6}$
(d) $1\frac{13}{20}$
(e) $1\frac{1}{2}$
(f) $4\frac{8}{15}$

5. (a) $1\frac{5}{12}$
(b) $2\frac{3}{4}$
(c) $3\frac{17}{20}$
(d) $5\frac{1}{8}$
(e) $4\frac{7}{10}$
(f) $\frac{9}{14}$

6. $1\frac{3}{8}$

Exercise 5.3a (page 67)

1. $\frac{1}{6}$
2. $\frac{2}{5}$
3. $\frac{2}{9}$
4. $\frac{2}{9}$
5. $2\frac{2}{3}$
6. $\frac{2}{3}$
7. $\frac{9}{10}$
8. $9\frac{3}{4}$
9. $5\frac{1}{2}$
10. $1\frac{3}{4}$
11. $1\frac{3}{5}$
12. $2\frac{2}{3}$

Exercise 5.4a (page 69)

1. 14
2. 6
3. 16.5
4. -11
5. -2
6. -12
7. 0.14
8. -46.5
   to 3 s.f.
9. 0.368
   to 3 s.f.
10. -22.6
   to 3 s.f.

Answers

Exercise 5.5a (page 71)

All answers are to 3 s.f.

1. (a) 209
   (b) 2.37
2. (a) 0.722
   (b) 1.26
   (c) 0.852
   (d) −0.649
3. (a) 33.7°
   (b) 74.5°
   (c) 65.5°
   (d) 21.8°
4. 83700
5. 7.57
6. 3.71×10^2
7. 600
8. 3.77
9. 0.0678
10. 7.46

Exercise 5.6a (page 72)

1. £20, £30, £50
2. 30°, 60°, 90°
3. £8
4. 3.2 litres
5. £150
6. £220
7. £146
8. 330 g
9. Michael £18.90;
   Iain £22.50
10. 1 : 4.43 : 0.732

Exercise 5.7a (page 75)

1. (a) 1.06.
   (b) 1.09
   (c) 1.175
   (d) 1.0125
   (e) $\frac{6}{5}$
   (f) $\frac{11}{9}$
2. (a) 0.94
   (b) 0.91
   (c) 0.825
   (d) 0.9875
   (e) $\frac{4}{5}$
   (f) $\frac{7}{9}$
3. £1340
4. 3525
5. £167
6. £38774
7. £19.26
8. £18 575
9. $(1.07)^{10} = 1.97$.
   So it does not quite
   double.
10. (a) £4051.69
    (b) £5033.40

Exercise 5.8a (page 78)

1. £53.75
2. 40
3. £75.05
4. £12 500
5. 1540
6. £2.25
7. £27 000
8. £24 000
9. £480
10. (a) 79p
    (b) 1.24

Revision exercise 5a (page 801)

1. (a) $1\frac{1}{6}$
   (b) $4\frac{13}{20}$
   (c) $\frac{7}{18}$
   (d) $\frac{7}{12}$
   (e) $2\frac{1}{3}$
   (f) $\frac{2}{5}$
   (g) $1\frac{1}{2}$
   (h) 8
   (i) $1\frac{1}{5}$
   (j) $2\frac{1}{2}$
2. $2\frac{1}{6}$ inches
3. (a) −8
   (b) −12
   (c) 4
4. (a) 11.16
   (b) −63.6
   (c) 0.147
   (d) 0.969
   (e) 21.4°
   (f) 2.94
   (g) 19 683
   (h) 1840
   (i) 1.44
   (j) 9.43
   (k) 1.74
   (l) −50.7
   (m) 2.52
   (n) 56.0°
   (o) 1.45
5. £375
6. 19
7. 11 865
8. 1679
9. 331
10. £520
11. 918
12. 234

Chapter 6

Exercise 6.1a (page 83)

1. $V = -21$
2. $P = 55$
3. $T = 2$
4. $M = 10$
5. $R = 24$
6. $L = 2\frac{1}{6}$
7. $D = \frac{8}{25}$
8. $M = 0.563$
9. (a) $S = 720$ m
   (b) $S = 30.625$ m
10. $A = 111.5$

Exercise 6.2a (page 86)

1. $5a + b$
2. $6ab - 4ac$
3. $-a^2 + 2b^2$
4. $2x^2 - 4xy + y^2$
5. $2b^2 - a^2$
6. Will not simplify.
7. $3a^3 + 7a^2$
8. $14abc$
9. $2x^2$
10. 0
11. $5a + 8$
12. $19x - 9$
13. $2b + 16$
14. $3x - 1$
15. $2x^2 + 5xy - 12y^2$

Exercise 6.3a (page 87)

1. $x^2 + 5x + 6$
2. $a^2 + 7a + 12$
3. $a^2 + 3a + 1$
4. $2x^2 - 3x - 2$
5. $2x^2 + x - 6$
6. $6a^2 - 4ab - 2b^2$
7. $4a^2 + 7ab - 2b^2$
8. $6a^2 - 13ab + 6b^2$
9. $8a^2 - 18ab + 9b^2$
10. $20 - 7b - 6b^2$
11. $6a^2 - 5ab + b^2$
12. $14a^2 + 13ab + 3b^2$
13. $a^2 + 4a + 4$
14. $16x^2 - 24xy + 9y^2$
15. $9x^2 - 6xy + y^2$
16. $a^2 - 4$
17. $9a^2 - b^2$
18. $25x^2 - 4y^2$
19. $4a^2 - ab - 3b^2$
20. $10a^2 + 3ab - 4b^2$

Exercise 6.4a (page 89)

1. $12a^5$
2. $2a^2$
3. $9a^6$
4. $6a^5b^3$
5. Cannot simplify
6. $5ab^2$
7. $3p^3$
8. $2abc^2$
9. $3t$
10. $2a^3b^3$

Exercise 6.5a (page 91)

1. $n^2 + 1$
2. $2n^2 - 1$
3. $n^2 + 4$
4. $3n^2 + 3$
5. $n^2 - 2$
6. $3n^2 + 4$
7. $4n^2 - 3$
8. $n^2 + 2n + 1$
9. $n^2 + 3n - 2$
10. $n^2 + n$

Exercise 6.6a (page 92)

1. $2(a + 4)$
2. $a(3 + 5a)$
3. $2a(b - 3c)$
4. $5ab(a + 2b)$
5. $x^2y(2y - 3x)$
6. $3ab(a - 2b)$
7. $2(6x - 3y + 4z)$
8. $3b(3a + 2b)$
9. $2ac(2a - c)$
10. $5y(3x - 1)$
11. $2a(3a^2 - 2a + 1)$
12. $3a^2b(1 - 3ab)$
13. $5abc(abc - 2)$
14. $a^2b(2 - 3b^2 + 7a^2)$
15. $a(4bc - 3c^2 + 2ab)$

Exercise 6.7a (page 94)

1. $(x + 3)(x + 2)$
2. $(x + 5)(x + 1)$
3. $(x + 4)(x + 2)$
4. $(x + 4)(x + 1)$
5. $(x + 1)(x + 1)$
6. $(x - 6)(x - 1)$
7. $(x - 2)(x - 5)$
8. $(x - 3)(x - 1)$
9. $(x - 7)(x - 2)$
10. $(x - 4)(x - 2)$
11. $(a + 6)(a + 2)$
12. $(a - 3)(a - 3)$
13. $(b - 8)(b - 4)$
14. $(x + 3)(x + 8)$
15. $(x - 5)(x - 4)$

Exercise 6.8a (page 95)

1. $(x - 4)(x + 2)$
2. $(x - 1)(x + 5)$
3. $(x + 2)(x - 3)$
4. $(x + 6)(x - 1)$
5. $(x + 3)(x - 1)$
6. $(x - 6)(x + 3)$
7. $(x - 10)(x + 1)$
8. $(x + 7)(x + 2)$
9. $(y + 11)(y - 2)$
10. $(x + 4)(x - 3)$
11. $(a - 2)(a + 10)$
12. $(a - 9)(a + 3)$
13. $(b + 2)(b + 10)$
14. $(b + 13)(b - 2)$
15. $(x - 3)(x - 6)$

Exercise 6.9a (page 96)

1. $b = a + c$
2. $x = \dfrac{3a}{y + w}$
3. $t = \dfrac{v - u}{a}$
4. $T = HA$
5. $T = \dfrac{P - C}{3}$
6. $u = 2P - v$
7. $r = \dfrac{C}{2\pi}$
8. $q = \sqrt{\dfrac{A - pr}{p}}$
9. $x = \frac{1}{2}P - y$
10. (a) $n = \dfrac{C - A}{32}$
    (b) $n = 56$

Exercise 6.10a (page 99)

1. (a) $x = -4, -3,$
        $-2, -1$
   (b) $x = 2, 3, 4, 5$
2. $x \leqslant 7$
3. $x > 2$
4. $x < 4$
5. $x \leqslant 1$
6. $x \geqslant 5$
7. $x > \frac{1}{2}$
8. $x < 3$
9. $x > 2.5$
10. $x \geqslant 4$
11. $x < -1$
12. $x \geqslant 2$
13. $x < 4$
14. $x > -3$
15. $x < -8.5$

1. $2x + 3 = 23$, $x = 10$, their ages are 10 and 13.
2. $3a + 15 = 180$, $a = 55$, the angles are 55°, 55°, 70°.
3. $30 + 20x \leqslant 240$, $x \leqslant 10.5$, the most lengths he can hang is 10.
4. $2x + 28 = 616$, $x = 294$, there are 294 boys and 322 girls.
5. (a) $2x + 60 \geqslant 225$, $x \geqslant 82.5$
   (b) The smallest distance is $82\frac{1}{2}$ miles (accept 83 miles).
6. (a) $5x - 6$
   (b) (i) $5x - 6 = 19$, $x = 5$
       (ii) Adult bikes £5, Child bikes £3.
7. (a) $6x \leqslant 40$, $x \leqslant 6\frac{2}{3}$ (b) 6 m by 12 m
8. Patrick has x cars. $3x + 11 = 41$, $x = 10$ Mark 14, Patrick 10, Iain 17

1. (a) $h = 20$
   (b) $h = 1$
   (c) $h = -11.8$
2. $A = 222$
3. (a) $5a$
   (b) $ab^2 + a^2b$
   (c) $4ab + 2ac$
   (d) $4x^2 + xy$
4. (a) $7x + 5$
   (b) $4x - 6$
   (c) $a + 16$
   (d) $4x + 4$
   (e) $4x - 1$
   (f) $3x^2 - 18xy + 4y^2$
5. (a) $x^2 + 8x + 7$
   (b) $a^2 + 2a - 15$
   (c) $2y^2 - 2y - 4$
   (d) $2x^2 - 9x - 5$
   (e) $4a^2 - 3ab - b^2$
   (f) $6 - 7c + 2c^2$
   (g) $x^2 - 25$
   (h) $x^2 + 4xy + 4y^2$
   (i) $14x^2 + 11xy - 15y^2$
6. (a) $2a^5$ (d) $24a^4b^4$
   (b) $5a$ (e) $3xz$
   (c) a^5 (f) $4a^2c$

7. (a) $n^2 + 3$
   (b) $2n^2 + 1$
   (c) $n^2 + n + 2$
8. (a) $3(a + 2b - 4c)$
   (b) $a(2 + 3b)$
   (c) $ab(a - 3b)$
   (d) $2xy(x - 3)$
   (e) $7ab(c + 2a)$
   (f) $3(3a^2 + b^2 - 2c^2)$
   (g) $5(pq - 2)$
   (h) $2a(1 - 2a + 3a^2)$
   (i) $50ac(2b - 1)$
9. (a) $(x + 4)(x + 1)$
   (b) $(x - 2)(x - 4)$
   (c) $(x - 8)(x - 2)$
   (d) $(x + 5)(x + 3)$
   (e) $(x - 7)(x + 1)$
   (f) $(x + 2)(x - 5)$
   (g) $(x - 6)(x - 2)$
   (h) $(x - 5)(x + 3)$
   (i) $(x - 10)(x + 7)$
   (j) $(x + 12)(x + 4)$
   (k) $(x - 9)(x + 2)$
   (l) $(x + 10)(x - 2)$

10. (a) $y = x + 3b$
    (b) $u = 2t - v$
    (c) $a = 2b - P$
    (d) $q = \dfrac{p - m}{x}$
    (e) $P = \dfrac{100I}{TR}$
    (f) $S = \dfrac{v^2 - u^2}{2a}$
11. (a) $x > 2\frac{1}{2}$ (f) $x \leqslant 2\frac{1}{3}$
    (b) $x \leqslant 2$ (g) $x > -2$
    (c) $x \geqslant 6$ (h) $x < \frac{1}{2}$
    (d) $x < 2$ (i) $x > -\frac{1}{4}$
    (e) $x \leqslant 8$
12. (a) $3x + 3$
    (b) $3x + 3 = 39$, $x = 12$
    (c) Their ages are 10, 12, 17.
13. (a) $24x + 320 \leqslant 500$,
        $x \leqslant 7.5$
    (b) She buys 7 packets of crisps.
14. (a) $5x + 110 = 360$, $x = 50$
    (b) The angles are 50°, 90°, 150°, 70°.

Chapter 7

Activity 4 (page 108)

Compost B

Height (h cm)	Frequency	Cumulative frequency
$0 \leqslant h < 10$	1	1
$10 \leqslant h < 20$	1	2
$20 \leqslant h < 30$	5	7
$30 \leqslant h < 40$	10	17
$40 \leqslant h < 50$	14	31
$50 \leqslant h < 60$	13	44
$60 \leqslant h < 70$	10	54
$70 \leqslant h < 80$	5	59
$80 \leqslant h < 90$	1	60

median = 49 cm
interquartile range = 61 cm − 38 cm = 23 cm

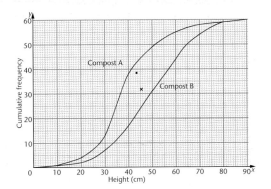

The median is higher for compost B but the interquartile range is wider. This implies a greater variation in plant heights.

Further work

Ideas for further work could include comparing:
- the heights of boys and girls
- the time spent on homework
- times at supermarket checkouts or in the school canteen
- weights, lengths... for animals (this data is readily available from encyclopedias).

Exercise 7.1a (page 111)

1. (a)

Speed (v km/h)	Cumulative frequency Policeman A	Cumulative frequency Policeman B
$10 \leqslant v < 30$	6	2
$30 \leqslant v < 50$	18	6
$50 \leqslant v < 70$	30	10
$70 \leqslant v < 90$	43	29
$90 \leqslant v < 110$	47	48
$110 \leqslant v < 130$	50	50

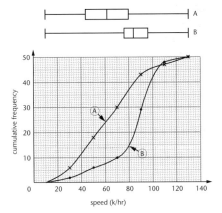

(b) medians: A = 62 km/h, B = 88 km/h
lower quartiles: A = 43 km/h, B = 76 km/h
upper quartiles: A = 80 km/h, B = 96 km/h

(c) For A the median speed is lower than for B and the interquartile range is higher than for B. A might be in a built-up area, B on a motorway

Exercise 7.1a (page III) – continued

2. (a) lower quartile at 4, median at 8, upper quartile at 15.5

   (b) lower quartile at 2.7, median at 5.4, upper quartile at 8.1

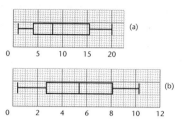

Revision exercise 7a (page II2)

1. (a)

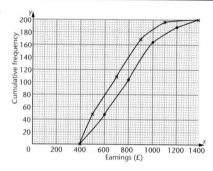

   (b) (i) £780   (iii) 60

   (ii) £940 − £600 = £340

2. (a)

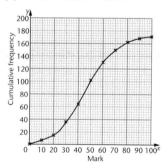

   (b) (i) 46   (iii) 170 − 118 = 52

   (ii) 58 − 32 = 26   (iv) 60% = 102

3. (a)

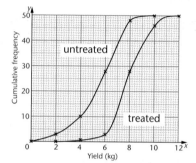

Treated: median = 7.8 kg, interquartile range 8.9 − 7.1 = 18 kg

Untreated: median = 5.8 kg, interquartile range 6.7 − 4.4 = 2.3 kg

The average yield is higher for the treated trees as there is less variation.

   (b) Yes, the chemical was effective.

4.

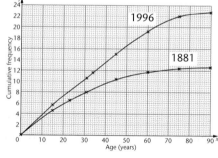

1881: median 22 years, interquartile range 40.5 − 10 = 30.5

1966: median 33 years, interquartile range 53 − 15 = 38

The average age was much higher in 1966 and the ages were more spread out.

5. (a)

Audience size	50–99	100–199	200–299	300–399	400–499	500–599
CF Wednesdays	11	31	41	47	51	52
CF Thursdays	3	6	24	43	48	53

(b) medians: Wednesday = 170, Thursday = 305
lower quartiles: Wednesday = 105, Thursday = 245
upper quartiles: Wednesday = 280, Thursday = 365

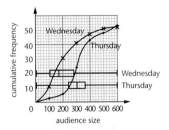

Chapter 8

Exercise 8.1a (page 114)

1. (a) $30 ÷ 5 = 6$, 6.4536
(b) $100 × 3 = 300$, 339.365
(c) $40 ÷ 10 = 4$, 5.0933
(d) $4 × 10 × 20 = 800$, 1153.26
2. (a) $(10 × 20) ÷ 60 = 3$, 5.4557
(b) $(5^2 × 50) ÷ 100 = 12.5$, 12.2409
(c) $\sqrt{(5 × 5)} = 5$, 5.047 77
3. (a) $0.4 × 90 ÷ 8 = 4.5$
(b) $10 ÷ 6 = 1.667$
(c) $10 × 0.07 = 0.7$
(d) $1 ÷ 5 = 0.2$
4. Students' own work

Exercise 8.2a (page 116)

1. (a) £330.75 − £300 = £30.75
(b) £1169.86 − £1000 = £169.86
(c) £491.73 − £450 = £41.73
(d) £5832 − £5000 = £832
(e) £39 323.88 − £30 000 = £9323.88
2. Five years at 8% produces £1469.32, four years at 9% produces £1411.58

Exercise 8.3a (page 118)

1. £168
2. £212
3. £25.99
4. £20.50
5. £33.24

Exercise 8.4a (page 120)

1. 60.48 m/s
2. 10.5 miles
3. 7.5 hours
4. £2.475 per kg,
£1.895 per kg, £1.96 per kg
5. 277.78 cm³
6. $2.45 × 10$ people/km²

Exercise 8.5a (page 121)

1. $3\frac{1}{2}$ minutes
2. 3 weeks
3. 5.7m
4. £16.10
5. 6650 km
6. 0.097 cm²

Revision exercise 8a (page 122)

1. (a) 960
(b) 1400
(c) 132
2. £271.84
3. compound interest = £135.69
simple interest = £126
difference = £9.69
4. 45.1 m.p.h
5. £65.27
6. 576 492
7. 5.19 litres/minute,
3.85 minutes or 3 minutes 51 seconds
8. 500 g
9. $1.43 × 10^3$ kg/m³
10. 11m
11. $1.44 × 10^8$ km
12. 75.36 kg

Chapter 9

Activity 2 (page 125)

(a) 15 cm²
(b) 351 cm²
(c) 168 cm²
(d) 200 cm²
(e) 152 cm²

Activity 3 (page 126)

(a) 5 cm
(b) 11.18 cm
(c) 5.39 cm
(d) 11.31 cm
(e) 11.4 cm
(f) 13 cm

Activity 4 (page 127)

● (a) 8 cm
 (b) 5.66 cm
 (c) 16 cm
 (d) 28.91 cm
 (e) 168.93 cm
 (f) 4 cm
 (g) 14.28 cm
 (h) 8.94 cm
● (a) 250.4 m
 (b) 28.62 m
 (c) 4.9 m
 (d) 30 + 21.2 + 37.08
  = 88.28 cm
 (e) 3.23 m

Activity 5 (page 128)

Students' own work

● (a) 13.61 cm
 (b) 7.28 cm
 (c) 3.62 cm
 (d) 41.71 cm
 (e) 7 cm
 (f) 11.44 cm

● (a) 36.87°
 (b) 39.8°
 (c) 26.57°
 (d) 21.8°
 (e) 70.87°

● (a) 4.36 cm
 (b) 1.66 cm
 (c) 4.15 cm
 (d) 6.8 cm
 (e) 4.14 cm

 (f) 42.1°
 (g) 61.3°
 (h) 26.5°
 (i) 51°
 (j) 60°

● (a) 68°
 (b) 4.14 m
 (c) 18.8 m
 (d) 44.1 km
 (e) 36.4°
 (f) 64°
 (g) 582 m
 (h) east 53.6 km,
  south 45 km

Activity 6 (page 134)

(a) $\sqrt{2}$
(b) $\sqrt{3}$, $\sin 30° = \frac{1}{2}$, $\cos 30° = \frac{\sqrt{3}}{2}$
(c) 2, $\cos 45° = \frac{\sqrt{2}}{2}$, $\sin 45° = \frac{\sqrt{2}}{2}$

Revision exercise 9a (page 135)

1. (a) 7.21 cm
 (b) 12.57 cm
 (c) 6.81 cm
2. 25.06 cm
3. 36.06 km
4. (a) 35.1°   (d) 8.43 cm
 (b) 61.0°   (e) 7.55 cm
 (c) 59.7°   (f) 16.49 cm

5. 43.5 m
6. 45.6°, 45.6°, 88.8°
7. 4.6 m
8. (a) west 4.83 km,
   north 1.29 km
 (b) 131.6°, 6.46 km

Chapter 10

Exercise 10.1a (page 137)

1. $x = 10$
2. $x = 0$
3. $x = 3$
4. $x = 2\frac{2}{3}$
5. $x = -5$
6. $x = 2\frac{3}{4}$
7. $x = 4$
8. $x = 6$
9. $x = 2$
10. $x = \frac{6}{7}$
11. $x = 25$
12. $x = 20$
13. $x = 12\frac{1}{2}$
14. $x = 2.74$
15. $x = 4.81$
16. $x = 1.63$
17. $x = 3.64$
18. $x = 5.30$
19. $x = -1.44$
20. $x = 0.511$

Exercise 10.2a (page 138)

1. $x < 1$
2. $x > 2$
3. $x > 3$
4. $x \geqslant 5$
5. $x > 6$
6. $x \leqslant -2$ or $x \geqslant 2$
7. $-5 < x < 5$
8. $x \leqslant -1$ or $x \geqslant 1$
9. $-4 \leqslant x \leqslant 4$
10. $-4 < x < 4$

Exercise 10.3a (page 140)

1. $x = 2(2x - 30)$
   $x = 20$
   Angles are 20° and 10°
2. $3(x + 4) = 27$
   $x = 5$
3. $x = 3(32 - x)$
   $x = 24$
   24 girls, 8 boys
4. $\frac{2}{3}x = x - 20$
   $x = 60$
5. $2n - 5 = 3(n - 2)$, $n = 1$
6. $4(p + 12) = 28p$, $p = 2$,
   children pay £2, adults £14
7. $3x + 5(x + 2) = £38$,
   $x = 3.5$, a one course meals
   cost £3.50
8. $x^2 < 36$, $-6 < x < 6$, the
   number lies between -6
   and $+6$

Exercise 10.4a (page 143)

1. $x = 4, y = 1$
2. $x = 2, y = 3$
3. $x = 1, y = 3$
4. $x = 2, y = 3$
5. $x = 5, y = 1$
6. $x = 4, y = 2$
7. $x = 2, y = 1$
8. $x = 3, y = 2$
9. $x = 2, y = 3$
10. $x = 1, y = 5$
11. $x = 2, y = 1$
12. $x = 2\frac{1}{2}, y = 1\frac{1}{2}$
13. $x = 2\frac{1}{2}, y = 1$
14. $x = 3, y = -1$
15. $x = 3\frac{1}{2}, y = 1$

Exercise 10.5a (page 145)

1. $x = 2, y = 3$
2. $x = 1, y = 1$
3. $x = 2, y = 3$
4. $x = 1, y = 2$
5. $x = 5, y = 6$
6. $x = 2, y = 1$
7. $x = -1, y = 2$
8. $x = -2, y = -3$
9. $x = -1, y = 4$
10. $x = 2\frac{9}{26}, y = 3\frac{5}{26}$

Exercise 10.6a (page 147)

1. $x = 2$ or 3
2. $x = 5$ or 1
3. $x = -2$ or -4
4. $x = -4$ or -1
5. $x = -1$ twice
6. $x = 6$ or 1
7. $x = 2$ or 5
8. $x = 1$ or 3
9. $x = 7$ or 2
10. $x = 2$ or 4
11. $x = 4$ or -2
12. $x = -5$ or 1
13. $x = 3$ or -2
14. $x = -6$ or 1
15. $x = -3$ or 1
16. $x = 6$ or -3
17. $x = 10$ or -1
18. $x = -7$ or -2
19. $x = -11$ or 2
20. $x = -4$ or 3

Exercise 10.7a (page 149)

1.

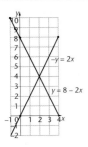

$x = 2, y = 4$

2.

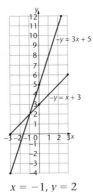

$x = -1, y = 2$

3.

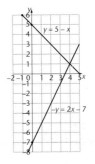

$x = 4, y = 1$

Answers

4.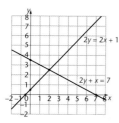

$x = 2, y = 2.5$

5. (a)

(b) $x = 2$ or 5.

6. (a)

(b) $x = -1$ or $+2$

7. (a)

(b) $x = -2.8$ or $+2.8$

8. (a)

(b) $x = -2.3$ or $+1.3$

9. (a)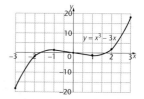

(b) $x = -1.7, 0$ or 1.7

10. (a)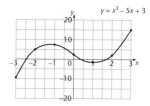

(b) $x = -2.5, 0.7$ or 1.8

Exercise 10.8a (page 151)

1. $x = 1.7$
2. $x = 2.8$
3. $x = 2.8$
4. $x = 4.6$
5. $x = 3.5$
6. $x = 2.29$
7. $x = -3.7$
8. $x = -2.5$
9. $x = 2.59$
10. $x = -2.62$

Exercise 10.9a (page 153)

1. (a) $x + y = 47, x - y = 9$
   (b) $x = 28, y = 19$
2. (a) $2c + 3d = 27.5, 3c + d = 18.5$
   (b) A cassette costs £4, a disc costs £6.50
3. (a) $s + 2b = 13, 2s + b = 11$
   (b) Small holds 3 litres, large holds 5 litres
4. $a + 2c = 31, 2a + 3c = 54$, adult costs £15, child costs £8
5. $x(x + 2) = 63$ or $x^2 + 2x - 63 = 0$, the numbers are 7 and 9

Exercise 10.10a (page 155)

1. $x > 2$
2. $y < 2x$
3. $3x + 4y > 12$
4. $y < 2x + 1$
5.
6.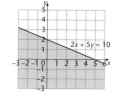

Answers

7.

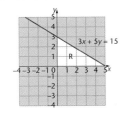

The region required is labelled R.

8.

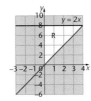

The required region is labelled R.

Exercise 10.11a (page 158)

1. $t = \dfrac{s}{a + 2b}$

2. $t = \dfrac{Pb}{b - a}$

3. $r = \sqrt{\dfrac{A}{\pi}}$

4. $a = \dfrac{cd}{b - c}$

5. $c = \dfrac{ab}{a + d}$

6. $s = \dfrac{bx + 2ax}{1 + b}$

7. $x = \dfrac{s + bs}{b + 2a}$

8. $t = \dfrac{ab}{1 - bs}$

9. $c = \sqrt{a - b}$

10. $P = \dfrac{100A}{100 + RT}$

Revision exercise 10a (page 159)

1. (a) $x = 3$
   (b) $x = 4$
   (c) $x = 6$
   (d) $x = 6$
   (e) $x = 4$
   (f) $x = 1\frac{2}{7}$
   (g) $x = 25$
   (h) $x = 5$

2. (a) $x < 3$
   (b) $x \leqslant 4$
   (c) $x > 5$
   (d) $-7 \leqslant x \leqslant 7$
   (e) $x \leqslant -4$ or $x \geqslant 4$
   (f) $-6 < x < 6$

3. $\dfrac{x}{3} = 3x - 24$, $x = 9$

4. (a) $x + 20$
   (b) $3x + 2(x + 20) = 340$,
      $x = 60$,
      a lolly costs 60p,
      an ice-cream costs 80p

5. (a) $x - 25$
   (b) $x - 25 = \dfrac{4x}{5}$, $x = 125$,

      Marcia is 125 cm,
      Carole is 100 cm

6. (a) $x = 7, y = 8$
   (b) $x = 2, y = 3$
   (c) $x = 3, y = 1$
   (d) $x = 5, y = 2$
   (e) $x = -1, y = 2$
   (f) $x = -2, y = 3$.
   (g) $x = 1, y = 2$
   (h) $x = \frac{1}{2}, y = 2\frac{1}{2}$
   (i) $x = \frac{1}{2}, y = -1$

7. (a) $x = 2$ or 4
   (b) $x = -2$ or -3
   (c) $x = 3$ or -1
   (d) $x = 5$ or -2
   (e) $x = 4$ or 1
   (f) $x = -5$ or -2
   (g) $x = 7$ or -2
   (h) $x = -15$ or -2
   (i) $x = 5$ or 4
   (j) $x = -3$ or -1
   (k) $x = 12$ or -3
   (l) $x = -9$ or 2

8. (a)

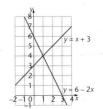

$x = 1, y = 4$

   (b)

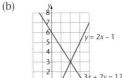

$x = 2, y = 3$

9. (a)

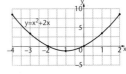

   (b) $x = -2$ or 0

10. (a)

(b) $x = 1.4$ or 3.6

11. (a)

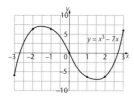

(b) $x = -2.6$, 0 or 2.6

12. (a) $x = 2.6$ (c) $x = 2.1$
(b) $x = 3.3$ (d) $x = -3.4$

13. $3c + 2a = 139$, $2c + a = 81$,
crisps cost 23p per packet,
apple juice costs 35p per
can.

14. $y - x = 200$
or $-x + y = 200$,
$3x + 2y = 2400$,
medium hold 400 g,
large hold 600 g

15. (a) $y < 3$
(b) $3x + 4y > 12$

16. (a)

(b)

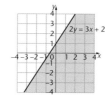

17.

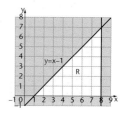

The region required is
labelled R.

18.

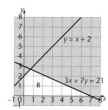

The region required is
labelled R.

Chapter II

Exercise II.Ia (page 162)

1. 7 cm (accept 6–8 cm)
2. 110° (accept 100°–120°)
3. 8–10 m
4. 25 g
5. 4 kg

Exercise II.2a (page 165)

1. discrete: 6-way, 2 pockets; continuous: 20 cm
2. discrete: 2 compartments, 3 pen holders;
   continuous: size (H)31.5 cm, (W)44.5 cm, (D)11.5 cm
3. 108 goals, 167 games, or first goal
4. 30 minutes, six minutes, 5 yards
5. Check students' own work
6. (c)
7. to nearest m or 10 m
8. (a) to nearest mile
   (b) to nearest $\frac{1}{4}$ or $\frac{1}{2}$ mile
9. to the age in years at the last birthday
10. to nearest ounce or nearest 25 g

Exercise II.3a (page 167)

1. (a) LB 26.5 cm, UB 27.5 cm
   (b) LB 29.5 cm, UB 30.5 cm
   (c) LB 127.5 cm, UB 128.5 cm
2. (a) LB 5 cm, UB 15 cm
   (b) LB 25 cm, UB 35 cm
   (c) LB 145 cm, UB 155 cm

3. (a) LB 5.55 cm, UB 5.65 cm
   (b) LB 0.75 cm, UB 0.85 cm
   (c) LB 11.95 cm, UB 12.05 cm
4. (a) LB 1.225 m, UB 1.235 m
   (b) LB 0.445 m, UB 0.455 m
   (c) LB 9.075 m, UB 9.085 m

5. (a) 10.615 s, UB 10.625 s
    (b) LB 9.805 s, UB 9.815 s
    (c) LB 48.095 s, US 48.105 s
6. 56.5 and 57.5

7. 4.65 and 4.75
8. 467.5 and 468.5
9. 34.905 and 34.915
10. 0.6335 and 0.6345

Exercise II.4a (page 168)

1. 50 mph
2. 4.5 m/s
3. 8.75 g/cm³
4. 7500 people/km²
5. 20 mph
6. 18 km/h
7. 6g
8. 20 square miles
9. 11.4 s
10. 75 km/h

Revision exercise IIa (page 169)

1. 85 cm–1 m
2. $\frac{1}{4}$ to $\frac{1}{3}$ mile or 0.4–0.5 km
3. (a) Check students' answers   (b) Check students' answers
4. (a) Jenny's
    (b) Jenny should have used cm. Her line was 10.2 cm long. Suni could not measure his line as accurately as 9.68 cm with a ruler.
5. nearest second
6. 16.5 cm by 27.5 cm
7. (a) 6.81 cm   (b) to the nearest $\frac{1}{100}$ cm
8. 7.36 m/s
9. 15 km/h
10. 8 cm³

Chapter 12

Exercise 12.1a (page 172)

1. (a) 5 minutes   (c) 10
    (b) 30 litres
2. (a) 9.30a.m.   (b) 11a.m.–12 noon
3.
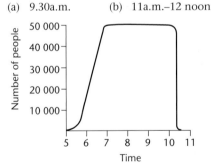

4. (a) £42   (c) (i) £30
    (b) 225   (ii) 8p
5.
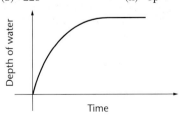

Exercise 12.2a (page 175)

1. (a) 2
    (b) −3
    (c) 1
2. (a) 2.5
    (b) 0.75
    (c) $-\frac{2}{3}$
3. (a) 6
    (b) 0
    (c) −5
    (d) $\frac{1}{4}$
4. (a) $-\frac{1}{2}$
    (b) 2.5
    (c) 1
    (d) 0.75
5. speed = 2 m/s
6. AB: 0.4, AC: 2.5, BC: −1

7. 0.26; the cost per minute, in £
8. Check students' graphs
    (a) 3
    (b) 3
9. Check students' graphs
    (a) 2
    (b) 5
    (c) 4
10. Check students' graphs
    (a) −2
    (b) −3
    (c) −1

1. (a) $y = 3x + 2$
   (b) $y = -x + 4$
   (c) $y = 5x$
2. (a) $y = 4x + 2$
   (b) $y = \frac{1}{3}x + 4$
   (c) $y = 2x$
3. (a) $y = -x + 5$
   (b) $y = -1.5x + 1$
   (c) $y = -\frac{1}{2}x - 3$
4. (a) $3, (0,-2)$
   (b) $5, (0,2)$
   (c) $-2, (0,7)$
5. (a) $-2, (0,5)$
   (b) $-2, (0,3.5)$
   (c) $-1.2, (0,2)$
6. $C = 0.08m + 30$
7. $C = 0.26x$
8.

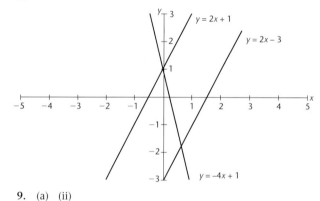

9. (a) (ii)
   (b) (i)
   (c) (iii)

10. (a)

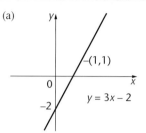

(b)

(c)

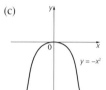

(d)

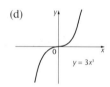

1. (a) 5 miles
   (b) The train was not moving
   (c) The train was braking for the station
   (d) CD
2.

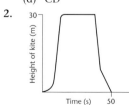

3. (a) 2.5
   (b) -1
   (c) 0
4. AB: -0.5, AC: 2.5, BC: $\frac{1}{4}$
5. (a) $2, (0, -3)$
   (b) $0.5, (0, 0)$
   (c) $\frac{1}{3}, (0, \frac{2}{3})$
   (d) $-0.4, (0, 2)$
6. (a) Check students' graphs
   (b) 1.2
   (c) 2.6 km
   (d) $d = 1.2t + 2.6$
7. (a) $y = 1.5x + 1$
   (b) $y = -0.5x + 2$
   (c) $y = -4x$
   (d) $y = 1.5x - 3$
8. Check students' sketches
9. (a)

(b)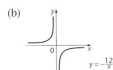

$y = -\frac{12}{x}$

(c)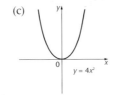

$y = 4x^2$

10. (a) (iii)
    (b) (iv)
    (c) (ii)
    (d) (i)

Chapter 13

Exercise 13.1a (page 189)

1.

First sock	Second sock
brown	brown
brown	red
brown	green
red	brown
red	red
red	green
green	brown
green	red
green	green

2.

First game	Second game	Third game
Alex	Alex	Alex
Alex	Alex	Meiling
Alex	Meiling	Alex
Meiling	Alex	Alex
Alex	Meiling	Meiling
Meiling	Alex	Meiling
Meiling	Meiling	Alex
Meiling	Meiling	Meiling

3.

First	Second	Third
B	B	B
B	B	G
B	G	B
G	B	B
B	G	G
G	B	G
G	G	B
G	G	G

(a) $\frac{1}{8}$
(b) $\frac{3}{8}$

4.

	5	6	7	8	9	10
	4	5	6	7	8	9
2nd Spin	3	4	5	6	7	8
	2	3	4	5	6	7
	1	2	3	4	5	6
		1	2	3	4	5

1st Spin

(a) $\frac{1}{25}$
(b) $\frac{4}{25}$

5.

C	X	X	X	X
D	X	X	X	X
S	X	X	X	X
H	X	X	X	X
	H	S	D	C

(a) $\frac{1}{16}$
(b) $\frac{4}{16} = \frac{1}{4}$

6.

6	X	X	X	X
5	X	X	X	X
4	X	X	X	X
3	X	X	X	X
2	X	X	X	X
1	X	X	X	X
	H	S	D	C

(a) $\frac{1}{24}$
(b) $\frac{2}{24} = \frac{1}{12}$
(c) $\frac{3}{24} = \frac{1}{8}$

7.

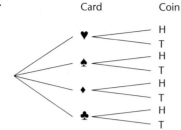

(a) $\frac{1}{8}$

(b) $\frac{2}{8} = \frac{1}{4}$

8.

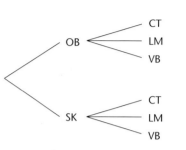

Answer $= \frac{1}{6}$

Exercise 13.2a (page 193)

1. $\frac{8}{10} = \frac{4}{5}$

2. 0.75

3. $\frac{8}{52} = \frac{2}{13}$

4. $\frac{9}{100} = 0.09$

5. 0.24

6. (a) $\frac{1}{3}$

   (b) $\frac{1}{9}$

7. $\frac{1}{169}$

8. 0.3, Likely to be influenced by one another, therefore not independent.

Exercise 13.3a (page 196)

1.

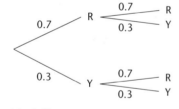

(a) 0.49

(b) 0.21

(c) 0.21

(d) 0.42

2.

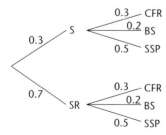

(a) 0.14

(b) 0.15

3.

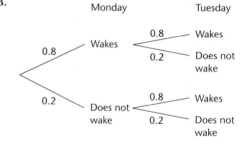

(a) 0.64

(b) 0.32

Exercise 13.3a (page 196) – continued

4. (a)

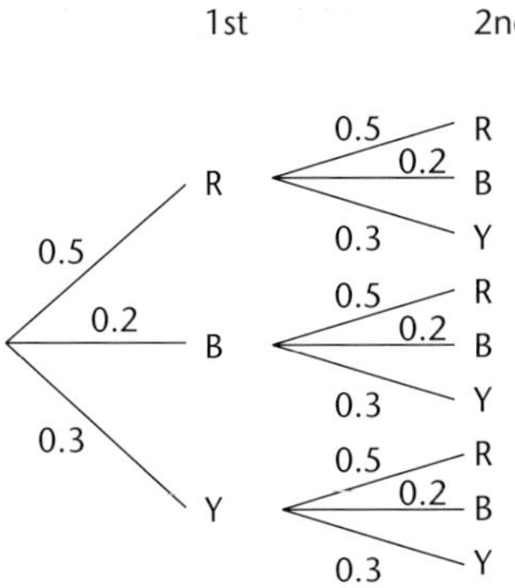

(b) (i) 0.25
(ii) 0.38

5.

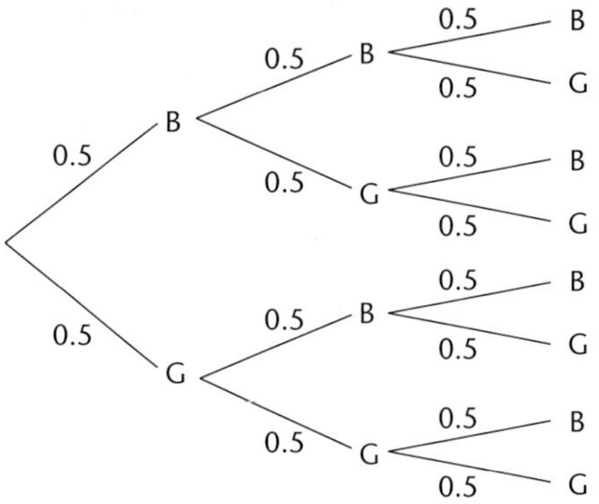

(a) 0.125
(b) 0.375

Revision exercise 13a (page 198)

1. 0.55

2. 0.06

3. $\frac{1}{100}$

4. 0.64

5.

2nd die						
6	6	12	18	24	30	36
5	5	10	15	20	25	30
4	4	8	12	16	20	24
3	3	6	9	12	15	18
2	2	4	6	8	10	12
1	1	2	3	4	5	6
1st die	1	2	3	4	5	6

(a) $\frac{1}{36}$
(b) $\frac{4}{36} = \frac{1}{9}$
(c) $\frac{3}{36} = \frac{1}{3}$

6.

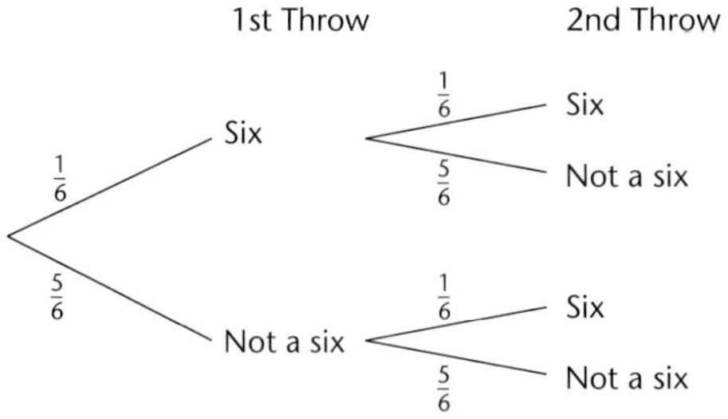

(a) $\frac{1}{36}$
(b) $\frac{11}{36}$

7.

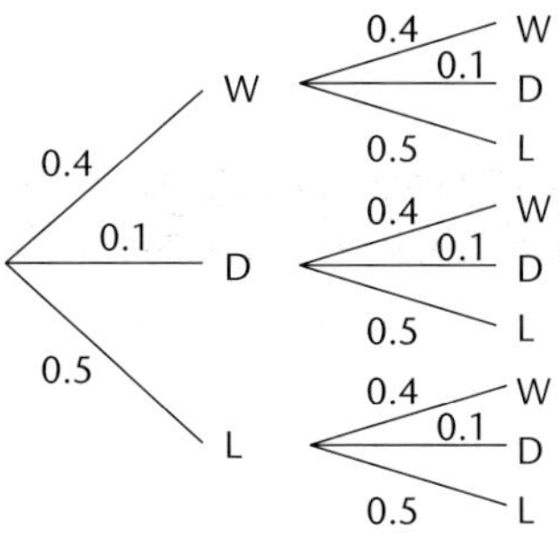

(a) 0.25
(b) 0.75
(c) 0.08

8. (a) 0.01
(b) 0.18

9.

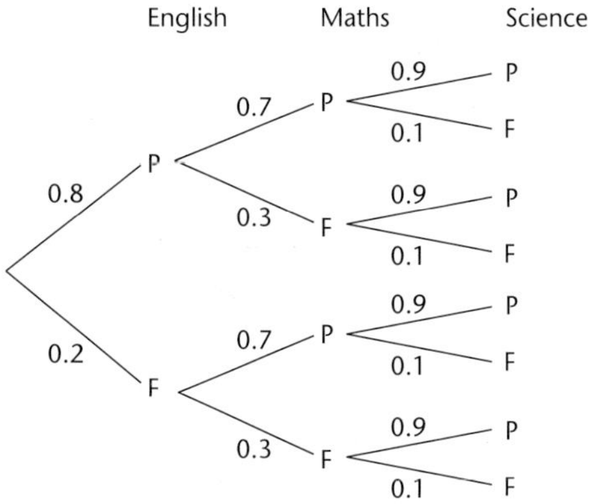

(a) 0.504
(b) 0.398

Chapter 14

1. (a) 40 cm²
   (b) 42 cm²
   (c) 30 cm²
2. (a) 46 cm²
   (b) 14 cm²
   (c) 42 cm²
3. (a) 24 cm²
   (b) 15 cm²
   (c) 21 cm²
4. $x = 8, y = 4, z = 8$
5. 3 cm

1. (a) 30 cm²
   (b) 16 cm²
   (c) 15 cm²
2. (a) 20 cm²
   (b) 12.5 cm²
   (c) 21 cm²
3. (a) 9 cm²
   (b) 18 cm²
   (c) 12 cm²
4. $a = 4, b = 3, c = 1\frac{1}{2}$
5. 9 cm

1. 837 cm³
2. 217 cm³
3. 402 cm³
4. (a) 525 cm³
   (b) 405 cm³
   (c) 67.5 cm³
5. 46.8 cm³
6. 1680 cm³
7. 16 cm
8. 9.07 cm
9. 5.1 cm
10. 6.44 m

1. (a) length
   (b) area
   (c) area
2. (b) and (c)
3. (a) and (c)
4. (a), (b) and (c)
5. (a) none
   (b) length
   (c) area

1. (a) 26.6 cm²
   (b) 27 cm²
   (c) 29.8 cm²
2. (a) 30.0 cm²
   (b) 30 cm²
   (c) 31.9 cm²
3. 550 cm³
4. 2.22
5. 15.3 cm
6. (a) area
   (b) length
   (c) volume

7. (a) 2
   (b) 2
   (c) 3
8. (a) 61.8 cm²
   (b) 23.4 cm³
9. (a) 23.5 cm²
   (b) 36.8 cm²
10. (a) 5.66 cm
    (b) 39.6 cm²

Chapter 15

1.
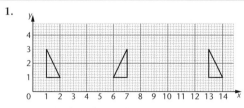

Translation through the vector $\begin{pmatrix} 12 \\ 0 \end{pmatrix}$.
Translation twice the distance between the mirror lines.

2. (a) Rotation through 180° about the midpoint of OC
   (b) Reflection in OD
   (c) Rotation through 180° about the midpoint of OE
   (d) Reflection in OF
   (e) Rotation through 180° about the midpoint of OG
   (f) Reflection in OH
   (g) Rotation through 180° about the midpoint of OA

3. (a) Rotation through 180° about O
    (b) Translation through vector $\overrightarrow{CO}$
    (c) Enlargement, centre C, scale factor 2
4. (a) Because triangle 1 can be reflected (in OD)
         onto triangle 4
    (b) Because triangle 1 can be translated
         (vector $\overrightarrow{OG}$) onto triangle 6
5. A can be mapped onto B by rotation through
    90° clockwise about O; A can be mapped onto
    C by translation through vector $\begin{pmatrix} -4 \\ -2 \end{pmatrix}$

    (Also B can be mapped onto C by rotation
    (through 90° anticlockwise about (−1, −3))

6. (a) 144°
    (b)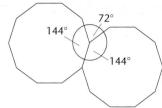

Since 2 × 144° = 288° there is a gap of 72°
that cannot be filled by a decagon.

1. (a) 14 cm
    (b) 60 m
2. Check students' drawings
3. (a) 5 cm
    (b) 3.5 km
4. (a) 2 km
    (b) 43.5 cm
    (c) 586 km
5. (a) 29.7 cm × 21 cm
    (b) 21 cm × 14.8 cm, yes, scale factor 1.4
    (c) size 14.8 cm × 10.5 cm, same scale factor
    (d) 42 cm × 29.7 cm

6. 8 cm
7. The sides are not proportional.
8. 4.2 cm, 5.88 cm
9. 3.4 cm, 4.4 cm
10. (a) Angle A is common, angle APQ = angle
         ABC (corresponding angles), angle AQP =
         angle ACB (corresponding angles); one of
         these can be substituted by 'angle sum of
         triangle'.
    (b) 6.27 cm

1. (a)–(d)
    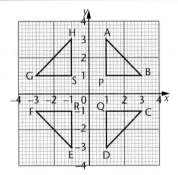
    (e) 4
    (f) No because, for example, AB ≠ BC
2. Because ABCD can be mapped onto GHAB by
    a rotation through 90° anticlockwise about O

3.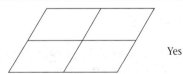
    Yes

4. (a) 9 cm, 7.75 cm
    (b) 4.75 cm, 2.25 cm
5. (a) 4 cm
    (b) 4.5 km
6. 2.4 m
7. 6 ÷ 8 = 0.75, 3 ÷ 5 = 0.6, the ratios are not
    equal so the triangles are not similar
8. (a) 180 − (40 + 55) = 85 so the angles are
         the same
    (b) 1.7
9. 6.64 cm, 6.24 cm
10. 7.14 m

Answers

481

Chapter 16

In comment questions, clearly students may use other words.
Answers read off graphs are approximate particularly from lines of best fit as different students will have different line

Exercise 16.1a (page 228)

1. Colin has, on average, lower scores. Vijay is more consistent. (ranges 25 and 16)
2. Town A's dental charges are higher but Town B has a greater spread of charges.
3. Nine numbers with a median of 7 and a greater range than 9.
4. Both means 18, ranges: Moralia 13, Sivarium 76, so on average they are the same but there is a much wider spread in Sivarium.
5. Tara: mean 14.8, range 4; Justin: mean 15.6, range 10; Justin, on average, is better but more inconsistent. Five homeworks is a very small sample on which to make judgement.
6. Jubilee Road: mode 1, range 6; Riverside Road: mode 3, range 8; Riverside Road has more letters and a wider spread.

7. Mean £4.30, range £4 to £5 (Cannot tell exactly, since the amounts are given to the nearest pound.)
   Class 9b on average get less pocket money but with a greater spread of amounts.
8. (a) A: median 12, IQR 8; B: median 13.5, IQR 4
   (b) Fire brigade A is quicker on average but has a greater spread (variation in times).
   (c)
   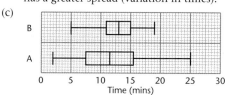
9. Probably LightGlo for greater guaranteed life. If buying large numbers, you may choose Britlite as the spread is not so important when buying in bulk.

Exercise 16.2a (page 233)

1. Fairly strong positive correlation
2. Weak negative correlation
3. (a)
   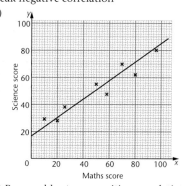
   (b) Reasonably strong positive correlation
   (d) (i) 45
       (ii) 84

4.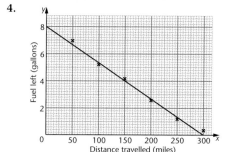
   (b) Strong negative correlation
   (d) 3.5 gallons

5.

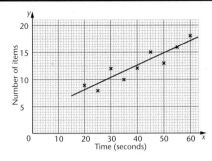

6. e.g.

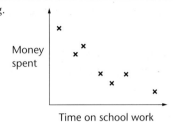

(b) Fairly strong positive correlation
(d) 11
(e) Too far out of the range of the given data

Exercise 16.3a (page 237)

1. (a), (c)

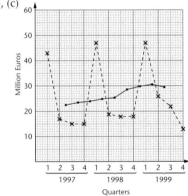

(b) moving averages 22.5, 23.5, 24, 24.75, 25.5, 28, 29.75, 30.75, 29.5
(d) general upward trend, though slight dip at end; always much higher in first quarter

2. (a), (c)

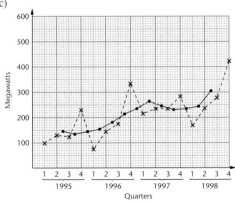

(b) moving averages 143.6, 138.0, 142.3, 154.8, 181.5, 217.1, 239.8, 255.2, 241.9, 230.0, 231.4, 243.3, 304
(d) general upward trend, with a few exceptions; first quarter always lowest, fourth quarter always highest

3. (a), (c)

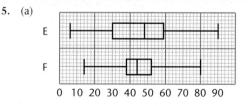

(b) moving averages 118, 112.5, 108.75, 111, 104.5, 100.25, 101.5, 98, 95.25, 94, 89.5, 86.75, 83

(d) general downward trend; third quarter always lowest

4. (a), (c)

(b) moving averages 420.7, 427.5, 436.7, 446.3, 460.7, 460.7, 464, 455.8, 449.2, 439.7, 432.5, 427.5, 424.7, 415.3, 397.3, 391, 359.5, 346.2, 344.3

(d) general trend upwards and then downwards; Monday always least, Friday and Saturday always highest

Revision exercise 16a (page 240)

1. David takes longer but his times are more consistent.

2. 10f median 15, range 21; 10g median 11, range 28; 10g students do question more quickly on average but with a wider spread of times. The interquartile range would eliminate extremes.

3. Mean £79 400, range a maximum of £120 000. House prices are higher in the south-east, with a wider spread of prices.

4. French adults drink more wine than English adults. Spread of amounts is similar but slightly wider in England.

5. (a)

(b) French: median 44, IQR 14; English: median 48, IQR 29; The French marks are higher but with a wider spread.

6. Both have positive correlation. Girls have stronger correlation than boys. Boys are heavier and taller than girls.

7. Negative

8. (a)
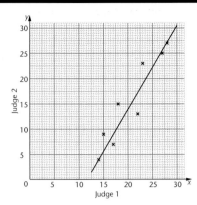

(b) A fair degree of positive correlation

(d) 22–23

9. (a)
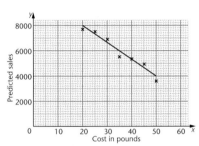

(b) Fairly strong negative correlation

(c) 6200

(d) Too far outside the range of the data.

10. e.g.
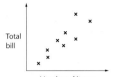

11. (a), (c) See graph

(b) moving averages 37 175, 25 200, 32 750, 30 000, 27 600, 25 800, 24 675, 24 075, 23 475, 22 775, 22 000, 21 175, 20 325

(d) general trend downwards; quarter up to January always highest, then steadily lower

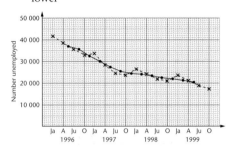

Chapter 17

Exercise 17.1a (page 245)

Check the accuracy of students' drawings. The diagrams in these answers are not accurate but are given as a guide.

1.
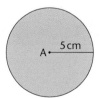

The locus is the shaded area.

2.
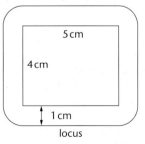

The locus is four straight lines and four quarter-circles, all 1 cm outside the rectangle.

3.

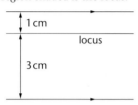

The line drawn is the bisector of AB. The region shaded is the locus.

4.

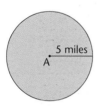

The locus is the line parallel to the two given lines.

5.

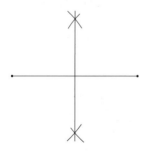

The region is inside a circle radius 5 miles.

6.

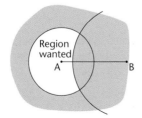

7.

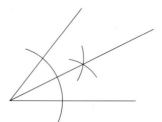

8.

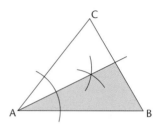

9.

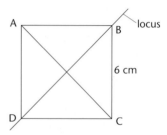

The locus passes through B and D.

10. Bisect angle C and the locus is the region on the side nearer to A.

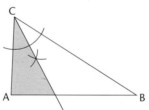

The regions **not** required are shaded in these answers.

1.

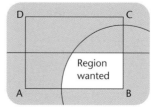

2.

3. The point equidistant from all sides is the intersection of the bisectors of the angles.

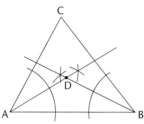

4.

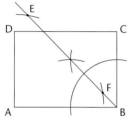

The points are marked E and F.

5. The region required is labelled R.

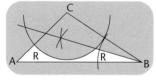

6. The region required is labelled R.

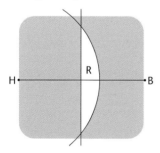

7. The regions required are labelled R.

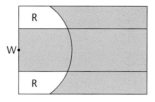

8. The region required is labelled R.

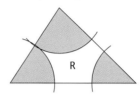

9. The region required is labelled R.

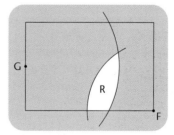

10. The region required is labelled R.

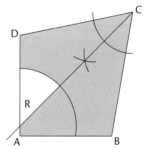

1.

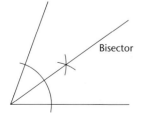

2.

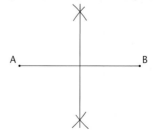

3.

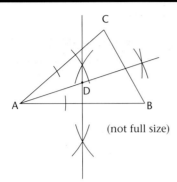

(not full size)

4. (Drawn half size)

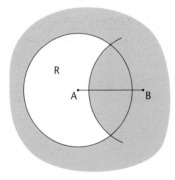

5. The region required is labelled R.

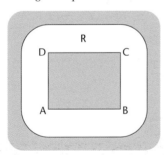

6. The region required is labelled R.

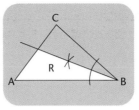

7. The region required is R. Note that it includes a region outside the triangle ABC. (Drawn half size)

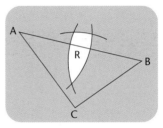

8.

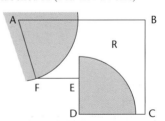

9. The region not covered by heat detectors is labelled R. (Drawn half size)

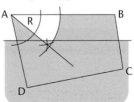

10. The region required is labelled R.

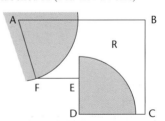

Chapter 18

Any equivalent form for an answer is acceptable. Various forms have been used.

Exercise 18.1a (page 251)

1. $y \propto x$
2. $y \propto x$
3. $t \propto \frac{1}{s}$
4. $p \propto w$
5. $p \propto \frac{1}{n}$
6. $y \propto x$
7. $y \propto \frac{1}{x}$
8. $y \propto \frac{1}{x}$
9. $y \propto x$
10. $y \propto x$

Exercise 18.2a (page 252)

1. $y = \frac{1}{3}x$
2. $xy = 30$
3. $xy = 80$
4. $y = 5x$
5. $y = \frac{2}{3}x$

Exercise 18.3a (page 253)

1. 12
2. 4
3. 8
4. 1
5. 1.25
6. 0.625
7. $4\frac{4}{9}$
8. 96
9. $\frac{3}{8}$ or 0.375
10. 3.9375
11. $y \propto x^2$
12. $y \propto \frac{1}{x^2}$
13. $y \propto x^3$
14. $y \propto \frac{1}{x}$
15. $y \propto \frac{1}{x^2}$

Exercise 18.4a (page 255)

1. $y = \frac{x^2}{12}$
2. $y = \frac{4x^2}{25}$
3. $y = \frac{x^3}{27}$
4. $y = \frac{64}{x^2}$
5. $y = \frac{5x^2}{36}$
6. $y = \frac{90}{x^2}$
7. $y = \frac{160}{x^2}$
8. $y = \frac{12x^3}{125}$
9. $y = 0.003x^3$
10. $y = \frac{7x^2}{64}$
11. $y = \frac{x^2}{5}$
12. $y = \frac{125}{x^2}$
13. $y = 0.04x^3$
14. $xy = 25$
15. $y = \frac{288}{x^2}$

Revision exercise 18a (page 255)

1. 17.5, $w = 3.5d$
2. 10, $dn = 30$
3. 0.06, $f = \frac{54}{d^2}$
4. $25, 125, 625, 1, 0.2$
5. (a) $y \propto \frac{1}{x}$, $xy = 50$
   (b) $y \propto x$, $y = 2x$
   (c) $y \propto \frac{1}{x}$, $xy = 0.2$
   (d) $y \propto x^2$, $y = 0.025x^2$
   (e) $y \propto \frac{1}{x^2}$, $y = \frac{25}{x^2}$
   (f) $y \propto x^3$, $y = 0.4x^3$

Chapter 19

Exercise 19.1a (page 258)

1. $(x + 6)(x + 1)$
2. $(x - 4)(x - 2)$
3. $2(x + 2)(x + 1)$
4. $(2x + 1)(x + 4)$
5. $3(2x - 1)(x - 2)$
6. $(3x - 2)(x - 3)$
7. $(3x - 5)(x - 2)$
8. $(2x + 3)(2x + 1)$
9. $(5x - 3)(x - 2)$
10. $(3x - 2)(2x - 5)$

Exercise 19.2a (page 260)

1. $(x - 3)(x + 2)$
2. $(x + 5)(x - 2)$
3. $(2x - 1)(x + 3)$
4. $(3x + 4)(x - 2)$
5. $(2x - 1)(x + 5)$
6. $5(x - 5)(x + 2)$
7. $(2x + 1)(2x - 3)$
8. $(3x - 7)(x + 2)$
9. $(2x - 7)(x + 3)$
10. $(2x - 7)(3x + 2)$

Exercise 19.3a (page 262)

1. $x = 3$ or -2
2. $x = -\frac{7}{2}$ or -1
3. $x = -\frac{5}{2}$ or 2
4. $x = 0$ or $\frac{2}{3}$
5. $x = \frac{1}{5}$ or -3
6. $x = 5$ or -5
7. $x = -\frac{3}{2}$ or 3
8. $x = -\frac{3}{2}$ or 7
9. $x = -0.84$ or -7.16
10. $x = -0.82$ or 1.82
11. $x = -1.85$ or 0.18
12. $x = 0.54$ or 1.86
13. $x = -2.32$ or 0.52
14. $x = -0.19$ or 5.19
15. $x = -2.27$ or -0.74

Exercise 19.4a (page 264)

1. $\dfrac{11x}{10}$

2. $\dfrac{-4x + 5}{6}$

3. $\dfrac{17x - 12}{30}$

4. $\dfrac{3x - 1}{x(x + 1)}$

5. $\dfrac{x + 6}{2x(x + 2)}$

6. $\dfrac{5x + 1}{(x + 1)(x - 1)}$

7. $\dfrac{2x^2 - 9x - 5}{(3x + 1)(x + 3)}$ or $\dfrac{(2x + 1)(x - 5)}{(3x + 1)(x + 3)}$

8. $\dfrac{4x^2 - x + 3}{(x - 1)(x + 2)}$

9. $\dfrac{7x^2 - 8x - 10}{5x(x + 1)}$

10. $\dfrac{23x^2 - 4x + 51}{9(x - 3)(x + 2)}$

11. $\dfrac{3a^2}{2b}$

12. $\dfrac{8b^4}{a^2c}$

13. $\dfrac{2}{x - 3}$

14. $\dfrac{3x}{x + 3}$

15. $\dfrac{x - 1}{x + 2}$

Exercise 19.5a (page 267)

1. $x = 5$
2. $x = 3$
3. $x = 0$
4. $x = -3$
5. $x = 1$
6. $x = -2$ or $+2$
7. $x = -1$ or 5
8. $x = -1$ or $\frac{3}{4}$
9. $x = -\frac{3}{2}$ or $\frac{5}{3}$
10. $x = -11$ or 2
11. $x > 3$
12. $x > 2$
13. $-2 < x < \frac{1}{3}$
14. $-3 < x < 2$
15. $x < -\frac{1}{2}$ or $x > 2$

Exercise 19.6a (page 269)

1. $t = \dfrac{s}{a + 2b}$

2. $t = \dfrac{Pb}{b - a}$

3. $x = \dfrac{s + bs}{b + 2a}$

4. $t = \dfrac{ab}{1 - bs}$

5. $c = \dfrac{1 - ab}{a}$

6. $d = \dfrac{b + c - a}{a - b}$

7. $c = \sqrt{(a - b)}$

8. $P = \dfrac{100A}{100 + RT}$

9. $x = \dfrac{a + b}{2a - b}$

10. $L = \dfrac{T^2 g}{4\pi^2}$

Exercise 19.7a (page 271)

1. Find where the curve crosses (a) $y = 0$ (b) $y = 2$
2. Find where the curve crosses $y = 5$.
3. $x^2 - 4x + 3 = 0$
4. $y = x^2 - 3$
5. $y = 3 - x$

6. (a)

x	-3	-2	-1	0	1	2	3
x^2	9	4	1	0	1	4	9
-5	-5	-5	-5	-5	-5	-5	-5
$y = x^2 - 5$	4	-1	-4	-5	-4	-1	4

(b) (i) $x = -2.2$ or $+2.2$
   (ii) Intersection with $y = -2$, $x = -1.7$ or $+1.7$

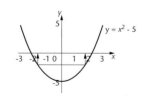

7. (a)

x	-2	-1	0	1	2	3	4
x^2	4	1	0	1	4	9	16
$2x^2$	8	2	0	2	8	18	32
$-3x$	6	3	0	-3	-6	-9	-12
$y = 2x^2 - 3x$	14	5	0	-1	2	9	20

(b) Solution of $2x^2 - 3x - 5 = 0$ is when $y = 5$, $x = -1$ or 2.5.

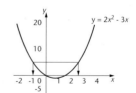

8. (a)

x	-2	-1	0	1	2	3	4
x^2	4	1	0	1	4	9	16
5	5	5	5	5	5	5	5
$y = x^2 + 5$	9	6	5	6	9	14	21

For $y = 3x + 7$, three points are
$(-2, 1)$, $(0, 7)$, $(4, 19)$

(b) At intersection $x^2 + 5 = 3x + 7$ or
$x^2 - 3x - 2 = 0$. Solution is $x = -0.6$ or 3.6.

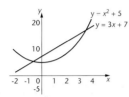

9. (a)

x	-3	-2	-1	0	1	2	3
x^3	-27	-8	-1	0	1	8	27
$-3x$	9	6	3	0	-3	-6	-9
$y = x^3 - 3x$	-18	-2	2	0	-2	2	18

(b) (i) $x^3 - 6x + 5 = 0$ is $x^3 - 3x - 3x + 5 = 0$
or $x^3 - 3x = 3x - 5$, so other graph is
$y = 3x - 5$; points $(-3, 14)$, $(0, -5)$, $(3, 4)$
(ii) Solution is $x = -2.8$ or 1 or 1.8

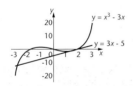

10. (a)

x	-2	-1	0	1	2	3	4
x^2	4	1	0	1	4	9	16
$-2x$	4	2	0	-2	-4	-6	-8
-4	-4	-4	-4	-4	-4	-4	-4
$y = x^2 - 2x - 4$	4	-1	-4	-5	-4	-1	4

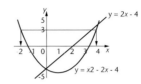

(b) (i) $x^2 - 2x - 7 = 0$ is the same as
$x^2 - 2x - 4 - 3 = 0$ or $x^2 - 2x - 4 = 3$,
where $y = 3$, so $x = -1.8$ or 3.8.
(ii) $x^2 - 4x = 0$ is the same as
$x^2 - 2x - 4 - 2x + 4 = 0$ or
$x^2 - 2x - 4 = 2x - 4$, where it crosses
$y = 2x - 4$, so $x = 0$ or 4.
(iii) $x^2 - 2x - 4 > 0$ above x-axis;
$x < 1.2$ or $x > 3.2$

Revision exercise 19a (page 273)

1. (a) $(x - 9)(x - 7)$
(b) $2(x + 3)(x - 7)$
(c) $(x - 2)(3x - 2)$
(d) $(x + 3)(2x - 5)$

(e) $3(x - 4)(x + 4)$
(f) $(2x + 3)(x - 7)$
(g) $3(2x + 1)(x - 5)$

(h) $(5x - 6)(x - 3)$
(i) $(2x + 1)(4x - 5)$
(j) $(3x + 2)(2x - 5)$

2. (a) $x = 4$ or -2
(b) $x = \frac{1}{2}$ or -5
(c) $x = \frac{5}{3}$ or 1
(d) $x = -\frac{7}{2}$ or 1

(e) $x = \frac{2}{3}$ or 2
(f) $x = 0$ or $\frac{5}{2}$
(g) $x = \frac{1}{6}$ or 1

(h) $x = -\frac{3}{2}$ or 4
(i) $x = \frac{2}{7}$ or 2
(j) $x = \frac{3}{2}$ or $-\frac{3}{2}$

3. (a) $x = 0.21$ or 4.79
(b) $x = -1.46$ or 0.46
(c) $x = 0.54$ or 1.86

4. (a) $\dfrac{5x + 2}{6}$

(b) $\dfrac{7x - 17}{20}$

(c) $\dfrac{5x}{(x + 1)(3x - 2)}$

(d) $\dfrac{x^2 + 10x - 1}{(x - 1)(x + 4)}$

(e) $\dfrac{2x}{x + 3}$

(f) $\dfrac{x - 2}{2x - 1}$

5. (a) $x = 3$
(b) $x = 2$
(c) $x = -4$ or 2
6. (a) $x < \frac{2}{5}$

(d) $x = 9$ or -3
(e) $x = 2$
(f) $x = -3$ or 1
(b) $0 < x < 2$

(g) $x = \frac{1}{2}$
(h) $x = 4$ twice

(c) $x < -5$ or $x > 6$

7. (a) $p = \dfrac{q}{7}$

   (b) $p = \dfrac{2}{2 - t}$

   (c) $p = \dfrac{qs}{s + q}$

   (d) $p = \dfrac{Tq}{2 + q}$

   (e) $p = \dfrac{1 + 2a}{4a - 1}$

   (f) $p = \pm\sqrt{2b - 4a}$

8. (a)

x	-6	-5	-4	-3	-2	-1	0	1	2	3
x^2	36	25	16	9	4	1	0	1	4	9
$+3x$	-18	-15	-12	-9	-6	-3	0	3	6	9
-7	-7	-7	-7	-7	-7	-7	-7	-7	-7	-7
$y = x^2 + 3x - 7$	11	3	-3	-7	-9	-7	-3	-3	3	11

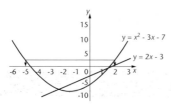

(b) (i) $x^2 + 3x - 7 = 0$ when $y = 0$, solution is $x = -4.5$ or 1.5

   (ii) $x^2 + 3x - 10 = 0$ is the same as $x^2 + 3x - 7 - 3 = 0$ or $x^2 + 3x - 7 = 3$.
   When $y = 3$, solution is -5 or 2.

(c) (i) $x^2 + x - 4 = 0$ is the same as $x^2 + 3x - 7 - 2x + 3 = 0$ or $x^2 + 3x - 7 = 2x - 3$.
   Equation is $y = 2x - 3$.

   (ii) Solution $x = -2.6$ or 1.6

Chapter 20

Exercise 20.1 (page 275)

1.

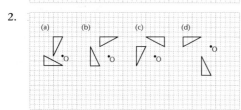

2.

3. (a) A′(−2, 1), B′(−5, 3), C′(−2, 6)
   (b) A′(6, −1), B′(9, −3), C′(6, −6)

Exercise 20.2a (page 276)

Students' diagrams should be checked. Coordinates of rotated shapes are given below:

1. A′(2, 2.4), B′(4.6, 3.9), C′(3.5, 5.6)
2. A′(1, 2), B′(−2.8, 3.3), C′(−1.1, 4.8)
3. A′(0, 2.8), B′(2, 5), C′(0, 7), D′(−2.2, 5)

Exercise 20.3a (page 277)

Students' diagrams should be checked.

1. Rotation of −90° about the point (−5, 1).
2. Rotation of 180° about the point (0.5, 1.5).
3. Rotation of 32° about the point (−2.5, 1.2).

Exercise 20.4a (page 279)

Students' diagrams should be checked.

1. A′(−6, −6), B′(−15, 0), C′(−15, 3), D′(−6, 3)
2. P′(−8, −4), Q′(−12, 2), R′(−4, 4)
3. A′(4, −4), B′(6, −4), C′(6, −8), D′(8, −8),
   E′(8, −10), F′(4, −10)

1. Triangle ABC is congruent to triangle KJL (S,S,S) or (S,A,S)
2. (a) Congruent (S,A,S)
   (b) not congruent
   (c) third angle = 80° therefore congruent, (A,S,A)
   (d) congruent, (R.H.S)
   (e) congruent (S,S,S)
   (f) not congruent
3.
   ABCD is a rectangle. In triangles ABD, ABC: AB is common to both, AD = BC, angles DAB and ABC both = 90° therefore triangle ABD is congruent to triangle BAC (S,A,S).
   Therefore BD = AC
4.
   AX, XC, AY, YB, BZ, ZC are all equal. The angles at A, B, C are equal.
   Therefore triangles CXZ, BZY, AYX are congruent (S,A,S)
   Therefore XZ = ZY = YX.
   Therefore XYZ must be an equilateral triangle.

1. 40° about the point (−7.6, 0.5)
2. A′(10, 7), B′(6, 7), C′(6, 5)
3. A′(6, 5), B′(3.5, 5), C′(3.5, 3)
4.
   Because joining the midpoints as shown creates isosceles triangles all the marked angles are 45°.
   Therefore the angles of the quadrilateral are 90°.
   The triangles ZAW, WBX, XCY, YDZ are congruent, (SAS).
   Therefore the sides ZW WX, XY, YZ are equal.
   Therefore ZWXY is a square.

Chapter 2I

1. students' own response
2. (a) e.g. biased only asking tennis players, and about tennis courts
   (b) students = own response
   (c) e.g. across age range, sex of respondents, and activities considered; possible strata suggested.

1. (a) no – e.g. mainly male
   (b) no – likely to exclude families with small children
   (c) no – excludes people who work
   (d no – would only include those who work in a particular area
   Representative sample obtained by e.g. systematic sampling

1. (a) e.g. localised response, only asking people who are not at work. Better to visit different locations/areas and extend the hours.
   (b) may not provide the right distribution of age and sex of students; better to choose by stratified or random sampling.
2. (a) by sampling
   (b) by sampling

Exercise 21.4 (page 291)

1. Total number of pupils = 972
   Y7 = 21.4 i.e. 21   Y8 = 19.86 i.e. 20
   Y9 = 20.27, i.e. 20   Y10 = 19.5 i.e. 20
   Y11 = 18.9 i.e. 19
2. Total pupils = 464, Y11 = 25
3. (If P = population)
   Day 1 catch 16.7%   implies P = 2695
   Day 2 catch 15.8%   implies P = 2848
   Day 3 catch 20%   implies P = 2250
   Day 4 catch 18.8%   implies P = 2394
   Mean value of P = 2547

4. Students' own work
   Example students' own work.
   The true mean is 1.429 cm

Exercise 21.5 (page 294)

1. (a) Label the rows and columns 0 to 9 so that
       0, 0 represents the mark of 14% and 3, 3 a
       mark of 46%. Use 10 random numbers to
       select the marks of 10 pupils and calculate
       the mean and median for the sample and
       hence for the 100 pupils.
   (b) Students' own work; mean = 42.09;
       median = 35
2. Students' own work

Revision exercise 21a (page 295)

1. (a) yes – because the number of pupils is
       significantly different
   (b) 14

Chapter 22

Exercise 22.1a (page 298)

1. (a) $n^{1/3}$ (b) n^{-3} (c) $n^{2/5}$
2. (a) $\frac{1}{4}$ (b) 2   (c) 1   (d) $\frac{1}{16}$ (e) 8
3. (a) 2   (b) $\frac{1}{8}$ (c) 16   (d) 64   (e) 8
4. (a) 8   (b) $\frac{1}{4}$ (c) 1   (d) 16   (e) 32
5. (a) 12   (b) 64   (c) $\frac{1}{3}$ (d) 27
6. (a) 9   (b) 16   (c) $\frac{16}{3} = 5\frac{1}{3}$ (d) 15
7. (a) 1.925 414 = 1.9254
   (b) 21.717 639 = 21.718
   (c) 1.045 910 = 1.0459
   (d) 0.003 538 869 = 0.003 538 9

8. (a) 31
   (b) 1.009 980 6 = 1.0100
   (c) 1.544 857 = 1.5449
   (d) 2.107 773 = 2.1078
9. (a) 106.1208 = 106.12
   (b) 13.427 845 = 13.428
   (c) 25.304 39 = 25.304
10. (a) 3.7711
    (b) 2.167 981 = 2.1680
    (c) 0

Exercise 22.2a (page 300)

1. (a) 3^3 (c) $3^{3/2}$ (e) 3^2
   (b) 3^{-1} (d) 3^6 (f) 3^{11n}
2. (a) 5^4 (d) $5^{-5/2}$
   (b) 5^2 (e) cannot simplify
   (c) 5^{-1} (f) 5^{7n}

3. (a) $2^3 \times 3$ (d) $2^2 \times 3^{-2}$ or $\dfrac{2^2}{3^2}$
   (b) $2^6 \times 3^2$ (e) $3^3 \times 2^{-1}$ or $\dfrac{3^3}{2}$
   (c) $2^{1/3} \times 3^{2/3}$ (f) $2^{4n} \times 3^{2n}$

4. (a) 3×5^2
    (b) $2^4 \times 3^2$
    (c) $2^2 \times 3 \times 5^2$
    (d) $2^2 \times 3^4$

5. (a) $12a^5b^3$
    (b) can't simplify
    (c) $2a$
    (d) $18a$

6. (a) $27a^6$
    (b) $\dfrac{1}{8b^3}$
    (c) $4a^2$
    (d) $2ab^3$
    (e) $\dfrac{a}{2}$

7. (a) $\dfrac{3a^2c}{b}$
    (b) $\dfrac{2a^2c + b}{3}$
    (c) $3a^2b + 4ab^2$

8. (a) $x = 4$
    (b) $x = -3$
    (c) $x = 2$
    (d) $x = 2$
    (e) $x = \frac{1}{2}$
    (f) $x = -\frac{1}{3}$
    (g) $x = 64$
    (h) $x = \pm\frac{1}{5}$

9. (a) $9a - 4$
    (b) $a + b$
    (c) $-\dfrac{3}{a^2} + a^2 - 2$

10. Order is x^4, x, $x^{\frac{1}{2}}$, x^{-2}

1. (a) (i) £2382.03 (ii) £4793.12
    (b) $A = 2000 \times 1.06^n$

2. (a) (i) £5397.26 (ii) £2506.51
    (b) $A = 9000 \times 0.88^n$

3. (a) 17.36 million (b) 25.66 million

4. (a) 36.45 g (b) 50×0.9^n
    (c) 6.6 years

5. $n = 2 \times 3^t$

6. (a) (i) 9.45 million (ii) 6.97 million
    (b) $N = 11 \times 0.97^n$

7.

x	-2	-1	0	1	2	3	4	5
y	0.25	0.5	1	2	4	8	16	32

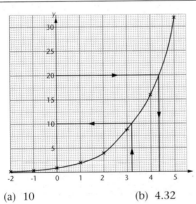

(a) 10 (b) 4.32

8.

x	0	0.5	1	1.5	2	2.5	3	3.5	4
y	1	0.577	0.333	0.192	0.111	0.064	0.039	0.021	0.012

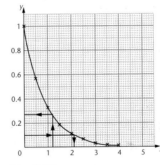

(a) 0.27 (b) 2.1

1. (a) n^{-1}
    (b) $m^{1/3}$
    (c) $n^{-1/2}$

2. (a) $\frac{1}{4}$
    (b) 1
    (c) 5
    (d) 16
    (e) 4
    (f) $\frac{1}{25}$
    (g) 2
    (h) 32
    (i) $1\frac{1}{2}$
    (j) 144

3. (a) 625
    (b) 80
    (c) 8
    (d) 8
    (e) 42
    (f) 500
    (c) 4096
    (g) 4
    (h) $2\frac{1}{12}$
    (d) 0.000 256 74

4. (a) 2.9242
    (b) 0.49842

5. (a) 9   (b) 1.6765   (c) 3.9842   (d) 512

6. (a) 2^7 (b) 3^6 (c) $7^{3/5}$ (d) 3^3 (e) 2^{6n+5}

7. (a) $2^3 \times 5$ (b) $2 \times 3^2 \times 5$ (c) $2^3 \times 17$ (d) $2^2 \times 3 \times 7^2$

8. (a) $3^2 \times 5^2$ (b) $2 \times 5^{1/3}$ (c) $2^4 \times 7^{10/3}$ (d) $2^3 \times 3^{5/2}$

9. (a) $8a^3b^6$ (c) $2b^{-1}$ or $\dfrac{2}{b}$ (e) $\dfrac{ba^{-2}}{4}$ or $\dfrac{b}{4a^2}$ (g) $5ab^2$

    (b) $3a^2$ (d) $2a^3bc^{-1}$ or $\dfrac{2a^3b}{c}$ (f) $7a^{-1}b$ or $\dfrac{7b}{a}$ (h) $\dfrac{b}{3}$

10. (a) (i) $x = 4$ (iii) $x = \frac{1}{2}$ (v) $x = \frac{1}{4}$ (vii) $x = 121$

       (ii) $x = -2$ (iv) $x = \frac{3}{2}$ (vi) $x = -\frac{5}{9}$ (viii) $x = \pm\frac{1}{13}$

    (b) Order is x^{-1}, $\sqrt[3]{x}$, $x^{\frac{1}{2}}$, x^4

11. (a) 382 884   (b) 488 668   (c) $300\,000 \times 1.05^n$ (d) 15 days

12.

x	0	0.5	1	1.5	2	2.5	3	3.5	4
y	1	0.707	0.5	0.354	0.25	0.177	0.125	0.088	0.063

(a) 0.29   (b) 0.75

Chapter 23

Exercise 23.1a (page 311)

1. (a) 3.56 cm
   (b) 13.6 cm
   (c) 27.0 cm
   (d) 12.4 cm
   (e) 8.41 cm
2. (a) 9.08 cm²
   (b) 25.1 cm²
   (c) 139 cm²
   (d) 59.5 cm²
   (e) 18.1 cm²
3. (a) 25.7 cm
   (b) 25.9 cm
   (c) 25.8 cm
4. (a) 43°
   (b) 100°
   (c) 185°
   (d) 58°
   (e) 148°
5. (a) 4.9 cm
   (b) 3.4 cm
   (c) 4.8 cm
   (d) 5.6 cm
   (e) 3.7 cm
   (f) 2.5 cm

Exercise 23.2a (page 316)

1. (a) 18 cm³
   (b) 54 cm³
   (c) 70 m³
2. (a) 103 cm³
   (b) 314 cm³
   (c) 51.5 cm³
3. (a) 524 cm³
   (b) 998 cm³
   (c) 33.5 mm³
4. (a) 242 cm²
   (b) 18.8 cm²
   (c) 101 cm²
5. (a) 92.4 cm²
   (b) 204 cm²
6. (a) 314 cm²
   (b) 483 cm²
   (c) 50.3 mm²
7. 117 ml
8. 88
9. 61.3 cm²
10. 3.17 cm

Exercise 23.3a (page 319)

1. 63.3 cm²
2. (a) 5.74 cm   (b) 11.8 cm
3. (a) 3 cm   (b) 1225 cm³
4. Similar triangles show that radius of cone is $2r$.
   So the volume of cone is $\frac{1}{2}\pi$
   $(2r)^2 \times 2h = \frac{8}{3}\pi r^2 h$.

Volume of frustum
$= \frac{8}{3}\pi r^2 h - \frac{1}{3}\pi r^2 h$
$= \frac{7}{3}\pi r^2 h$

5. (a) 3.54 cm   (b) 29.5 cm³
6. (b) 6.13 cm
7. (a) 3.34 cm   (b) 72.0 cm³

8. 484 cm²
9. 38.4 cm²
10. 169 cm³

Exercise 23.4a (page 322)

1. (a) 4
   (b) 9
   (c) 25
2. (a) 1000
   (b) 64
   (c) 125
3. (a) 4
   (b) 6
4. 25 cm^2

5. 1 litre
6. 360 cm^2
7. 1 : 50
8. 12.6
9. 27 : 64 : 125
10. (a) 2 m
    (b) 3 m^2
    (c) 18 750 cm^3

Revision exercise 23a (page 324)

1. (a) 8.51 cm
   (b) 27.7 cm^2
2. (a) 66.0°
   (b) 144°
3. (a) 6.21 cm
   (b) 4.84 cm
4. 7240 cm^3

5. 136 m^3
6. 800 ml
7. 7.42 cm
8. 18.7 cm^2
9. 65.6 cm^2
10. 44

Chapter 24

Exercise 24.1a (page 326)

1. (a) 61.2 s
   (b) 24.51 s
   (c) 12.4 m
   (d) 1.747 kg
2. (a) 61 s
   (b) 24.49 s
   (c) 12.38 m
   (d) 1.745 kg

3. (a) 704 g
   (b) 6.7 cm
   (c) 790 g
   (d) 4.4 s
4. (a) 702 g
   (b) 6.5 cm
   (c) 770 g
   (d) 4.2 s
5. 50.8 cm

Exercise 24.2a (page 328)

1. (a) 16.3625 m^2
   (b) 20.507 175 m^2
   (c) 56.910 875 m^2
   (d) 40.1625 m^2
2. (a) 15.5625 m^2
   (b) 20.415 675 m^2
   (c) 56.759 175 m^2
   (d) 38.8825 m^2

3. (a) 5.08 cm/s
   (b) 1.25 m/s
   (c) 10.5 m/s
4. (a) 5.61 cm/s
   (b) 1.28 m/s
   (c) 10.7 m/s
5. 0.022 88 km/cm^3

Revision exercise 24a (page 330)

1. 535 g, 505 g
2. (a) 31.2 cm   (b) 8.2 cm
3. 15 min 24.16 s
4. (a) UB of space = 1000.5 mm
       UB of each unit = 500.5 mm,
       so UB of two units = 1001 mm
       (or other valid explanation).
   (b) 1.5 mm
5. (a) 4.075 cm   (b) 394 cm^3
6. 101 cm^3, 94.2 cm^3
7. 4.06 cm
8. (a) 7.38 m/s   (b) 7.35 m/s
9. 978.75 m
10. 602 people/km^2

Chapter 25

Exercise 25.1a (page 334)

1. (a) 41.6°
   (b) 15 cm
   (c) 17 cm
   (d) 28.1°
2. (a) 5.29 cm
   (b) 48.6°
   (c) 12.8 cm
   (d) 24.4°
3. (a) AC = 102.5 m
      BC = 64.0 m
   (b) 120.9 m
   (c) 328°

4. (a) 8.47 cm
   (b) 45.1°
5. (a) 45°
   (b) 73.4°
   (c) 11.3 cm
   (d) 5.66 cm
   (e) 12.8 cm
   (f) 66.2°

Exercise 25.2a (page 338)

1. (a)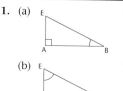
   (b)
   (c)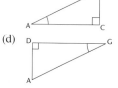
   (d)

2. (a) 32°
   (b) 58°
3. (a) 33.7°

   (c) 26.6°
   (d) 32.5°
   (b) 36.5°

Exercise 25.3a (page 343)

1. c = 5.39 cm, A = 46°, a = 5.22 cm
2. p = 11.6 cm, R = 26°, r = 5.50 cm
3. g = 14.6 cm, E = 55°, e = 15.2 cm
4. b = 271 m, C = 68.5°, c = 260 m
5. B = 66°, C = 72°, c = 7.39 cm
6. M = 71.4°, L = 28.6°, l = 6.46 cm
7. E = 34.2°, D = 120°, d = 9.11 cm
8. B = 94.3°
9. AT = 85.7 m, BT = 60.5 m, TC = 38.9 m
10. AB = 25.7 m, BC = 42.7 m, width = 23.9 m

Exercise 25.4a (page 346)

1. 14.2 cm
2. 3.91 cm
3. 13.7 cm
4. 21.6 cm
5. 48.5°
6. 50.7°
7. 34.9°
8. 110.7°
9. 4.79 km
10. A = 45.7°,
    B = 62.5°,
    C = 71.7°

Exercise 25.5a (page 350)

1. 8.94 cm²
2. 19.7 cm²
3. 20.5 cm²
4. 15 cm²
5. 35.7 cm²

Revision exercise 25a – Section A (page 351)

1. (a) 56.8°
   (b) 8.96 m
2. 11.0 cm
3. (a) 49.5 cm²
   (b) AS (angle SBD = 13.3°
      and angle SAD = 14.0°)
   (c) 48 cm³

4. (a) angle BHC
   (b) angle AGB
5. (a) angle CAD = 35.0°
   (b) angle YBV = 51.1°
6. (a) 149°
   (b) 5.85 km
   (c) 4.9°

Revision exercise 25a – Section B (page 352)

1. (a) 13.8 cm
   (b) 73°
   (c) 15.4 cm
2. (a) 44.3°
   (b) 17 600 m²

3. (a) 12.3°
   (b) 132°
   (c) 8.30 m
4. (a) 13 cm
   (b) 32.2°
   (c) 52.0 cm²

5. (a) 38.2°
   (b) 60°
6. (a) 73 km
   (b) 11.6°
7. (a) 14.7 miles
   (b) 15.8 miles

8. (a) 996 m
   (b) 258 m
9. (a) 65.7°
   (b) 159 cm
10. 6000 m²

Chapter 26

1. $\frac{5}{8}$

2. $\frac{2}{499}$

3. (a)

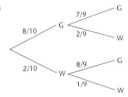

   (b) $\frac{2}{90} = \frac{1}{45}$

   (c) $\frac{32}{90} = \frac{16}{45}$

4. $\frac{2}{999\,000} = \frac{1}{499\,500}$

5. $\frac{68}{110} = \frac{34}{55}$

6. (a) $\frac{20}{90} = \frac{2}{9}$

   (b) $\frac{28}{90} = \frac{14}{45}$

7. (a)

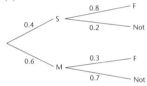

   (b) 0.5

8. (a)

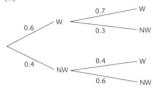

   (b) 0.34
   (c) 0.76

9. (a)

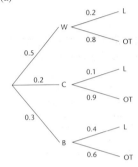

   (b) 0.76

10. 0.86

1. $\frac{3}{1999}$

2. $\frac{3}{13}$

3. $\frac{9}{49}$

4. $\frac{106}{165}$

5. 0.038

6. (a) $\frac{1}{21}$

   (b) $\frac{10}{21}$

7. (a) $\frac{91}{228}$ (b) $\frac{35}{76}$

8. $\frac{17}{42}$

9. (a) 0.64
   (b) 0.592

10. (a) 0.0225
    (b) 0.7515

Chapter 27

Pupils' answers may use different letters and different units which, provided they are well defined, are equally valid.

1. Let c = number of chairs made in a week
    t = number of tables made in a week
    T = total time in hours
    $T = 5c + 4t$

2. Let m= number of minibuses
    t = number of taxis
    n = total number of people carried
    $n = 10m + 4t$

3. Let the numbers be a and b.
    Let G = the geometric mean
    $$G = \sqrt{(ab)}$$
4. Let number = n, $n = 10a + b$
5. Let c = number of cars
    l = number of lorries
    $20c + 50l \leqslant 5500$
6. (a) If U_n = the nth term, $U_n = 4 \times 5^{n-1}$
    (b) 7 812 500
7. (a) If U_n = the nth term, $U_n = 128 \times (\frac{1}{2})^{n-1}$ or
        equivalent e.g. 2^{8-n}
    (b) $\frac{1}{4}$

8. Let t = time in seconds
    d = distance in metres
    (a) $d \propto t^2$
    (b) $d = kt^2$
9. Let amount the investment is worth = £A
    (a) $A = P \times 1.05$ or $1.05P$
    (b) $A = P \times 1.05^2$
    (c) $A = P \times 1.05^n$
10. $PQ = \sqrt{(c-a)^2 + (d-b)^2}$

Pupils will choose their own scales for graphs. Answers for a and b will be approximate.

1. (a)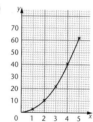

    (b)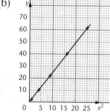

    (c) $a = 2.5$

2. (a)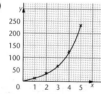

    (b)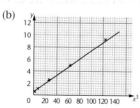

    (c) $a = 1.8$, $b = 13$

3. (a)

    (b)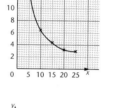

    (c) $a = 63$

4. (a) 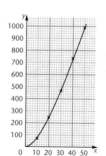 (b)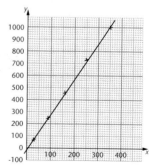

    (c) $a = 3$. $b = -22$

Pupils' answers may use different letters and different units which, provided they are well defined, are equally valid.

Pupils will choose their own scales for graphs. Answers for a and b will be approximate

1. Let j = number of jackets made in a week
    t = number of trousers made in a week
    $5j + 2t \leqslant 40$
2. Let l = length of cuboid in cm
    w = width of cuboid in cm
    h = height of cuboid in cm
    d = length of diagonal in cm
    $d = \sqrt{(l^2 + w^2 + h^2)}$
3. (a) No units
    (b) No consideration of waste, circles do not fit exactly, or equivalent.
4. (a) Let n = first number, $n = 10a + b$
    (b) Let n' = second number, $n' = 10b + a$
    (c) $n + n' = 11a + 11b$
    (d) 11
5. Let t = time of swing in seconds,
    l = length of pendulum in m.
    (a) $t \propto \sqrt{l}$
    (b) $t = k\sqrt{l}$
6. (a) If U_n = the nth term $U_n = 4 \times 1.5^{n-1}$
    (b) 1167.717
7. (a) If U_n = the nth term $U_n = \dfrac{2n - 1}{5 \times 2^{n-1}}$
    (b) $\dfrac{39}{2\,621\,440}$

8. Let p = number of points
    l = number of lines
    (a) $l = \dfrac{p(p - 1)}{2}$
    (b) 435
9. Let A = the amount the investment is worth in pounds.
    (a) $A = P \times 1.04^n$
    (b) $A = P \times 1.06^n$
    (c) $A = P\left(1 + \dfrac{r}{100}\right)^n$
10.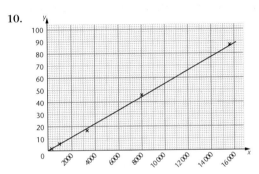

Chapter 28

1. $b = 140°$ (angle at the circumference = $\frac{1}{2}$ angle at the centre)
2. $c = 45°$ (angle at the centre = $2 \times$ angle at the circumference)
    $p = 45°$ (isosceles triangle)
3. $e = 100°$ (isosceles triangle)
    $d = 50°$ (angle at the circumference = $\frac{1}{2}$ angle at the centre)
4. $q = 60°$ (sum of angles on a straight line)
    $r = 120°$ (angle at the centre = $2 \times$ angle at the circumference)

1. $a = 50°$; $b = 100°$
2. $c = 110°$; $d = 110°$
3. $e = 45°$, $f = 45°$
4. $g = 45°$, $h = 45°$, $i = 45°$

1. AC is a diameter
    angle OAB = 40°
    angle b = 40°
    angle c = 40°
    angle DOC = 100°
    angle a = 50°
2. s = 60°
    angle CEA = 120°
    $p = 180° - (40° + 120°) = 20°$
    $q = 20°$

angle ABC = 90° (angle in semi-circle)
(angle sum of triangle ABC)
(angle sum of triangle ABO)
(angles subtended by same arc)
(vertically opposite angles)
(angle at centre and circumference)
(angles in same segment)
(angles on straight line)
(angle sum of triangle)
(angles in same segment)

3. $f = 69°$ (angle at centre and circumference)
   $g = 69° ÷ 2 = 34.5°$ (exterior angle of triangle ADC = sum of interior opposite angles)
4. $y = 80°$ (angle at centre)
   $z = 50°$ (angles in isosceles triangle)
   $x = 90°$ (angle in semi-circle)

Exercise 28.4a (page 377)

1. $a = 90° − 40° = 50°$
   (angle between tangent and radius)
2. $b = 50°$
   (angles at X and y = 90°, angle sum of quadrilateral)
3. $d = 20°$
   $e = 70°$
   (angle between tangent and radius)
4. $6x = 90°$
   $x = 15°$
   $5x = 75°$
   $y = 180° − 150° = 30°$

Exercise 28.5a (page 379)

1. $a = 70°$ (angle between chord and tangent)
   $b = 50°$
2. triangle is equilateral
   $c = 60°$ and $d = 60°$ (angle between chord and tangent)
3. angle CXA = 30°   (angles on straight line)
   angle ABC = 150°   (opposite angles of cyclic quadrilateral)
   $e = f = 15°$ (base angles of isosceles triangle)
4. $x = 80°$ (angle at centre and circumference)
   $z = 180° − (90° + 80°) = 10°$
        (angle between radius and tangent = 90°)
   $y = 180° − (90° + 40°) = 50°$
        (angle at circumference = 40°)
5. TD = TA (tangents from T)
   UA = UB (tangents from U)
   VB = VC (tangents from V)
   WC = WD (tangents from W)
   also TU = TA + AU = TD + UB
   VW = VC + CW = VB + WD
   therefore TU + WV = (TD + UB) + (VB + WD) = (TD + DW)
   + (UB + VB) = WT + UV

Revision exercise 28a (page 380)

1. $y = 85°$ (angle at the circumference = $\frac{1}{2}$ angle at the centre)
   $x = 95°$ (sum of angles on a straight line)
2. $e = 240°$ (opposite angles of a cyclic quadrilateral)
   $f = 120°$ (angle at centre and circumference)
   $g = 240°$
3. angle at centre = 160°   (angle at centre and circumference)
   $d = 10°$ (base angle of isosceles triangle)
4. angle DAB = 70°   (base angle of isosceles triangle)
   therefore angle OAB = angle DAB − angle EAO = 70° − 40° = 30°
   therefore angle AOB = 120°   (angle sum of isosceles triangle)
   therefore $x = 60°$ (angle at centre and circumference)
5. angle at B = 70°   (base angle of isosceles triangle)
   therefore $x = 70°$ (angle between chord and tangent)
6. $b = 55°$ (base angle of isosceles triangle)
   therefore $d = 70°$ (angle sum of triangle)
   $a = 55°$ (angle between chord and tangent)
   $c = 70°$ (angle between chord and tangent)
7. third angle of triangle = 70°   (angle between chord and tangent)
   therefore $y = 70°$ (base angle of isosceles triangle)
   $x = 40°$

Chapter 29

Exercise 29.1a (page 382)

1. (a) $x = 9$ or -2
   (b) $x = \frac{1}{2}$ or -3
   (c) $x = \frac{1}{3}$ or 3
2. (a) $x = 5.65$ or 0.35
   (b) $x = -1.72$ or 0.39
3. (a) $\dfrac{5x + 4}{6}$

   (b) $\dfrac{2x - 17}{20}$

   (c) $\dfrac{3x}{(x + 1)(x - 2)}$

   (d) $x = 0$ or $\frac{7}{2}$
   (e) $x = \frac{1}{3}$ or $\frac{1}{2}$

   (c) $x = 3.22$ or 0.78

   (d) $\dfrac{x^2 + 6x - 1}{(x - 1)(x + 2)}$

   (e) $\dfrac{3x}{2x + 1}$

4. (a) $x = 6$
   (b) $x = 1\frac{5}{7}$
   (c) $x = -5$ or 3
   (d) $x = 4$ or -3
5. (a) $x = \dfrac{7 + 3y}{2}$

   (b) $x = \dfrac{8x + 9y}{5}$

   (c) $x = \dfrac{4 - 2y}{3}$

6. (a) $x = 5,\ y = 1$
   (b) $x = 3,\ y = 2$
   (c) $x = 1,\ y = \frac{1}{2}$

   (e) $x = -2$
   (f) $x = 3$ or -5
   (g) $x = 4$ or 5

   (d) $x = \dfrac{4y - 5z}{5}$

   (e) $x = \dfrac{15y - 7}{6}$

   (d) $x = 2,\ y = -1$
   (e) $x = \frac{1}{2},\ y = 1\frac{1}{2}$

Exercise 29.2a (page 386)

1. $x = 2,\ y = 3$
2. $x = 2,\ y = 3$
3. $x = 1,\ y = 2$
4. $x = 5,\ y = 6$
5. $x = 4,\ y = 2$ or $x = -1,\ y = 12$
6. $x = -1,\ y = 3$ or $x = 8,\ y = 39$
7. $x = -1,\ y = 5$ or $x = \frac{1}{2},\ y = 2\frac{3}{4}$
8. $x = -2,\ y = 5$ or $x = \frac{1}{2},\ y = 3\frac{3}{4}$

9. (a) $y = x^2 - 5x + 5$

x	-2	-1	0	1	2	3	4	5
y	19	11	5	1	-1	-1	1	5

$2x + y = 9$

x	-2	0	5
y	13	9	-1

Cross at $(-1, 11)$, $(4, 1)$

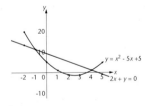

(b) $x = -1,\ y = 11$ or $x = 4,\ y = 1$

10. (a) $y = x^2 - 3x - 1$

x	-4	-3	-2	-1	0	1	2	3
y	27	17	9	3	-1	-3	-3	-1

$4x + y = 5$

x	-4	0	3
y	21	5	-7

Cross at $(-3, 17)$, $(2, -3)$

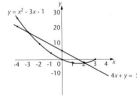

(b) $x = -3,\ y = 17$ or $x = 2,\ y = -3$

Exercise 29.3a (page 389)

The diagrams are not to size in this exercise

1.

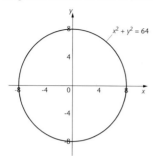

2. (a)

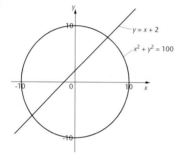

(b) Cross at $(-6, -8)$, $(6, 8)$.

3. (a)

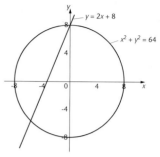

(b) Cross at $(-6.4, -4.8)$, $(0, 8)$

4. $x = 0$, $y = 7$ or $x = 7$, $y = 0$

5. $x = 5$, $y = 12$ or $x = -12$, $y = -5$

6. $x = 0$, $y = 5$ or $x = 5$, $y = 0$

7. $x = 6$, $y = 8$ or $x = -8$, $y = -6$

8. $x = 0$, $y = 8$ or $x = -6.4$, $y = -4.8$

Exercise 29.4a (page 394)

1. (a) 4
(b) 4
(c) -3

2. (a) $3y = x + 6$
(b) $y + 2x = 6$

3. (a) $y = 2x + 4$
(b) $y + 3x = 8$
(c) $y = 2x + 1$

4. $y = x + 3$

5. $y + 3x = 3$

6. $2y + x = 8$

7. $y = 2x + 2$

8. $2y - 3x = 5$ and
$6y + 4x = 1$ are
perpendicular.

9. $3y = x + 4$

10. (a) $y = 2x + 2$
(b) $2y + x = 4$
(c) $(0, 2)$

Revision exercise 29a (page 396)

1. (a) $x = -6$ or 2
(b) $x = -2$ or $\frac{2}{3}$

2. $x = 0.27$ or 3.73

3. (a) $\dfrac{x}{2}$

4. (a) $x = 2\frac{1}{3}$

5. (a) $a = c + 2b$
(b) $a = \dfrac{3c + 3b}{2}$

6. (a) $x = 6$, $y = 1$
(b) $x = 5$, $y = 2$

(c) $x = 5$ or 9
(d) $x = 0$ or $2\frac{1}{4}$
(b) $x = -2.69$ or 0.19
(b) $\dfrac{6x + 2}{(x + 3)(x - 1)}$
(b) $x = 2\frac{3}{5}$
(c) $a = 2b$
(d) $a = \dfrac{2b + 5c}{8}$
(c) $x = 3$, $y = 2$
(d) $x = 1\frac{1}{2}$, $y = \frac{1}{2}$

(e) $x = 2$ or $2\frac{1}{2}$
(c) $x = -0.24$ or -2.76.
(c) $\dfrac{3x^2 - 11x + 4}{(3x - 1)(3x + 1)}$
(c) $x = 3\frac{1}{3}$
(e) $a = 2b$
(e) $x = 2$, $y = -1$

7. (a)

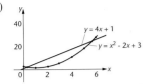

(b) $x = 0.4, y = 2.4$ or $x = 5.6, y = 24$

8. (a)

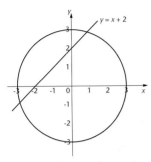

(b) $x = -2.9, y = -0.9$ or $x = 0.9, y = 2.9$

9. (a) $x = 1, y = 2$ or $x = 3, y = 6$
  (b) $x = 1, y = 2$ or $x = 2, y = 5$
10. (a) $y + 3x = 3$
11. $2y + x = 2$
12. $y = 2x + 3$

  (c) $x = 1, y = 2$ or $x = -1, y = 10$
  (d) $x = 0, y = 6$ or $x = -6, y = 0$
  (b) $y = 8x + 17$ (c) $y = 2x - 5$

Chapter 30

Exercise 30.1a (page 398)

1.

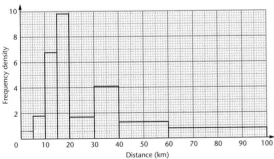

2.

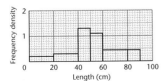

3.

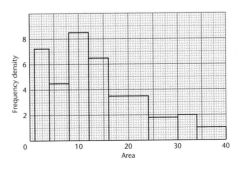

Answers

4. (a)

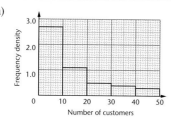

(b) There were more customers after the refit and less variation in the numbers.

Exercise 30.2a (page 401)

1. (a)   130   (b)   28
2. (a)   31   (b)   43 kg

Revision exercise 30a (page 406)

1.

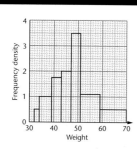

2. 50
3.

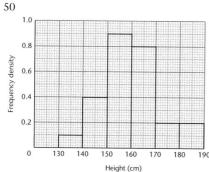

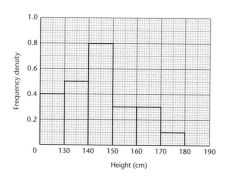

Chapter 31

Exercise 31.1a (page 411)

1.

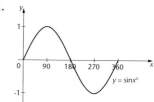

2.

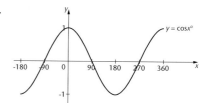

±72.5°, 287.5°
3. 117°, 297°
4.   45, 225

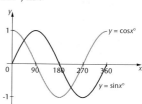

5. 120°, 240°, 480°, 600°

1.

2.

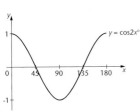

3. (a) 3   (b) 4   (c) 2

4. (a) 360°   (b) 180°   (c) 720°

5. $a = 5$ $b = 0.5$

6. $a = 0.5$ $b = 3$

7.

8. 15°, 75°, 195°, 255°

9. 45°, 135°, 225°, 315°

10.

One solution of $\sin x = \cos 2x$

1. (a)

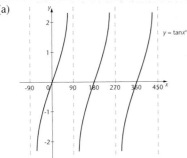

2. 45°, 225°

3. 217°

4. 210°, 330°

5. 78.5°, 281.5°

6. 336

7.

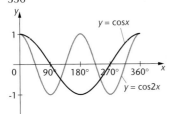

8. 45, 225

9. A (60, 0), B (30, 2)

10.

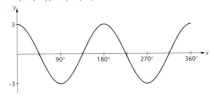

Chapter 32

Exercise 32.la (page 420)

1. (a) R   (e) I   (i) I
    (b) R   (f) R   (j) R
    (c) I   (g) R
    (d) R   (h) I

2. (a) $0.6\dot{3}$ (c) $0.0\dot{4}2857\dot{1}$ (e) $0.4\dot{1}6\dot{2}$
    (b) $0.\dot{4}2857\dot{1}$ (d) $0.2\dot{5}$

3. (a) $\frac{2}{9}$ (c) $\frac{7}{30}$ (e) $2\frac{2}{11}$
    (b) $\frac{16}{33}$ (d) $\frac{44}{333}$

Exercise 32.2a (page 423)

1. (a) $2\sqrt{3}$, I   (c) $3\sqrt{5}$, I   (e) $5\sqrt{3}$, I   (g) $6\sqrt{10}$, I   (i) $20\sqrt{10}$, I
    (b) $10\sqrt{10}$, I   (d) $10\sqrt{3}$, I   (f) 4, R   (h) 2, R   (j) $15\sqrt{15}$, I

2. (a) 8   (b) $2\sqrt{3}$ (c) 13

3. (a) $7 - 2\sqrt{5}$ (b) $-1 + 4\sqrt{5}$ (c) $14 + 6\sqrt{5}$

4. (a) $5\sqrt{3} + 6$ (b) $37 + 20\sqrt{3}$ (c) $34 - 21\sqrt{2}$

5. (a) $\dfrac{\sqrt{2}}{2}$ (b) $\dfrac{2\sqrt{5}}{5}$ (c) $\dfrac{5\sqrt{7}}{7}$ (d) $\dfrac{11\sqrt{2}}{6}$ (e) $\dfrac{9\sqrt{5}}{10}$

6. (a) $\dfrac{3\sqrt{2}}{2}$ (b) $\dfrac{\sqrt{3}}{5}$ (c) $\dfrac{4\sqrt{3}}{5}$ (d) $\dfrac{2\sqrt{6}}{3}$

Revision exercise 32a (page 424)

1. (a) R   (c) I   (e) R
    (b) R   (d) I

2. (a) $0.4\dot{5}$ (b) $0.2\dot{1}\dot{2}$ (c) $0.07\dot{4}$

3. (a) $\frac{6}{11}$ (b) $3\frac{73}{495}$ (c) $\frac{226}{1111}$

4. (a) $4\sqrt{2}$ (d) 30
    (b) $5\sqrt{6}$ (e) $6\sqrt{5}$
    (c) $8\sqrt{2}$ (f) $2\sqrt{2}$ (g) $48\sqrt{6}$

5. (a) $8 - 3\sqrt{7}$ (c) $-13 - 7\sqrt{7}$
    (b) $-2 + 5\sqrt{7}$

6. (a) $37 + 20\sqrt{3}$ (b) $37 - 20\sqrt{3}$ (c) 13

7. $65\sqrt{10} + 200$

8. (a) $\dfrac{11\sqrt{2}}{2}$ (b) $\dfrac{5\sqrt{3}}{3}$ (c) $\dfrac{2\sqrt{3}}{3}$

Chapter 33

Exercise 33.la (page 426)

1. (a) 1
    (b) -17

2. (a) (i) 6
       (ii) 30
    (b) 2 or 3

3. (a) 45 and 78
    (b) 1.75

4. (a) $18x - 1$
    (b) $27x - 3$
    (c) $9x + 4$

5. (a) $\cos x + 3$
    (b) $3 \cos x + 6$
    (c) $\cos 2x + 2$
    (d) $5 \cos 3x + 10$

Exercise 33.2a (page 429)

1.

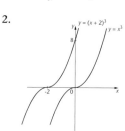

Translation of $\begin{pmatrix} 0 \\ 3 \end{pmatrix}$

2.

Translation of $\begin{pmatrix} -2 \\ 0 \end{pmatrix}$

3. 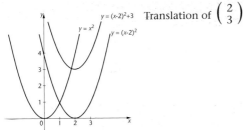 Translation of $\begin{pmatrix} 2 \\ 3 \end{pmatrix}$

6.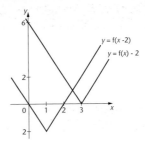

4.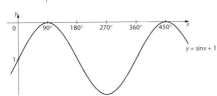

$y = \sin x - 1$

5. (a) $y = f(x) - 5$ (b) $y = f(x + 2)$

7.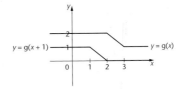

8. $y = (x - 1)^2 = 2$

9. $y = \cos x + 2$

10. $y = (x + 2)^2 + 3$

Exercise 33.3a (page 433)

1.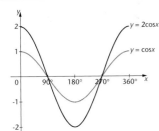

One-way stretch parallel to y-axis with scale factor 2

2.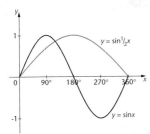

One-way stretch parallel to x-axis with scale factor 2

3. One-way stretch parallel to x-axis with scale factor $\frac{1}{3}$.

4. (a) reflection in the y-axis
(b) reflection in the x-axis
(c) one way stretch parallel to the y-axis with s.f. 3

5. $y = \cos 3x$

6. (a) $y = x^2 + 5$ (b) $y = -x^2 - 5$

7. (a) $y = \dfrac{3}{x}$ (b) $y = \dfrac{1}{2x}$

8. (a) translation of $\begin{pmatrix} 0 \\ 1 \end{pmatrix}$

(b) one-way stretch parallel to the y-axis with s.f. 3
(c) one-way stretch parallel to the x-axis with s.f. $\frac{1}{2}$
(d) one-way stretch parallel to the x-axis with s.f. 3 and one-way stretch parallel to the y-axis with s.f. 5

9. (a) $y = -x^3$
(b) $y = -x^3$
(c) $y = 8x^3$

10. (a) $y = \dfrac{x^2}{4}$

(b) $(2, 1)$

(c) (i) $\dfrac{1}{4}$

(ii) $\left(1, \dfrac{1}{4}\right)$

Answers

509

Exercise 33.4a (page 435)

1. (a) y against x^2 (c) C against $\sqrt{m}$
   (b) V against d^3
2. (a) $y = 4x^3 + 7$ (b) $s = 5t^2$
3. (a) $y = 6 - 2x^2$ (b) $C = \dfrac{12}{m}$

4. (a) 4, 25, 36, 81   (b) $y = 3x^2 - 10$
5. $a = 0.6$ $b = 2.4$
6. $x = 0.4t^3 + 6$

Exercise 33.5a (page 438)

1. (a) 702.46, 786.76, 881.2
   (b) 3.6
2. (a)

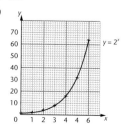

   (b) 7.6–7.7
3. (a) 25
   (b)

   (c) 35 minutes
   (d) 9510 to 3 s.f.
4. (a) £103.32
   (b) £85 × 1.05^x
   (c) 14(.2) or 15
5. (a)

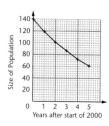

   (b) 3.4

6.

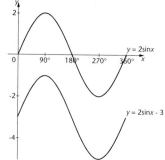

7. (a) 4 m
   (b) 1 m
   (c) 12
   (d) between 0 and 2 and between 10 and 12.
8. (a) $V = x^2 (8 - x)$
   (b)

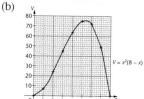

   (c) 5.3 cm, 5.3 cm, 2.7 cm
9. (a) 9 cm
   (b) 6 cm
10. $a = 30, b = 2$

1. (a) 34
   (b) 14
2. (a) $2 - 15x$
   (b) $8 - 20x$
   (c) $2 + 5x$
3. (a) one-way stretch parallel to the x-axis with scale factor $\frac{1}{3}$
   (b) one-way stretch parallel to the y-axis with scale factor 4
   (c) reflection in the y-axis
4. (a)

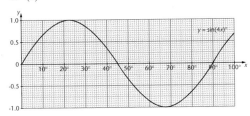

   (b) $-7.5, 52.5, 82.5$ etc.

5. (a)

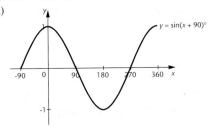

   (b) $y = \cos x$
6. (a) $y = \cos x + 3$
   (b) $y = \cos 4x$
7. (a) $y = 3x^2 - 5$
   (b) $P = -3\sqrt{t} + 2$
8. $a = 4.6, b = 9.2$
9. (a) 100
   (b) 249
   (c) 12.6–13
10. $a = 10, b = 0.8$

Chapter 34

Exercise 34.1a (page 445)

1. $\overrightarrow{AB} = 2\mathbf{a}$, $\quad \overrightarrow{CD} = -4\mathbf{a}$, $\quad \overrightarrow{EF} = 3\mathbf{a}$, $\quad \overrightarrow{GH} = -2\mathbf{a}$, $\quad \overrightarrow{PQ} = -\frac{1}{2}\mathbf{a}$, $\quad \overrightarrow{RS} = \frac{7}{2}\mathbf{a}$
2. $\overrightarrow{AB} = \mathbf{a}$, $\quad \overrightarrow{CD} = -\mathbf{b}$, $\quad \overrightarrow{EF} = 2\mathbf{b}$, $\quad \overrightarrow{GH} = -\frac{1}{2}\mathbf{a}$, $\quad \overrightarrow{PQ} = -\frac{1}{2}\mathbf{b}$, $\quad \overrightarrow{RS} = 3\mathbf{a}$
3. $\overrightarrow{AB} = 2\mathbf{a}$, $\quad \overrightarrow{CD} = -2\mathbf{a}$, $\quad \overrightarrow{EB} = \mathbf{a}$, $\quad \overrightarrow{GD} = -\mathbf{a}$, $\quad \overrightarrow{HF} = 2\mathbf{a}$, $\quad \overrightarrow{FC} = \mathbf{b}$
4. $\overrightarrow{AB} = \begin{pmatrix} 4 \\ 1 \end{pmatrix}$, $\quad \overrightarrow{CD} = \begin{pmatrix} 2 \\ 0 \end{pmatrix}$, $\quad \overrightarrow{CB} = \begin{pmatrix} 1 \\ 4 \end{pmatrix}$, $\quad \overrightarrow{AD} = \begin{pmatrix} 5 \\ -3 \end{pmatrix}$, $\quad \overrightarrow{CA} = \begin{pmatrix} -3 \\ 3 \end{pmatrix}$
5. $\overrightarrow{EF} = \begin{pmatrix} 4 \\ 3 \end{pmatrix}$, $\quad \overrightarrow{GH} = \begin{pmatrix} -2 \\ -2 \end{pmatrix}$, $\quad \overrightarrow{EH} = \begin{pmatrix} 6 \\ 1 \end{pmatrix}$, $\quad \overrightarrow{GF} = \begin{pmatrix} -4 \\ 0 \end{pmatrix}$, $\quad \overrightarrow{FH} = \begin{pmatrix} 2 \\ -2 \end{pmatrix}$

6.

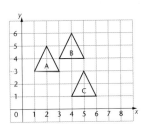

7. (a) Translation of $\begin{pmatrix} 2 \\ -6 \end{pmatrix}$ (b) Translation of $\begin{pmatrix} -8 \\ 1 \end{pmatrix}$ (c) Translation of $\begin{pmatrix} -6 \\ -5 \end{pmatrix}$

8. (a) $\begin{pmatrix} 0 \\ 2 \end{pmatrix}$ (b) $\begin{pmatrix} -4 \\ 0 \end{pmatrix}$ (c) $\begin{pmatrix} -2 \\ 3 \end{pmatrix}$ (d) $\begin{pmatrix} 1 \\ 7 \end{pmatrix}$ (e) $\begin{pmatrix} 8 \\ -6 \end{pmatrix}$ (f) $\begin{pmatrix} -6 \\ 4 \end{pmatrix}$

Exercise 34.2a (page 449)

1. (a) $\begin{pmatrix} 4 \\ 6 \end{pmatrix}$ (b) $\begin{pmatrix} 9 \\ 3 \end{pmatrix}$ (c) $\begin{pmatrix} 2 \\ 3 \end{pmatrix}$ (d) $\begin{pmatrix} 1 \\ 0 \end{pmatrix}$ (e) $\begin{pmatrix} 5 \\ 12 \end{pmatrix}$

2. (a) $\begin{pmatrix} -6 \\ 0 \end{pmatrix}$ (b) $\begin{pmatrix} -1 \\ -2 \end{pmatrix}$ (c) $\begin{pmatrix} 0.5 \\ -1.5 \end{pmatrix}$ (d) $\begin{pmatrix} 6 \\ 1 \end{pmatrix}$ (e) $\begin{pmatrix} 0 \\ 1 \end{pmatrix}$

3. (a) $\begin{pmatrix} 12 \\ 6 \end{pmatrix}$ (b) $\begin{pmatrix} -6 \\ -3 \end{pmatrix}$ (c) $\begin{pmatrix} 24 \\ 12 \end{pmatrix}$ (d) $\begin{pmatrix} 3 \\ 1.5 \end{pmatrix}$ (e) $\begin{pmatrix} -2 \\ -1 \end{pmatrix}$

4. (a) $\begin{pmatrix} 3 \\ 9 \end{pmatrix}$ (b) $\begin{pmatrix} 4 \\ 7 \end{pmatrix}$ (c) $\begin{pmatrix} 2 \\ 1 \end{pmatrix}$ (d) $\begin{pmatrix} 5 \\ 10 \end{pmatrix}$ (e) $\begin{pmatrix} -3 \\ 1 \end{pmatrix}$

5. (a) $\begin{pmatrix} -3 \\ -9 \end{pmatrix}$ (b) $\begin{pmatrix} 2 \\ -20 \end{pmatrix}$ (c) $\begin{pmatrix} 4 \\ -4 \end{pmatrix}$ (d) $\begin{pmatrix} -7 \\ 12 \end{pmatrix}$ (e) $\begin{pmatrix} 4.5 \\ -1 \end{pmatrix}$

Exercise 34.3a (page 452)

1.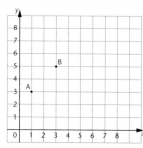

(a) $\begin{pmatrix} 2 \\ 2 \end{pmatrix}$

(b) (i) $\begin{pmatrix} 2 \\ 2 \end{pmatrix}$ (ii) $\begin{pmatrix} 2 \\ 2 \end{pmatrix}$ (iii) $\begin{pmatrix} 2 \\ 2 \end{pmatrix}$

(c) They are all $\begin{pmatrix} 2 \\ 2 \end{pmatrix}$.

2.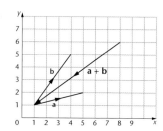

3. (a) (i) $\overrightarrow{AB} = \begin{pmatrix} 6 \\ 2 \end{pmatrix}$ (ii) $\overrightarrow{BC} = \begin{pmatrix} 3 \\ 1 \end{pmatrix}$.

(b) $\overrightarrow{AB} = 2 \times \overrightarrow{BC}$, so ABC is a straight line and $AB = 2 \times BC$.

4. $\overrightarrow{BC} = \overrightarrow{BA} + \overrightarrow{AC} = -\mathbf{a} + 2\mathbf{b} = 2\mathbf{b} - \mathbf{a}$

5. (a) $\overrightarrow{AB} = -\mathbf{a} - \mathbf{b}$
   (b) $\overrightarrow{BC} = 3\mathbf{b} - 4\mathbf{a}$
   (c) $\overrightarrow{AC} = 2\mathbf{b} - 5\mathbf{a}$

6. $\overrightarrow{BC} = \mathbf{b}$, $\overrightarrow{CD} = -\mathbf{a}$, $\overrightarrow{BD} = \mathbf{b} - \mathbf{a}$, and $\overrightarrow{AC} = \mathbf{a} + \mathbf{b}$

7. $\overrightarrow{AB} = \mathbf{b} - \mathbf{a}$, $\overrightarrow{CB} = \frac{1}{3}(\mathbf{b} - \mathbf{a})$, $\overrightarrow{OC} = \frac{1}{3}\mathbf{a} + \frac{2}{3}\mathbf{b}$

8. $\overrightarrow{EB} = \frac{1}{2}\mathbf{a} - \mathbf{b}$

9. $\overrightarrow{CD} = \frac{1}{2}\mathbf{b} - \mathbf{a}$

10. (a) $\overrightarrow{AE} = 3\mathbf{a}$, $\overrightarrow{AF} = 3\mathbf{b}$, $\overrightarrow{BC} = \mathbf{b} - \mathbf{a}$, $\overrightarrow{EF} = 3\mathbf{b} - 3\mathbf{a}$

(b) $\overrightarrow{EF} = 3 \times \overrightarrow{BC}$ so EF and BC are parallel and $EF = 3 \times BC$ in length.

Revision exercise 34a (page 454)

1. (a) (i) $\overrightarrow{AB} = \begin{pmatrix} 6 \\ 5 \end{pmatrix}$, $\overrightarrow{BC} = \begin{pmatrix} 1 \\ -6 \end{pmatrix}$, $\overrightarrow{CD} = \begin{pmatrix} -6 \\ 4 \end{pmatrix}$ (ii) Sum $= \begin{pmatrix} 1 \\ 3 \end{pmatrix}$

(b) $\overrightarrow{AD} = \begin{pmatrix} 1 \\ 3 \end{pmatrix}$, $\overrightarrow{AD}$ the same as the sum of the first three.

2.

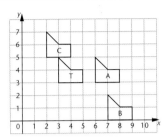

3. (a) Translation of $\begin{pmatrix} 6 \\ 1 \end{pmatrix}$ (b) Translation of $\begin{pmatrix} 5 \\ 5 \end{pmatrix}$ (c) Translation of $\begin{pmatrix} -1 \\ 4 \end{pmatrix}$.

4. (a) $\begin{pmatrix} 2 \\ 4 \end{pmatrix}$ (c) $\begin{pmatrix} 2 \\ -2 \end{pmatrix}$ (e) $\begin{pmatrix} 1 \\ 0 \end{pmatrix}$ (g) $\begin{pmatrix} 5 \\ 13 \end{pmatrix}$ (i) $\begin{pmatrix} 3.5 \\ 2.5 \end{pmatrix}$

   (b) $\begin{pmatrix} 3 \\ 1 \end{pmatrix}$ (d) $\begin{pmatrix} -3 \\ 4 \end{pmatrix}$ (f) $\begin{pmatrix} 0.5 \\ 1 \end{pmatrix}$) (h) $\begin{pmatrix} -0.5 \\ 2 \end{pmatrix}$

5. (a) $(-1, 1)$ (b) $(0, 0)$ (c) $(5, -5)$
6. $\vec{BC} = 2\mathbf{b} - \mathbf{a}$
7. (a) $\vec{AB} = 2\mathbf{b} - 2\mathbf{a}$, $\vec{BC} = 4\mathbf{b} - 4\mathbf{a}$
   (b) ABC is a straight line and BC is twice the length of AB.
8. (a) $\vec{EB} = \frac{1}{2}\mathbf{p}$, $\vec{BF} = \frac{1}{2}\mathbf{q}$, $\vec{EF} = \frac{1}{2}\mathbf{p} + \frac{1}{2}\mathbf{q}$, $\vec{HD} = \frac{1}{2}\mathbf{q}$, $\vec{DG} = \frac{1}{2}\mathbf{p}$, $\vec{HG} = \frac{1}{2}\mathbf{p} + \frac{1}{2}\mathbf{q}$
   (b) HG and EF are equal and parallel.
9. $\vec{EB} = \frac{1}{3}\mathbf{p} - \frac{2}{3}\mathbf{q}$
10. Draw the diagram, and work out $\vec{DC} = 5\mathbf{p}$. So AB and DC are parallel. So the shape is a trapezium.

Index

proportion 71–72, 250–251, 255
proportional change 74–75, 80
pyramids, volume 314
Pythagoras' theorem 123–127, 135

Q

quadratic equations 145–146, 152, 158
quadratic equations, factorising
145–146, 260–261, 273
quadratic equations, solving by formula
261–262, 273
quadratic expressions, factorising
256–258, 259, 273
quadrilaterals, cyclic 28, 29
quartiles 109, 110–111, 227
questionnaires 105–107, 112, 285, 294
questions, closed 107, 112
quota (stratified) sampling 287, 294

R

random numbers 291–293, 294
random sampling 287, 289–290, 294
range 31, 35, 36, 40, 226, 240
ranges, interquartile 109, 112
rate of change 170, 174–175, 183
ratio 12, 20, 71–72
rational numbers 417
reciprocals 19, 20
recurring decimals 419
reflections 42–43, 56, 58, 213, 214, 431,
440
representative sample 286
resultant of two vectors 450–451, 454
roots 18
rotations 44–46, 56, 58, 247, 274, 275,
276–277, 282

rounding numbers 6–7, 8, 9, 20, 114,
121, 164

S

sampling 286–287
scale drawings 217–218, 223
scale factors 51, 52, 58, 218, 223,
278–279, 321
scatter graphs 231, 232, 240
sectors of circles 309–310, 323
semicircles, angles in 24
sequences 361–362
sequences, nth term 90–91, 103,
361–362
shading regions on graphs 154–155, 158
significant figures, rounding to 9, 20,
114, 164
similar shapes 219, 220, 223
similar triangles 219–220, 223
simultaneous equations 141–142, 144,
152, 158, 383–386, 396
sine 129, 135, 408, 409, 412, 413
sine rule 340–342, 351
skewed distribution 39
solving equations, elimination method
141–142, 383
solving equations, factorisation
145–146
solving equations, graphical methods
147–148, 269–272, 273, 385
solving equations, substitution method
384, 385, 386, 389
solving equations, trial and
improvement method 150, 158
solving, quadratic equations 260–261,
273
speed 118–119, 122, 167–168
spheres, surface area 315

W